SIR WALTER SCOTT
NOVELS

WAVERLEY

OR
'TIS SIXTY YEARS SINCE

VOLUME II

HERON BOOKS LONDON

LIST OF ILLUSTRATIONS

WAVERLEY

OR
'TIS SIXTY YEARS SINCE

CHAPTER I

SHOWS THAT THE LOSS OF A HORSE'S SHOE MAY BE A SERIOUS INCONVENIENCE

THE manner and air of Waverley, but, above all, the glittering contents of his purse, and the indifference with which he seemed to regard them, somewhat overawed his companion, and deterred him from making any attempts to enter upon conversation. His own reflections were moreover agitated by various surmises, and by plans of self-interest, with which these were intimately connected. The travellers journeyed, therefore, in silence, until it was interrupted by the annunciation, on the part of the guide, that his "naig had lost a forefoot shoe, which doubtless his honour would consider it was his part to replace."

This was what lawyers call a "fishing question," calculated to ascertain how far Waverley was disposed to submit to petty imposition. "My part to replace your horse's shoe, you rascal?" said Waverley, mistaking the purport of the intimation.

"Indubitably," answered Mr. Cruickshanks; "though there was no preceese clause to that effect, it canna be expected that I am to pay for the casualties whilk may befall the puir naig while in your honour's service. Nathless, if your honour —"

"Oh, you mean I am to pay the farrier. But where shall we find one?"

Rejoiced at discerning there would be no objection made on the part of his temporary master, Mr. Cruickshanks assured him that Cairnvreckan, a village which they were about to enter, was happy in an excellent blacksmith; "but as he was a professor, he would drive a nail for no man on the Sabbath, or kirk-fast, unless it were in a case of absolute necessity, for which he always charged sixpence each shoe." The most important part of this communication, in the opinion of the speaker, made a very slight impression on the hearer, who only internally wondered what college this veterinary professor belonged to, — not aware that the word was used to denote any person who pretended to uncommon sanctity of faith and manner.

As they entered the village of Cairnvreckan, they speedily distinguished the smith's house. Being also a "public," it was two stories high, and proudly reared its crest, covered with gray slate, above the thatched hovels by which it was surrounded. The adjoining smithy betokened none of the Sabbatical silence and repose which Ebenezer had augured from the sanctity of his friend. On the contrary, hammer clashed and anvil rang, the bellows groaned, and the whole apparatus of Vulcan appeared to be in full activity. Nor was the labour of a rural and pacific nature. The master

smith, — benempt, as his sign intimated, John
Mucklewrath, — with two assistants, toiled busily
in arranging, repairing, and furbishing old muskets,
pistols, and swords, which lay scattered around his
workshop in military confusion. The open shed,
containing the forge, was crowded with persons
who came and went as if receiving and communicating important news ; and a single glance at the
aspect of the people who traversed the street in
haste, or stood assembled in groups, with eyes elevated and hands uplifted, announced that some
extraordinary intelligence was agitating the public
mind of the municipality of Cairnvreckan. "There
is some news," said mine host of the Candlestick,
pushing his lantern-jawed visage and bareboned
nag rudely forward into the crowd, — "there is
some news ; and if it please my Creator, I will
forthwith obtain speirings thereof."

Waverley, with better regulated curiosity than
his attendant's, dismounted, and gave his horse to
a boy who stood idling near. It arose perhaps
from the shyness of his character in early youth
that he felt dislike at applying to a stranger even
for casual information, without previously glancing
at his physiognomy and appearance. While he
looked about in order to select the person with
whom he would most willingly hold communication, the buzz around saved him in some degree
the trouble of interrogatories. The names of Lochiel, Clanronald, Glengarry, and other distinguished Highland chiefs, among whom Vich Ian
Vohr was repeatedly mentioned, were as familiar
in men's mouths as household words ; and from the
alarm generally expressed, he easily conceived that
their descent into the Lowlands, at the head of their

3

armed tribes, had either already taken place, or was instantly apprehended.

Ere Waverley could ask particulars, a strong, large-boned, hard-featured woman, about forty, dressed as if her clothes had been flung on with a pitchfork, her cheeks flushed with a scarlet red where they were not smutted with soot and lamp-black, jostled through the crowd, and brandishing high a child of two years old, which she danced in her arms, without regard to its screams of terror, sang forth, with all her might, —

> " Charlie is my darling, my darling, my darling,
>   Charlie is my darling,
>   The young Chevalier! "

" D' ye hear what 's come ower ye now," continued the virago, " ye whingeing Whig carles ? D' ye hear wha 's coming to cow yer cracks ?

> ' Little wot ye wha 's coming,
>   Little wot ye wha 's coming, —
>   A' the wild Macraws are coming.' "

The Vulcan of Cairnvreckan, who acknowledged his Venus in this exulting Bacchante, regarded her with a grim and ire-foreboding countenance, while some of the senators of the village hastened to interpose.

" Whisht, gudewife ! Is this a time, or is this a day, to be singing your ranting fule sangs in ? — a time when the wine of wrath is poured out without mixture in the cup of indignation, and a day when the land should give testimony against popery and prelacy and quakerism and independency and supremacy and erastianism and antinomianism and a' the errors of the church ? "

" And that 's a' your Whiggery," re-echoed the

Jacobite heroine, — " that 's a' your Whiggery, and
your presbytery, ye cut-lugged, graning carles!
What! d' ye think the lads wi' the kilts will care
for yer synods and yer presbyteries and yer buttock-mail and yer stool o' repentance ?   Vengeance
on the black face o't! mony an honester woman 's
been set upon it than streeks doon beside ony Whig
in the country.   I mysell — "

Here John Mucklewrath, who dreaded her entering upon a detail of personal experience, interposed his matrimonial authority.   " Gae hame, and
be d—— (that I should say sae!), and put on the
sowens for supper."

" And you, ye doil'd dotard," replied his gentle
helpmate, her wrath, which had hitherto wandered
abroad over the whole assembly, being at once and
violently impelled into its natural channel, " *ye* stand
there hammering dog-heads for fules that will never
snap them at a Highlandman, instead of earning
bread for your family and shoeing this winsome
young gentleman's horse that 's just come frae the
North!   I'se warrant him nane of your whingeing
King George folk, but a gallant Gordon, at the
least o' him."

The eyes of the assembly were now turned upon
Waverley, who took the opportunity to beg the
smith to shoe his guide's horse with all speed, as
he wished to proceed on his journey; for he had
heard enough to make him sensible that there
would be danger in delaying long in this place.
The smith's eyes rested on him with a look of
displeasure and suspicion, not lessened by the
eagerness with which his wife enforced Waverley's
mandate.   " D' ye hear what the weel-favoured
young gentleman says, ye drunken ne'er-do-good ?"

5

"And what may your name be, sir?" quoth Mucklewrath.

"It is of no consequence to you, my friend, provided I pay your labour."

"But it may be of consequence to the state, sir," replied an old farmer, smelling strongly of whisky and peat-smoke; "and I doubt we maun delay your journey till you have seen the laird."

"You certainly," said Waverley, haughtily, "will find it both difficult and dangerous to detain me, unless you can produce some proper authority."

There was a pause and a whisper among the crowd, — "Secretary Murray;" "Lord Lewis Gordon;" "Maybe the Chevalier himsell!" Such were the surmises that passed hurriedly among them, and there was obviously an increased disposition to resist Waverley's departure. He attempted to argue mildly with them; but his voluntary ally, Mrs. Mucklewrath, broke in upon and drowned his expostulations, taking his part with an abusive violence which was all set down to Edward's account by those on whom it was bestowed. "*Ye'll* stop ony gentleman that's the Prince's freend?" for she too, though with other feelings, had adopted the general opinion respecting Waverley. "I daur ye to touch him," spreading abroad her long and muscular fingers, garnished with claws which a vulture might have envied. "I'll set my ten commandments in the face o' the first loon that lays a finger on him."

"Gae hame, gudewife," quoth the farmer aforesaid; "it wad better set you to be nursing the gudeman's bairns than to be deaving us here."

"*His* bairns?" retorted the Amazon, regarding her husband with a grin of ineffable contempt, — "*His* bairns!

6

' O gin ye were dead, gudeman,
    And a green turf on your head, gudeman!
Then I wad ware my widowhood
    Upon a ranting Highlandman.' "

This canticle, which excited a suppressed titter
among the younger part of the audience, totally
overcame the patience of the taunted man of the
anvil. "Deil be in me but I'll put this het gad
down her throat!" cried he, in an ecstasy of wrath,
snatching a bar from the forge; and he might have
executed his threat, had he not been withheld by a
part of the mob, while the rest endeavoured to force
the termagant out of his presence.

Waverley meditated a retreat in the confusion,
but his horse was nowhere to be seen. At length
he observed, at some distance, his faithful attendant, Ebenezer, who, as soon as he had perceived the
turn matters were likely to take, had withdrawn
both horses from the press, and mounted on the
one and holding the other, answered the loud and
repeated calls of Waverley for his horse: "Na, na!
if ye are nae friend to kirk and the king, and are
detained as siccan a person, ye maun answer to
honest men of the country for breach of contract;
and I maun keep the naig and the walise for
damage and expense, in respect my horse and mysell will lose to-morrow's day's-wark, besides the
afternoon preaching."

Edward, out of patience, hemmed in and hustled
by the rabble on every side, and every moment expecting personal violence, resolved to try measures
of intimidation, and at length drew a pocket-pistol,
threatening, on the one hand, to shoot whomsoever
dared to stop him, and on the other, menacing
Ebenezer with a similar doom if he stirred a foot

7

with the horses. The sapient Partridge says that
one man with a pistol is equal to a hundred un-
armed, because, though he can shoot but one of the
multitude, yet no one knows but that he himself
may be that luckless individual. The *levy en masse*
of Cairnvreckan would therefore probably have
given way, nor would Ebenezer, whose natural pale-
ness had waxed three shades more cadaverous, have
ventured to dispute a mandate so enforced, had not
the Vulcan of the village, eager to discharge upon
some more worthy object the fury which his helpmate had provoked, and not ill satisfied to find such
an object in Waverley, rushed at him with the red-
hot bar of iron with such determination as made the
discharge of his pistol an act of self-defence. The
unfortunate man fell; and while Edward, thrilled
with a natural horror at the incident, neither had
presence of mind to unsheathe his sword nor to
draw his remaining pistol, the populace threw themselves upon him, disarmed him, and were about to
use him with great violence, when the appearance
of a venerable clergyman, the pastor of the parish,
put a curb on their fury.

This worthy man (none of the Goukthrapples or
Rentowels) maintained his character with the common people, although he preached the practical
fruits of Christian faith, as well as its abstract tenets, and was respected by the higher orders, notwithstanding he declined soothing their speculative
errors by converting the pulpit of the gospel into
a school of heathen morality. Perhaps it is owing
to this mixture of faith and practice in his doctrine
that although his memory has formed a sort of era
in the annals of Cairnvreckan, so that the parishioners, to denote what befell Sixty Years since, still

say it happened "in good Mr. Morton's time," I
have never been able to discover which he belonged
to, the evangelical, or the moderate party in the
kirk. Nor do I hold the circumstance of much
moment, since, in my own remembrance, the one was
headed by an Erskine, the other by a Robertson.[1]

Mr. Morton had been alarmed by the discharge
of the pistol and the increasing hubbub around the
smithy. His first attention, after he had directed
the bystanders to detain Waverley, but to abstain
from injuring him, was turned to the body of
Mucklewrath, over which his wife, in a revulsion
of feeling, was weeping, howling, and tearing her
elf-locks, in a state little short of distraction. On
raising up the smith, the first discovery was that
he was alive, and the next that he was likely to
live as long as if he had never heard the report of
a pistol in his life. He had made a narrow escape,
however; the bullet had grazed his head, and
stunned him for a moment or two, which trance
terror and confusion of spirit had prolonged somewhat longer. He now arose to demand vengeance
on the person of Waverley, and with difficulty acquiesced in the proposal of Mr. Morton that he
should be carried before the laird, as a justice of
peace, and placed at his disposal. The rest of the
assistants unanimously agreed to the measure
recommended; even Mrs. Mucklewrath, who had

[1] The Rev. John Erskine, D.D., an eminent Scottish divine and
a most excellent man, headed the Evangelical party in the Church
of Scotland at the time when the celebrated Dr. Robertson, the
historian, was the leader of the Moderate party. These two distinguished persons were colleagues in the Old Gray Friars' Church,
Edinburgh; and however much they differed in church politics,
preserved the most perfect harmony as private friends, and as
clergymen serving the same cure.

begun to recover from her hysterics, whimpered forth, " She wadna say naething against what the minister proposed ; he was e'en ower gude for his trade, and she hoped to see him wi' a dainty decent bishop's gown on his back, — a comelier sight than your Geneva cloaks and bands, I wis."

All controversy being thus laid aside, Waverley, escorted by the whole inhabitants of the village who were not bed-ridden, was conducted to the house of Cairnvreckan, which was about half a mile distant.

CHAPTER II

MAJOR MELVILLE of Cairnvreckan, an elderly gentleman who had spent his youth in the military service, received Mr. Morton with great kindness, and our hero with civility, which the equivocal circumstances wherein Edward was placed rendered constrained and distant.

The nature of the smith's hurt was inquired into; and as the actual injury was likely to prove trifling, and the circumstances in which it was received rendered the infliction, on Edward's part, a natural act of self-defence, the major conceived he might dismiss that matter, on Waverley's depositing in his hands a small sum for the benefit of the wounded person.

" I could wish, sir," continued the major, " that my duty terminated here; but it is necessary that we should have some further inquiry into the cause of your journey through the country at this unfortunate and distracted time."

Mr. Ebenezer Cruickshanks now stood forth, and communicated to the magistrate all he knew or suspected, from the reserve of Waverley and the evasions of Callum Beg. The horse upon which Edward rode, he said, he knew to belong to Vich Ian Vohr, though he dared not tax Edward's former attendant with the fact, lest he should have his

11

house and stables burned over his head some night by that godless gang, the Mac-Ivors. He concluded by exaggerating his own services to kirk and state, as having been the means, under God (as he modestly qualified the assertion), of attaching this suspicious and formidable delinquent. He intimated hopes of future reward, and of instant reimbursement for loss of time, and even of character, by travelling on the state business on the fast-day.

To this Major Melville answered, with great composure, that so far from claiming any merit in this affair, Mr. Cruickshanks ought to deprecate the imposition of a very heavy fine for neglecting to lodge, in terms of the recent proclamation, an account with the nearest magistrate of any stranger who came to his inn; that as Mr. Cruickshanks boasted so much of religion and loyalty, he should not impute this conduct to disaffection, but only suppose that his zeal for kirk and state had been lulled asleep by the opportunity of charging a stranger with double horse-hire; that, however, feeling himself incompetent to decide singly upon the conduct of a person of such importance, he should reserve it for consideration of the next quarter-sessions. Now, our history for the present saith no more of him of the Candlestick, who wended, dolorous and malcontent, back to his own dwelling.

Major Melville then commanded the villagers to return to their homes, excepting two, who officiated as constables, and whom he directed to wait below. The apartment was thus cleared of every person but Mr. Morton, whom the major invited to remain, a sort of factor, who acted as clerk, and Waverley himself. There ensued a painful and embarrassed pause, till Major Melville, looking upon Waverley

12

with much compassion, and often consulting a paper or memorandum which he held in his hand, requested to know his name.

"Edward Waverley."

"I thought so. Late of the —— dragoons, and nephew of Sir Everard Waverley, of Waverley Honour?"

"The same."

"Young gentleman, I am extremely sorry that this painful duty has fallen to my lot."

"Duty, Major Melville, renders apologies superfluous."

"True, sir; permit me, therefore, to ask you how your time has been disposed of since you obtained leave of absence from your regiment, several weeks ago, until the present moment?"

"My reply," said Waverley, "to so general a question must be guided by the nature of the charge which renders it necessary. I request to know what that charge is, and upon what authority I am forcibly detained to reply to it?"

"The charge, Mr. Waverley, I grieve to say, is of a very high nature, and affects your character both as a soldier and a subject. In the former capacity, you are charged with spreading mutiny and rebellion among the men you commanded, and setting them the example of desertion, by prolonging your own absence from the regiment, contrary to the express orders of your commanding officer. The civil crime of which you stand accused is that of high treason and levying war against the king, — the highest delinquency of which a subject can be guilty."

"And by what authority am I detained to reply to such heinous calumnies?"

"By one which you must not dispute, nor I disobey."

He handed to Waverley a warrant from the Supreme Criminal Court of Scotland, in full form, for apprehending and securing the person of Edward Waverley, Esq., suspected of treasonable practices and other high crimes and misdemeanours.

The astonishment which Waverley expressed at this communication was imputed by Major Melville to conscious guilt, while Mr. Morton was rather disposed to construe it into the surprise of innocence unjustly suspected. There was something true in both conjectures; for although Edward's mind acquitted him of the crime with which he was charged, yet a hasty review of his own conduct convinced him he might have great difficulty in establishing his innocence to the satisfaction of others.

"It is a very painful part of this painful business," said Major Melville, after a pause, "that, under so grave a charge, I must necessarily request to see such papers as you have on your person."

"You shall, sir, without reserve," said Edward, throwing his pocket-book and memorandums upon the table; "there is but one with which I could wish you would dispense."

"I am afraid, Mr. Waverley, I can indulge you with no reservation."

"You shall see it then, sir; and as it can be of no service, I beg it may be returned."

He took from his bosom the lines he had that morning received, and presented them, with the envelope. The major perused them in silence, and directed his clerk to make a copy of them. He then wrapped the copy in the envelope, and placing it on the table before him, returned the original to Waverley, with an air of melancholy gravity.

After indulging the prisoner — for such our hero must now be considered—with what he thought a reasonable time for reflection, Major Melville resumed his examination, premising that as Mr. Waverley seemed to object to general questions, his interrogatories should be as specific as his information permitted. He then proceeded in his investigation, dictating, as he went on, the import of the questions and answers to the amanuensis, by whom it was written down.

"Did Mr. Waverley know one Humphry Houghton, a non-commissioned officer in Gardiner's dragoons ? "

"Certainly; he was sergeant of my troop, and son of a tenant of my uncle."

" Exactly; and had a considerable share of your confidence, and an influence among his comrades ? "

" I had never occasion to repose confidence in a person of his description," answered Waverley. " I favoured Sergeant Houghton as a clever, active young fellow, and I believe his fellow-soldiers respected him accordingly."

" But you used through this man," answered Major Melville, " to communicate with such of your troop as were recruited upon Waverley Honour ? "

" Certainly ; the poor fellows, finding themselves in a regiment chiefly composed of Scotch or Irish, looked up to me in any of their little distresses, and naturally made their countryman, and sergeant, their spokesman on such occasions."

" Sergeant Houghton's influence," continued the major, " extended, then, particularly over those

15

soldiers who followed you to the regiment from your uncle's estate ? "

" Surely. But what is that to the present purpose ? "

" To that I am just coming, and I beseech your candid reply. Have you, since leaving the regiment, held any correspondence, direct or indirect, with this Sergeant Houghton ? "

" I! — I hold correspondence with a man of his rank and situation ? How, or for what purpose ? "

" That you are to explain. But did you not, for example, send to him for some books ? "

" You remind me of a trifling commission," said Waverley, " which I gave Sergeant Houghton, because my servant could not read. I do recollect I bade him, by letter, select some books, of which I sent him a list, and send them to me at Tully-Veolan."

" And of what description were those books ? "

" They related almost entirely to elegant literature ; they were designed for a lady's perusal."

" Were there not, Mr. Waverley, treasonable tracts and pamphlets among them ? "

" There were some political treatises, into which I hardly looked. They had been sent to me by the officiousness of a kind friend whose heart is more to be esteemed than his prudence or political sagacity ; they seemed to be dull compositions."

" That friend," continued the persevering inquirer, " was a Mr. Pembroke, a nonjuring clergyman, the author of two treasonable works, of which the manuscripts were found among your baggage ? "

" But of which, I give you my honour as a gentleman," replied Waverley, " I never read six pages."

" I am not your judge, Mr. Waverley ; your exami-

16

nation will be transmitted elsewhere. And now to proceed. Do you know a person that passes by the name of Wily Will, or Will Ruthven ? "

" I never heard of such a name till this moment."

" Did you never through such a person, or any other person, communicate with Sergeant Humphry Houghton, instigating him to desert, with as many of his comrades as he could seduce to join him, and unite with the Highlanders and other rebels now in arms under the command of the young Pretender ? "

" I assure you I am not only entirely guiltless of the plot you have laid to my charge, but I detest it from the very bottom of my soul, nor would I be guilty of such treachery to gain a throne, either for myself or any other man alive."

" Yet when I consider this envelope, in the handwriting of one of those misguided gentlemen who are now in arms against their country, and the verses which it enclosed, I cannot but find some analogy between the enterprise I have mentioned and the exploit of Wogan, which the writer seems to expect you should imitate."

Waverley was struck with the coincidence, but denied that the wishes or expectations of the letter-writer were to be regarded as proofs of a charge otherwise chimerical.

" But if I am rightly informed, your time was spent, during your absence from the regiment, between the house of this Highland chieftain and that of Mr. Bradwardine of Bradwardine, also in arms for this unfortunate cause ? "

" I do not mean to disguise it ; but I do deny most resolutely being privy to any of their designs against the government."

17

" You do not, however, I presume, intend to deny that you attended your host, Glennaquoich, to a rendezvous, where, under a pretence of a general hunting-match, most of the accomplices of his treason were assembled to concert measures for taking arms ? "

" I acknowledge having been at such a meeting," said Waverley; " but I neither heard nor saw anything which could give it the character you affix to it."

" From thence you proceeded," continued the magistrate, " with Glennaquoich and a part of his clan to join the army of the young Pretender, and returned, after having paid your homage to him, to discipline and arm the remainder, and unite them to his bands on their way southward ? "

" I never went with Glennaquoich on such an errand. I never so much as heard that the person whom you mention was in the country."

He then detailed the history of his misfortune at the hunting-match, and added that on his return he found himself suddenly deprived of his commission, and did not deny that he then, for the first time, observed symptoms which indicated a disposition in the Highlanders to take arms; but added that having no inclination to join their cause, and no longer any reason for remaining in Scotland, he was now on his return to his native country, to which he had been summoned by those who had a right to direct his motions, as Major Melville would perceive from the letters on the table.

Major Melville accordingly perused the letters of Richard Waverley, of Sir Everard, and of Aunt Rachel; but the inferences he drew from them were different from what Waverley expected. They held

the language of discontent with government, threw
out no obscure hints of revenge, and that of poor
Aunt Rachel, which plainly asserted the justice of
the Stewart cause, was held to contain the open
avowal of what the others only ventured to insinuate.

"Permit me another question, Mr. Waverley,"
said Major Melville, — "Did you not receive repeated letters from your commanding-officer, warning you and commanding you to return to your
post, and acquainting you with the use made of
your name to spread discontent among your
soldiers ? "

"I never did, Major Melville. One letter, indeed, I received from him, containing a civil intimation of his wish that I would employ my leave
of absence otherwise than in constant residence at
Bradwardine, as to which, I own, I thought he was
not called on to interfere; and, finally, I received,
on the same day on which I observed myself superseded in the Gazette, a second letter from Colonel
Gardiner, commanding me to join the regiment, —
an order which, owing to my absence, already mentioned and accounted for, I received too late to be
obeyed. If there were any intermediate letters, —
and certainly from the colonel's high character I
think it probable that there were, — they have
never reached me."

"I have omitted, Mr. Waverley," continued
Major Melville, " to inquire after a matter of less
consequence, but which has nevertheless been publicly talked of to your disadvantage. It is said
that, a treasonable toast having been proposed in
your hearing and presence, you, holding his Majesty's commission, suffered the task of resenting it

19

to devolve upon another gentleman of the company. This, sir, cannot be charged against you in a court of justice; but if, as I am informed, the officers of your regiment requested an explanation of such a rumour, as a gentleman and soldier I cannot but be surprised that you did not afford it to them."

This was too much. Beset and pressed on every hand by accusations in which gross falsehoods were blended with such circumstances of truth as could not fail to procure them credit, — alone, unfriended, and in a strange land, Waverley almost gave up his life and honour for lost; and leaning his head upon his hand, resolutely refused to answer any further questions, since the fair and candid statement he had already made had only served to furnish arms against him.

Without expressing either surprise or displeasure at the change in Waverley's manner, Major Melville proceeded composedly to put several other queries to him. "What does it avail me to answer you?" said Edward, sullenly. "You appear convinced of my guilt, and wrest every reply I have made to support your own preconceived opinion. Enjoy your supposed triumph, then, and torment me no further. If I am capable of the cowardice and treachery your charge burdens me with, I am not worthy to be believed in any reply I can make to you. If I am not deserving of your suspicion, — and God and my own conscience bear evidence with me that it is so, — then I do not see why I should, by my candour, lend my accusers arms against my innocence. There is no reason I should answer a word more, and I am determined to abide by this resolution." And again he resumed his posture of sullen and determined silence.

"Allow me," said the magistrate, "to remind you of one reason that may suggest the propriety of a candid and open confession. The inexperience of youth, Mr. Waverley, lays it open to the plans of the more designing and artful; and one of your friends, at least, — I mean Mac-Ivor of Glennaquoich, — ranks high in the latter class, as, from your apparent ingenuousness, youth, and unacquaintance with the manners of the Highlands, I should be disposed to place you among the former. In such a case, a false step, or error, like yours, which I shall be happy to consider as involuntary, may be atoned for, and I would willingly act as intercessor. But as you must necessarily be acquainted with the strength of the individuals in this country who have assumed arms, with their means, and with their plans, I must expect you will merit this mediation on my part by a frank and candid avowal of all that has come to your knowledge upon these heads. In which case, I think I can venture to promise that a very short personal restraint will be the only ill consequence that can arise from your accession to these unhappy intrigues."

Waverley listened with great composure until the end of this exhortation, when, springing from his seat with an energy he had not yet displayed, he replied : "Major Melville, — since that is your name, — I have hitherto answered your questions with candour, or declined them with temper, because their import concerned myself alone; but as you presume to esteem me mean enough to commence informer against others, who received me, whatever may be their public misconduct, as a guest and friend, — I declare to you that I consider your questions as an insult infinitely more offensive

21

than your calumnious suspicions; and that since my hard fortune permits me no other mode of resenting them than by verbal defiance, you should sooner have my heart out of my bosom than a single syllable of information on subjects which I could only become acquainted with in the full confidence of unsuspecting hospitality."

Mr. Morton and the major looked at each other; and the former, who in the course of the examination had been repeatedly troubled with a sorry rheum, had recourse to his snuff-box and his handkerchief.

"Mr. Waverley," said the major, "my present situation prohibits me alike from giving or receiving offence, and I will not protract a discussion which approaches to either. I am afraid I must sign a warrant for detaining you in custody; but this house shall for the present be your prison. I fear I cannot persuade you to accept a share of our supper? — [Edward shook his head] — but I will order refreshments in your apartment."

Our hero bowed and withdrew, under guard of the officers of justice, to a small but handsome room, where, declining all offers of food or wine, he flung himself on the bed, and stupefied by the harassing events and mental fatigue of this miserable day, he sunk into a deep and heavy slumber. This was more than he himself could have expected; but it is mentioned of the North American Indians, when at the stake of torture, that on the least intermission of agony they will sleep until the fire is applied to awaken them.

CHAPTER III

MAJOR MELVILLE had detained Mr. Morton during his examination of Waverley, both because he thought he might derive assistance from his practical good sense and approved loyalty, and also because it was agreeable to have a witness of unimpeached candour and veracity to proceedings which touched the honour and safety of a young Englishman of high rank and family, and the expectant heir of a large fortune. Every step he knew would be rigorously canvassed, and it was his business to place the justice and integrity of his own conduct beyond the limits of question.

When Waverley retired, the laird and clergyman of Cairnvreckan sat down in silence to their evening meal. While the servants were in attendance, neither chose to say anything on the circumstances which occupied their minds, and neither felt it easy to speak upon any other. The youth and apparent frankness of Waverley stood in strong contrast to the shades of suspicion which darkened around him, and he had a sort of *naïveté* and openness of demeanour that seemed to belong to one unhackneyed in the ways of intrigue, and which pleaded highly in his favour.

Each mused over the particulars of the examination, and each viewed it through the medium of his

23

own feelings. Both were men of ready and acute talent, and both were equally competent to combine various parts of evidence, and to deduce from them the necessary conclusions. But the wide difference of their habits and education often occasioned a great discrepancy in their respective deductions from admitted premises.

Major Melville had been versed in camps and cities; he was vigilant by profession and cautious from experience, had met with much evil in the world, and therefore, though himself an upright magistrate and an honourable man, his opinions of others were always strict, and sometimes unjustly severe. Mr. Morton, on the contrary, had passed from the literary pursuits of a college, where he was beloved by his companions and respected by his teachers, to the ease and simplicity of his present charge, where his opportunities of witnessing evil were few, and never dwelt upon but in order to encourage repentance and amendment, and where the love and respect of his parishioners repaid his affectionate zeal in their behalf, by endeavouring to disguise from him what they knew would give him the most acute pain, — namely, their own occasional transgressions of the duties which it was the business of his life to recommend. Thus it was a common saying in the neighbourhood (though both were popular characters) that the laird knew only the ill in the parish, and the minister only the good.

A love of letters, though kept in subordination to his clerical studies and duties, also distinguished the pastor of Cairnvreckan, and had tinged his mind in earlier days with a slight feeling of romance, which no after incidents of real life had entirely dissipated. The early loss of an amiable young woman whom he had married for love, and who was quickly followed to the grave by an only child, had also served, even after the lapse of many years, to soften a disposition naturally mild and contemplative. His feelings on the present occasion were therefore likely to differ from those of the severe disciplinarian, strict magistrate, and distrustful man of the world.

When the servants had withdrawn, the silence of both parties continued, until Major Melville, filling his glass and pushing the bottle to Mr. Morton, commenced.

"A distressing affair this, Mr. Morton. I fear this youngster has brought himself within the compass of a halter."

"God forbid!" answered the clergyman.

"Marry, and amen," said the temporal magistrate; "but I think even your merciful logic will hardly deny the conclusion."

"Surely, Major," answered the clergyman, "I should hope it might be averted, for aught we have heard to-night?"

"Indeed!" replied Melville. "But, my good parson, you are one of those who would communicate to every criminal the benefit of clergy."

"Unquestionably I would. Mercy and long-suffering are the grounds of the doctrine I am called to teach."

"True, religiously speaking; but mercy to a criminal may be gross injustice to the community. I don't speak of this young fellow in particular, who I heartily wish may be able to clear himself, for I like both his modesty and his spirit; but I fear he has rushed upon his fate."

"And why? Hundreds of misguided gentlemen are now in arms against the government, many, doubtless, upon principles which education and early prejudice have gilded with the names of patriotism and heroism. Justice, when she selects her victims from such a multitude (for surely all will not be destroyed), must regard the moral motive. He whom ambition or hope of personal advantage has led to disturb the peace of a well-ordered government, let him fall a victim to the laws; but surely youth, misled by the wild visions of chivalry and imaginary loyalty, may plead for pardon."

"If visionary chivalry and imaginary loyalty come within the predicament of high treason," replied the magistrate, "I know no court in Christendom, my dear Mr. Morton, where they can sue out their Habeas Corpus."

"But I cannot see that this youth's guilt is at all established to my satisfaction," said the clergyman.

"Because your good-nature blinds your good sense," replied Major Melville. "Observe now: this young man, descended of a family of hereditary Jacobites, his uncle the leader of the Tory interest in the county of ——, his father a disobliged and discontented courtier, his tutor a non-juror and the author of two treasonable volumes, — this youth, I say, enters into Gardiner's dragoons, bringing with him a body of young fellows from his uncle's estate who have not stickled at avowing, in their way, the High-Church principles they learned at Waverley Honour, in their disputes with their comrades. To these young men Waverley is unusually attentive; they are supplied with money beyond a soldier's wants and inconsistent with his discipline, and are under the management of a favourite ser-

26

geant, through whom they hold an unusually close communication with their captain, and affect to consider themselves as independent of the other officers, and superior to their comrades."

"All this, my dear Major, is the natural consequence of their attachment to their young landlord, and of their finding themselves in a regiment levied chiefly in the north of Ireland and the west of Scotland, and of course among comrades disposed to quarrel with them, both as Englishmen and as members of the Church of England."

"Well said, parson!" replied the magistrate; "I would some of your synod heard you. But let me go on. This young man obtains leave of absence, goes to Tully-Veolan, — the principles of the Baron of Bradwardine are pretty well known, not to mention that this lad's uncle brought him off in the year Fifteen; he engages there in a brawl, in which he is said to have disgraced the commission he bore. Colonel Gardiner writes to him, first mildly, then more sharply, — I think you will not doubt his having done so, since he says so; the mess invite him to explain the quarrel, in which he is said to have been involved : he neither replies to his commander nor his comrades. In the meanwhile his soldiers become mutinous and disorderly, and at length, when the rumour of this unhappy rebellion becomes general, his favourite, Sergeant Houghton, and another fellow are detected in correspondence with a French emissary, accredited, as he says, by Captain Waverley, who urges him, according to the men's confession, to desert with the troop and join their captain, who was with Prince Charles. In the meanwhile this trusty captain is, by his own admission, residing at Glennaquoich with the most

27

active, subtle, and desperate Jacobite in Scotland; he goes with him at least as far as their famous hunting rendezvous, and I fear a little farther. Meanwhile two other summonses are sent him, one warning him of the disturbances in his troop, another peremptorily ordering him to repair to the regiment, — which, indeed, common sense might have dictated, when he observed rebellion thickening all round him. He returns an absolute refusal, and throws up his commission."

"He had been already deprived of it," said Mr. Morton.

"But he regrets," replied Melville, "that the measure had anticipated his resignation. His baggage is seized at his quarters and at Tully-Veolan, and is found to contain a stock of pestilent jacobitical pamphlets, enough to poison a whole country, besides the unprinted lucubrations of his worthy friend and tutor Mr. Pembroke."

"He says he never read them," answered the minister.

"In an ordinary case I should believe him," replied the magistrate; "for they are as stupid and pedantic in composition as mischievous in their tenets. But can you suppose anything but value for the principles they maintain would induce a young man of his age to lug such trash about with him? Then, when news arrive of the approach of the rebels, he sets out in a sort of disguise, refusing to tell his name, and, if yon old fanatic tell truth, attended by a very suspicious character, and mounted on a horse known to have belonged to Glennaquoich, and bearing on his person letters from his family expressing high rancour against the house of Brunswick, and a copy of verses in praise of one Wogan,

who abjured the service of the Parliament to join
the Highland insurgents, when in arms to restore
the house of Stewart, with a body of English cavalry, — the very counterpart of his own plot, —
and summed up with a ' Go thou and do likewise,'
from that loyal subject and most safe and peaceable
character, Fergus Mac-Ivor of Glennaquoich, Vich
Ian Vohr, and so forth. And, lastly," continued
Major Melville, warming in the detail of his arguments, " where do we find this second edition of
Cavalier Wogan ? Why, truly, in the very track
most proper for execution of his design, and pistol-
ling the first of the king's subjects who ventures to
question his intentions."

Mr. Morton prudently abstained from argument,
which he perceived would only harden the magistrate in his opinion, and merely asked how he intended to dispose of the prisoner ?

"It is a question of some difficulty, considering
the state of the country," said Major Melville.

"Could you not detain him (being such a gentle-
man-like young man) here in your own house, out
of harm's way, till this storm blow over ? "

" My good friend," said Major Melville, " neither
your house nor mine will be long out of harm's
way, even were it legal to confine him here. I
have just learned that the commander-in-chief, who
marched into the Highlands to seek out and disperse the insurgents, has declined giving them battle at Corryerick, and marched on northward with
all the disposable force of government to Inverness,
John-o'-Groat's House, or the devil, for what I
know, leaving the road to the Low Country open
and undefended to the Highland army."

" Good God ! " said the clergyman. " Is the man
a coward, a traitor, or an idiot ? "

"None of the three, I believe," answered Melville. "Sir John has the commonplace courage of a common soldier, is honest enough, does what he is commanded, and understands what is told him; but is as fit to act for himself in circumstances of importance as I, my dear parson, to occupy your pulpit."

This important public intelligence naturally diverted the discourse from Waverley for some time; at length, however, the subject was resumed.

"I believe," said Major Melville, "that I must give this young man in charge to some of the detached parties of armed volunteers who were lately sent out to overawe the disaffected districts. They are now recalled towards Stirling, and a small body comes this way to-morrow or next day, commanded by the westland man — what's his name? You saw him, and said he was the very model of one of Cromwell's military saints."

"Gilfillan the Cameronian," answered Mr. Morton. "I wish the young gentleman may be safe with him. Strange things are done in the heat and hurry of minds in so agitating a crisis, and I fear Gilfillan is of a sect which has suffered persecution without learning mercy."

"He has only to lodge Mr. Waverley in Stirling Castle," said the major; "I will give strict injunctions to treat him well. I really cannot devise any better mode for securing him, and I fancy you would hardly advise me to encounter the responsibility of setting him at liberty."

"But you will have no objection to my seeing him to-morrow in private?" said the minister.

"None, certainly; your loyalty and character are my warrant. But with what view do you make the request?"

"Simply," replied Mr. Morton, "to make the experiment whether he may not be brought to communicate to me some circumstances which may hereafter be useful to alleviate, if not to exculpate his conduct."

The friends now parted and retired to rest, each filled with the most anxious reflections on the state of the country.

CHAPTER IV

WAVERLEY awoke in the morning, from troubled dreams and unrefreshing slumbers, to a full consciousness of the horrors of his situation. How it might terminate he knew not. He might be delivered up to military law, which, in the midst of civil war, was not likely to be scrupulous in the choice of its victims or the quality of the evidence. Nor did he feel much more comfortable at the thoughts of a trial before a Scottish court of justice, where he knew the laws and forms differed in many respects from those of England, and had been taught to believe, however erroneously, that the liberty and rights of the subject were less carefully protected. A sentiment of bitterness rose in his mind against the government, which he considered as the cause of his embarrassment and peril, and he cursed internally his scrupulous rejection of MacIvor's invitation to accompany him to the field.

"Why did not I," he said to himself, "like other men of honour, take the earliest opportunity to welcome to Britain the descendant of her ancient kings and lineal heir of her throne ? Why did not I —

> Unthread the rude eye of rebellion,
> And welcome home again discarded faith,
> Seek out Prince Charles, and fall before his feet ?

32

All that has been recorded of excellence and worth in the house of Waverley has been founded upon their loyal faith to the house of Stewart. From the interpretation which this Scotch magistrate has put upon the letters of my uncle and father, it is plain that I ought to have understood them as marshalling me to the course of my ancestors; and it has been my gross dulness, joined to the obscurity of expression which they adopted for the sake of security, that has confounded my judgment. Had I yielded to the first generous impulse of indignation when I learned that my honour was practised upon, how different had been my present situation! I had then been free and in arms, fighting, like my forefathers, for love, for loyalty, and for fame. And now I am here, netted and in the toils, at the disposal of a suspicious, stern, and cold-hearted man, perhaps to be turned over to the solitude of a dungeon, or the infamy of a public execution. Oh, Fergus, how true has your prophecy proved; and how speedy, how very speedy, has been its accomplishment!"

While Edward was ruminating on these painful subjects of contemplation, and very naturally, though not quite so justly, bestowing upon the reigning dynasty that blame which was due to chance, or, in part at least, to his own unreflecting conduct, Mr. Morton availed himself of Major Melville's permission to pay him an early visit.

Waverley's first impulse was to intimate a desire that he might not be disturbed with questions or conversation; but he suppressed it upon observing the benevolent and reverend appearance of the clergyman who had rescued him from the immediate violence of the villagers.

"I believe, sir," said the unfortunate young man, "that in any other circumstances I should have had as much gratitude to express to you as the safety of my life may be worth; but such is the present tumult of my mind, and such is my anticipation of what I am yet likely to endure, that I can hardly offer you thanks for your interposition."

Mr. Morton replied "that, far from making any claim upon his good opinion, his only wish and the sole purpose of his visit was to find out the means of deserving it. My excellent friend Major Melville," he continued, "has feelings and duties, as a soldier and public functionary, by which I am not fettered; nor can I always coincide in opinions which he forms, perhaps with too little allowance for the imperfections of human nature." He paused, and then proceeded: "I do not intrude myself on your confidence, Mr. Waverley, for the purpose of learning any circumstances, the knowledge of which can be prejudicial either to yourself or to others; but I own my earnest wish is, that you would intrust me with any particulars which could lead to your exculpation. I can solemnly assure you they will be deposited with a faithful and, to the extent of his limited powers, a zealous agent."

"You are, sir, I presume, a Presbyterian clergyman?" Mr. Morton bowed. "Were I to be guided by the prepossessions of education, I might distrust your friendly professions in my case; but I have observed that similar prejudices are nourished in this country against your professional brethren of the Episcopal persuasion, and I am willing to believe them equally unfounded in both cases."

"Evil to him that thinks otherwise," said Mr.

Morton, " or who holds church government and ceremonies as the exclusive gauge of Christian faith or moral virtue."

" But," continued Waverley, " I cannot perceive why I should trouble you with a detail of particulars out of which, after revolving them as carefully as possible in my recollection, I find myself unable to explain much of what is charged against me. I know, indeed, that I am innocent, but I hardly see how I can hope to prove myself so."

" It is for that very reason, Mr. Waverley," said the clergyman, " that I venture to solicit your confidence. My knowledge of individuals in this country is pretty general, and can upon occasion be extended. Your situation will, I fear, preclude your taking those active steps for recovering intelligence or tracing imposture which I would willingly undertake in your behalf ; and if you are not benefited by my exertions, at least they cannot be prejudicial to you."

Waverley, after a few minutes' reflection, was convinced that his reposing confidence in Mr. Morton, so far as he himself was concerned, could hurt neither Mr. Bradwardine nor Fergus Mac-Ivor, both of whom had openly assumed arms against the government, and that it might possibly, if the professions of his new friend corresponded in sincerity with the earnestness of his expression, be of some service to himself. He therefore ran briefly over most of the events with which the reader is already acquainted, suppressing his attachment to Flora, and indeed neither mentioning her nor Rose Bradwardine in the course of his narrative.

Mr. Morton seemed particularly struck with the account of Waverley's visit to Donald Bean Lean.

"I am glad," he said, "you did not mention this circumstance to the major. It is capable of great misconstruction on the part of those who do not consider the power of curiosity and the influence of romance as motives of youthful conduct. When I was a young man like you, Mr. Waverley, any such harebrained expedition (I beg your pardon for the expression) would have had inexpressible charms for me. But there are men in the world who will not believe that danger and fatigue are often incurred without any very adequate cause, and therefore who are sometimes led to assign motives of action entirely foreign to the truth. This man Bean Lean is renowned through the country as a sort of Robin Hood, and the stories which are told of his address and enterprise are the common tales of the winter fireside. He certainly possesses talents beyond the rude sphere in which he moves; and being neither destitute of ambition, nor encumbered with scruples, he will probably attempt, by every means, to distinguish himself during the period of these unhappy commotions." Mr. Morton then made a careful memorandum of the various particulars of Waverley's interview with Donald Bean, and the other circumstances which he had communicated.

The interest which this good man seemed to take in his misfortunes, above all the full confidence he appeared to repose in his innocence, had the natural effect of softening Edward's heart, whom the coldness of Major Melville had taught to believe that the world was leagued to oppress him. He shook Mr. Morton warmly by the hand, and assuring him that his kindness and sympathy had relieved his mind of a heavy load, told him that

36

whatever might be his own fate, he belonged to a family who had both gratitude and the power of displaying it. The earnestness of his thanks called drops to the eyes of the worthy clergyman, who was doubly interested in the cause for which he had volunteered his services, by observing the genuine and undissembled feelings of his young friend.

Edward now inquired if Mr. Morton knew what was likely to be his destination.

"Stirling Castle," replied his friend; "and so far I am well pleased for your sake, for the governor is a man of honour and humanity. But I am more doubtful of your treatment upon the road; Major Melville is involuntarily obliged to intrust the custody of your person to another."

"I am glad of it," answered Waverley. "I detest that cold-blooded, calculating Scotch magistrate. I hope he and I shall never meet more. He had neither sympathy with my innocence nor with my wretchedness; and the petrifying accuracy with which he attended to every form of civility, while he tortured me by his questions, his suspicions, and his inferences, was as tormenting as the racks of the Inquisition. Do not vindicate him, my dear sir, for that I cannot bear with patience; tell me rather who is to have the charge of so important a state prisoner as I am."

"I believe a person called Gilfillan, — one of the sect who are termed Cameronians."

"I never heard of them before."

"They claim," said the clergyman, "to represent the more strict and severe Presbyterians, who, in Charles Second's and James Second's days, refused to profit by the Toleration, or Indulgence, as it was called, which was extended to others of that religion. They held conventicles in the open fields, and being treated with great violence and cruelty by the Scottish government, more than once took arms during those reigns. They take their name from their leader, Richard Cameron."

"I recollect," said Waverley. "But did not the triumph of Presbytery at the Revolution extinguish that sect?"

"By no means," replied Morton; "that great event fell yet far short of what they proposed, which was nothing less than the complete establishment of the Presbyterian Church, upon the grounds of the old Solemn League and Covenant. Indeed, I believe they scarce knew what they wanted; but being a numerous body of men, and not unacquainted with the use of arms, they kept themselves together as a separate party in the state, and at the time of the Union had nearly formed a most unnatural league with their old enemies, the Jacobites, to oppose that important national measure. Since that time their numbers have gradually diminished; but a good many are still to be found in the western counties, and several, with a better temper than in 1707, have now taken arms for government. This person, whom they call Gifted Gilfillan, has been long a leader among them, and now heads a small party, which will pass here to-day or to-morrow, on their march towards Stirling, under whose escort Major Melville proposes you shall travel. I would willingly speak to Gilfillan in your behalf; but having deeply imbibed all the prejudices of his sect, and being of the same fierce disposition, he would pay little regard to the remonstrances of an Erastian divine, as he would politely term me. And now farewell, my young friend, for the present; I must not weary out the major's indulgence, that I may obtain his permission to visit you again in the course of the day."

CHAPTER V

ABOUT noon Mr. Morton returned, and brought an invitation from Major Melville that Mr. Waverley would honour him with his company to dinner, notwithstanding the unpleasant affair which detained him at Cairnvreckan, from which he should heartily rejoice to see Mr. Waverley completely extricated. The truth was that Mr. Morton's favourable report and opinion had somewhat staggered the preconceptions of the old soldier concerning Edward's supposed accession to the mutiny in the regiment; and in the unfortunate state of the country, the mere suspicion of disaffection, or an inclination to join the insurgent Jacobites, might infer criminality indeed, but certainly not dishonour. Besides, a person whom the major trusted had reported to him (though, as it proved, inaccurately) a contradiction of the agitating news of the preceding evening. According to this second edition of the intelligence, the Highlanders had withdrawn from the Lowland frontier, with the purpose of following the army in their march to Inverness. The major was at a loss, indeed, to reconcile his information with the well-known abilities of some of the gentlemen in the Highland army; yet it was the course which was likely to be most agreeable to others. He remembered the same policy had detained them

40

in the North in the year 1715, and he anticipated a
similar termination to the insurrection as upon that
occasion.

This news put him in such good-humour that he
readily acquiesced in Mr. Morton's proposal to pay
some hospitable attention to his unfortunate guest,
and voluntarily added, he hoped the whole affair
would prove a youthful escapade which might be
easily atoned by a short confinement. The kind
mediator had some trouble to prevail on his young
friend to accept the invitation. He dared not urge
to him the real motive, which was a good-natured
wish to secure a favourable report of Waverley's
case from Major Melville to Governor Blakeney.
He remarked, from the flashes of our hero's spirit,
that touching upon this topic would be sure to defeat his purpose. He therefore pleaded that the
invitation argued the major's disbelief of any part
of the accusation which was inconsistent with
Waverley's conduct as a soldier and man of honour,
and that to decline his courtesy might be interpreted into a consciousness that it was unmerited.
In short, he so far satisfied Edward that the manly
and proper course was to meet the major on easy
terms, that, suppressing his strong dislike again to
encounter his cold and punctilious civility, Waverley agreed to be guided by his new friend.

The meeting at first was stiff and formal enough.
But Edward, having accepted the invitation, and
his mind being really soothed and relieved by the
kindness of Morton, held himself bound to behave
with ease, though he could not affect cordiality.
The major was somewhat of a *bon vivant*, and his
wine was excellent. He told his old campaign
stories, and displayed much knowledge of men and

41

manners. Mr. Morton had an internal fund of
placid and quiet gaiety which seldom failed to enliven any small party in which he found himself
pleasantly seated. Waverley, whose life was a
dream, gave ready way to the predominating impulse, and became the most lively of the party. He
had at all times remarkable natural powers of conversation, though easily silenced by discouragement.
On the present occasion he piqued himself upon
leaving on the minds of his companions a favourable impression of one who, under such disastrous
circumstances, could sustain his misfortunes with
ease and gaiety. His spirits, though not unyield-
ing, were abundantly elastic, and soon seconded
his efforts. The trio were engaged in very lively
discourse, apparently delighted with each other, and
the kind host was pressing a third bottle of Bur-
gundy, when the sound of a drum was heard at
some distance. The major, who in the glee of an
old soldier had forgot the duties of a magistrate,
cursed, with a muttered military oath, the circumstances which recalled him to his official functions.
He rose and went towards the window, which commanded a very near view of the high-road, and he
was followed by his guests.

The drum advanced, beating no measured martial tune, but a kind of rub-a-dub-dub, like that
with which the fire-drum startles the slumbering
artisans of a Scotch burgh. It is the object of this
history to do justice to all men; I must therefore
record, in justice to the drummer, that he protested
he could beat any known march or point of war
known in the British army, and had accordingly
commenced with "Dumbarton's Drums," when he
was silenced by Gifted Gilfillan, the commander of

the party, who refused to permit his followers to
move to this profane, and even, as he said, "perse-
cutive" tune, and commanded the drummer to beat
the 119th Psalm. As this was beyond the capacity
of the drubber of sheepskin, he was fain to have
recourse to the inoffensive row-dow-dow as a harm-
less substitute for the sacred music which his instrument or skill was unable to achieve. This
may be held a trifling anecdote; but the drummer
in question was no less than town-drummer of An-
derton. I remember his successor in office, a
member of that enlightened body, the British
Convention; be his memory, therefore, treated with
due respect.

CHAPTER VI

On hearing the unwelcome sound of the drum, Major Melville hastily opened a sashed door and stepped out upon a sort of terrace which divided his house from the high-road from which the martial music proceeded. Waverley and his new friend followed him, though probably he would have dispensed with their attendance. They soon recognized in solemn march, first, the performer upon the drum; secondly, a large flag of four compartments, on which were inscribed the words, Covenant, Kirk, King, Kingdoms. The person who was honoured with this charge was followed by the commander of the party, — a thin, dark, rigid-looking man about sixty years old. The spiritual pride which in mine Host of the Candlestick mantled in a sort of supercilious hypocrisy, was in this man's face elevated and yet darkened by genuine and undoubting fanaticism. It was impossible to behold him without imagination placing him in some strange crisis where religious zeal was the ruling principle. A martyr at the stake, a soldier in the field, a lonely and banished wanderer consoled by the intensity and supposed purity of his faith under every earthly privation, perhaps a persecuting inquisitor, as terrific in power as unyield-

44

ing in adversity, — any of these seemed congenial
characters to this personage. With these high
traits of energy there was something in the affected
precision and solemnity of his deportment and discourse that bordered upon the ludicrous ; so that,
according to the mood of the spectator's mind, and
the light under which Mr. Gilfillan presented himself, one might have feared, admired, or laughed at
him. His dress was that of a west-country peasant,
of better materials, indeed, than that of the lower
rank, but in no respect affecting either the mode of
the age, or of the Scottish gentry at any period.
His arms were a broadsword and pistols, which,
from the antiquity of their appearance, might have
seen the rout of Pentland or Bothwell Brigg.

As he came up a few steps to meet Major Melville, and touched solemnly, but slightly, his huge
and overbrimmed blue bonnet, in answer to the
major, who had courteously raised a small trian-
gular gold-laced hat, Waverley was irresistibly impressed with the idea that he beheld a leader of
the Roundheads of yore in conference with one of
Marlborough's captains.

The group of about thirty armed men who followed this gifted commander was of a motley description. They were in ordinary Lowland dresses,
of different colours, which, contrasted with the
arms they bore, gave them an irregular and mob-
bish appearance, — so much is the eye accustomed
to connect uniformity of dress with the military
character. In front were a few who apparently
partook of their leader's enthusiasm, — men obviously to be feared in a combat where their natural
courage was exalted by religious zeal. Others
puffed and strutted, filled with the importance of

45

carrying arms, and all the novelty of their situation, while the rest, apparently fatigued with their march, dragged their limbs listlessly along, or straggled from their companions to procure such refreshments as the neighbouring cottages and alehouses afforded. " Six grenadiers of Ligonier's," thought the major to himself, as his mind reverted to his own military experience, "would have sent all these fellows to the right about."

Greeting, however, Mr. Gilfillan civilly, he requested to know if he had received the letter he had sent to him upon his march, and could undertake the charge of the state prisoner whom he there mentioned, as far as Stirling Castle. " Yea," was the concise reply of the Cameronian leader, in a voice which seemed to issue from the very *penetralia* of his person.

"But your escort, Mr. Gilfillan, is not so strong as I expected," said Major Melville.

"Some of the people," replied Gilfillan, "hungered and were athirst by the way, and tarried until their poor souls were refreshed with the Word."

"I am sorry, sir," replied the major, "you did not trust to your refreshing your men at Cairnvreckan; whatever my house contains is at the command of persons employed in the service."

"It was not of creature-comforts I spake," answered the Covenanter, regarding Major Melville with something like a smile of contempt, — "howbeit, I thank you; but the people remained waiting upon the precious Mr. Jabesh Rentowel for the outpouring of the afternoon exhortation."

"And have you, sir," said the major, " when the rebels are about to spread themselves through this country, actually left a great part of your command at a field-preaching?"

Gilfillan again smiled scornfully as he made this indirect answer: "Even thus are the children of this world wiser in their generation than the children of light!"

"However, sir," said the major, "as you are to take charge of this gentleman to Stirling, and deliver him, with these papers, into the hands of Governor Blakeney, I beseech you to observe some rules of military discipline upon your march. For example, I would advise you to keep your men more closely together, and that each, in his march, should cover his file-leader, instead of straggling like geese upon a common; and for fear of surprise, I further recommend to you to form a small advance-party of your best men, with a single vidette in front of the whole march, so that when you approach a village or a wood — " Here the major interrupted himself. "But as I don't observe you listen to me, Mr. Gilfillan, I suppose I need not give myself the trouble to say more upon the subject. You are a better judge, unquestionably, than I am of the measures to be pursued; but one thing I would have you well aware of, that you are to treat this gentleman, your prisoner, with no rigour nor incivility, and are to subject him to no other restraint than is necessary for his security."

"I have looked into my commission," said Mr. Gilfillan, "subscribed by a worthy and professing nobleman, William, Earl of Glencairn; nor do I find it therein set down that I am to receive any charges or commands anent my doings from Major William Melville of Cairnvreckan."

Major Melville reddened even to the well-powdered ears which appeared beneath his neat military side-curls, the more so as he observed Mr. Morton smile at the same moment. "Mr. Gilfillan," he answered, with some asperity, "I beg ten thousand pardons for interfering with a person of your importance. I thought, however, that as you have been bred a grazier, if I mistake not, there might be occasion to remind you of the difference between Highlanders and Highland cattle; and if you should happen to meet with any gentleman who has seen service, and is disposed to speak upon the subject, I should still imagine that listening to him would do you no sort of harm. But I have done, and have only once more to recommend this gentleman to your civility, as well as to your custody. Mr. Waverley, I am truly sorry we should part in this way; but I trust, when you are again in this country, I may have an opportunity to render Cairnvreckan more agreeable than circumstances have permitted on this occasion."

So saying, he shook our hero by the hand. Morton also took an affectionate farewell, and Waverley, having mounted his horse, with a musketeer leading it by the bridle, and a file upon each side to prevent his escape, set forward upon the march with Gilfillan and his party. Through the little village they were accompanied with the shouts of the children, who cried out, "Eh, see to the Southland gentleman that's gaun to be hanged for shooting lang John Mucklewrath, the smith!"

CHAPTER VII

AN INCIDENT

THE dinner-hour of Scotland Sixty Years since was two o'clock. It was therefore about four o'clock of a delightful autumn afternoon that Mr. Gilfillan commenced his march, in hopes, although Stirling was eighteen miles distant, he might be able, by becoming a borrower of the night for an hour or two, to reach it that evening. He therefore put forth his strength, and marched stoutly along at the head of his followers, eyeing our hero from time to time as if he longed to enter into controversy with him. At length, unable to resist the temptation, he slackened his pace till he was alongside of his prisoner's horse, and after marching a few steps in silence abreast of him, he suddenly asked : "Can ye say wha the carle was wi' the black coat and the mousted head that was wi' the Laird of Cairnvreckan ? "

"A Presbyterian clergyman," answered Waverley.

"Presbyterian ! " answered Gilfillan contemptuously, — " a wretched Erastian, or rather an obscured Prelatist; a favourer of the black Indulgence; ane of thae dumb dogs that canna bark : they tell ower a clash o' terror and a clatter o' comfort in their sermons, without ony sense, or savour, or life. Ye 've been fed in siccan a fauld, belike ? "

"No ; I am of the Church of England," said Waverley.

49

"And they're just neighbour-like," replied the Covenanter; "and nae wonder they gree sae weel. Wha wad hae thought the goodly structure of the Kirk of Scotland, built up by our fathers in 1642, wad hae been defaced by carnal ends and the corruptions of the time; ay, wha wad hae thought the carved work of the sanctuary would hae been sae soon cut down!"

To this lamentation, which one or two of the assistants chorussed with a deep groan, our hero thought it unnecessary to make any reply. Whereupon Mr. Gilfillan, resolving that he should be a hearer at least, if not a disputant, proceeded in his Jeremiade.

"And now is it wonderful, when, for lack of exercise anent the call to the service of the altar and the duty of the day, ministers fall into sinful compliances with patronage and indemnities and oaths and bonds, and other corruptions, — is it wonderful, I say, that you, sir, and other sic-like unhappy persons, should labour to build up your auld Babel of iniquity, as in the bluidy persecuting, saint-killing times? I trow, gin ye werena blinded wi' the graces and favours, and services and enjoyments, and employments and inheritances, of this wicked world, I could prove to you, by the Scripture, in what a filthy rag ye put your trust, and that your surplices, and your copes and vestments, are but cast-off garments of the muckle harlot, that sitteth upon seven hills and drinketh of the cup of abomination. But I trow ye are deaf as adders upon that side of the head, — ay, ye are deceived with her enchantments, and ye traffic with her merchandise, and ye are drunk with the cup of her fornication!"

How much longer this military theologist might

50

have continued his invective, in which he spared
nobody but the scattered remnant of *hill-folk*, as
he called them, is absolutely uncertain. His matter was copious, his voice powerful, and his memory
strong; so that there was little chance of his ending his exhortation till the party had reached Stirling, had not his attention been attracted by a
pedlar who had joined the march from a cross-road,
and who sighed, or groaned, with great regularity
at all fitting pauses of his homily.

"And what may ye be, friend?" said the Gifted
Gilfillan.

"A puir pedlar that's bound for Stirling, and
craves the protection of your honour's party in these
kittle times. Ah! your honour has a notable faculty in searching and explaining the secret, — ay,
the secret and obscure and incomprehensible causes
of the backslidings of the land; ay, your honour
touches the root o' the matter."

"Friend," said Gilfillan, with a more complacent
voice than he had hitherto used, "honour not me.
I do not go out to park-dikes and to steadings and
to market-towns to have herds and cottars and
burghers pull off their bonnets to me as they do to
Major Melville o' Cairnvreckan, and ca' me laird, or
captain, or honour, — no; my sma' means, whilk
are not aboon twenty thousand merk, have had the
blessing of increase, but the pride of my heart has
not increased with them; nor do I delight to be
called captain, though I have the subscribed commission of that gospel-searching nobleman, the Earl
of Glencairn, in whilk I am so designated. While
I live, I am and will be called Habakkuk Gilfillan,
who will stand up for the standards of doctrine
agreed on by the ance-famous Kirk of Scotland

51

before she trafficked with the accursed Achan, while he has a plack in his purse, or a drap o' bluid in his body."

"Ah," said the pedlar, "I have seen your land about Mauchlin, — a fertile spot! Your lines have fallen in pleasant places! And siccan a breed o' cattle is not in ony laird's land in Scotland."

"Ye say right, ye say right, friend," retorted Gilfillan eagerly; for he was not inaccessible to flattery upon this subject, — "ye say right; they are the real Lancashire, and there's no the like o' them even at the Mains of Kilmaurs;" and he then entered into a discussion of their excellences, to which our readers will probably be as indifferent as our hero. After this excursion, the leader returned to his theological discussions, while the pedlar, less profound upon those mystic points, contented himself with groaning, and expressing his edification at suitable intervals.

"What a blessing it would be to the puir blinded popish nations, among whom I hae sojourned, to have siccan a light to their paths! I hae been as far as Muscovia, in my sma' trading way, as a travelling merchant; and I hae been through France, and the Low Countries, and a' Poland, and maist feck o' Germany, and oh! it would grieve your honour's soul to see the murmuring, and the singing and massing, that's in the kirk, and the piping that's in the quire, and the heathenish dancing and dicing upon the Sabbath!"

This set Gilfillan off upon the Book of Sports and the Covenant, and the Engagers, and the Protesters, and the Whiggamore's Raid, and the Assembly of Divines at Westminster, and the Longer and Shorter Catechism, and the Excommunication at Torwood, and the slaughter of Archbishop Sharp.

This last topic, again, led him into the lawfulness of defensive arms, on which subject he uttered much more sense than could have been expected from some other parts of his harangue, and attracted even Waverley's attention, who had hitherto been lost in his own sad reflections. Mr. Gilfillan then considered the lawfulness of a private man's standing forth as the avenger of public oppression; and as he was labouring with great earnestness the cause of Mas James Mitchell, who fired at the Archbishop of St. Andrews some years before the prelate's assassination on Magus Muir, an incident occurred which interrupted his harangue.

The rays of the sun were lingering on the very verge of the horizon as the party ascended a hollow and somewhat steep path which led to the summit of a rising ground. The country was unenclosed, being part of a very extensive heath, or common, but it was far from level, exhibiting in many places hollows filled with furze and broom; in others, little dingles of stunted brushwood. A thicket of the latter description crowned the hill up which the party ascended. The foremost of the band, being the stoutest and most active, had pushed on, and, having surmounted the ascent, were out of ken for the present. Gilfillan, with the pedlar and the small party who were Waverley's more immediate guard, were near the top of the ascent, and the remainder straggled after them at a considerable interval.

Such was the situation of matters when the pedlar, missing, as he said, a little doggie which belonged to him, began to halt and whistle for the animal. This signal, repeated more than once, gave offence to the rigour of his companion, the rather because it appeared to indicate inattention to the treasures of theological and controversial knowledge which were pouring out for his edification. He therefore signified, gruffly, that he could not waste his time in waiting for an useless cur.

"But if your honour wad consider the case of Tobit — "

"Tobit!" exclaimed Gilfillan, with great heat, — "Tobit and his dog baith are altogether heathenish and apocryphal, and none but a prelatist or a papist would draw them into question. I doubt I hae been mista'en in you, friend."

"Very likely," answered the pedlar, with great composure; "but ne'ertheless I shall take leave to whistle again upon puir Bawty."

This last signal was answered in an unexpected manner; for six or eight stout Highlanders, who lurked among the copse and brushwood, sprung into the hollow way, and began to lay about them with their claymores. Gilfillan, unappalled at this undesirable apparition, cried out manfully, "The sword of the Lord and of Gideon!" and drawing his broadsword, would probably have done as much credit to the good old cause as any of its doughty champions at Drumclog, when behold! the pedlar, snatching a musket from the person who was next him, bestowed the butt of it with such emphasis on the head of his late instructor in the Cameronian creed that he was forthwith levelled to the ground. In the confusion which ensued, the horse which bore our hero was shot by one of Gilfillan's party as he discharged his firelock at random. Waverley fell with, and indeed under, the animal, and sustained some severe contusions. But he was almost instantly extricated from the fallen steed by two Highlanders, who, each seizing him by the arm,

54

hurried him away from the scuffle and from the high-road. They ran with great speed, half supporting and half dragging our hero, who could, however, distinguish a few dropping shots fired about the spot which he had left. This, as he afterwards learned, proceeded from Gilfillan's party, who had now assembled, the stragglers in front and rear having joined the others. At their approach the Highlanders drew off, but not before they had rifled Gilfillan and two of his people, who remained on the spot grievously wounded. A few shots were exchanged betwixt them and the Westlanders; but the latter, now without a commander, and apprehensive of a second ambush, did not make any serious effort to recover their prisoner, judging it more wise to proceed on their journey to Stirling, carrying with them their wounded captain and comrades.

CHAPTER VIII

THE velocity, and indeed violence, with which Waverley was hurried along, nearly deprived him of sensation; for the injury he had received from his fall prevented him from aiding himself so effectually as he might otherwise have done. When this was observed by his conductors, they called to their aid two or three others of the party, and swathing our hero's body in one of their plaids, divided his weight by that means among them, and transported him at the same rapid rate as before, without any exertion of his own. They spoke little, and that in Gaelic, and did not slacken their pace till they had run nearly two miles, when they abated their extreme rapidity, but continued still to walk very fast, relieving each other occasionally.

Our hero now endeavoured to address them, but was only answered with "Cha n'eil Beurl' agam," — *i. e.* "I have no English," — being, as Waverley well knew, the constant reply of a Highlander when he either does not understand, or does not choose to reply to, an Englishman or Lowlander. He then mentioned the name of Vich Ian Vohr, concluding that he was indebted to his friendship for his rescue from the clutches of Gifted Gilfillan; but neither did this produce any mark of recognition from his escort.

The twilight had given place to moonshine when the party halted upon the brink of a precipitous glen, which, as partly enlightened by the moonbeams, seemed full of trees and tangled brushwood. Two of the Highlanders dived into it by a small foot-path, as if to explore its recesses, and one of them, returning in a few minutes, said something to his companions, who instantly raised their burden, and bore him, with great attention and care, down the narrow and abrupt descent. Notwithstanding their precautions, however, Waverley's person came more than once into contact, rudely enough, with the projecting stumps and branches which overhung the pathway.

At the bottom of the descent, and, as it seemed, by the side of a brook (for Waverley heard the rushing of a considerable body of water, although its stream was invisible in the darkness), the party again stopped before a small and rudely constructed hovel. The door was open, and the inside of the premises appeared as uncomfortable and rude as its situation and exterior foreboded. There was no appearance of a floor of any kind ; the roof seemed rent in several places ; the walls were composed of loose stones and turf, and the thatch of branches of trees. The fire was in the centre, and filled the whole wigwam with smoke, which escaped as much through the door as by means of a circular aperture in the roof. An old Highland sibyl, the only inhabitant of this forlorn mansion, appeared busy in the preparation of some food. By the light which the fire afforded, Waverley could discover that his attendants were not of the clan of Ivor, for Fergus was particularly strict in requiring from his followers that they should wear the tartan striped in the mode peculiar to their race, — a mark of distinction anciently general through the Highlands, and still maintained by those chiefs who were proud of their lineage, or jealous of their separate and exclusive authority.

Edward had lived at Glennaquoich long enough to be aware of a distinction which he had repeatedly heard noticed; and now satisfied that he had no interest with his attendants, he glanced a disconsolate eye around the interior of the cabin. The only furniture, excepting a washing-tub and a wooden press, called in Scotland an "ambry," sorely decayed, was a large wooden bed, planked, as is usual, all around, and opening by a sliding panel. In this recess the Highlanders deposited Waverley, after he had by signs declined any refreshment. His slumbers were broken and unrefreshing; strange visions passed before his eyes, and it required constant and reiterated efforts of mind to dispel them. Shivering, violent headache, and shooting pains in his limbs, succeeded these symptoms; and in the morning it was evident to his Highland attendants or guard, for he knew not in which light to consider them, that Waverley was quite unfit to travel.

After a long consultation among themselves, six of the party left the hut with their arms, leaving behind an old and a young man. The former addressed Waverley, and bathed the contusions, which swelling and livid colour now made conspicuous. His own portmanteau, which the Highlanders had not failed to bring off, supplied him with linen, and, to his great surprise, was, with all its undiminished contents, freely resigned to his use. The bedding of his couch seemed clean and comfortable, and his aged attendant closed the door of the bed, for it had no curtain, after a few words of Gaelic, from which Waverley gathered that he exhorted him to repose. So behold our hero for a second time the patient of a Highland Esculapius, but in a situation much more uncomfortable than when he was the guest of the worthy Tomanrait.

The symptomatic fever which accompanied the injuries he had sustained, did not abate till the third day, when it gave way to the care of his attendants and the strength of his constitution, and he could now raise himself in his bed, though not without pain. He observed, however, that there was a great disinclination on the part of the old woman who acted as his nurse, as well as on that of the elderly Highlander, to permit the door of the bed to be left open, so that he might amuse himself with observing their motions ; and at length, after Waverley had repeatedly drawn open, and they had as frequently shut, the hatchway of his cage, the old gentleman put an end to the contest by securing it on the outside with a nail so effectually that the door could not be drawn till this exterior impediment was removed.

While musing upon the cause of this contradictory spirit in persons whose conduct intimated no purpose of plunder, and who in all other points appeared to consult his welfare and his wishes, it occurred to our hero that during the worst crisis of his illness a female figure, younger than his old Highland nurse, had appeared to flit around his couch. Of this, indeed, he had but a very indistinct recollection ; but his suspicions were confirmed when, attentively listening, he often heard, in the course of the day, the voice of another female conversing in whispers with his attendant. Who could

59

it be ? And why should she apparently desire concealment ? Fancy immediately roused herself, and turned to Flora Mac-Ivor. But after a short conflict between his eager desire to believe she was in his neighbourhood, guarding, like an angel of mercy, the couch of his sickness, Waverley was compelled to conclude that his conjecture was altogether improbable ; since to suppose she had left her comparatively safe situation at Glennaquoich to descend into the Low Country, now the seat of civil war, and to inhabit such a lurking-place as this, was a thing hardly to be imagined. Yet his heart bounded as he sometimes could distinctly hear the trip of a light female step glide to or from the door of the hut, or the suppressed sounds of a female voice, of softness and delicacy, hold dialogue with the hoarse inward croak of old Janet, — for so he understood his antiquated attendant was denominated.

Having nothing else to amuse his solitude, he employed himself in contriving some plan to gratify his curiosity, in despite of the sedulous caution of Janet and the old Highland janizary, — for he had never seen the young fellow since the first morning. At length, upon accurate examination, the infirm state of his wooden prison-house appeared to supply the means of gratifying his curiosity, for out of a spot which was somewhat decayed he was able to extract a nail. Through this minute aperture he could perceive a female form, wrapped in a plaid, in the act of conversing with Janet. But since the days of our grandmother Eve, the gratification of inordinate curiosity has generally borne its penalty in disappointment. The form was not that of Flora, nor was the face visible ; and to crown his vexation, while he laboured with the nail to enlarge the hole, that he might obtain a more complete view, a slight noise betrayed his purpose, and the object of his curiosity instantly disappeared, — nor, so far as he could observe, did she again revisit the cottage.

All precautions to blockade his view were from that time abandoned, and he was not only permitted, but assisted, to rise, and quit what had been, in a literal sense, his couch of confinement. But he was not allowed to leave the hut; for the young Highlander had now rejoined his senior, and one or other was constantly on the watch. Whenever Waverley approached the cottage door, the sentinel upon duty civilly, but resolutely, placed himself against it and opposed his exit, accompanying his action with signs which seemed to imply there was danger in the attempt, and an enemy in the neighbourhood. Old Janet appeared anxious and upon the watch; and Waverley, who had not yet recovered strength enough to attempt to take his departure in spite of the opposition of his hosts, was under the necessity of remaining patient. His fare was, in every point of view, better than he could have conceived; for poultry, and even wine, were no strangers to his table. The Highlanders never presumed to eat with him, and unless in the circumstance of watching him, treated him with great respect. His sole amusement was gazing from the window — or rather the shapeless aperture which was meant to answer the purpose of a window — upon a large and rough brook which raged and foamed through a rocky channel, closely canopied with trees and bushes, about ten feet beneath the site of his house of captivity.

Upon the sixth day of his confinement, Waverley found himself so well that he began to meditate his escape from this dull and miserable prison-house, thinking any risk which he might incur in the attempt preferable to the stupefying and intolerable uniformity of Janet's retirement. The question, indeed, occurred, whither he was to direct his course when again at his own disposal. Two schemes seemed practicable, yet both attended with danger and difficulty. One was to go back to Glennaquoich and join Fergus Mac-Ivor, by whom he was sure to be kindly received; and in the present state of his mind, the rigour with which he had been treated fully absolved him, in his own eyes, from his allegiance to the existing government. The other project was to endeavour to attain a Scottish seaport, and thence to take shipping for England. His mind wavered between these plans; and probably, if he had effected his escape in the manner he proposed, he would have been finally determined by the comparative facility by which either might have been executed. But his fortune had settled that he was not to be left to his option.

Upon the evening of the seventh day the door of the hut suddenly opened, and two Highlanders entered, whom Waverley recognized as having been a part of his original escort to this cottage. They conversed for a short time with the old man and his companion, and then made Waverley understand, by very significant signs, that he was to prepare to accompany them. This was a joyful communication. What had already passed during his confinement made it evident that no personal injury was designed to him; and his romantic spirit, having recovered during his repose much of that elasticity which anxiety, resentment, disappointment, and the mixture of unpleasant feelings excited

62

by his late adventures had for a time subjugated, was now wearied with inaction. His passion for the wonderful, although it is the nature of such dispositions to be excited by that degree of danger which merely gives dignity to the feeling of the individual exposed to it, had sunk under the extraordinary and apparently insurmountable evils by which he appeared environed at Cairnvreckan. In fact, this compound of intense curiosity and exalted imagination forms a peculiar species of courage, which somewhat resembles the light usually carried by a miner, — sufficiently competent, indeed, to afford him guidance and comfort during the ordinary perils of his labour, but certain to be extinguished should he encounter the more formidable hazard of earth-damps or pestiferous vapours. It was now, however, once more rekindled, and with a throbbing mixture of hope, awe, and anxiety, Waverley watched the group before him as those who were just arrived snatched a hasty meal, and the others assumed their arms and made brief preparations for their departure.

As he sat in the smoky hut, at some distance from the fire around which the others were crowded, he felt a gentle pressure upon his arm. He looked round, — it was Alice, the daughter of Donald Bean Lean. She showed him a packet of papers in such a manner that the motion was remarked by no one else, put her finger for a second to her lips, and passed on, as if to assist old Janet in packing Waverley's clothes in his portmanteau. It was obviously her wish that he should not seem to recognize her; yet she repeatedly looked back at him, as an opportunity occurred of doing so unobserved, and when she saw that he remarked what she did, she folded the packet with great address and speed in one of his shirts, which she deposited in the portmanteau.

Here, then, was fresh food for conjecture. Was Alice his unknown warden, and was this maiden of the cavern the tutelar genius that watched his bed during his sickness ? Was he in the hands of her father ? and if so, what was his purpose ? Spoil, his usual object, seemed in this case neglected; for not only Waverley's property was restored, but his purse, which might have tempted this professional plunderer, had been all along suffered to remain in his possession. All this perhaps the packet might explain ; but it was plain, from Alice's manner, that she desired he should consult it in secret. Nor did she again seek his eye after she had satisfied herself that her manœuvre was observed and understood ; on the contrary, she shortly afterwards left the hut, and it was only as she tripped out from the door that, favoured by the obscurity, she gave Waverley a parting smile and nod of significance ere she vanished in the dark glen.

The young Highlander was repeatedly despatched by his comrades as if to collect intelligence. At length, when he had returned for the third or fourth time, the whole party arose, and made signs to our hero to accompany them. Before his departure, however, he shook hands with old Janet, who had been so sedulous in his behalf, and added substantial marks of his gratitude for her attendance.

" God bless you ! God prosper you, Captain Waverley ! " said Janet, in good Lowland Scotch, though he had never hitherto heard her utter a syllable, save in Gaelic. But the impatience of his attendants prohibited his asking any explanation.

CHAPTER IX

A NOCTURNAL ADVENTURE

THERE was a moment's pause when the whole party had got out of the hut; and the Highlander who assumed the command, and who, in Waverley's awakened recollection, seemed to be the same tall figure who had acted as Donald Bean Lean's lieutenant, by whispers and signs imposed the strictest silence. He delivered to Edward a sword and steel pistol, and pointing up the track, laid his hand on the hilt of his own claymore, as if to make him sensible they might have occasion to use force to make good their passage. He then placed himself at the head of the party, who moved up the pathway in single or Indian file, Waverley being placed nearest to their leader. He moved with great precaution, as if to avoid giving any alarm, and halted as soon as he came to the verge of the ascent. Waverley was soon sensible of the reason, for he heard at no great distance an English sentinel call out "All's well." The heavy sound sunk on the night wind down the woody glen, and was answered by the echoes of its banks. A second, third, and fourth time the signal was repeated fainter and fainter, as if at a greater and greater distance. It was obvious that a party of soldiers were near, and upon their guard, though not sufficiently so to detect men skilful in every art of predatory warfare,

65

like those with whom he now watched their ineffectual precautions.

When these sounds had died upon the silence
of the night, the Highlanders began their march
swiftly, yet with the most cautious silence. Waverley had little time, or indeed disposition, for observation, and could only discern that they passed
at some distance from a large building, in the windows of which a light or two yet seemed to twin-
kle. A little farther on, the leading Highlander
snuffed the wind like a setting spaniel, and then
made a signal to his party again to halt. He
stooped down upon all fours, wrapped up in his
plaid, so as to be scarce distinguishable from the
heathy ground on which he moved, and advanced
in this posture to reconnoitre. In a short time he
returned, and dismissed his attendants excepting
one; and intimating to Waverley that he must
imitate his cautious mode of proceeding, all three
crept forward on hands and knees.

After proceeding a greater way in this inconvenient manner than was at all comfortable to his
knees and shins, Waverley perceived the smell of
smoke, which probably had been much sooner distinguished by the more acute nasal organs of his
guide. It proceeded from the corner of a low and
ruinous sheep-fold, the walls of which were made
of loose stones, as is usual in Scotland. Close by
this low wall the Highlander guided Waverley, and
in order, probably, to make him sensible of his
danger, or perhaps to obtain the full credit of his
own dexterity, he intimated to him, by sign and
example, that he might raise his head so as to peep
into the sheep-fold. Waverley did so, and beheld
an out-post of four or five soldiers lying by their

watch-fire. They were all asleep, except the sentinel, who paced backwards and forwards with his firelock on his shoulder, which glanced red in the light of the fire as he crossed and re-crossed before it in his short walk, casting his eye frequently to that part of the heavens from which the moon, hitherto obscured by mist, seemed now about to make her appearance.

In the course of a minute or two, by one of those sudden changes of atmosphere incident to a mountainous country, a breeze arose, and swept before it the clouds which had covered the horizon, and the night planet poured her full effulgence upon a wide and blighted heath, skirted indeed with copsewood and stunted trees in the quarter from which they had come, but open and bare to the observation of the sentinel in that to which their course tended. The wall of the sheep-fold indeed concealed them as they lay, but any advance beyond its shelter seemed impossible without certain discovery.

The Highlander eyed the blue vault; but far from blessing the useful light with Homer's, or rather Pope's, benighted peasant, he muttered a Gaelic curse upon the unseasonable splendour of *Mac-Farlane's buat* (*i. e.*, lantern [1]). He looked anxiously around for a few minutes, and then apparently took his resolution. Leaving his attendant with Waverley, after motioning to Edward to remain quiet, and giving his comrade directions in a brief whisper, he retreated, favoured by the irregularity of the ground, in the same direction and in the same manner as they had advanced. Edward, turning his head after him, could perceive him crawl-

[1] Note I. — Mac-Farlane's Lantern

ing on all fours with the dexterity of an Indian,
availing himself of every bush and inequality to
escape observation, and never passing over the
more exposed parts of his track until the sentinel's
back was turned from him. At length he reached
the thickets and underwood which partly covered
the moor in that direction, and probably extended
to the verge of the glen where Waverley had been
so long an inhabitant. The Highlander disappeared;
but it was only for a few minutes, for he suddenly
issued forth from a different part of the thicket,
and advancing boldly upon the open heath, as if
to invite discovery, he levelled his piece and fired
at the sentinel. A wound in the arm proved a disagreeable interruption to the poor fellow's meteoro-
logical observations, as well as to the tune of "Nancy
Dawson," which he was whistling. He returned
the fire ineffectually, and his comrades, starting up
at the alarm, advanced alertly towards the spot
from which the first shot had issued. The Highlander, after giving them a full view of his person,
dived among the thickets, for his *ruse de guerre* had
now perfectly succeeded.

While the soldiers pursued the cause of their
disturbance in one direction, Waverley, adopting
the hint of his remaining attendant, made the best
of his speed in that which his guide originally intended to pursue, and which now (the attention of
the soldiers being drawn to a different quarter)
was unobserved and unguarded. When they had
run about a quarter of a mile, the brow of a rising
ground, which they had surmounted, concealed
them from further risk of observation. They still
heard, however, at a distance the shouts of the
soldiers as they hallooed to each other upon the

heath, and they could also hear the distant roll of a drum beating to arms in the same direction. But these hostile sounds were now far in their rear, and died away upon the breeze as they rapidly proceeded.

When they had walked about half an hour, still along open and waste ground of the same description, they came to the stump of an ancient oak, which, from its relics, appeared to have been at one time a tree of very large size. In an adjacent hollow they found several Highlanders, with a horse or two. They had not joined them above a few minutes, which Waverley's attendant employed, in all probability, in communicating the cause of their delay, — for the words "Duncan Duroch" were often repeated, — when Duncan himself appeared, out of breath indeed, and with all the symptoms of having run for his life, but laughing, and in high spirits at the success of the stratagem by which he had baffled his pursuers. This, indeed, Waverley could easily conceive might be a matter of no great difficulty to the active mountaineer, who was perfectly acquainted with the ground, and traced his course with a firmness and confidence to which his pursuers must have been strangers. The alarm which he excited seemed still to continue, for a dropping shot or two were heard at a great distance, which seemed to serve as an addition to the mirth of Duncan and his comrades.

The mountaineer now resumed the arms with which he had intrusted our hero, giving him to understand that the dangers of the journey were happily surmounted. Waverley was then mounted upon one of the horses, — a change which the fatigue of the night and his recent illness rendered exceedingly acceptable. His portmanteau was placed on another pony, Duncan mounted a third, and they set forward at a round pace, accompanied by their escort. No other incident marked the course of that night's journey, and at the dawn of morning they attained the banks of a rapid river. The country around was at once fertile and romantic. Steep banks of wood were broken by cornfields, which this year presented an abundant harvest, already in a great measure cut down.

On the opposite bank of the river, and partly surrounded by a winding of its stream, stood a large and massive castle, the half-ruined turrets of which were already glittering in the first rays of the sun.[1] It was in form an oblong square, of size sufficient to contain a large court in the centre. The towers at each angle of the square rose higher than the walls of the building, and were in their turn surmounted by turrets, differing in height, and irregular in shape. Upon one of these a sentinel watched, whose bonnet and plaid, streaming in the wind, declared him to be a Highlander, as a broad white ensign, which floated from another tower, announced that the garrison was held by the insurgent adherents of the house of Stewart.

Passing hastily through a small and mean town, where their appearance excited neither surprise nor curiosity in the few peasants whom the labours of the harvest began to summon from their repose, the party crossed an ancient and narrow bridge of several arches, and turning to the left, up an avenue of huge old sycamores, Waverley found himself in front of the gloomy yet picturesque structure which he had admired at a distance. A huge iron-grated

[1] Note II. —Castle of Doune.

door, which formed the exterior defence of the gateway, was already thrown back to receive them; and a second, heavily constructed of oak, and studded thickly with iron nails, being next opened, admitted them into the interior court-yard. A gentleman dressed in the Highland garb, and having a white cockade in his bonnet, assisted Waverley to dismount from his horse, and with much courtesy bid him welcome to the castle.

The governor — for so we must term him — having conducted Waverley to a half-ruinous apartment, where, however, there was a small camp-bed, and having offered him any refreshment which he desired, was then about to leave him.

"Will you not add to your civilities," said Waverley, after having made the usual acknowledgment, "by having the kindness to inform me where I am, and whether or not I am to consider myself as a prisoner?"

"I am not at liberty to be so explicit upon this subject as I could wish. Briefly, however, you are in the Castle of Doune, in the district of Menteith, and in no danger whatever."

"And how am I assured of that?"

"By the honour of Donald Stewart, governor of the garrison, and lieutenant-colonel in the service of his Royal Highness Prince Charles Edward." So saying, he hastily left the apartment, as if to avoid further discussion.

Exhausted by the fatigues of the night, our hero now threw himself upon the bed, and was in a few minutes fast asleep.

CHAPTER X

BEFORE Waverley awakened from his repose the day was far advanced, and he began to feel that he had passed many hours without food. This was soon supplied in form of a copious breakfast; but Colonel Stewart, as if wishing to avoid the queries of his guest, did not again present himself. His compliments were, however, delivered by a servant, with an offer to provide anything in his power that could be useful to Captain Waverley on his journey, which he intimated would be continued that evening. To Waverley's further inquiries the servant opposed the impenetrable barrier of real or affected ignorance and stupidity. He removed the table and provisions, and Waverley was again consigned to his own meditations.

As he contemplated the strangeness of his fortune, which seemed to delight in placing him at the disposal of others, without the power of directing his own motions, Edward's eye suddenly rested upon his portmanteau, which had been deposited in his apartment during his sleep. The mysterious appearance of Alice in the cottage of the glen immediately rushed upon his mind, and he was about to secure and examine the packet which she had deposited among his clothes, when the servant of

72

Colonel Stewart again made his appearance, and took up the portmanteau upon his shoulders.

"May I not take out a change of linen, my friend?"

"Your honour sall get ane o' the Colonel's ain ruffled sarks, but this maun gang in the baggage-cart."

And so saying, he very coolly carried off the portmanteau, without waiting further remonstrance, leaving our hero in a state where disappointment and indignation struggled for the mastery. In a few minutes he heard a cart rumble out of the rugged court-yard, and made no doubt that he was now dispossessed, for a space at least, if not forever, of the only documents which seemed to promise some light upon the dubious events which had of late influenced his destiny. With such melancholy thoughts he had to beguile about four or five hours of solitude.

When this space was elapsed, the trampling of horse was heard in the court-yard, and Colonel Stewart soon after made his appearance to request his guest to take some further refreshment before his departure. The offer was accepted; for a late breakfast had by no means left our hero incapable of doing honour to dinner, which was now presented. The conversation of his host was that of a plain country gentleman, mixed with some soldier-like sentiments and expressions. He cautiously avoided any reference to the military operations or civil politics of the time; and to Waverley's direct inquiries concerning some of these points, replied that he was not at liberty to speak upon such topics.

When dinner was finished, the governor arose, and, wishing Edward a good journey, said that

having been informed by Waverley's servant that his
baggage had been sent forward, he had taken the
freedom to supply him with such changes of linen
as he might find necessary till he was again possessed of his own.   With this compliment he disappeared.   A servant acquainted Waverley an instant afterwards that his horse was ready.

Upon this hint he descended into the court-yard,
and found a trooper holding a saddled horse, on
which he mounted, and sallied from the portal of
Doune Castle, attended by about a score of armed
men on horseback.   These had less the appearance
of regular soldiers than of individuals who had suddenly assumed arms from some pressing motive
of unexpected emergency.   Their uniform, which
was blue and red, — an affected imitation of that of
French chasseurs, — was in many respects incom-
plete, and sat awkwardly upon those who wore it.
Waverley's eye, accustomed to look at a well-disci-
plined regiment, could easily discover that the
motions and habits of his escort were not those of
trained soldiers, and that although expert enough in
the management of their horses, their skill was that
of huntsmen or grooms rather than of troopers.   The
horses were not trained to the regular pace so necessary to execute simultaneous and combined movements and formations ; nor did they seem "bitted"
(as it is technically expressed) for the use of the
sword.   The men, however, were stout, hardy-look-
ing fellows, and might be individually formidable
as irregular cavalry.   The commander of this small
party was mounted upon an excellent hunter, and
although dressed in uniform, his change of apparel
did not prevent Waverley from recognizing his old
acquaintance, Mr. Falconer of Balmawhapple.

Now, although the terms upon which Edward had parted with this gentleman were none of the most friendly, he would have sacrificed every recollection of their foolish quarrel for the pleasure of enjoying once more the social intercourse of question and answer, from which he had been so long secluded. But apparently the remembrance of his defeat by the Baron of Bradwardine, of which Edward had been the unwilling cause, still rankled in the mind of the low-bred and yet proud laird. He carefully avoided giving the least sign of recognition, riding doggedly at the head of his men, who, though scarce equal in numbers to a sergeant's party, were denominated Captain Falconer's troop, being preceded by a trumpet, which sounded from time to time, and a standard, borne by Cornet Falconer, the laird's younger brother. The lieutenant, an elderly man, had much the air of a low sportsman and boon companion; an expression of dry humour predominated in his countenance over features of a vulgar cast, which indicated habitual intemperance. His cocked hat was set knowingly upon one side of his head, and while he whistled the "Bob of Dumblain," under the influence of half a mutchkin of brandy, he seemed to trot merrily forward, with a happy indifference to the state of the country, the conduct of the party, the end of the journey, and all other sublunary matters whatever.

From this wight, who now and then dropped alongside of his horse, Waverley hoped to acquire some information, or at least to beguile the way with talk.

"A fine evening, sir," was Edward's salutation.

"Ow, ay, sir! a bra' night," replied the lieutenant, in broad Scotch of the most vulgar description.

"And a fine harvest, apparently," continued Waverly, following up his first attack.

"Ay, the aits will be got bravely in; but the farmers, deil burst them, and the corn-mongers, will make the auld price gude against them as has horses till keep."

"You perhaps act as quartermaster, sir?"

"Ay, quartermaster, riding-master, and lieutenant," answered this officer of all work. "And, to be sure, wha's fitter to look after the breaking and the keeping of the poor beasts than mysell, that bought and sold every ane o' them?"

"And pray, sir, if it be not too great a freedom, may I beg to know where we are going just now?"

"A fule's errand, I fear," answered this communicative personage.

"In that case," said Waverley, determined not to spare civility, "I should have thought a person of your appearance would not have been found on the road."

"Vera true, vera true, sir," replied the officer; "but every why has its wherefore. Ye maun ken, the laird there bought a' thir beasts frae me to munt his troop, and agreed to pay for them according to the necessities and prices of the time. But then he hadna the ready penny, and I hae been advised his bond will not be worth a boddle against the estate, and then I had a' my dealers to settle wi' at Martinmas; and so as he very kindly offered me this commission, and as the auld *Fifteen* [1] wad never help me to my siller for sending out naigs against the government, why, conscience! sir, I thought my best chance for payment was e'en to

[1] The Judges of the Supreme Court of Session in Scotland are proverbially termed, among the country people, "The Fifteen."

76

gae out[1] mysell; and ye may judge, sir, as I hae dealt a' my life in halters, I think na mickle o' putting my craig in peril of a St. Johnstone's tippet."

"You are not, then, by profession a soldier?" said Waverley.

"Na, na, thank God," answered this doughty partisan, "I wasna bred at sae short a tether; I was brought up to hack and manger. I was bred a horse-couper, sir; and if I might live to see you at Whitson-tryst, or at Stagshawbank, or the winter fair at Hawick, and ye wanted a spanker that would lead the field, I 'se be caution I would serve ye easy; for Jamie Jinker was ne'er the lad to impose upon a gentleman. Ye 're a gentleman, sir, and should ken a horse's points. Ye see that through-ganging thing that Balmawhapple 's on: I selled her till him. She was bred out of Lick-the-Ladle, that wan the king's plate at Caverton-Edge, by Duke Hamilton's White-Foot," &c. &c. &c.

But as Jinker was entered full sail upon the pedigree of Balmawhapple's mare, having already got as far as great-grandsire and great-grand-dam, and while Waverley was watching for an opportunity to obtain from him intelligence of more interest, the noble captain checked his horse until they

---

[1] "To go out," or "to have been out," in Scotland, was a conventional phrase similar to that of the Irish respecting a man having been "up," both having reference to an individual who had been engaged in insurrection. It was accounted ill-breeding in Scotland, about forty years since, to use the phrase "rebellion" or "rebel," which might be interpreted by some of the parties present as a personal insult. It was also esteemed more polite even for stanch Whigs to denominate Charles Edward the Chevalier, than to speak of him as the Pretender; and this kind of accommodating courtesy was usually observed in society where individuals of each party mixed on friendly terms.

77

came up, and then, without directly appearing to notice Edward, said sternly to the genealogist: " I thought, Lieutenant, my orders were preceese, that no one should speak to the prisoner ? "

The metamorphosed horse-dealer was silenced, of course, and slunk to the rear, where he consoled himself by entering into a vehement dispute upon the price of hay with a farmer who had reluctantly followed his laird to the field rather than give up his farm, whereof the lease had just expired. Waverley was therefore once more consigned to silence, foreseeing that further attempts at conversation with any of the party would only give Balmawhapple a wished-for opportunity to display the insolence of authority, and the sulky spite of a temper naturally dogged, and rendered more so by habits of low indulgence and the incense of servile adulation.

In about two hours' time the party were near the Castle of Stirling, over whose battlements the union flag was brightened as it waved in the evening sun. To shorten his journey, or perhaps to display his importance and insult the English garrison, Balmawhapple, inclining to the right, took his route through the royal park which reaches to and surrounds the rock upon which the fortress is situated.

With a mind more at ease, Waverley could not have failed to admire the mixture of romance and beauty which renders interesting the scene through which he was now passing, — the field which had been the scene of the tournaments of old ; the rock from which the ladies beheld the contest, while each made vows for the success of some favourite knight ; the towers of the Gothic church, where these vows might be paid ; and, surmounting all, the fortress itself, at once a castle and palace, where

78

valour received the prize from royalty, and knights and dames closed the evening amid the revelry of the dance, the song, and the feast. All these were objects fitted to arouse and interest a romantic imagination.

But Waverley had other objects of meditation, and an incident soon occurred of a nature to disturb meditation of any kind. Balmawhapple, in the pride of his heart, as he wheeled his little body of cavalry round the base of the castle, commanded his trumpet to sound a flourish, and his standard to be displayed. This insult produced apparently some sensation ; for when the cavalcade was at such distance from the southern battery as to admit of a gun being depressed so as to bear upon them, a flash of fire issued from one of the embrasures upon the rock, and ere the report with which it was attended could be heard, the rushing sound of a cannon-ball passed over Balmawhapple's head, and the bullet, burying itself in the ground at a few yards' distance, covered him with the earth which it drove up. There was no need to bid the party trudge. In fact, every man, acting upon the impulse of the moment, soon brought Mr. Jinker's steeds to show their mettle, and the cavaliers, retreating with more speed than regularity, never took to a trot, as the lieutenant afterwards observed, until an intervening eminence had secured them from any repetition of so undesirable a compliment on the part of Stirling Castle. I must do Balmawhapple, however, the justice to say that he not only kept the rear of his troop, and laboured to maintain some order among them, but, in the height of his gallantry, answered the fire of the castle by discharging one of his horse-pistols at the battlements : although, the distance

79

being nearly half a mile, I could never learn that this measure of retaliation was attended with any particular effect.

The travellers now passed the memorable field of Bannockburn, and reached the Torwood, — a place glorious or terrible to the recollections of the Scottish peasant, as the feats of Wallace, or the cruelties of Wude Willie Grime, predominate in his recollection. At Falkirk, — a town formerly famous in Scottish history, and soon to be again distinguished as the scene of military events of importance, — Balmawhapple proposed to halt and repose for the evening. This was performed with very little regard to military discipline, his worthy quartermaster being chiefly solicitous to discover where the best brandy might be come at. Sentinels were deemed unnecessary, and the only vigils performed were those of such of the party as could procure liquor. A few resolute men might easily have cut off the detachment; but of the inhabitants, some were favourable, many indifferent, and the rest overawed. So nothing memorable occurred in the course of the evening, except that Waverley's rest was sorely interrupted by the revellers hallooing forth their Jacobite songs, without remorse or mitigation of voice.

Early in the morning they were again mounted and on the road to Edinburgh, though the pallid visages of some of the troop betrayed that they had spent a night of sleepless debauchery. They halted at Linlithgow, distinguished by its ancient palace, which, Sixty Years since, was entire and habitable, and whose venerable ruins, *not quite Sixty Years since*, very narrowly escaped the unworthy fate of being converted into a barrack for French prisoners.

May repose and blessings attend the ashes of the patriotic statesman who, amongst his last services to Scotland, interposed to prevent this profanation!

As they approached the metropolis of Scotland, through a champaign and cultivated country, the sounds of war began to be heard. The distant yet distinct report of heavy cannon, fired at intervals, apprised Waverley that the work of destruction was going forward. Even Balmawhapple seemed moved to take some precautions, by sending an advanced party in front of his troop, keeping the main body in tolerable order, and moving steadily forward.

Marching in this manner, they speedily reached an eminence, from which they could view Edinburgh stretching along the ridgy hill which slopes eastward from the castle. The latter, being in a state of siege, or rather of blockade, by the Northern insurgents, who had already occupied the town for two or three days, fired at intervals upon such parties of Highlanders as exposed themselves, either on the main street, or elsewhere in the vicinity of the fortress. The morning being calm and fair, the effect of this dropping fire was to invest the castle in wreaths of smoke, the edges of which dissipated slowly in the air, while the central veil was darkened ever and anon by fresh clouds poured forth from the battlements; the whole giving, by the partial concealment, an appearance of grandeur and gloom rendered more terrific when Waverley reflected on the cause by which it was produced, and that each explosion might ring some brave man's knell.

Ere they approached the city, the partial cannonade had wholly ceased. Balmawhapple, however,

having in his recollection the unfriendly greeting
which his troop had received from the battery at
Stirling, had apparently no wish to tempt the
forbearance of the artillery of the castle.   He
therefore left the direct road, and sweeping considerably to the southward, so as to keep out of the
range of the cannon, approached the ancient palace
of Holyrood, without having entered the walls of
the city.   He then drew up his men in front of
that venerable pile, and delivered Waverley to the
custody of a guard of Highlanders, whose officer
conducted him into the interior of the building.

A long, low, and ill-proportioned gallery, hung
with pictures affirmed to be the portraits of kings,
who, if they ever flourished at all, lived several
hundred years before the invention of painting in
oil-colours, served as a sort of guard-chamber, or
vestibule, to the apartments which the adventurous
Charles Edward now occupied in the palace of his
ancestors.   Officers, both in the Highland and Lowland garb, passed and repassed in haste, or loitered
in the hall, as if waiting for orders.   Secretaries
were engaged in making out passes, musters, and
returns.   All seemed busy, and earnestly intent
upon something of importance ; but Waverley was
suffered to remain seated in the recess of a window,
unnoticed by any one, in anxious reflection upon
the crisis of his fate, which seemed now rapidly
approaching.

CHAPTER XI

AN OLD AND A NEW ACQUAINTANCE

WHILE he was deep sunk in his reverie, the rustle of tartans was heard behind him, a friendly arm clasped his shoulders, and a friendly voice exclaimed, —

"Said the Highland prophet sooth? Or must second-sight go for nothing?"

Waverley turned, and was warmly embraced by Fergus Mac-Ivor. "A thousand welcomes to Holyrood, once more possessed by her legitimate sovereign! Did I not say we should prosper, and that you would fall into the hands of the Philistines if you parted from us?"

"Dear Fergus!" said Waverley, eagerly returning his greeting. "It is long since I have heard a friend's voice. Where is Flora?"

"Safe, and a triumphant spectator of our success."

"In this place?" said Waverley.

"Ay, in this city, at least," answered his friend, "and you shall see her; but first you must meet a friend whom you little think of, who has been frequent in his inquiries after you."

Thus saying, he dragged Waverley by the arm out of the guard-chamber, and ere he knew where he was conducted, Edward found himself in a presence-room, fitted up with some attempt at royal state.

A young man, wearing his own fair hair, distinguished by the dignity of his mien and the noble expression of his well-formed and regular features, advanced out of a circle of military gentlemen and Highland chiefs, by whom he was surrounded. In his easy and graceful manners Waverley afterwards thought he could have discovered his high birth and rank, although the star on his breast and the embroidered garter at his knee had not appeared as its indications.

"Let me present to your Royal Highness — " said Fergus, bowing profoundly.

"The descendant of one of the most ancient and loyal families in England," said the young Chevalier, interrupting him. "I beg your pardon for interrupting you, my dear Mac-Ivor ; but no master of ceremonies is necessary to present a Waverley to a Stewart."

Thus saying, he extended his hand to Edward with the utmost courtesy, who could not, had he desired it, have avoided rendering him the homage which seemed due to his rank, and was certainly the right of his birth. "I am sorry to understand, Mr. Waverley, that owing to circumstances which have been as yet but ill explained, you have suffered some restraint among my followers in Perthshire and on your march here ; but we are in such a situation that we hardly know our friends, and I am even at this moment uncertain whether I can have the pleasure of considering Mr. Waverley as among mine."

He then paused for an instant; but before Edward could adjust a suitable reply, or even arrange his ideas as to its purport, the prince took out a paper, and then proceeded: "I should indeed have no doubts upon this subject, if I could trust to this proclamation, set forth by the friends of the Elector of Hanover, in which they rank Mr. Waverley among the nobility and gentry who are menaced with the pains of high treason for loyalty to their legitimate sovereign. But I desire to gain no adherents save from affection and conviction ; and if Mr. Waverley inclines to prosecute his journey to the South, or to join the forces of the Elector, he shall have my passport and free permission to do so ; and I can only regret that my present power will not extend to protect him against the probable consequences of such a measure. But," continued Charles Edward, after another short pause, "if Mr. Waverley should, like his ancestor, Sir Nigel, determine to embrace a cause which has little to recommend it but its justice, and follow a prince who throws himself upon the affections of his people to recover the throne of his ancestors or perish in the attempt, 1 can only say that among these nobles and gentlemen he will find worthy associates in a gallant enterprise, and will follow a master who may be unfortunate, but, I trust, will never be ungrateful."

The politic chieftain of the race of Ivor knew his advantage in introducing Waverley to this personal interview with the royal Adventurer. Unaccustomed to the address and manners of a polished court, in which Charles was eminently skilful, his words and his kindness penetrated the heart of our hero, and easily outweighed all prudential motives. To be thus personally solicited for assistance by a prince whose form and manners, as well as the spirit which he displayed in this singular enterprise, answered his ideas of a hero of romance; to be courted by him in the ancient halls of his paternal palace, recovered by the sword which he was already bending towards other conquests, — gave Edward, in his own eyes, the dignity and importance which he had ceased to consider as his attributes. Rejected, slandered, and threatened upon the one side, he was irresistibly attracted to the cause which the prejudices of education and the political principles of his family had already recommended as the most just. These thoughts rushed through his mind like a torrent, sweeping before them every consideration of an opposite tendency, — the time, besides, admitted of no deliberation, — and Waverley, kneeling to Charles Edward, devoted his heart and sword to the vindication of his rights.

The prince (for although unfortunate in the faults and follies of his forefathers, we shall here and elsewhere give him the title due to his birth) raised Waverley from the ground, and embraced him with an expression of thanks too warm not to be genuine. He also thanked Fergus Mac-Ivor repeatedly for having brought him such an adherent, and presented Waverley to the various noblemen, chieftains, and officers who were about his person, as a young gentleman of the highest hopes and prospects, in whose bold and enthusiastic avowal of his cause they might see an evidence of the sentiments of the English families of rank at this important crisis.[1] Indeed, this was a point much doubted among the adherents of the house of Stewart; and

[1] The Jacobite sentiments were general among the western counties and in Wales; but although the great families of the Wynnes, the Wyndhams, and others, had come under an actual obligation to join Prince Charles if he should land, they had done so under the express stipulation that he should be assisted by an auxiliary army of French, without which they foresaw the enterprise would be desperate. Wishing well to his cause, therefore,

as a well-founded disbelief in the co-operation of the English Jacobites kept many Scottish men of rank from his standard, and diminished the courage of those who had joined it, nothing could be more seasonable for the Chevalier than the open declaration in his favour of the representative of the house of Waverley Honour, so long known as cavaliers and royalists. This Fergus had foreseen from the beginning. He really loved Waverley, because their feelings and projects never thwarted each other ; he hoped to see him united with Flora, and he rejoiced that they were effectually engaged in the same cause. But, as we before hinted, he also exulted as a politician in beholding secured to his party a partisan of such consequence ; and he was far from being insensible to the personal importance which he himself gained with the prince from having so materially assisted in making the acquisition.

Charles Edward, on his part, seemed eager to show his attendants the value which he attached to his new adherent by entering immediately, as in confidence, upon the circumstances of his situation. "You have been secluded so much from intelligence, Mr. Waverley, from causes of which I am but indistinctly informed, that I presume you are even yet unacquainted with the important particulars of my present situation. You have, however, heard of my landing in the remote district of Moi-

and watching an opportunity to join him, they did not, nevertheless, think themselves bound in honour to do so, as he was only supported by a body of wild mountaineers speaking an uncouth dialect and wearing a singular dress. The race up to Derby struck them with more dread than admiration. But it was difficult to say what the effect might have been had either the battle of Preston or Falkirk been fought and won during the advance into England.

87

dart with only seven attendants, and of the numerous chiefs and clans whose loyal enthusiasm at once placed a solitary adventurer at the head of a gallant army. You must also, I think, have learned that the commander-in-chief of the Hanoverian Elector, Sir John Cope, marched into the Highlands at the head of a numerous and well-appointed military force, with the intention of giving us battle, but that his courage failed him when we were within three hours' march of each other, so that he fairly gave us the slip, and marched northward to Aberdeen, leaving the Low Country open and undefended. Not to lose so favourable an opportunity, I marched on to this metropolis, driving before me two regiments of horse, Gardiner's and Hamilton's, who had threatened to cut to pieces every Highlander that should venture to pass Stirling; and while discussions were carrying forward among the magistracy and citizens of Edinburgh whether they should defend themselves or surrender, my good friend Lochiel [laying his hand on the shoulder of that gallant and accomplished chieftain] saved them the trouble of further deliberation by entering the gates with five hundred Camerons. Thus far, therefore, we have done well; but in the meanwhile, this doughty general's nerves being braced by the keen air of Aberdeen, he has taken shipping for Dunbar, and I have just received certain information that he landed there yesterday. His purpose must unquestionably be to march towards us to recover possession of the capital. Now there are two opinions in my council of war : one, that being inferior probably in numbers, and certainly in discipline and military appointments, not to mention our total want of artillery, and the weakness of our cavalry, it will be safest to fall back towards the mountains and there protract the war, until fresh succours arrive from France, and the whole body of the Highland clans shall have taken arms in our favour. The opposite opinion maintains that a retrograde movement in our circumstances is certain to throw utter discredit on our arms and undertaking, and far from gaining us new partisans, will be the means of disheartening those who have joined our standard. The officers who use these last arguments—among whom is your friend Fergus Mac-Ivor — maintain that if the Highlanders are strangers to the usual military discipline of Europe, the soldiers whom they are to encounter are no less strangers to their peculiar and formidable mode of attack; that the attachment and courage of the chiefs and gentlemen are not to be doubted; and that as they will be in the midst of the enemy, their clansmen will as surely follow them, — in fine, that having drawn the sword we should throw away the scabbard, and trust our cause to battle and to the God of Battles. Will Mr. Waverley favour us with his opinion in these arduous circumstances ? "

Waverley coloured high betwixt pleasure and modesty at the distinction implied in this question, and answered, with equal spirit and readiness, that he could not venture to offer an opinion as derived from military skill, but that the counsel would be far the most acceptable to him which should first afford him an opportunity to evince his zeal in his Royal Highness's service.

"Spoken like a Waverley ! " answered Charles Edward; "and that you may hold a rank in some degree corresponding to your name, allow me, instead of the captain's commission which you have lost, to offer you the brevet rank of major in my service, with the advantage of acting as one of my aides-de-camp until you can be attached to a regiment, of which I hope several will be speedily embodied."

"Your Royal Highness will forgive me," answered Waverley, for his recollection turned to Balmawhapple and his scanty troop, "if I decline accepting any rank until the time and place where I may have interest enough to raise a sufficient body of men to make my command useful to your Royal Highness's service. In the meanwhile, I hope for your permission to serve as a volunteer under my friend Fergus Mac-Ivor."

"At least," said the prince, who was obviously pleased with this proposal, "allow me the pleasure of arming you after the Highland fashion." With these words, he unbuckled the broadsword which he wore, the belt of which was plated with silver, and the steel basket-hilt richly and curiously inlaid. "The blade," said the prince, "is a genuine Andrea Ferrara, — it has been a sort of heirloom in our family; but I am convinced I put it into better hands than my own, and will add to it pistols of the same workmanship. Colonel Mac-Ivor, you must have much to say to your friend; I will detain you no longer from your private conversation, but remember we expect you both to attend us in the evening. It may be perhaps the last night we may enjoy in these halls, and as we go to the field with a clear conscience, we will spend the eve of battle merrily."

Thus licensed, the chief and Waverley left the presence-chamber.

CHAPTER XII

"How do you like him?" was Fergus's first question as they descended the large stone staircase.

"A prince to live and die under," was Waverley's enthusiastic answer.

"I knew you would think so when you saw him, and I intended you should have met earlier, but was prevented by your sprain. And yet he has his foibles, or rather he has difficult cards to play, and his Irish officers,[1] who are much about him, are but sorry advisers, — they cannot discriminate among the numerous pretensions that are set up. Would you think it, — I have been obliged for the present to suppress an earl's patent, granted for services rendered ten years ago, for fear of exciting the jealousy, forsooth, of C—— and M——. But you

[1] Divisions early showed themselves in the Chevalier's little army, not only amongst the independent chieftains, who were far too proud to brook subjection to each other, but betwixt the Scotch and Charles's governor, O'Sullivan, an Irishman by birth, who, with some of his countrymen bred in the Irish Brigade in the service of the king of France, had an influence with the Adventurer, much resented by the Highlanders, who were sensible that their own clans made the chief, or rather the only, strength of his enterprise. There was a feud, also, between Lord George Murray and John Murray of Broughton, the prince's secretary, whose disunion greatly embarrassed the affairs of the adventurer. In general, a thousand different pretensions divided their little army, and finally contributed in no small degree to its overthrow.

91

were very right, Edward, to refuse the situation of aide-de-camp. There are two vacant, indeed, but Clanronald and Lochiel, and almost all of us, have requested one for young Aberchallader, and the Lowlanders and the Irish party are equally desirous to have the other for the Master of F——. Now, if either of these candidates were to be superseded in your favour, you would make enemies. And then I am surprised that the prince should have offered you a majority, when he knows very well that nothing short of lieutenant-colonel will satisfy others, who cannot bring one hundred and fifty men to the field. 'But patience, cousin, and shuffle the cards!' It is all very well for the present, and we must have you properly equipped for the evening in your new costume; for, to say truth, your outward man is scarce fit for a court."

"Why," said Waverley, looking at his soiled dress, "my shooting jacket has seen service since we parted; but that, probably, you, my friend, know as well or better than I."

"You do my second-sight too much honour," said Fergus. "We were so busy, first with the scheme of giving battle to Cope, and afterwards with our operations in the Lowlands, that I could only give general directions to such of our people as were left in Perthshire to respect and protect you, should you come in their way. But let me hear the full story of your adventures, for they have reached us in a very partial and mutilated manner."

Waverley then detailed at length the circumstances with which the reader is already acquainted, to which Fergus listened with great attention. By this time they had reached the door of his quarters, which he had taken up in a small paved court, retiring from the street called the Canongate, at the house of a buxom widow of forty, who seemed to smile very graciously upon the handsome young chief, she being a person with whom good looks and good-humour were sure to secure an interest, whatever might be the party's political opinions. Here Callum Beg received them with a smile of recognition. "Callum," said the chief, "call Shemus an Snachad" (James of the Needle). This was the hereditary tailor of Vich Ian Vohr. "Shemus, Mr. Waverley is to wear the *cath dath* [battle colour, or tartan]; his trews must be ready in four hours. You know the measure of a well-made man, — two double nails to the small of the leg — "

"Eleven from haunch to heel, seven round the waist. I give your honour leave to hang Shemus if there's a pair of sheers in the Highlands that has a baulder sneck than hers ain at the *cumadh an truais*" (shape of the trews).

"Get a plaid of Mac-Ivor tartan, and sash," continued the chieftain, "and a blue bonnet of the prince's pattern, at Mr. Mouat's, in the Crames. My short green coat, with silver lace and silver buttons, will fit him exactly, and I have never worn it. Tell Ensign Maccombich to pick out a handsome target from among mine. The prince has given Mr. Waverley broadsword and pistols, I will furnish him with a dirk and purse; add but a pair of low-heeled shoes, and then, my dear Edward [turning to him], you will be a complete son of Ivor."

These necessary directions given, the chieftain resumed the subject of Waverley's adventures. "It is plain," he said, "that you have been in the custody of Donald Bean Lean. You must know that when I marched away my clan to join the prince, I laid my injunctions on that worthy member of society to perform a certain piece of service, which done, he was to join me with all the force he could muster. But instead of doing so, the gentleman, finding the coast clear, thought it better to make war on his own account, and has scoured the country, plundering, I believe, both friend and foe, under pretence of levying black-mail, sometimes as if by my authority, and sometimes (and be cursed to his consummate impudence) in his own great name! Upon my honour, if I live to see the cairn of Benmore again, I shall be tempted to hang that fellow! I recognize his hand particularly in the mode of your rescue from that canting rascal Gilfillan, and I have little doubt that Donald himself played the part of the pedlar on that occasion; but how he should not have plundered you, or put you to ransom, or availed himself in some way or other of your captivity for his own advantage, passes my judgment."

"When and how did you hear the intelligence of my confinement?" asked Waverley.

"The prince himself told me," said Fergus, "and inquired very minutely into your history. He then mentioned your being at that moment in the power of one of our Northern parties, — you know I could not ask him to explain particulars, — and requested my opinion about disposing of you. I recommended that you should be brought here as a prisoner, because I did not wish to prejudice you farther with the English government, in case you pursued your purpose of going southward. I knew nothing, you must recollect, of the charge brought against you of aiding and abetting high treason, which, I presume, had some share in changing your original plan. That sullen, good-for-nothing brute, Balma-whapple, was sent to escort you from Doune, with what he calls his troop of horse. As to his be-haviour, in addition to his natural antipathy to everything that resembles a gentleman, I presume his adventure with Bradwardine rankles in his recollection, the rather that I daresay his mode of telling that story contributed to the evil reports which reached your quondam regiment."

"Very likely," said Waverley; "but now surely, my dear Fergus, you may find time to tell me something of Flora."

"Why," replied Fergus, "I can only tell you that she is well, and residing for the present with a relation in this city. I thought it better she should come here, as since our success a good many ladies of rank attend our military court. And I assure you that there is a sort of consequence annexed to the near relative of such a person as Flora Mac-Ivor; and where there is such a justling of claims and requests, a man must use every fair means to enhance his importance."

There was something in this last sentence which grated on Waverley's feelings. He could not bear that Flora should be considered as conducing to her brother's preferment by the admiration which she must unquestionably attract; and although it was in strict correspondence with many points of Fergus's character, it shocked him as selfish, and unworthy of his sister's high mind and his own in-dependent pride. Fergus, to whom such manœuvres were familiar, as to one brought up at the French court, did not observe the unfavourable impression which he had unwarily made upon his friend's mind,

95

and concluded by saying, that they could hardly
see Flora before the evening, when she would be
at the concert and ball with which the prince's
party were to be entertained. "She and I had a
quarrel about her not appearing to take leave of
you. I am unwilling to renew it by soliciting her
to receive you this morning ; and perhaps my doing
so might not only be ineffectual, but prevent your
meeting this evening."

While thus conversing, Waverley heard in the
court, before the windows of the parlour, a well-
known voice. "I aver to you, my worthy friend,"
said the speaker, "that it is a total dereliction of
military discipline ; and were you not, as it were, a
tyro, your purpose would deserve strong reprobation. For a prisoner of war is on no account to be
coerced with fetters, or debinded *in ergastulo*, as
would have been the case had you put this gentleman into the pit of the peel-house at Balmawhapple. I grant, indeed, that such a prisoner may for
security be coerced *in carcere ;* that is, in a public
prison."

The growling voice of Balmawhapple was heard
as taking leave in displeasure ; but the word "landlouper" alone was distinctly audible. He had disappeared before Waverley reached the house, in order
to greet the worthy Baron of Bradwardine. The
uniform in which he was now attired, — a blue coat,
namely, with gold lace, a scarlet waistcoat and
breeches, and immense jack-boots, — seemed to have
added fresh stiffness and rigidity to his tall, perpen-
dicular figure; and the consciousness of military
command and authority had increased, in the same
proportion, the self-importance of his demeanour,
and dogmatism of his conversation.

96

He received Waverley with his usual kindness, and expressed immediate anxiety to hear an explanation of the circumstances attending the loss of his commission in Gardiner's dragoons,—" not," he said, "that he had the least apprehension of his young friend having done aught which could merit such ungenerous treatment as he had received from government, but because it was right and seemly that the Baron of Bradwardine should be, in point of trust and in point of power, fully able to refute all calumnies against the heir of Waverley Honour, whom he had so much right to regard as his own son."

Fergus Mac-Ivor, who had now joined them, went hastily over the circumstances of Waverley's story, and concluded with the flattering reception he had met from the young Chevalier. The Baron listened in silence, and at the conclusion shook Waverley heartily by the hand, and congratulated him upon entering the service of his lawful prince. "For," continued he, "although it has been justly held in all nations a matter of scandal and dishonour to infringe the *sacramentum militare,* and that whether it was taken by each soldier singly, whilk the Romans denominated *per conjurationem,* or by one soldier in name of the rest, yet no one ever doubted that the allegiance so sworn was discharged by the *dimissio,* or discharging of a soldier, whose case would be as hard as that of colliers, salters, and other *adscripti glebæ,* or slaves of the soil, were it to be accounted otherwise. This is something like the brocard expressed by the learned Sanchez in his work *De Jure-jurando,* which you have questionless consulted upon this occasion. As for those who have calumniated you by leasing-making, I protest to

Heaven I think they have justly incurred the penalty of the *Memnonia lex*, also called *Lex Rhemnia*, which is prelected upon by Tullius in his oration *In Verrem*. I should have deemed, however, Mr. Waverley, that before destining yourself to any special service in the army of the prince, ye might have inquired what rank the old Bradwardine held there, and whether he would not have been peculiarly happy to have had your services in the regiment of horse which he is now about to levy."

Edward eluded this reproach by pleading the necessity of giving an immediate answer to the prince's proposal, and his uncertainty at the moment whether his friend the Baron was with the army, or engaged upon service elsewhere.

This punctilio being settled, Waverley made inquiry after Miss Bradwardine, and was informed she had come to Edinburgh with Flora Mac-Ivor, under guard of a party of the chieftain's men. This step was indeed necessary, Tully-Veolan having become a very unpleasant, and even dangerous place of residence for an unprotected young lady, on account of its vicinity to the Highlands, and also to one or two large villages which, from aversion as much to the caterans as zeal for presbytery, had declared themselves on the side of government, and formed irregular bodies of partisans, who had frequent skirmishes with the mountaineers, and sometimes attacked the houses of the Jacobite gentry in the braes, or frontier betwixt the mountain and plain.

" I would propose to you," continued the Baron, " to walk as far as my quarters in the Luckenbooths, and to admire in your passage the High

Street, whilk is, beyond a shadow of dubitation, finer than any street, whether in London or Paris. But Rose, poor thing, is sorely discomposed with the firing of the castle, though I have proved to her from Blondel and Coehorn that it is impossible a bullet can reach these buildings ; and, besides, I have it in charge from his Royal Highness to go to the camp, or leaguer of our army, to see that the men do *conclamare vasa* — that is, truss up their bag and baggage — for to-morrow's march."·

"That will be easily done by most of us," said Mac-Ivor, laughing.

"Craving your pardon, Colonel Mac-Ivor, not quite so easily as ye seem to opine. I grant most of your folk left the Highlands expedited, as it were, and free from the encumbrance of baggage ; but it is unspeakable the quantity of useless sprechery which they have collected on their march. I saw one fellow of yours (craving your pardon once more) with a pier-glass upon his back."

"Ay," said Fergus, still in good-humour, "he would have told you, if you had questioned him, ' A ganging foot is aye getting.' But come, my dear Baron, you know as well as I that a hundred Uhlans, or a single troop of Schmirschitz's Pandours, would make more havoc in a country than the knight of the mirror and all the rest of our clans put together."

"And that is very true likewise," replied the Baron ; "they are, as the heathen author says, ' ferociores in aspectu, mitiores in actu,' ' of a horrid and grim visage, but more benign in demeanour than their physiognomy or aspect might infer.' But I stand here talking to you two youngsters when I should be in the King's Park."

"But you will dine with Waverley and me on your return? I assure you, Baron, though I can live like a Highlander when needs must, I remember my Paris education, and understand perfectly *faire la meilleure chère.*"

"And wha the deil doubts it," quoth the Baron, laughing, "when ye bring only the cookery, and the gude toun must furnish the materials? Weel, I have some business in the toun too; but I 'll join you at three, if the vivers can tarry so long."

So saying, he took leave of his friends, and went to look after the charge which had been assigned him.

CHAPTER XIII

A SOLDIER'S DINNER

JAMES OF THE NEEDLE was a man of his word when whisky was no party to the contract; and upon this occasion Callum Beg, who still thought himself in Waverley's debt, since he had declined accepting compensation at the expense of mine host of the Candlestick's person, took the opportunity of discharging the obligation by mounting guard over the hereditary tailor of Sliochd nan Ivor, and, as he expressed himself, "targed him tightly" till the finishing of the job. To rid himself of this restraint, Shemus's needle flew through the tartan like lightning; and as the artist kept chanting some dreadful skirmish of Fin Macoul, he accomplished at least three stitches to the death of every hero. The dress was therefore soon ready, for the short coat fitted the wearer, and the rest of the apparel required little adjustment.

Our hero having now fairly assumed the "garb of old Gaul," well calculated as it was to give an appearance of strength to a figure which, though tall and well made, was rather elegant than robust, I hope my fair readers will excuse him if he looked at himself in the mirror more than once, and could not help acknowledging that the reflection seemed that of a very handsome young fellow. In fact, there was no disguising it. His light-brown hair —

101

for he wore no periwig, notwithstanding the universal fashion of the time — became the bonnet which
surmounted it. His person promised firmness and
agility, to which the ample folds of the tartan added
an air of dignity. His blue eye seemed of that
kind, —

"Which melted in love, and which kindled in war;"

and an air of bashfulness, which was in reality the
effect of want of habitual intercourse with the world,
gave interest to his features, without injuring their
grace or intelligence.

"He's a pratty man, a very pratty man," said
Evan Dhu (now Ensign Maccombich) to Fergus's
buxom landlady.

"He's vera weel," said the Widow Flockhart,
"but no naething sae weel-far'd as your colonel,
Ensign."

"I wasna comparing them," quoth Evan, "nor
was I speaking about his being weel-favoured; but
only that Mr. Waverley looks clean-made and *deliver*, and like a proper lad o' his quarters, that will
not cry barley in a brulzie. And, indeed, he's gleg
aneuch at the broadsword and target. I hae played
wi' him mysell at Glennaquoich, and sae has Vich
Ian Vohr often of a Sunday afternoon."

"Lord forgie ye, Ensign Maccombich," said the
alarmed Presbyterian; "I'm sure the colonel wad
never do the like o' that!"

"Hout! hout! Mrs. Flockhart," replied the ensign, "we're young blude, ye ken; and young saints,
auld deils."

"But will ye fight wi' Sir John Cope the morn,
Ensign Maccombich?" demanded Mrs. Flockhart
of her guest.

"Troth, I 'se insure him, an he 'll bide us, Mrs. Flockhart," replied the Gael.

"And will ye face thae tearing chields the dragoons, Ensign Maccombich ?" again inquired the landlady.

"Claw for claw, as Conan said to Satan, Mrs. Flockhart, and the deevil tak the shortest nails."

"And will the colonel venture on the bagganets himsell ?"

"Ye may swear it, Mrs. Flockhart; the very first man will he be, by Saint Phedar !"

"Merciful goodness ! and if he 's killed amang the red-coats !" exclaimed the soft-hearted widow.

"Troth, if it should sae befall, Mrs. Flockhart, I ken ane that will no be living to weep for him. But we maun a' live the day and have our dinner; and there 's Vich Ian Vohr has packed his *dorlach*, and Mr. Waverley's wearied wi' majoring yonder afore the muckle pier glass; and that gray auld stoor carle, the Baron o' Bradwardine, that shot young Ronald of Ballenkeiroch, he 's coming down the close wi' that droghling coghling bailie body they ca' Macwhupple, just like the Laird o' Kittlegab's French cook, wi' his turnspit doggie trindling ahint him; and I am as hungry as a gled, my bonny dow; sae bid Kate set on the broo', and do ye put on your pinners, for ye ken Vich Ian Vohr winna sit down till ye be at the head o' the table, — and dinna forget the pint bottle o' brandy, my woman."

This hint produced dinner. Mrs. Flockhart, smiling in her weeds like the sun through a mist, took the head of the table, thinking within herself, perhaps, that she cared not how long the rebellion lasted, that brought her into company so much above her usual associates. She was supported by

103

Waverley and the Baron, with the advantage of the chieftain *vis-à-vis*. The men of peace and of war, — that is, Bailie Macwheeble and Ensign Maccombich, — after many profound *congés* to their superiors and each other, took their places on each side of the chieftain. Their fare was excellent, time, place, and circumstances considered, and Fergus's spirits were extravagantly high. Regardless of danger, and sanguine from temper, youth, and ambition, he saw in imagination all his prospects crowned with success, and was totally indifferent to the probable alternative of a soldier's grave. The Baron apologized slightly for bringing Macwheeble. They had been providing, he said, for the expenses of the campaign. "And by my faith," said the old man, "as I think this will be my last, so I just end where I began, — I hae evermore found the sinews of war, as a learned author calls the *caisse militaire*, mair difficult to come by than either its flesh, blood, or bones."

"What! have you raised our only efficient body of cavalry, and got ye none of the louis-d'or out of the 'Doutelle' to help you?" [1]

"No, Glennaquoich; cleverer fellows have been before me."

"That's a scandal," said the young Highlander; "but you will share what is left of my subsidy. It will save you an anxious thought to-night, and will be all one to-morrow, for we shall all be provided for, one way or other, before the sun sets."

Waverley, blushing deeply, but with great earnestness, pressed the same request.

[1] The "Doutelle" was an armed vessel which brought a small supply of money and arms from France for the use of the insurgents.

"I thank ye baith, my good lads," said the Baron, "but I will not infringe upon your *peculium*. Bailie Macwheeble has provided the sum which is necessary."

Here the bailie shifted and fidgeted about in his seat, and appeared extremely uneasy. At length, after several preliminary hems, and much tautological expression of his devotion to his honour's service, by night or day, living or dead, he began to insinuate, "that the Banks had removed a' their ready cash into the Castle; that, nae doubt, Sandie Goldie, the silversmith, would do mickle for his honour; but there was little time to get the wadset made out, and, doubtless, if his honour Glennaquoich, or Mr. Wauverley, could accommodate"—

"Let me hear of no such nonsense, sir," said the Baron, in a tone which rendered Macwheeble mute, "but proceed as we accorded before dinner, if it be your wish to remain in my service."

To this peremptory order the bailie, though he felt as if condemned to suffer a transfusion of blood from his own veins into those of the Baron, did not presume to make any reply. After fidgeting a little while longer, however, he addressed himself to Glennaquoich, and told him, if his honour had mair ready siller than was sufficient for his occasions in the field, he could put it out at use for his honour in safe hands, and at great profit, at this time.

At this proposal Fergus laughed heartily, and answered, when he had recovered his breath: "Many thanks, Bailie; but you must know it is a general custom among us soldiers to make our landlady our banker. Here, Mrs. Flockhart," said he, taking four or five broad pieces out of a well-filled purse,

and tossing the purse itself, with its remaining contents, into her apron, " these will serve my occasions ; do you take the rest. Be my banker if I
live, and my executor if I die ; but take care to
give something to the Highland *cailliachs*[1] that
shall cry the coronach loudest for the last Vich
Ian Vohr."

" It is the *testamentum militare,*" quoth the Baron,
" whilk, amang the Romans, was privilegiate to be
nuncupative." But the soft heart of Mrs. Flockhart was melted within her at the chieftain's
speech ; she set up a lamentable blubbering, and
positively refused to touch the bequest, which Fergus was therefore obliged to resume.

" Well, then," said the chief, " if I fall, it will go
to the grenadier that knocks my brains out, and I
shall take care he works hard for it."

Bailie Macwheeble was again tempted to put in
his oar ; for where cash was concerned, he did not
willingly remain silent. " Perhaps he had better
carry the gowd to Miss Mac-Ivor, in case of mortality or accidents of war. It might tak the form
of a *mortis causa* donation in the young leddie's
favour, and wad cost but the scrape of a pen to
mak it out."

" The young lady," said Fergus, " should such an
event happen, will have other matters to think of
than these wretched louis-d'or."

" True, undeniable, there 's nae doubt o' that ; but
your honour kens that a full sorrow — "

" Is endurable by most folk more easily than a
hungry one ? True, Bailie, very true ; and I believe there may even be some who would be con-

[1] Old women on whom devolved the duty of lamenting for the
dead, which the Irish call *Keenning.*

soled by such a reflection for the loss of the whole existing generation. But there is a sorrow which knows neither hunger nor thirst; and poor Flora — " He paused, and the whole company sympathized in his emotion.

The Baron's thoughts naturally reverted to the unprotected state of his daughter, and the big tear came to the veteran's eye. " If I fall, Macwheeble, you have all my papers and know all my affairs ; be just to Rose."

The bailie was a man of earthly mould, after all ; a good deal of dirt and dross about him, undoubtedly, but some kindly and just feelings he had, especially where the Baron or his young mistress were concerned. He set up a lamentable howl. " If that doleful day should come, while Duncan Macwheeble had a boddle it should be Miss Rose's. He wald scroll for a plack the sheet, or she kenn'd what it was to want ; if indeed a' the bonnie baronie o' Bradwardine and Tully-Veolan, with the fortalice and manor-place thereof [he kept sobbing and whining at every pause], tofts, crofts, mosses, muirs, outfield, infield, buildings, orchards, dovecotes, with the right of net and coble in the water and loch of Veolan, teinds, parsonage and vicarage, annexis, connexis, rights of pasturage, fuel, feal, and divot, parts, pendicles, and pertinents whatsoever [here he had recourse to the end of his long cravat to wipe his eyes, which overflowed, in spite of him, at the ideas which this technical jargon conjured up], — all as more fully described in the proper evidents and titles thereof, and lying within the parish of Bradwardine, and the shire of Perth, — if, as aforesaid, they must a' pass from my master's child to Inch-Grabbit, wha 's a Whig and a Hanoverian, and

107

be managed by his doer, Jamie Howie, wha 's no fit to be a birlieman, let be a bailie —"

The beginning of this lamentation really had something affecting; but the conclusion rendered laughter irresistible. "Never mind, Bailie," said Ensign Maccombich, "for the gude auld times of rugging and riving [pulling and tearing] are come back again, an' Sneckus Mac-Snackus [meaning, probably, annexis, connexis], and a' the rest of your friends, maun gie place to the langest claymore."

"And that claymore shall be ours, Bailie," said the chieftain, who saw that Macwheeble looked very blank at this intimation.

> " We 'll give them the metal our mountain affords,
> >   Lillibulero, bullen a la,
> And in place of broad-pieces, we 'll pay with broadswords,
> >   Lero, lero, etc.
> With duns and with debts we will soon clear our score,
> >   Lillibulero, etc.
> For the man that 's thus paid will crave payment no more,
> >   Lero, lero, etc. [1]

But come, Bailie, be not cast down, drink your wine with a joyous heart; the Baron shall return safe and victorious to Tully-Veolan, and unite Killancureit's lairdship with his own, since the cowardly, half-bred swine will not turn out for the prince like a gentleman."

"To be sure, they lie maist ewest," [2] said the bailie, wiping his eyes, "and should naturally fa' under the same factory."

"And I," proceeded the chieftain, "shall take care of myself too; for you must know, I have to

---

[1] These lines, or something like them, occur in an old magazine of the period.

[2] That is, contiguous.

complete a good work here, by bringing Mrs. Flockhart into the bosom of the Catholic Church, or at
least half way, and that is to your Episcopal meeting-
house. Oh, Baron, if you heard her fine counter-
tenor admonishing Kate and Matty in the morning,
you, who understand music, would tremble at the
idea of hearing her shriek in the psalmody of
Haddo's Hole."

"Lord forgie you, Colonel, how ye rin on! But I
hope your honours will tak tea before ye gang to
the palace, and I maun gang and mask it for you."

So saying, Mrs. Flockhart left the gentlemen to
their own conversation, which, as might be supposed,
turned chiefly upon the approaching events of the
campaign.

CHAPTER XIV

THE BALL.

ENSIGN MACCOMBICH having gone to the Highland camp upon duty, and Bailie Macwheeble having retired to digest his dinner and Evan Dhu's intimation of martial law, in some blind change-house, Waverley, with the Baron and the chieftain, proceeded to Holyrood House. The two last were in full tide of spirits, and the Baron rallied in his way our hero upon the handsome figure which his new dress displayed to advantage. "If you have any design upon the heart of a bonny Scotch lassie, I would premonish you, when you address her, to remember and quote the words of Virgilius, —

> Nunc insanus amor duri me Martis in armis,
> Tela inter media atque adversos detinet hostes;

whilk verses Robertson of Struan, chief of the Clan Donnochy (unless the claims of Lude ought to be preferred *primo loco*), has thus elegantly rendered : —

> For cruel love has gartan'd low my leg,
> And clad my hurdies in a philabeg, —

although, indeed, ye wear the trews, a garment whilk I approve maist of the twa, as mair ancient and seemly."

110

" Or rather," said Fergus, " hear my song, —

> She wadna hae a Lowland laird,
> Nor be an English lady ;
> But she 's away with Duncan Græme,
> And he 's row'd her in his plaidy. "

By this time they reached the palace of Holyrood, and were announced respectively as they entered the apartments.

It is but too well known how many gentlemen of rank, education, and fortune took a concern in the ill-fated and desperate undertaking of 1745. The ladies, also, of Scotland very generally espoused the cause of the gallant and handsome young prince, who threw himself upon the mercy of his country-men rather like a hero of romance than a calculat-ing politician. It is not, therefore, to be wondered that Edward, who had spent the greater part of his life in the solemn seclusion of Waverley Honour, should have been dazzled at the liveliness and elegance of the scene now exhibited in the long-deserted halls of the Scottish palace. The accom-paniments, indeed, fell short of splendour, being such as the confusion and hurry of the time admit-ted ; still, however, the general effect was striking, and, the rank of the company considered, might well be called brilliant.

It was not long before the lover's eye discovered the object of his attachment. Flora Mac-Ivor was in the act of returning to her seat, near the top of the room, with Rose Bradwardine by her side. Among much elegance and beauty, they had at-tracted a great degree of the public attention, being certainly two of the handsomest women present. The prince took much notice of both, particularly of

Flora, with whom he danced, — a preference which she probably owed to her foreign education, and command of the French and Italian languages.

When the bustle attending the conclusion of the dance permitted, Edward, almost intuitively, followed Fergus to the place where Miss Mac-Ivor was seated. The sensation of hope, with which he had nursed his affection in absence of the beloved object, seemed to vanish in her presence, and, like one striving to recover the particulars of a forgotten dream, he would have given the world at that moment to recollect the grounds on which he had founded expectations which now seemed so delusive. He accompanied Fergus with downcast eyes, tingling ears, and the feelings of the criminal who, while the melancholy cart moves slowly through the crowds that have assembled to behold his execution, receives no clear sensation either from the noise which fills his ears, or the tumult on which he casts his wandering look.

Flora seemed a little — a very little — affected and discomposed at his approach. "I bring you an adopted son of Ivor," said Fergus.

"And I receive him as a second brother," replied Flora.

There was a slight emphasis on the word, which would have escaped every ear but one that was feverish with apprehension. It was, however, distinctly marked, and, combined with her whole tone and manner, plainly intimated, "I will never think of Mr. Waverley as a more intimate connection." Edward stopped, bowed, and looked at Fergus, who bit his lip, — a movement of anger which proved that he also had put a sinister interpretation on the reception which his sister had given his friend.

112

"This, then, is an end of my day-dream!" Such was Waverley's first thought, and it was so exquisitely painful as to banish from his cheek every drop of blood.

"Good God," said Rose Bradwardine, "he is not yet recovered!"

These words, which she uttered with great emotion, were overheard by the Chevalier himself, who stepped hastily forward, and taking Waverley by the hand, inquired kindly after his health, and added that he wished to speak with him. By a strong and sudden effort, which the circumstances rendered indispensable, Waverley recovered himself so far as to follow the Chevalier in silence to a recess in the apartment.

Here the prince detained him some time, asking various questions about the great Tory and Catholic families of England, their connections, their influence, and the state of their affections towards the house of Stewart. To these queries Edward could not at any time have given more than general answers, and it may be supposed that in the present state of his feelings his responses were indistinct even to confusion. The Chevalier smiled once or twice at the incongruity of his replies, but continued the same style of conversation, although he found himself obliged to occupy the principal share of it, until he perceived that Waverley had recovered his presence of mind. It is probable that this long audience was partly meant to further the idea which the prince desired should be entertained among his followers, that Waverley was a character of political influence. But it appeared, from his concluding expressions, that he had a different and good-natured motive, personal to our hero, for pro-

113

longing the conference. "I cannot resist the temptation," he said, "of boasting of my own discretion
as a lady's confidant. You see, Mr. Waverley, that
I know all, and I assure you I am deeply interested
in the affair. But, my good young friend, you
must put a more severe restraint upon your feelings. There are many here whose eyes can see as
clearly as mine, but the prudence of whose tongues
may not be equally trusted."

So saying, he turned easily away, and joined a
circle of officers at a few paces' distance, leaving
Waverley to meditate upon his parting expression,
which, though not intelligible to him in its whole
purport, was sufficiently so in the caution which
the last word recommended. Making, therefore, an
effort to show himself worthy of the interest which
his new master had expressed, by instant obedience
to his recommendation, he walked up to the spot
where Flora and Miss Bradwardine were still seated,
and having made his compliments to the latter, he
succeeded, even beyond his own expectation, in entering into conversation upon general topics.

If, my dear reader, thou hast ever happened to
take post-horses at ——, or at —— (one at least
of which blanks, or more probably both, you will
be able to fill up from an inn near your own residence), you must have observed, and doubtless with
sympathetic pain, the reluctant agony with which
the poor jades at first apply their galled necks to
the collars of the harness. But when the irresistible arguments of the post-boy have prevailed upon
them to proceed a mile or two, they will become
callous to the first sensation; and being "warm in
the harness," as the said post-boy may term it, proceed as if their withers were altogether unwrung.

114

This simile so much corresponds with the state of Waverley's feelings in the course of this memorable evening that I prefer it (especially as being, I trust, wholly original) to any more splendid illustration, with which Byshe's " Art of Poetry " might supply me.

Exertion, like virtue, is its own reward ; and our hero had, moreover, other stimulating motives for persevering in a display of affected composure and indifference to Flora's obvious unkindness. Pride, which supplies its caustic as an useful, though severe, remedy for the wounds of affection, came rapidly to his aid. Distinguished by the favour of a prince ; destined, he had room to hope, to play a conspicuous part in the revolution which awaited a mighty kingdom ; excelling, probably, in mental acquirements, and equalling at least in personal accomplishments, most of the noble and distinguished persons with whom he was now ranked ; young, wealthy, and high-born, — could he, or ought he, to droop beneath the frown of a capricious beauty ?

> " O nymph, unrelenting and cold as thou art,
> My bosom is proud as thine own."

With the feeling expressed in these beautiful lines (which, however, were not then written), [1] Waverley determined upon convincing Flora that he was not to be depressed by a rejection in which his vanity whispered that perhaps she did her own prospects as much injustice as his. And to aid this change of feeling, there lurked the secret and unacknowledged hope that she might learn to prize his affection more highly, when she did not conceive it to

[1] They occur in Miss Seward's fine verses, beginning, —
To thy rocks, stormy Lannow, adieu.

be altogether within her own choice to attract or repulse it. There was a mystic tone of encouragement, also, in the Chevalier's words, though he feared they only referred to the wishes of Fergus in favour of an union between him and his sister. But the whole circumstances of time, place, and incident combined at once to awaken his imagination, and to call upon him for a manly and decisive tone of conduct, leaving to fate to dispose of the issue. Should he appear to be the only one sad and disheartened on the eve of battle, how greedily would the tale be commented upon by the slander which had been already but too busy with his fame? Never, never, he internally resolved, shall my unprovoked enemies possess such an advantage over my reputation.

Under the influence of these mixed sensations, and cheered at times by a smile of intelligence and approbation from the prince as he passed the group, Waverley exerted his powers of fancy, animation, and eloquence, and attracted the general admiration of the company. The conversation gradually assumed the tone best qualified for the display of his talents and acquisitions. The gaiety of the evening was exalted in character, rather than checked, by the approaching dangers of the morrow. All nerves were strung for the future, and prepared to enjoy the present. This mood of mind is highly favourable for the exercise of the powers of imagination, for poetry, and for that eloquence which is allied to poetry. Waverley, as we have elsewhere observed, possessed at times a wonderful flow of rhetoric; and on the present occasion he touched more than once the higher notes of feeling, and then again ran off in a wild voluntary of fanciful mirth. He was supported and excited by kindred spirits, who felt the same impulse of mood and time; and even those of more cold and calculating habits were hurried along by the torrent. Many ladies declined the dance, which still went forward, and, under various pretences, joined the party to which the "handsome young Englishman" seemed to have attached himself. He was presented to several of the first rank, and his manners, which for the present were altogether free from the bashful restraint by which, in a moment of less excitation, they were usually clouded, gave universal delight.

Flora Mac-Ivor appeared to be the only female present who regarded him with a degree of coldness and reserve; yet even she could not suppress a sort of wonder at talents which, in the course of their acquaintance, she had never seen displayed with equal brilliancy and impressive effect. I do not know whether she might not feel a momentary regret at having taken so decisive a resolution upon the addresses of a lover who seemed fitted so well to fill a high place in the highest stations of society. Certainly she had hitherto accounted among the incurable deficiencies of Edward's disposition the *mauvaise honte*, which, as she had been educated in the first foreign circles, and was little acquainted with the shyness of English manners, was, in her opinion, too nearly related to timidity and imbecility of disposition. But if a passing wish occurred that Waverley could have rendered himself uniformly thus amiable and attractive, its influence was momentary; for circumstances had arisen since they met which rendered, in her eyes, the resolution she had formed respecting him, final and irrevocable.

117

With opposite feelings, Rose Bradwardine bent her whole soul to listen. She felt a secret triumph at the public tribute paid to one whose merit she had learned to prize too early and too fondly. Without a thought of jealousy, without a feeling of fear, pain, or doubt, and undisturbed by a single selfish consideration, she resigned herself to the pleasure of observing the general murmur of applause. When Waverley spoke, her ear was exclusively filled with his voice; when others answered, her eye took its turn of observation, and seemed to watch his reply. Perhaps the delight which she experienced in the course of that evening, though transient, and followed by much sorrow, was in its nature the most pure and disinterested which the human mind is capable of enjoying.

"Baron," said the Chevalier, "I would not trust my mistress in the company of your young friend. He is really, though perhaps somewhat romantic, one of the most fascinating young men whom I have ever seen."

"And by my honour, sir," replied the Baron, "the lad can sometimes be as dowff as a sexagenary like myself. If your Royal Highness had seen him dreaming and dozing about the banks of Tully-Veolan like an hypochondriac person, or, as Burton's 'Anatomia' hath it, a phrenesiac or lethargic patient, you would wonder where he hath sae suddenly acquired all this fine sprack festivity and jocularity."

"Truly," said Fergus Mac-Ivor, "I think it can only be the inspiration of the tartans; for though Waverley be always a young fellow of sense and honour, I have hitherto often found him a very absent and inattentive companion."

" We are the more obliged to him," said the prince,
" for having reserved for this evening qualities which
even such intimate friends had not discovered. But
come, gentlemen, the night advances, and the business of to-morrow must be early thought upon.
Each take charge of his fair partner, and honour
a small refreshment with your company."

He led the way to another suite of apartments,
and assumed the seat and canopy at the head of a
long range of tables, with an air of dignity mingled
with courtesy which well became his high birth
and lofty pretensions. An hour had hardly flown
away when the musicians played the signal for
parting, so well known in Scotland.[1]

" Good-night, then," said the Chevalier, rising;
" good-night, and joy be with you ! Good-night, fair
ladies, who have so highly honoured a proscribed
and banished prince. Good-night, my brave friends ;
may the happiness we have this evening experienced
be an omen of our return to these our paternal halls
speedily and in triumph, and of many and many future meetings of mirth and pleasure in the palace of
Holyrood ! "

When the Baron of Bradwardine afterwards mentioned this adieu of the Chevalier, he never failed
to repeat, in a melancholy tone, —

> "Audiit, et voti Phœbus succedere partem
> Mente dedit ; partem volucres dispersit in auras,—

which," as he added, " is weel rendered into English
metre by my friend Bangour ,—

> Ae half the prayer wi' Phœbus grace did find ;
> The t'other half he whistled down the wind."

[1] Which is, or was wont to be, the old air of "Good-night, and
joy be wi' you a' ! "

119

CHAPTER XV

THE conflicting passions and exhausted feelings of
Waverley had resigned him to late but sound repose. He was dreaming of Glennaquoich, and had
transferred to the halls of Ian nan Chaistel the
festal train which so lately graced those of Holyrood. The pibroch, too, was distinctly heard, —
and this, at least, was no delusion ; for the " proud
step of the chief piper " of the " chlain Mac-Ivor "
was perambulating the court before the door of his
chieftain's quarters, and, as Mrs. Flockhart, apparently no friend to his minstrelsy, was pleased to
observe, " garring the very stane-and-lime wa's din-
gle wi' his screeching." Of course it soon became
too powerful for Waverley's dream, with which it
had at first rather harmonized.

The sound of Callum's brogues in his apartment
(for Mac-Ivor had again assigned Waverley to his
care) was the next note of parting. " Winna yere
honour bang up ? Vich Ian Vohr and ta prince are
awa to the lang green glen ahint the clachan, tat
they ca' the King's Park,[1] and mony ane 's on his
ain shanks the day that will be carried on ither
folk's ere night."

[1] The main body of the Highland army encamped, or rather
bivouacked, in that part of the King's Park which lies towards
the village of Duddingston.

Waverley sprung up, and, with Callum's assistance and instructions, adjusted his tartans in proper costume. Callum told him also "tat his leather *dorlach* wi' the lock on her was come frae Doune, and she was awa again in the wain wi' Vich Ian Vohr's walise."

By this periphrasis Waverley readily apprehended his portmanteau was intended. He thought upon the mysterious packet of the maid of the cavern, which seemed always to escape him when within his very grasp. But this was no time for indulgence of curiosity; and having declined Mrs. Flockhart's compliment of a *morning,* — *i. e.*, a matutinal dram, — being probably the only man in the Chevalier's army by whom such a courtesy would have been rejected, he made his adieus, and departed with Callum.

"Callum," said he, as they proceeded down a dirty close to gain the southern skirts of the Canongate, "what shall I do for a horse?"

"Ta deil ane ye maun think o'," said Callum. "Vich Ian Vohr's marching on foot at the head o' his kin (not to say ta prince, wha does the like), wi' his target on his shoulder; and ye maun e'en be neighbour-like."

"And so I will, Callum, — give me my target; so, there we are fixed. How does it look?"

"Like the bra' Highlander tat's painted on the board afore the mickle change-house they ca' Luckie Middlemass's," answered Callum, — meaning, I must observe, a high compliment; for, in his opinion, Luckie Middlemass's sign was an exquisite specimen of art. Waverley, however, not feeling the full force of this polite simile, asked him no further questions.

Upon extricating themselves from the mean and dirty suburbs of the metropolis, and emerging into the open air, Waverley felt a renewal both of health and spirits, and turned his recollection with firmness upon the events of the preceding evening, and with hope and resolution towards those of the approaching day.

When he had surmounted a small craggy eminence called St. Leonard's Hill, the King's Park, or the hollow between the mountain of Arthur's Seat, and the rising grounds on which the southern part of Edinburgh is now built, lay beneath him, and displayed a singular and animating prospect. It was occupied by the army of the Highlanders, now in the act of preparing for their march. Waverley had already seen something of the kind at the hunting-match which he attended with Fergus Mac-Ivor; but this was on a scale of much greater magnitude and incomparably deeper interest. The rocks, which formed the background of the scene, and the very sky itself, rang with the clang of the bagpipers, summoning forth, each with his appropriate pibroch, his chieftain and clan. The mountaineers, rousing themselves from their couch under the canopy of heaven, with the hum and bustle of a confused and irregular multitude, like bees alarmed and arming in their hives, seemed to possess all the pliability of movement fitted to execute military manœuvres. Their motions appeared spontaneous and confused, but the result was order and regularity; so that a general must have praised the conclusion, though a martinet might have ridiculed the method by which it was attained.

The sort of complicated medley created by the hasty arrangements of the various clans under their respective banners, for the purpose of getting into the order of march, was in itself a gay and lively spectacle. They had no tents to strike, having generally, and by choice, slept upon the open field, although the autumn was now waning, and the nights began to be frosty. For a little space, while they were getting into order, there was exhibited a changing, fluctuating, and confused appearance of waving tartans and floating plumes, and of banners displaying the proud gathering word of Clanronald, "Ganion Coheriga" (Gainsay who dares); "Loch-Sloy," the watchword of the Mac-Farlanes; "Forth, fortune, and fill the fetters," the motto of the Marquis of Tullibardine; "Bydand," that of Lord Lewis Gordon; and the appropriate signal words and emblems of many other chieftains and clans.

At length the mixed and wavering multitude arranged themselves into a narrow and dusky column of great length, stretching through the whole extent of the valley. In the front of the column the standard of the Chevalier was displayed, bearing a red cross upon a white ground, with the motto "Tandem Triumphans." The few cavalry, being chiefly Lowland gentry, with their domestic servants and retainers, formed the advanced guard of the army; and their standards, of which they had rather too many, in respect of their numbers, were seen waving upon the extreme verge of the horizon. Many horsemen of this body — among whom Waverley accidentally remarked Balmawhapple and his lieutenant, Jinker (which last, however, had been reduced, with several others, by the advice of the Baron of Bradwardine, to the situation of what he called reformed officers, or reformadoes), — added

123

to the liveliness, though by no means to the regularity, of the scene, by galloping their horses as fast forward as the press would permit, to join their proper station in the van. The fascinations of the Circes of the High Street, and the potations of strength with which they had been drenched over night, had probably detained these heroes within the walls of Edinburgh somewhat later than was consistent with their morning duty. Of such loiterers, the prudent took the longer and circuitous, but more open route, to attain their place in the march, by keeping at some distance from the infantry, and making their way through the enclosures to the right, at the expense of leaping over or pulling down the dry-stone fences. The irregular appearance and vanishing of these small parties of horsemen, as well as the confusion occasioned by those who endeavoured, though generally without effect, to press to the front through the crowd of Highlanders, maugre their curses, oaths, and opposition, added to the picturesque wildness what it took from the military regularity of the scene.

While Waverley gazed upon this remarkable spectacle, rendered yet more impressive by the occasional discharge of cannon-shot from the castle at the Highland guards as they were withdrawn from its vicinity to join their main body, Callum, with his usual freedom of interference, reminded him that Vich Ian Vohr's folk were nearly at the head of the column of march, which was still distant, and that "they would gang very fast after the cannon fired." Thus admonished, Waverley walked briskly forward, yet often casting a glance upon the darksome clouds of warriors who were collected before and beneath him. A nearer view, indeed, rather diminished the effect impressed on the mind by the more distant appearance of the army. The leading men of each clan were well armed with broadsword, target, and fusee, to which all added the dirk, and most the steel pistol. But these consisted of gentlemen, — that is, relations of the chief, however distant, and who had an immediate title to his countenance and protection. Finer and hardier men could not have been selected out of any army in Christendom; while the free and independent habits which each possessed, and which each was yet so well taught to subject to the command of his chief, and the peculiar mode of discipline adopted in Highland warfare, rendered them equally formidable by their individual courage and high spirit, and from their rational conviction of the necessity of acting in unison and of giving their national mode of attack the fullest opportunity of success.

But in a lower rank to these there were found individuals of an inferior description, the common peasantry of the Highland country, who, although they did not allow themselves to be so called, and claimed often, with apparent truth, to be of more ancient descent than the masters whom they served, bore, nevertheless, the livery of extreme penury, being indifferently accoutred and worse armed, half naked, stunted in growth, and miserable in aspect. Each important clan had some of those Helots attached to them; — thus, the Mac-Couls, though tracing their descent from Comhal, the father of Finn, or Fingal, were a sort of Gibeonites, or hereditary servants, to the Stewarts of Appine; the Macbeths, descended from the unhappy

125

monarch of that name, were subjects to the Morays, and clan Donnochy, or Robertsons of Athole; and many other examples might be given, were it not for the risk of hurting any pride of clanship which may yet be left, and thereby drawing a Highland tempest into the shop of my publisher. Now these same Helots, though forced into the field by the arbitrary authority of the chieftains under whom they hewed wood and drew water, were, in general, very sparingly fed, ill dressed, and worse armed. The latter circumstance was indeed owing chiefly to the general Disarming Act, which had been carried into effect ostensibly through the whole Highlands, although most of the chieftains contrived to elude its influence, by retaining the weapons of their own immediate clansmen, and delivering up those of less value, which they collected from these inferior satellites. It followed, as a matter of course, that, as we have already hinted, many of these poor fellows were brought to the field in a very wretched condition.

From this it happened that, in bodies, the van of which were admirably well armed in their own fashion, the rear resembled actual banditti. Here was a pole-axe, there a sword without a scabbard; here a gun without a lock, there a scythe set straight upon a pole; and some had only their dirks, and bludgeons or stakes pulled out of hedges. The grim, uncombed, and wild appearance of these men, most of whom gazed with all the admiration of ignorance upon the most ordinary production of domestic art, created surprise in the Lowlands, but it also created terror. So little was the condition of the Highlands known at that late period that the character and appearance of their population,

126

while thus sallying forth as military adventurers, conveyed to the south-country Lowlanders as much surprise as if an invasion of African negroes or Esquimaux Indians had issued forth from the northern mountains of their own native country. It cannot therefore be wondered if Waverley, who had hitherto judged of the Highlanders generally from the samples which the policy of Fergus had from time to time exhibited, should have felt damped and astonished at the daring attempt of a body not then exceeding four thousand men, and of whom not above half the number, at the utmost, were armed, to change the fate and alter the dynasty of the British kingdoms.

As he moved along the column, which still remained stationary, an iron gun, the only piece of artillery possessed by the army which meditated so important a revolution, was fired as the signal of march. The Chevalier had expressed a wish to leave this useless piece of ordnance behind him; but, to his surprise, the Highland chiefs interposed to solicit that it might accompany their march, pleading the prejudices of their followers, who, little accustomed to artillery, attached a degree of absurd importance to this field-piece, and expected it would contribute essentially to a victory which they could only owe to their own muskets and broadswords. Two or three French artillerymen were therefore appointed to the management of this military engine, which was drawn along by a string of Highland ponies, and was, after all, only used for the purpose of firing signals.[1]

No sooner was its voice heard upon the present occasion than the whole line was in motion. A

[1] Note III. — Field-piece in the Highland army.

wild cry of joy from the advancing battalions rent the air, and was then lost in the shrill clangour of the bagpipes, as the sound of these, in their turn, was partially drowned by the heavy tread of so many men put at once into motion. The banners glittered and shook as they moved forward, and the horse hastened to occupy their station as the advanced guard, and to push on reconnoitring parties to ascertain and report the motions of the enemy. They vanished from Waverley's eye as they wheeled round the base of Arthur's Seat, under the remarkable ridge of basaltic rocks which fronts the little lake of Duddingston.

The infantry followed in the same direction, regulating their pace by another body which occupied a road more to the southward. It cost Edward some exertion of activity to attain the place which Fergus's followers occupied in the line of march.

CHAPTER XVI

AN INCIDENT GIVES RISE TO UNAVAILING
REFLECTIONS

WHEN Waverley reached that part of the column which was filled by the clan of Mac-Ivor, they halted, formed, and received him with a triumphant flourish upon the bagpipes and a loud shout of the men, most of whom knew him personally, and were delighted to see him in the dress of their country and of their sept. "You shout," said a Highlander of a neighbouring clan to Evan Dhu, "as if the chieftain were just come to your head."

"Mar e Bran is e a brathair (If it be not Bran, it is Bran's brother)," was the proverbial reply of Maccombich.[1]

"Oh, then, it is the handsome Sassenach Duinhé-wassel, that is to be married to Lady Flora?"

"That may be, or it may not be; and it is neither your matter nor mine, Gregor."

Fergus advanced to embrace the volunteer and afford him a warm and hearty welcome; but he thought it necessary to apologize for the diminished numbers of his battalion (which did not exceed three hundred men), by observing, he had sent a good many out upon parties.

[1] Bran, the well-known dog of Fingal, is often the theme of Highland proverb as well as song.

The real fact, however, was that the defection of
Donald Bean Lean had deprived him of at least
thirty hardy fellows whose services he had fully
reckoned upon, and that many of his occasional adherents had been recalled by their several chiefs to
the standards to which they most properly owed
their allegiance. The rival chief of the great northern branch also of his own clan had mustered his
people, although he had not yet declared either for
the government or for the Chevalier, and by his
intrigues had in some degree diminished the force
with which Fergus took the field. To make amends
for these disappointments, it was universally admitted that the followers of Vich Ian Vohr, in point
of appearance, equipment, arms, and dexterity in
using them, equalled the most choice troops which
followed the standard of Charles Edward. Old
Ballenkeiroch acted as his major, and, with the
other officers who had known Waverley when at
Glennaquoich, gave our hero a cordial reception,
as the sharer of their future dangers and expected
honours.

The route pursued by the Highland army after
leaving the village of Duddingston was for some
time the common post-road betwixt Edinburgh and
Haddington, until they crossed the Esk at Musselburgh, when, instead of keeping the low grounds
towards the sea, they turned more inland, and occupied the brow of the eminence called Carberry Hill,
— a place already distinguished in Scottish history
as the spot where the lovely Mary surrendered herself to her insurgent subjects. This direction was
chosen because the Chevalier had received notice
that the army of the government, arriving by sea
from Aberdeen, had landed at Dunbar and quartered

the night before to the west of Haddington, with
the intention of falling down towards the seaside
and approaching Edinburgh by the lower coast-
road. By keeping the height, which overhung that
road in many places, it was hoped the Highlanders
might find an opportunity of attacking them to
advantage. The army therefore halted upon the
ridge of Carberry Hill, both to refresh the soldiers
and as a central situation from which their march
could be directed to any point that the motions of
the enemy might render most advisable. While
they remained in this position, a messenger arrived
in haste to desire Mac-Ivor to come to the prince,
adding that their advanced post had had a skirmish
with some of the enemy's cavalry, and that the
Baron of Bradwardine had sent in a few prisoners.

Waverley walked forward out of the line to satisfy his curiosity, and soon observed five or six of
the troopers, who, covered with dust, had galloped
in to announce that the enemy were in full march
westward along the coast. Passing still a little
farther on, he was struck with a groan which issued from a hovel. He approached the spot, and
heard a voice in the provincial English of his native county, which endeavoured, though frequently
interrupted by pain, to repeat the Lord's Prayer.
The voice of distress always found a ready answer
in our hero's bosom. He entered the hovel, which
seemed to be intended for what is called, in the
pastoral counties of Scotland, a " smearing-house ; "
and in its obscurity Edward could only at first
discern a sort of red bundle ; for those who had
stripped the wounded man of his arms, and part of
his clothes, had left him the dragoon-cloak in which
he was enveloped.

131

"For the love of God," said the wounded man, as he heard Waverley's step, "give me a single drop of water!"

"You shall have it," answered Waverley, at the same time raising him in his arms, bearing him to the door of the hut, and giving him some drink from his flask.

"I should know that voice," said the man; but, looking on Waverley's dress with a bewildered look, — "no, this is not the young squire!"

This was the common phrase by which Edward was distinguished on the estate of Waverley Honour, and the sound now thrilled to his heart with the thousand recollections which the well-known accents of his native country had already contributed to awaken. "Houghton!" he said, gazing on the ghastly features which death was fast disfiguring, "can this be you?"

"I never thought to hear an English voice again," said the wounded man; "they left me to live or die here as I could, when they found I would say nothing about the strength of the regiment. But oh, squire, how could you stay from us so long, and let us be tempted by that fiend of the pit Ruffin? We should have followed you through flood and fire, to be sure."

"Ruffin! I assure you, Houghton, you have been vilely imposed upon."

"I often thought so," said Houghton, "though they showed us your very seal; and so Timms was shot, and I was reduced to the ranks."

"Do not exhaust your strength in speaking," said Edward; "I will get you a surgeon presently."

He saw Mac-Ivor approaching, who was now returning from headquarters, where he had attended a council of war, and hastened to meet him. "Brave news!" shouted the chief; "we shall be at it in less than two hours. The prince has put himself at the head of the advance, and as he drew his sword, called out, 'My friends, I have thrown away the scabbard.' Come, Waverley, we move instantly."

"A moment, a moment; this poor prisoner is dying. Where shall I find a surgeon?"

"Why, where should you? We have none, you know, but two or three French fellows, who, I believe, are little better than *garçons apothicaires*."

"But the man will bleed to death."

"Poor fellow!" said Fergus, in a momentary fit of compassion; then instantly added, "But it will be a thousand men's fate before night, so come along."

"I cannot; I tell you he is a son of a tenant of my uncle's."

"Oh, if he's a follower of yours, he must be looked to. I'll send Callum to you; but *diaoul! ceade millia molligheart*," continued the impatient chieftain, "what made an old soldier like Bradwardine send dying men here to cumber us?"

Callum came with his usual alertness; and indeed Waverley rather gained than lost in the opinion of the Highlanders by his anxiety about the wounded man. They would not have understood the general philanthropy which rendered it almost impossible for Waverley to pass any person in such distress; but as apprehending that the sufferer was one of his "following,"[1] they unanimously allowed that Waverley's conduct was that of a kind and considerate chieftain who merited the attachment

[1] *Scottice* for followers

133

of his people. In about a quarter of an hour poor Humphrey breathed his last, praying his young master, when he returned to Waverley Honour, to be kind to old Job Houghton and his dame, and conjuring him not to fight with these wild petticoatmen against Old England.

When his last breath was drawn, Waverley, who had beheld with sincere sorrow and no slight tinge of remorse the final agonies of mortality, now witnessed for the first time, commanded Callum to remove the body into the hut. This the young Highlander performed, — not without examining the pockets of the defunct, which, however, he remarked, had been pretty well sponged. He took the cloak, however, and proceeding with the provident caution of a spaniel hiding a bone, concealed it among some furze, and carefully marked the spot, observing that if he chanced to return that way, it would be an excellent rokelay for his auld mother Elspat.

It was by a considerable exertion that they regained their place in the marching column, which was now moving rapidly forward to occupy the high grounds above the village of Tranent, between which and the sea lay the purposed march of the opposite army.

This melancholy interview with his late sergeant forced many unavailing and painful reflections upon Waverley's mind. It was clear, from the confession of the man, that Colonel Gardiner's proceedings had been strictly warranted, and even rendered indispensable, by the steps taken in Edward's name to induce the soldiers of his troop to mutiny. The circumstance of the seal he now, for the first time, recollected, and that he had lost it in the

134

cavern of the robber, Bean Lean. That the artful villain had secured it, and used it as the means of carrying on an intrigue in the regiment for his own purposes, was sufficiently evident ; and Edward had now little doubt that in the packet placed in his portmanteau by his daughter, he should find farther light upon his proceedings. In the meanwhile the repeated expostulation of Houghton, " Ah, squire, why did you leave us ? " rung like a knell in his ears.

" Yes," he said, " I have indeed acted towards you with thoughtless cruelty. I brought you from your paternal fields and the protection of a generous and kind landlord, and when I had subjected you to all the rigour of military discipline, I shunned to bear my own share of the burden, and wandered from the duties I had undertaken, leaving alike those whom it was my business to protect, and my own reputation, to suffer under the artifices of villany. Oh, indolence and indecision of mind, if not in yourselves vices, to how much exquisite misery and mischief do you frequently prepare the way ! "

CHAPTER XVII

ALTHOUGH the Highlanders marched on very fast, the sun was declining when they arrived upon the brow of those high grounds which command an open and extensive plain stretching northward to the sea, on which are situated, but at a considerable distance from each other, the small villages of Seaton and Cockenzie, and the larger one of Preston. One of the low coast-roads to Edinburgh passed through this plain, issuing upon it from the enclosures of Seaton House, and at the town, or village, of Preston again entering the defiles of an enclosed country. By this way the English general had chosen to approach the metropolis, both as most commodious for his cavalry, and being probably of opinion that, by doing so, he would meet in front with the Highlanders advancing from Edinburgh in the opposite direction. In this he was mistaken; for the sound judgment of the Chevalier, or of those to whose advice he listened, left the direct passage free, but occupied the strong ground by which it was overlooked and commanded.

When the Highlanders reached the heights above the plain described, they were immediately formed in array of battle along the brow of the hill. Almost at the same instant the van of the English appeared issuing from among the trees and enclosures of Seaton, with the purpose of occupying the level plain between the high ground and the sea; the space which divided the armies being only about half a mile in breadth. Waverley could plainly see the squadrons of dragoons issue, one after another, from the defiles, with their videttes in front, and form upon the plain, with their front opposed to that of the Prince's army. They were followed by a train of field-pieces, which, when they reached the flank of the dragoons, were also brought into line and pointed against the heights. The march was continued by three or four regiments of infantry marching in open column, their fixed bayonets showing like successive hedges of steel, and their arms glancing like lightning, as, at a signal given, they also at once wheeled up, and were placed in direct opposition to the Highlanders. A second train of artillery, with another regiment of horse, closed the long march, and formed on the left flank of the infantry, the whole line facing southward.

While the English army went through these evolutions, the Highlanders showed equal promptitude and zeal for battle. As fast as the clans came upon the ridge which fronted their enemy they were formed into line, so that both armies got into complete order of battle at the same moment. When this was accomplished, the Highlanders set up a tremendous yell, which was re-echoed by the heights behind them. The regulars, who were in high spirits, returned a loud shout of defiance, and fired one or two of their cannon upon an advanced post of the Highlanders. The latter displayed great earnestness to proceed instantly to the attack, Evan Dhu urging to Fergus, by way of argument, that

"the *sidier roy* was tottering like an egg upon a
staff, and that they had a' the vantage of the onset,
for even a haggis (God bless her!) could charge
down hill."

But the ground through which the mountaineers
must have descended, although not of great extent,
was impracticable in its character, being not only
marshy, but intersected with walls of dry stone,
and traversed in its whole length by a very broad
and deep ditch, — circumstances which must have
given the musketry of the regulars dreadful advantages before the mountaineers could have used
their swords, on which they were taught to rely.
The authority of the commanders was therefore
interposed to curb the impetuosity of the Highlanders, and only a few marksmen were sent down
the descent to skirmish with the enemy's advanced
posts and to reconnoitre the ground.

Here then was a military spectacle of no ordinary
interest or usual occurrence. The two armies, so
different in aspect and discipline, yet each admirably trained in its own peculiar mode of war, upon
whose conflict the temporary fate, at least, of Scotland appeared to depend, now faced each other like
two gladiators in the arena, each meditating upon
the mode of attacking their enemy. The leading
officers and the general's staff of each army could
be distinguished in front of their lines, busied with
spy-glasses to watch each other's motions, and occupied in despatching the orders and receiving the
intelligence conveyed by the aides-de-camp and
orderly men, who gave life to the scene by galloping along in different directions, as if the fate of
the day depended upon the speed of their horses.
The space between the armies was at times occu-

138

pied by the partial and irregular contest of individual sharpshooters, and a hat or bonnet was occasionally seen to fall, as a wounded man was borne off by his comrades. These, however, were but trifling skirmishes, for it suited the views of neither party to advance in that direction. From the neighbouring hamlets, the peasantry cautiously showed themselves, as if watching the issue of the expected engagement; and at no great distance in the bay were two square-rigged vessels bearing the English flag, whose tops and yards were crowded with less timid spectators.

When this awful pause had lasted for a short time, Fergus, with another chieftain, received orders to detach their clans towards the village of Preston, in order to threaten the right flank of Cope's army, and compel him to a change of position. To enable him to execute these orders, the Chief of Glennaquoich occupied the churchyard of Tranent, — a commanding situation and a convenient place, as Evan Dhu remarked, " for any gentleman who might have the misfortune to be killed, and chanced to be curious about Christian burial." To check or dislodge this party, the English general detached two guns, escorted by a strong party of cavalry. They approached so near that Waverley could plainly recognize the standard of the troop he had formerly commanded, and hear the trumpets and kettle-drums sound the signal of advance, which he had so often obeyed. He could hear, too, the well-known word, given in the English dialect, by the equally well-distinguished voice of the commanding officer, for whom he had once felt so much respect. It was at that instant that, looking around him, he saw the wild dress and appearance of his Highland

139

associates, heard their whispers in an uncouth and
unknown language, looked upon his own dress, so
unlike that which he had worn from his infancy,
and wished to awake from what seemed at the
moment a dream, strange, horrible, and unnatural.
"Good God!" he muttered; "am I then a traitor
to my country, a renegade to my standard, and a
foe, as that poor dying wretch expressed himself,
to my native England?"

Ere he could digest or smother the recollection,
the tall military form of his late commander came
full in view, for the purpose of reconnoitring. "I
can hit him now," said Callum, cautiously raising
his fusee over the wall under which he lay couched,
at scarce sixty yards' distance.

Edward felt as if he was about to see a parricide
committed in his presence; for the venerable gray
hair and striking countenance of the veteran recalled the almost paternal respect with which his
officers universally regarded him. But ere he could
say "Hold!" an aged Highlander, who lay beside
Callum Beg, stopped his arm. "Spare your shot,"
said the seer; "his hour is not yet come. But let
him beware of to-morrow, — I see his winding-sheet
high upon his breast."

Callum, flint to other considerations, was pene-
trable to superstition. He turned pale at the words
of the *taishatr*, and recovered his piece. Colonel
Gardiner, unconscious of the danger he had escaped,
turned his horse round, and rode slowly back to
the front of his regiment.

By this time the regular army had assumed a
new line, with one flank inclined towards the sea,
and the other resting upon the village of Preston;
and as similar difficulties occurred in attacking their

new position, Fergus and the rest of the detachment were recalled to their former post. This alteration created the necessity of a corresponding change in General Cope's army, which was again brought into a line parallel with that of the Highlanders. In these manœuvres on both sides the daylight was nearly consumed, and both armies prepared to rest upon their arms for the night in the lines which they respectively occupied.

"There will be nothing done to-night," said Fergus to his friend Waverley; "ere we wrap ourselves in our plaids, let us go see what the Baron is doing in the rear of the line."

When they approached his post, they found the good old careful officer, after having sent out his night patrols and posted his sentinels, engaged in reading the Evening Service of the Episcopal Church to the remainder of his troop. His voice was loud and sonorous, and though his spectacles upon his nose, and the appearance of Saunders Saunderson, in military array, performing the functions of clerk, had something ludicrous, yet the circumstances of danger in which they stood, the military costume of the audience, and the appearance of their horses, saddled and picketed behind them, gave an impressive and solemn effect to the office of devotion.

"I have confessed to-day, ere you were awake," whispered Fergus to Waverley; "yet I am not so strict a Catholic as to refuse to join in this good man's prayers."

Edward assented, and they remained till the Baron had concluded the service.

As he shut the book, " Now, lads," said he, " have at them in the morning, with heavy hands

141

and light consciences." He then kindly greeted Mac-Ivor and Waverley, who requested to know his opinion of their situation. "Why, you know Tacitus saith, 'In rebus bellicis maxime dominatur Fortuna,' which is equiponderate with our vernacular adage, 'Luck can maist in the mellee.' But credit me, gentlemen, yon man is not a deacon o' his craft. He damps the spirits of the poor lads he commands by keeping them on the defensive, — whilk of itself implies inferiority or fear. Now will they lie on their arms yonder, as anxious and as ill at ease as a toad under a harrow, while our men will be quite fresh and blithe for action in the morning. Well, good night. One thing troubles me; but if to-morrow goes well off, I will consult you about it, Glennaquoich."

"I could almost apply to Mr. Bradwardine the character which Henry gives of Fluellen," said Waverley, as his friend and he walked towards their bivouac:—

> "Though it appears a little out of fashion,
> There is much care and valour in this 'Scotchman.' "

"He has seen much service," answered Fergus, "and one is sometimes astonished to find how much nonsense and reason are mingled in his composition. I wonder what can be troubling his mind, — probably something about Rose. Hark! the English are setting their watch."

The roll of the drum and shrill accompaniment of the fifes swelled up the hill, died away, resumed its thunder, and was at length hushed. The trumpets and kettledrums of the cavalry were next heard to perform the beautiful and wild point of war appropriated as a signal for that piece of nocturnal duty, and then finally sunk upon the wind with a shrill and mournful cadence.

The friends, who had now reached their post, stood and looked round them ere they lay down to rest. The western sky twinkled with stars, but a frost-mist, rising from the ocean, covered the eastern horizon, and rolled in white wreaths along the plain where the adverse army lay couched upon their arms. Their advanced posts were pushed as far as the side of the great ditch at the bottom of the descent, and had kindled large fires at different intervals, gleaming with obscure and hazy lustre through the heavy fog which encircled them with a doubtful halo.

The Highlanders, "thick as leaves in Valombrosa," lay stretched upon the ridge of the hill, buried (excepting their sentinels) in the most profound repose. "How many of these brave fellows will sleep more soundly before to-morrow night, Fergus!" said Waverley, with an involuntary sigh.

"You must not think of that," answered Fergus, whose ideas were entirely military. "You must only think of your sword, and by whom it was given. All other reflections are now TOO LATE."

With the opiate contained in this undeniable remark, Edward endeavoured to lull the tumult of his conflicting feelings. The chieftain and he, combining their plaids, made a comfortable and warm couch. Callum, sitting down at their head (for it was his duty to watch upon the immediate person of the chief), began a long, mournful song in Gaelic, to a low and uniform tune, which, like the sound of the wind at a distance, soon lulled them to sleep.

CHAPTER XVIII

WHEN Fergus Mac-Ivor and his friend had slept for a few hours, they were awakened, and summoned to attend the prince. The distant village-clock was heard to toll three as they hastened to the place where he lay. He was already surrounded by his principal officers and the chiefs of clans. A bundle of pease-straw, which had been lately his couch, now served for his seat. Just as Fergus reached the circle, the consultation had broken up. "Courage, my brave friends," said the Chevalier, "and each one put himself instantly at the head of his command! A faithful friend[1] has offered to guide us by a practicable, though narrow and circuitous, route, which, sweeping to our right, traverses the broken ground and morass, and enables us to gain the firm and open plain upon which the enemy are lying. This difficulty surmounted, Heaven and your good swords must do the rest."

The proposal spread unanimous joy, and each leader hastened to get his men into order with as little noise as possible. The army, moving by their right from off the ground on which they had rested, soon entered the path through the morass, conducting their march with astonishing silence and great rapidity. The mist had not risen to the

[1] Note IV. — Anderson of Whitburgh

higher grounds, so that for some time they had the advantage of starlight. But this was lost as the stars faded before approaching day, and the head of the marching column, continuing its descent, plunged as it were into the heavy ocean of fog which rolled its white waves over the whole plain, and over the sea by which it was bounded. Some difficulties were now to be encountered, inseparable from darkness, a narrow, broken, and marshy path, and the necessity of preserving union in the march. These, however, were less inconvenient to Highlanders, from their habits of life, than they would have been to any other troops, and they continued a steady and swift movement.

As the clan of Ivor approached the firm ground, following the track of those who preceded them, the challenge of a patrol was heard through the mist, though they could not see the dragoon by whom it was made, — "Who goes there?"

"Hush," cried Fergus, "hush! Let none answer, as he values his life. Press forward;" and they continued their march with silence and rapidity.

The patrol fired his carabine upon the body, and the report was instantly followed by the clang of his horse's feet as he galloped off. "Hylax in limine latrat," said the Baron of Bradwardine, who heard the shot; "that loon will give the alarm."

The clan of Fergus had now gained the firm plain, which had lately borne a large crop of corn. But the harvest was gathered in, and the expanse was unbroken by tree, bush, or interruption of any kind. The rest of the army were following fast, when they heard the drums of the enemy beat the general. Surprise, however, had made no part of their plan, so they were not disconcerted by this intimation that the foe was upon his guard and prepared to receive them. It only hastened their dispositions for the combat, which were very simple.

The Highland army, which now occupied the eastern end of the wide plain, or stubble field, so often referred to, was drawn up in two lines, extending from the morass towards the sea. The first was destined to charge the enemy, the second to act as a reserve. The few horse, whom the prince headed in person, remained between the two lines. The Adventurer had intimated a resolution to charge in person at the head of his first line; but his purpose was deprecated by all around him, and he was with difficulty induced to abandon it.

Both lines were now moving forward, the first prepared for instant combat. The clans, of which it was composed, formed each a sort of separate phalanx, narrow in front, and in depth ten, twelve, or fifteen files, according to the strength of the following. The best-armed and best-born, — for the words were synonymous, — were placed in front of each of these irregular subdivisions. The others in the rear shouldered forward the front, and by their pressure added both physical impulse and additional ardour and confidence to those who were first to encounter the danger.

"Down with your plaid, Waverley!" cried Fergus, throwing off his own; "we'll win silks for our tartans before the sun is above the sea."

The clansmen on every side stripped their plaids, prepared their arms, and there was an awful pause of about three minutes, during which the men, pulling off their bonnets, raised their faces to heaven and uttered a short prayer, then pulled their bonnets over their brows, and began to move forward at first slowly. Waverley felt his heart at that moment throb as it would have burst from his bosom. It was not fear, it was not ardour; it was a compound of both, — a new and deeply energetic impulse, that with its first emotion chilled and astounded, then fevered and maddened his mind. The sounds around him combined to exalt his enthusiasm; the pipes played, and the clans rushed forward, each in its own dark column. As they advanced they mended their pace, and the muttering sounds of the men to each other began to swell into a wild cry.

At this moment the sun, which was now risen above the horizon, dispelled the mist. The vapours rose like a curtain, and showed the two armies in the act of closing. The line of the regulars was formed directly fronting the attack of the Highlanders; it glittered with the appointments of a complete army, and was flanked by cavalry and artillery. But the sight impressed no terror on the assailants.

"Forward, sons of Ivor," cried their chief, "or the Camerons will draw the first blood!" They rushed on with a tremendous yell.

The rest is well known. The horse, who were commanded to charge the advancing Highlanders in the flank, received an irregular fire from their fusees as they ran on, and seized with a disgraceful panic, wavered, halted, disbanded, and galloped from the field. The artillerymen, deserted by the cavalry, fled after discharging their pieces, and the Highlanders, who dropped their guns when fired, and drew their broadswords, rushed with headlong fury against the infantry.

It was at this moment of confusion and terror that Waverley remarked an English officer, apparently of high rank, standing alone and unsupported by a field-piece, which, after the flight of the men by whom it was wrought, he had himself levelled and discharged against the clan of Mac-Ivor, the nearest group of Highlanders within his aim. Struck with his tall martial figure, and eager to save him from inevitable destruction, Waverley outstripped for an instant even the speediest of the warriors, and, reaching the spot first, called to him to surrender. The officer replied by a thrust with his sword, which Waverley received in his target, and in turning it aside the Englishman's weapon broke. At the same time the battle-axe of Dugald Mahony was in the act of descending upon the officer's head. Waverley intercepted and prevented the blow, and the officer, perceiving further resistance unavailing, and struck with Edward's generous anxiety for his safety, resigned the fragment of his sword, and was committed by Waverley to Dugald, with strict charge to use him well, and not to pillage his person, promising him, at the same time, full indemnification for the spoil.

On Edward's right the battle for a few minutes raged fierce and thick. The English infantry, trained in the wars in Flanders, stood their ground with great courage; but their extended files were pierced and broken in many places by the close masses of the clans, and in the personal struggle which ensued, the nature of the Highlanders' weapons, and their extraordinary fierceness and activity, gave them a decided superiority over those who had been accustomed to trust much to their array and discipline, and felt that the one was broken and the other useless. Waverley, as he cast his eyes towards this scene of smoke and slaughter, observed Colonel Gardiner, deserted by his own soldiers, in spite of all his attempts to rally them, yet spurring his horse through the field to take the command of a small body of infantry who, with their backs arranged against the wall of his own park (for his house was close by the field of battle), continued a desperate and unavailing resistance. Waverley could perceive that he had already received many wounds, his clothes and saddle being marked with blood. To save this good and brave man became the instant object of his most anxious exertions. But he could only witness his fall. Ere Edward could make his way among the Highlanders, who, furious and eager for spoil, now thronged upon each other, he saw his former commander brought from his horse by the blow of a scythe, and beheld him receive, while on the ground, more wounds than would have let out twenty lives. When Waverley came up, however, perception had not entirely fled. The dying warrior seemed to recognize Edward, for he fixed his eye upon him with an upbraiding, yet sorrowful look, and appeared to struggle for utterance. But he felt that death was dealing closely with him, and resigning his purpose, and folding his hands as if in devotion, he gave up his soul to his Creator. The look with which he regarded Waverley in his dying moments did not strike him so deeply at that crisis of hurry and confusion as when it recurred to his imagination at the distance of some time.[1]

Loud shouts of triumph now echoed over the whole field. The battle was fought and won, and

[1] Note V. — Death of Colonel Gardiner

the whole baggage, artillery, and military stores of the regular army remained in possession of the victors. Never was a victory more complete. Scarce any escaped from the battle, excepting the cavalry, who had left it at the very onset; and even these were broken into different parties and scattered all over the country. So far as our tale is concerned, we have only to relate the fate of Balmawhapple, who, mounted on a horse as headstrong and stiffnecked as his rider, pursued the flight of the dragoons above four miles from the field of battle, when some dozen of the fugitives took heart of grace, turned round, and cleaving his skull with their broadswords, satisfied the world that the unfortunate gentleman had actually brains, the end of his life thus giving proof of a fact greatly doubted during its progress. His death was lamented by few. Most of those who knew him agreed in the pithy observation of Ensign Maccombich, that there " was mair *tint* [lost] at Sheriff-Muir." His friend Lieutenant Jinker bent his eloquence only to exculpate his favourite mare from any share in contributing to the catastrophe. "He had tauld the laird a thousand times," he said, "that it was a burning shame to put a martingale upon the puir thing, when he would needs ride her wi' a curb of half a yard lang; and that he could na but bring himsell (not to say her) to some mischief, by flinging her down, or otherwise; whereas, if he had had a wee bit rinnin ring on the snaffle, she wad ha' rein'd as cannily as a cadger's pownie."

Such was the elegy of the Laird of Balmawhapple.[1]

[1] Note VI. — Laird of Balmawhapple.

CHAPTER XIX

AN UNEXPECTED EMBARRASSMENT

WHEN the battle was over, and all things coming into order, the Baron of Bradwardine, returning from the duty of the day, and having disposed those under his command in their proper stations, sought the Chieftain of Glennaquoich and his friend Edward Waverley. He found the former busied in determining disputes among his clansmen about points of precedence and deeds of valour, besides sundry high and doubtful questions concerning plunder. The most important of the last respected the property of a gold watch, which had once belonged to some unfortunate English officer. The party against whom judgment was awarded consoled himself by observing, " She [that is, the watch, which he took for a living animal] died the very night Vich Ian Vohr gave her to Murdoch ; " the machine having, in fact, stopped for want of winding up.

It was just when this important question was decided that the Baron of Bradwardine, with a careful and yet important expression of countenance, joined the two young men. He descended from his reeking charger, the care of which he recommended to one of his grooms. " I seldom ban, sir," said he to the man ; " but if you play any of your hound's-foot tricks, and leave puir Berwick before he's sorted, to rin after spuilzie, deil be wi' me if I do not give your craig a thraw." He then stroked with great complacency the animal which had borne him through the fatigues of the day, and having taken a tender leave of him, "Weel, my good young friends, a glorious and decisive victory," said he ; "but these loons of troopers fled ower soon. I should have liked to have shown you the true points of the *prælium equestre*, or equestrian combat, whilk their cowardice has postponed, and which I hold to be the pride and terror of warfare. Weel, I have fought once more in this old quarrel, though I admit I could not be so far *ben* as you lads, being that it was my point of duty to keep together our handful of horse. And no cavalier ought in any wise to begrudge honour that befalls his companions, even though they are ordered upon thrice his danger, whilk another time, by the blessing of God, may be his own case. But, Glennaquoich, and you, Mr. Waverley, I pray ye to give me your best advice on a matter of mickle weight, and which deeply affects the honour of the house of Bradwardine. I crave your pardon, Ensign Maccombich, and yours, Inveraughlin, and yours, Edderalshendrach, and yours, sir."

The last person he addressed was Ballenkeiroch, who, remembering the death of his son, lowered on him with a look of savage defiance. The Baron, quick as lightning at taking umbrage, had already bent his brow, when Glennaquoich dragged his major from the spot, and remonstrated with him, in the authoritative tone of a chieftain, on the madness of reviving a quarrel in such a moment.

"The ground is cumbered with carcases," said the old mountaineer, turning sullenly away ; "*one more* would hardly have been kenned upon it; and if it wasna for yoursell, Vich Ian Vohr, that one should be Bradwardine's or mine."

The chief soothed while he hurried him away, and then returned to the Baron. "It is Ballenkeiroch," he said, in an under and confidential voice, "father of the young man who fell eight years since in the unlucky affair at the Mains."

"Ah!" said the Baron, instantly relaxing the doubtful sternness of his features, "I can take mickle frae a man to whom I have unhappily rendered sic a displeasure as that. Ye were right to apprise me, Glennaquoich; he may look as black as midnight at Martinmas ere Cosmo Comyne Bradwardine shall say he does him wrang. Ah! I have nae male lineage, and I should bear with one I have made childless, though you are aware the blood-wit was made up to your ain satisfaction by assythment, and that I have since expedited letters of slains. Weel, as I have said, I have no male issue, and yet it is needful that I maintain the honour of my house; and it is on that score I prayed ye for your peculiar and private attention."

The two young men awaited to hear him, in anxious curiosity.

"I doubt na, lads," he proceeded, "but your education has been sae seen to that ye understand the true nature of the feudal tenures?"

Fergus, afraid of an endless dissertation, answered, "Intimately, Baron," and touched Waverley, as a signal to express no ignorance.

"And ye are aware, I doubt not, that the holding of the barony of Bradwardine is of a nature alike honourable and peculiar, being blanch (which Craig opines ought to be Latinated *blancum*, or rather *francum*, a free holding), *pro servitio detrahendi, seu*

153

exuendi, caligas regis post battalliam." Here Fergus
turned his falcon eye upon Edward, with an almost
imperceptible rise of his eyebrow, to which his
shoulders corresponded in the same degree of eleva-
tion. "Now, twa points of dubitation occur to me
upon this topic. First, whether this service, or
feudal homage, be at any event due to the person of
the prince, the words being, *per expressum, caligas*
REGIS, the boots of the king himself; and I pray
your opinion anent that particular before we proceed
farther."

"Why, he is Prince Regent," answered Mac-Ivor,
with laudable composure of countenance; "and in
the court of France all the honours are rendered
to the person of the regent which are due to that of
the king. Besides, were I to pull off either of their
boots, I would render that service to the young
Chevalier ten times more willingly than to his
father."

"Ay, but I talk not of personal predilections.
However, your authority is of great weight as to
the usages of the court of France; and doubtless
the prince, as *alter ego*, may have a right to claim
the *homagium* of the great tenants of the Crown,
since all faithful subjects are commanded, in the
commission of regency, to respect him as the king's
own person. Far, therefore, be it from me to
diminish the lustre of his authority by withholding
this act of homage, so peculiarly calculated to give
it splendour; for I question if the Emperor of
Germany hath his boots taken off by a free baron
of the empire. But here lieth the second difficulty,
— the prince wears no boots, but simply brogues
and trews."

This last dilemma had almost disturbed Fergus's
gravity.

"Why," said he, "you know, Baron, the proverb tells us, 'It's ill taking the breeks off a Highlandman;' and the boots are here in the same predicament."

"The word *caligæ*, however," continued the Baron, "though I admit, that, by family tradition, and even in our ancient evidents, it is explained lie BOOTS ... means, in its primitive sense, rather sandals; and Caius Cæsar, the nephew and successor of Caius Tiberius, received the agnomen of Caligula, 'a caligulis, sive caligis levioribus, quibus adolescentior usus fuerat in exercitu Germanici patris sui.' And the *caligæ* were also proper to the monastic bodies; for we read in an ancient Glossarium, upon the rule of Saint Benedict, in the Abbey of St. Amand, that *caligæ* were tied with latchets."

"That will apply to the brogues," said Fergus.

"It will so, my dear Glennaquoich, and the words are express: 'Caligæ dictæ sunt quia ligantur; nam socci non ligantur, sed tantum intromittuntur;' that is, *caligæ* are denominated from the ligatures wherewith they are bound; whereas *socci*, which may be analogous to our mules, whilk the English denominate 'slippers,' are only slipped upon the feet. The words of the charter are also alternative, 'exuere, seu detrahere;' that is, to *undo*, as in the case of sandals or brogues, and to *pull off*, as we say vernacularly, concerning boots. Yet I would we had more light; but I fear there is little chance of finding hereabout any erudite author *de re vestiaria*."

"I should doubt it very much," said the chieftain, looking around on the straggling Highlanders, who were returning loaded with spoils of the slain, "though the *res vestiaria* itself seems to be in some request at present."

This remark coming within the Baron's idea of jocularity, he honoured it with a smile, but immediately resumed what to him appeared very serious business.

"Bailie Macwheeble, indeed, holds an opinion that this honorary service is due, from its very nature, *si petatur tantum*, only if his Royal Highness shall require of the great tenant of the Crown to perform that personal duty; and indeed he pointed out the case in Dirleton's 'Doubts and Queries,' Grippit *versus* Spicer, anent the eviction of an estate *ob non solutum canonem*, that is, for non-payment of a feu-duty of three pepper-corns a year, whilk were taxt to be worth seven eighths of a penny Scots, in whilk the defender was assoilzied. But I deem it safest, wi' your good favour, to place myself in the way of rendering the prince this service, and to proffer performance thereof; and I shall cause the bailie to attend with a schedule of a protest, whilk he has here prepared (taking out a paper), intimating that if it shall be his Royal Highness's pleasure to accept of other assistance at pulling off his *caligæ* (whether the same shall be rendered boots or brogues), save that of the said Baron of Bradwardine, who is in presence ready and willing to perform the same, it shall in no wise impinge upon or prejudice the right of the said Cosmo Comyne Bradwardine to perform the said service in future, nor shall it give any esquire, valet of the chamber, squire, or page, whose assistance it may please his Royal Highness to employ, any right, title, or ground for evicting from the said Cosmo Comyne Bradwardine the estate and barony of Bradwardine, and others held as aforesaid, by the due and faithful performance thereof."

Fergus highly applauded this arrangement; and the Baron took a friendly leave of them, with a smile of contented importance upon his visage.

"Long live our dear friend the Baron," exclaimed the chief, as soon as he was out of hearing, "for the most absurd original that exists north of the Tweed! I wish to Heaven I had recommended him to attend the circle this evening with a boot-ketch under his arm. I think he might have adopted the suggestion, if it had been made with suitable gravity."

"And how can you take pleasure in making a man of his worth so ridiculous?"

"Begging pardon, my dear Waverley, you are as ridiculous as he. Why, do you not see that the man's whole mind is wrapped up in this ceremony? He has heard and thought of it since infancy as the most august privilege and ceremony in the world; and I doubt not but the expected pleasure of performing it was a principal motive with him for taking up arms. Depend upon it, had I endeavoured to divert him from exposing himself, he would have treated me as an ignorant, conceited coxcomb, or perhaps might have taken a fancy to cut my throat, — a pleasure which he once proposed to himself upon some point of etiquette not half so important, in his eyes, as this matter of boots or brogues, or whatever the *caligæ* shall finally be pronounced by the learned. But I must go to headquarters· to prepare the prince for this extraordinary scene. My information will be well taken, for it will give him a hearty laugh at present, and put him on his guard against laughing when it might be very malapropos. So *au revoir*, my dear Waverley."

157

CHAPTER XX

THE first occupation of Waverley, after he departed from the chieftain, was to go in quest of the officer whose life he had saved. He was guarded, along with his companions in misfortune, who were very numerous, in a gentleman's house near the field of battle.

On entering the room where they stood crowded together, Waverley easily recognized the object of his visit, not only by the peculiar dignity of his appearance, but by the appendage of Dugald Mahony with his battle-axe, who had stuck to him from the moment of his captivity, as if he had been skewered to his side. This close attendance was perhaps for the purpose of securing his promised reward from Edward, but it also operated to save the English gentleman from being plundered in the scene of general confusion; for Dugald sagaciously argued that the amount of the salvage which he might be allowed would be regulated by the state of the prisoner when he should deliver him over to Waverley. He hastened to assure Waverley, therefore, with more words than he usually employed, that he had " keepit ta *sidier roy* haill, and that he wasna a plack the waur since the fery moment when his honour forbad her to gie him a bit clamhewit wi' her Lochaber-axe."

158

Waverley assured Dugald of a liberal recompense, and, approaching the English officer, expressed his anxiety to do anything which might contribute to his convenience under his present unpleasant circumstances.

"I am not so inexperienced a soldier, sir," answered the Englishman, "as to complain of the fortune of war. I am only grieved to see those scenes acted in our own island, which I have often witnessed elsewhere with comparative indifference."

"Another such day as this," said Waverley, "and I trust the cause of your regrets will be removed, and all will again return to peace and order."

The officer smiled and shook his head. "I must not forget my situation so far as to attempt a formal confutation of that opinion ; but notwithstanding your success, and the valour which achieved it, you have undertaken a task to which your strength appears wholly inadequate."

At this moment Fergus pushed into the press.

"Come, Edward, come along ; the Prince has gone to Pinkie House for the night, and we must follow, or lose the whole ceremony of the *caligæ*. Your friend the Baron has been guilty of a great piece of cruelty, — he has insisted upon dragging Bailie Macwheeble out to the field of battle. Now, you must know the bailie's greatest horror is an armed Highlander or a loaded gun ; and there he stands, listening to the Baron's instructions concerning the protest, ducking his head like a seagull at the report of every gun and pistol that our idle boys are firing upon the fields, and undergoing, by way of penance, at every symptom of flinching, a severe rebuke from his patron, who would not admit the discharge of a whole battery of cannon,

159

within point-blank distance, as an apology for neglecting a discourse in which the honour of his family is interested."

" But how has Mr. Bradwardine got him to venture so far ? " said Edward.

" Why, he had come as far as Musselburgh, I fancy, in hopes of making some of our wills; and the peremptory commands of the Baron dragged him forward to Preston after the battle was over. He complains of one or two of our ragamuffins having put him in peril of his life by presenting their pieces at him ; but as they limited his ransom to an English penny, I don't think we need trouble the provost-marshal upon that subject. So come along, Waverley."

" Waverley ! " said the English officer, with great emotion, — " the nephew of Sir Everard Waverley, of ——shire ? "

" The same, sir," replied our hero, somewhat surprised at the tone in which he was addressed.

" I am at once happy and grieved," said the prisoner, " to have met with you."

" I am ignorant, sir," answered Waverley, " how I have deserved so much interest."

" Did your uncle never mention a friend called Talbot ? "

" I have heard him talk with great regard of such a person," replied Edward, — " a colonel, I believe, in the army, and the husband of Lady Emily Blandeville ; but I thought Colonel Talbot had been abroad."

" I am just returned," answered the officer ; " and being in Scotland, thought it my duty to act where my services promised to be useful. Yes, Mr. Waverley, I am that Colonel Talbot, the husband of the lady you have named; and I am proud to acknowledge that I owe alike my professional rank and my domestic happiness to your generous and noble-minded relative. Good God! that I should find his nephew in such a dress, and engaged in such a cause!"

"Sir," said Fergus, haughtily, "the dress and cause are those of men of birth and honour."

"My situation forbids me to dispute your assertion," said Colonel Talbot; "otherwise it were no difficult matter to show that neither courage nor pride of lineage can gild a bad cause. But with Mr. Waverley's permission, and yours, sir, if yours also must be asked, I would willingly speak a few words with him on affairs connected with his own family."

"Mr. Waverley, sir, regulates his own motions. You will follow me, I suppose, to Pinkie," said Fergus, turning to Edward, "when you have finished your discourse with this new acquaintance?" So saying, the Chief of Glennaquoich adjusted his plaid with rather more than his usual air of haughty assumption, and left the apartment.

The interest of Waverley readily procured for Colonel Talbot the freedom of adjourning to a large garden belonging to his place of confinement. They walked a few paces in silence, Colonel Talbot apparently studying how to open what he had to say; at length he addressed Edward.

"Mr. Waverley, you have this day saved my life; and yet I would to God that I had lost it ere I had found you wearing the uniform and cockade of these men."

"I forgive your reproach, Colonel Talbot; it is well meant, and your education and prejudices render it natural. But there is nothing extraordinary

161

in finding a man, whose honour has been publicly and unjustly assailed, in the situation which promised most fair to afford him satisfaction on his calumniators."

"I should rather say, in the situation most likely to confirm the reports which they have circulated," said Colonel Talbot, "by following the very line of conduct ascribed to you. Are you aware, Mr. Waverley, of the infinite distress, and even danger, which your present conduct has occasioned to your nearest relatives?"

"Danger!"

"Yes, sir, danger. When I left England, your uncle and father had been obliged to find bail to answer a charge of treason, to which they were only admitted by the exertion of the most powerful interest. I came down to Scotland with the sole purpose of rescuing you from the gulf into which you have precipitated yourself; nor can I estimate the consequences to your family of your having openly joined the rebellion, since the very suspicion of your intention was so perilous to them. Most deeply do I regret that I did not meet you before this last and fatal error."

"I am really ignorant," said Waverley, in a tone of reserve, "why Colonel Talbot should have taken so much trouble on my account."

"Mr. Waverley," answered Talbot, "I am dull at apprehending irony, and therefore I shall answer your words according to their plain meaning. I am indebted to your uncle for benefits greater than those which a son owes to a father. I acknowledge to him the duty of a son; and as I know there is no manner in which I can requite his kindness so well as by serving you, I will serve you, if possible, whether you will permit me or no. The personal obligation which you have this day laid me under (although, in common estimation, as great as one human being can bestow on another), adds nothing to my zeal on your behalf, nor can that zeal be abated by any coolness with which you may please to receive it."

" Your intentions may be kind, sir," said Waverley, drily, "but your language is harsh, or at least peremptory."

"On my return to England," continued Colonel Talbot, "after long absence, I found your uncle, Sir Everard Waverley, in the custody of a king's messenger, in consequence of the suspicion brought upon him by your conduct. He is my oldest friend, — how often shall I repeat it ! — my best benefactor ! he sacrificed his own views of happiness to mine ; he never uttered a word, he never harboured a thought, that benevolence itself might not have thought or spoken. I found this man in confinement, rendered harsher to him by his habits of life, his natural dignity of feeling, and — forgive me, Mr. Waverley — by the cause through which this calamity had come upon him. I cannot disguise from you my feelings upon this occasion; they were most painfully unfavourable to you. Having by my family interest, which you probably know is not inconsiderable, succeeded in obtaining Sir Everard's release, I set out for Scotland. I saw Colonel Gardiner, a man whose fate alone is sufficient to render this insurrection for ever execrable. In the course of conversation with him, I found that, from late circumstances, from a re-examination of the persons engaged in the mutiny, and from his original good opinion of your character, he

163

was much softened towards you; and I doubted not that if I could be so fortunate as to discover you, all might yet be well. But this unnatural rebellion has ruined all. I have for the first time, in a long and active military life, seen Britons disgrace themselves by a panic flight, and that before a foe without either arms or discipline. And now I find the heir of my dearest friend — the son, I may say, of his affections — sharing a triumph for which he ought the first to have blushed. Why should I lament Gardiner? — his lot was happy compared to mine!"

There was so much dignity in Colonel Talbot's manner, such a mixture of military pride and manly sorrow, and the news of Sir Everard's imprisonment was told in so deep a tone of feeling, that Edward stood mortified, abashed, and distressed in presence of the prisoner who owed to him his life not many hours before. He was not sorry when Fergus interrupted their conference a second time.

"His Royal Highness commands Mr. Waverley's attendance." Colonel Talbot threw upon Edward a reproachful glance, which did not escape the quick eye of the Highland chief. "His *immediate* attendance," he repeated, with considerable emphasis. Waverley turned again towards the colonel.

"We shall meet again," he said; "in the meanwhile, every possible accommodation — "

"I desire none," said the colonel; "let me fare like the meanest of those brave men who, on this day of calamity, have preferred wounds and captivity to flight. I would almost exchange places with one of those who have fallen, to know that my words have made a suitable impression on your mind."

"Let Colonel Talbot be carefully secured," said Fergus to the Highland officer who commanded the guard over the prisoners; "it is the prince's particular command; he is a prisoner of the utmost importance."

"But let him want no accommodation suitable to his rank," said Waverley.

"Consistent always with secure custody," reiterated Fergus.

The officer signified his acquiescence in both commands, and Edward followed Fergus to the garden-gate, where Callum Beg, with three saddle-horses, awaited them. Turning his head, he saw Colonel Talbot re-conducted to his place of confinement by a file of Highlanders; he lingered on the threshold of the door, and made a signal with his hand towards Waverley, as if enforcing the language he had held towards him.

"Horses," said Fergus, as he mounted, "are now as plenty as blackberries; every man may have them for the catching. Come, let Callum adjust your stirrups, and let us to Pinkie House [1] as fast as these *ci-devant* dragoon-horses choose to carry us."

[1] Charles Edward took up his quarters after the battle at Pinkie House, adjoining to Musselburgh.

CHAPTER XXI

"I WAS turned back," said Fergus to Edward, as they galloped from Preston to Pinkie House, "by a message from the prince. But I suppose you know the value of this most noble Colonel Talbot as a prisoner? He is held one of the best officers among the red-coats, — a special friend and favourite of the Elector himself, and of that dreadful hero, the Duke of Cumberland, who has been summoned from his triumphs at Fontenoy to come over and devour us poor Highlanders alive. Has he been telling you how the bells of St. James's ring? Not 'turn again, Whittington,' like those of Bow, in the days of yore?"

"Fergus!" said Waverley, with a reproachful look.

"Nay, I cannot tell what to make of you," answered the chief of Mac-Ivor; "you are blown about with every wind of doctrine. Here have we gained a victory unparalleled in history, and your behaviour is praised by every living mortal to the skies, and the prince is eager to thank you in person, and all our beauties of the White Rose are pulling caps for you, — and you, the *preux chevalier* of the day, are stooping on your horse's neck like a butter-woman riding to market, and looking as black as a funeral!"

166

"I am sorry for poor Colonel Gardiner's death; he was once very kind to me."

"Why, then, be sorry for five minutes, and then be glad again; his chance to-day may be ours to-morrow. And what does it signify? The next best thing to victory is honourable death; but it is a *pis-aller*, and one would rather a foe had it than one's self."

"But Colonel Talbot has informed me that my father and uncle are both imprisoned by government on my account."

"We'll put in bail, my boy; old Andrew Ferrara [1] shall lodge his security, — and I should like to see him put to justify it in Westminster Hall!"

"Nay, they are already at liberty, upon bail of a more civic disposition."

"Then why is thy noble spirit cast down, Edward? Dost think that the Elector's ministers are such doves as to set their enemies at liberty at this critical moment if they could or durst confine and punish them? Assure thyself that either they have no charge against your relations on which they can continue their imprisonment, or else they are afraid of our friends the jolly cavaliers of Old England. At any rate, you need not be apprehensive upon their account, and we will find some means of conveying to them assurances of your safety."

Edward was silenced, but not satisfied, with these reasons. He had now been more than once shocked at the small degree of sympathy which Fergus exhibited for the feelings even of those whom he loved, if they did not correspond with his own mood at the time, and more especially if they

[1] Note VII. — Andrea de Ferrara

167

thwarted him while earnest in a favourite pursuit. Fergus sometimes indeed observed that he had offended Waverley, but always intent upon some favourite plan or project of his own, he was never sufficiently aware of the extent or duration of his displeasure, so that the reiteration of these petty offences somewhat cooled the volunteer's extreme attachment to his officer.

The Chevalier received Waverley with his usual favour, and paid him many compliments on his distinguished bravery. He then took him apart, made many inquiries concerning Colonel Talbot, and when he had received all the information which Edward was able to give concerning him and his connections, he proceeded: " I cannot but think, Mr. Waverley, that since this gentleman is so particularly connected with our worthy and excellent friend Sir Everard Waverley, and since his lady is of the house of Blandeville, whose devotion to the true and loyal principles of the Church of England is so generally known, the colonel's own private sentiments cannot be unfavourable to us, whatever mask he may have assumed to accommodate himself to the times."

" If I am to judge from the language he this day held to me, I am under the necessity of differing widely from your Royal Highness."

" Well, it is worth making a trial, at least. I therefore intrust you with the charge of Colonel Talbot, with power to act concerning him as you think most advisable ; and I hope you will find means of ascertaining what are his real dispositions towards our royal father's restoration."

" I am convinced," said Waverley, bowing, " that if Colonel Talbot chooses to grant his parole, it may be securely depended upon ; but if he refuses it, I trust your Royal Highness will devolve on some other person than the nephew of his friend the task of laying him under the necessary restraint."

" I will trust him with no person but you," said the prince, smiling, but peremptorily repeating his mandate ; " it is of importance to my service that there should appear to be a good intelligence between you, even if you are unable to gain his confidence in earnest. You will therefore receive him into your quarters, and in case he declines giving his parole, you must apply for a proper guard. I beg you will go about this directly. We return to Edinburgh to-morrow."

Being thus remanded to the vicinity of Preston, Waverley lost the Baron of Bradwardine's solemn act of homage. So little, however, was he at this time in love with vanity that he had quite forgotten the ceremony in which Fergus had laboured to engage his curiosity. But next day a formal Gazette was circulated, containing a detailed account of the battle of Gladsmuir, as the Highlanders chose to denominate their victory. It concluded with an account of the court afterwards held by the Chevalier at Pinkie House, which contained this among other high-flown descriptive paragraphs : —

" Since that fatal treaty which annihilates Scotland as an independent nation, it has not been our happiness to see her princes receive, and her nobles discharge, those acts of feudal homage which, founded upon the splendid actions of Scottish valour, recall the memory of her early history, with the manly and chivalrous simplicity of the ties which united to the Crown the homage of the warriors by whom it was repeatedly up-

169

held and defended. But on the evening of the 20th our memories were refreshed with one of those ceremonies which belong to the ancient days of Scotland's glory. After the circle was formed, Cosmo Comyne Bradwardine, of that ilk, colonel in the service, etc., came before the prince, attended by Mr. D. Macwheeble, the bailie of his ancient barony of Bradwardine (who, we understand, has been lately named a commissary), and, under form of instrument, claimed permission to perform, to the person of his Royal Highness, as representing his father, the service used and wont, for which, under a charter of Robert Bruce (of which the original was produced and inspected by the Masters of his Royal Highness's Chancery for the time being), the claimant held the barony of Bradwardine and lands of Tully-Veolan. His claim being admitted and registered, his Royal Highness, having placed his foot upon a cushion, the Baron of Bradwardine, kneeling upon his right knee, proceeded to undo the latchet of the brogue, or low-heeled Highland shoe, which our gallant young hero wears, in compliment to his brave followers. When this was performed, his Royal Highness declared the ceremony completed, and embracing the gallant veteran, protested that nothing but compliance with an ordinance of Robert Bruce could have induced him to receive even the symbolical performance of a menial office from hands which had fought so bravely to put the crown upon the head of his father. The Baron of Bradwardine then took instruments in the hands of Mr. Commissary Macwheeble, bearing, that all points and circumstances of the act of homage had been *rite et solenniter acta et peracta ;* and a corresponding entry was made in the protocol of the Lord High Chamberlain and in the record of Chancery. We understand that it is in contemplation of his Royal Highness, when his Majesty's pleasure can be known, to raise Colonel Bradwardine to the peerage, by the title of Viscount Bradwardine, of Bradwardine and

Tully-Veolan, and that, in the meanwhile, his Royal Highness, in his father's name and authority, has been pleased to grant him an honourable augmentation to his paternal coat-of-arms, being a budget or boot-jack, disposed saltier-wise with a naked broadsword to be borne in the dexter cantle of the shield; and as an additional motto, on a scroll beneath, the words, 'Draw and draw off.' "

" Were it not for the recollection of Fergus's raillery," thought Waverley to himself, when he had perused this long and grave document, " how very tolerably would all this sound, and how little should I have thought of connecting it with any ludicrous idea ! Well, after all, everything has its fair as well as its seamy side ; and truly I do not see why the Baron's boot-jack may not stand as fair in heraldry as the water-buckets, waggons, cart-wheels, plough-socks, shuttles, candlesticks, and other ordinaries, conveying ideas of anything save chivalry, which appear in the arms of some of our most ancient gentry."

This, however, is an episode in respect to the principal story.

When Waverley returned to Preston and rejoined Colonel Talbot, he found him recovered from the strong and obvious emotions with which a concurrence of unpleasing events had affected him. He had regained his natural manner, which was that of an English gentleman and soldier, manly, open, and generous, but not unsusceptible of prejudice against those of a different country, or who opposed him in political tenets. When Waverley acquainted Colonel Talbot with the Chevalier's purpose to commit him to his charge, " I did not think to have owed so much obligation to that young gentleman," he said, "as is implied in this destination. I can at least cheerfully join in the prayer of the honest Presbyterian clergyman that, as he has come among us seeking an earthly crown, his labours may be speedily rewarded with a heavenly one.[1] I shall willingly give my parole not to attempt an escape without your knowledge, since, in fact, it was to meet you that I came to Scotland; and I am glad it has happened even under this predicament. But I suppose we shall be but a short time together. Your Chevalier (that is a name we may both give to him), with his plaids and blue caps, will, I presume, be continuing his crusade southward?"

"Not, as I hear; I believe the army makes some stay in Edinburgh, to collect reinforcements."

"And to besiege the Castle?" said Talbot, smiling sarcastically. "Well, unless my old commander, General Preston, turn false metal, or the Castle sink into the North Loch, — events which I deem equally probable, — I think we shall have some time to make up our acquaintance. I have a guess that this gallant Chevalier has a design that I should be your proselyte; and as I wish you to be mine, there cannot be a more fair proposal than to afford us fair conference together. But as I spoke to-day under the influence of feelings I rarely give way to, I hope you will excuse my entering again upon controversy till we are somewhat better acquainted."

[1] The clergyman's name was Mac-Vicar. Protected by the cannon of the Castle, he preached every Sunday in the West Kirk while the Highlanders were in possession of Edinburgh; and it was in presence of some of the Jacobites that he prayed for Prince Charles Edward in the terms quoted in the text.

172

CHAPTER XXII

IT is not necessary to record in these pages the triumphant entrance of the Chevalier into Edinburgh after the decisive affair of Preston. One circumstance, however, may be noticed, because it illustrates the high spirit of Flora Mac-Ivor. The Highlanders, by whom the Prince was surrounded, in the license and extravagance of this joyful moment, fired their pieces repeatedly, and one of these having been accidentally loaded with ball, the bullet grazed the young lady's temple as she waved her handkerchief from a balcony.[1] Fergus, who beheld the accident, was at her side in an instant; and on seeing that the wound was trifling, he drew his broadsword, with the purpose of rushing down upon the man by whose carelessness she had incurred so much danger, when, holding him by the plaid, " Do not harm the poor fellow," she cried ; " for Heaven's sake, do not harm him, but thank God with me that

---

[1] The incident here said to have happened to Flora Mac-Ivor, actually befell Miss Nairne, a lady with whom the Author had the pleasure of being acquainted. As the Highland army rushed into Edinburgh, Miss Nairne, like other ladies who approved of their cause, stood waving her handkerchief from a balcony, when a ball from a Highlander's musket, which was discharged by accident, grazed her forehead. " Thank God," said she, the instant she recovered, " that the accident happened to me, whose principles are known. Had it befallen a Whig, they would have said it was done on purpose. '

the accident happened to Flora Mac-Ivor; for had it befallen a Whig, they would have pretended that the shot was fired on purpose."

Waverley escaped the alarm which this accident would have occasioned to him, as he was unavoidably delayed by the necessity of accompanying Colonel Talbot to Edinburgh.

They performed the journey together on horseback, and for some time, as if to sound each other's feelings and sentiments, they conversed upon general and ordinary topics.

When Waverley again entered upon the subject which he had most at heart, the situation, namely, of his father and his uncle, Colonel Talbot seemed now rather desirous to alleviate than to aggravate his anxiety. This appeared particularly to be the case when he heard Waverley's history, which he did not scruple to confide to him.

"And so," said the colonel, "there has been no malice prepense, as lawyers, I think, term it, in this rash step of yours; and you have been trepanned into the service of this Italian knight-errant by a few civil speeches from him and one or two of his Highland recruiting sergeants? It is sadly foolish, to be sure, but not nearly so bad as I was led to expect. However, you cannot desert, even from the Pretender, at the present moment, — that seems impossible. But I have little doubt that, in the dissensions incident to this heterogeneous mass of wild and desperate men, some opportunity may arise, by availing yourself of which, you may extricate yourself honourably from your rash engagement before the bubble burst. If this can be managed, I would have you go to a place of safety in Flanders, which I shall point out. And I think I can secure your pardon from government after a few months' residence abroad."

" I cannot permit you, Colonel Talbot," answered Waverley, "to speak of any plan which turns on my deserting an enterprise in which I may have engaged hastily, but certainly voluntarily, and with the purpose of abiding the issue."

"Well," said Colonel Talbot, smiling, "leave me my thoughts and hopes at least at liberty, if not my speech. But have you never examined your mysterious packet ?"

" It is in my baggage," replied Edward; " we shall find it in Edinburgh."

In Edinburgh they soon arrived. Waverley's quarters had been assigned to him, by the prince's express orders, in a handsome lodging, where there was accommodation for Colonel Talbot. His first business was to examine his portmanteau, and after a very short search, out tumbled the expected packet. Waverley opened it eagerly. Under a blank cover, simply addressed to E. Waverley, Esq., he found a number of open letters. The uppermost were two from Colonel Gardiner addressed to himself. The earliest in date was a kind and gentle remonstrance for neglect of the writer's advice respecting the disposal of his time during his leave of absence, the renewal of which, he reminded Captain Waverley, would speedily expire. "Indeed," the letter proceeded, "had it been otherwise, the news from abroad, and my instructions from the War-Office, must have compelled me to recall it, as there is great danger, since the disaster in Flanders, both of foreign invasion and insurrection among the disaffected at home. I therefore entreat you will repair, as soon as possible, to the headquarters of

175

the regiment; and I am concerned to add that this is still the more necessary, as there is some discontent in your troop, and I postpone inquiry into particulars until I can have the advantage of your assistance."

The second letter, dated eight days later, was in such a style as might have been expected from the colonel's receiving no answer to the first. It reminded Waverley of his duty as a man of honour, an officer, and a Briton; took notice of the increasing dissatisfaction of his men, and that some of them had been heard to hint that their captain encouraged and approved of their mutinous behaviour; and, finally, the writer expressed the utmost regret and surprise that he had not obeyed his commands by repairing to headquarters, reminded him that his leave of absence had been recalled, and conjured him, in a style in which paternal remonstrance was mingled with military authority, to redeem his error by immediately joining his regiment. "That I may be certain," concluded the letter, "that this actually reaches you, I despatch it by Corporal Tims, of your troop, with orders to deliver it into your own hand."

Upon reading these letters, Waverley, with great bitterness of feeling, was compelled to make the *amende honorable* to the memory of the brave and excellent writer; for surely, as Colonel Gardiner must have had every reason to conclude they had come safely to hand, less could not follow, on their being neglected, than that third and final summons, which Waverley actually received at Glennaquoich, though too late to obey it. And his being superseded, in consequence of his apparent neglect of this last command, was so far from being a harsh or severe proceeding, that it was plainly inevitable. The next letter he unfolded was from the major of the regiment, acquainting him that a report, to the disadvantage of his reputation, was public in the country, stating that one Mr. Falconer of Ballihopple, or some such name, had proposed in his presence a treasonable toast, which he permitted to pass in silence, although it was so gross an affront to the royal family that a gentleman in company, not remarkable for his zeal for government, had nevertheless taken the matter up, and that, supposing the account true, Captain Waverley had thus suffered another, comparatively unconcerned, to resent an affront directed against him personally as an officer, and to go out with the person by whom it was offered. The major concluded that no one of Captain Waverley's brother officers could believe this scandalous story, but that it was necessarily their joint opinion that his own honour, equally with that of the regiment, depended upon its being instantly contradicted by his authority, &c. &c. &c.

"What do you think of all this ? " said Colonel Talbot, to whom Waverley handed the letters after he had perused them.

"Think! it renders thought impossible; it is enough to drive me mad."

"Be calm, my young friend; let us see what are these dirty scrawls that follow."

The first was addressed, —

" For Master W. Ruffin These.

DEAR SUR, sum of our yong gulpins will not bite, thof I tuold them you shoed me the squoire's own seel. But Tims will deliver you the lettrs as desired, and tell ould Addem he gave them to squoir's hond, as to

177

be sure yours is the same, and shall be ready for signal, and hoy for Hoy Church and Sachefrel, as fadur sings at harvest-whome.

Yours, deer Sur,

H. H.

Poscriff. — Do'e tell squoire we longs to heer from him, and has dootings about his not writing himself, and Lifetenant Bottler is smoky."

"This Ruffin, I suppose, then, is your Donald of the Cavern, who has intercepted your letters, and carried on a correspondence with the poor devil Houghton, as if under your authority?"

"It seems too true. But who can Addem be?"

"Possibly Adam, — for poor Gardiner, a sort of pun on his name."

The other letters were to the same purpose, and they soon received yet more complete light upon Donald Bean's machinations.

John Hodges, one of Waverley's servants, who had remained with the regiment and had been taken at Preston, now made his appearance. He had sought out his master, with the purpose of again entering his service. From this fellow they learned that some time after Waverley had gone from the headquarters of the regiment, a pedlar called Ruthven, Ruffin, or Rivane, known among the soldiers by the name of Wily Will, had made frequent visits to the town of Dundee. He appeared to possess plenty of money, sold his commodities very cheap, seemed always willing to treat his friends at the ale-house, and easily ingratiated himself with many of Waverley's troop, particularly Sergeant Houghton and one Tims, also a non-commissioned officer. To these he unfolded, in Waverley's name, a plan for leaving the regiment and joining him in the Highlands, where report said the clans had already taken arms in great numbers. The men, who had been educated as Jacobites, so far as they had any opinion at all, and who knew their landlord, Sir Everard, had always been supposed to hold such tenets, easily fell into the snare. That Waverley was at a distance in the Highlands, was received as a sufficient excuse for transmitting his letters through the medium of the pedlar; and the sight of his well-known seal seemed to authenticate the negotiations in his name, where writing might have been dangerous. The cabal, however, began to take air, from the premature mutinous language of those concerned. Wily Will justified his appellative; for after suspicion arose, he was seen no more. When the Gazette appeared, in which Waverley was superseded, great part of his troop broke out into actual mutiny, but were surrounded and disarmed by the rest of the regiment. In consequence of the sentence of a court-martial, Houghton and Tims were condemned to be shot, but afterwards permitted to cast lots for life. Houghton, the survivor, showed much penitence, being convinced, from the rebukes and explanations of Colonel Gardiner, that he had really engaged in a very heinous crime. It is remarkable that as soon as the poor fellow was satisfied of this, he became also convinced that the instigator had acted without authority from Edward, saying, " If it was dishonourable and against Old England, the squire could know nought about it; he never did, or thought to do, anything dishonourable, no more did n't Sir Everard, nor none of them afore him; and in that belief he would live and die, that Ruffin had done it all of his own head."

179

The strength of conviction with which he expressed himself upon this subject, as well as his assurances that the letters intended for Waverley had been delivered to Ruthven, made that revolution in Colonel Gardiner's opinion which he expressed to Talbot.

The reader has long since understood that Donald Bean Lean played the part of tempter on this occasion. His motives were shortly these. Of an active and intriguing spirit, he had been long employed as a subaltern agent and spy, by those in the confidence of the Chevalier, to an extent beyond what was suspected even by Fergus Mac-Ivor, whom, though obliged to him for protection, he regarded with fear and dislike. To success in this political department he naturally looked for raising himself by some bold stroke above his present hazardous and precarious trade of rapine. He was particularly employed in learning the strength of the regiments in Scotland, the character of the officers, etc., and had long had his eye upon Waverley's troop, as open to temptation. Donald even believed that Waverley himself was at bottom in the Stewart interest, which seemed confirmed by his long visit to the Jacobite Baron of Bradwardine. When, therefore, he came to his cave with one of Glennaquoich's attendants, the robber, who could never appreciate his real motive, which was mere curiosity, was so sanguine as to hope that his own talents were to be employed in some intrigue of consequence, under the auspices of this wealthy young Englishman. Nor was he undeceived by Waverley's neglecting all hints and openings afforded for explanation. His conduct passed for prudent reserve, and somewhat piqued Donald

Bean, who, supposing himself left out of a secret where confidence promised to be advantageous, determined to have his share in the drama, whether a regular part were assigned him or not. For this purpose, during Waverley's sleep he possessed himself of his seal, as a token to be used to any of the troopers whom he might discover to be possessed of the captain's confidence. His first journey to Dundee, the town where the regiment was quartered, undeceived him in his original supposition, but opened to him a new field of action. He knew there would be no service so well rewarded by the friends of the Chevalier as seducing a part of the regular army to his standard. For this purpose he opened the machinations with which the reader is already acquainted, and which form a clew to all the intricacies and obscurities of the narrative previous to Waverley's leaving Glennaquoich.

By Colonel Talbot's advice, Waverley declined detaining in his service the lad whose evidence had thrown additional light on these intrigues. He represented to him it would be doing the man an injury to engage him in a desperate undertaking, and that, whatever should happen, his evidence would go some length, at least, in explaining the circumstances under which Waverley himself had embarked in it. Waverley therefore wrote a short state of what had happened, to his uncle and his father, cautioning them, however, in the present circumstances, not to attempt to answer his letter. Talbot then gave the young man a letter to the commander of one of the English vessels of war cruising in the Frith, requesting him to put the bearer ashore at Berwick, with a pass to proceed to ——shire. He was then furnished with money to make an

181

expeditious journey, and directed to get on board the
ship by means of bribing a fishing-boat, which, as
they afterwards learned, he easily effected.

Tired of the attendance of Callum Beg, who, he
thought, had some disposition to act as a spy on
his motions, Waverley hired as a servant a simple
Edinburgh swain, who had mounted the white cockade in a fit of spleen and jealousy because Jenny
Jop had danced a whole night with Corporal
Bullock of the Fusileers.

CHAPTER XXIII

INTRIGUES OF SOCIETY AND LOVE

COLONEL TALBOT became more kindly in his demeanour towards Waverley after the confidence he
had reposed in him, and as they were necessarily
much together, the character of the colonel rose
in Waverley's estimation. There seemed at first
something harsh in his strong expressions of dislike
and censure, although no one was in the general
case more open to conviction. The habit of authority had also given his manners some peremptory
hardness, notwithstanding the polish which they
had received from his intimate acquaintance with
the higher circles. As a specimen of the military
character, he differed from all whom Waverley had
as yet seen. The soldiership of the Baron of Bradwardine was marked by pedantry; that of Major
Melville by a sort of martinet attention to the
minutiæ and technicalities of discipline rather suitable to one who was to manœuvre a battalion, than
to him who was to command an army; the military
spirit of Fergus was so much warped and blended
with his plans and political views that it was less
that of a soldier than of a petty sovereign. But
Colonel Talbot was in every point the English soldier. His whole soul was devoted to the service
of his king and country, without feeling any pride
in knowing the theory of his art with the Baron,

183

or its practical minutiæ with the major, or in applying his science to his own particular plans of ambition, like the Chieftain of Glennaquoich. Added to this, he was a man of extended knowledge and cultivated taste, although strongly tinged, as we have already observed, with those prejudices which are peculiarly English.

The character of Colonel Talbot dawned upon Edward by degrees; for the delay of the Highlanders in the fruitless siege of Edinburgh Castle occupied several weeks, during which Waverley had little to do, excepting to seek such amusement as society afforded. He would willingly have persuaded his new friend to become acquainted with some of his former intimates. But the colonel, after one or two visits, shook his head, and declined further experiment. Indeed, he went further, and characterized the Baron as the most intolerable formal pedant he had ever had the misfortune to meet with, and the Chief of Glennaquoich as a Frenchified Scotchman possessing all the cunning and plausibility of the nation where he was educated, with the proud, vindictive, and turbulent humour of that of his birth. " If the devil," he said, " had sought out an agent expressly for the purpose of embroiling this miserable country, I do not think he could find a better than such a fellow as this, whose temper seems equally active, supple, and mischievous, and who is followed, and implicitly obeyed, by a gang of such cutthroats as those whom you are pleased to admire so much."

The ladies of the party did not escape his censure. He allowed that Flora Mac-Ivor was a fine woman, and Rose Bradwardine a pretty girl. But he alleged that the former destroyed the effect of her beauty by an affectation of the grand airs which she had probably seen practised in the mock court of St. Germains. As for Rose Bradwardine, he said it was impossible for any mortal to admire such a little uninformed thing, whose small portion of education was as ill adapted to her sex or youth as if she had appeared with one of her father's old campaign-coats upon her person for her sole garment. Now, much of this was mere spleen and prejudice in the excellent colonel, with whom the white cockade on the breast, the white rose in the hair, and the Mac at the beginning of a name, would have made a devil out of an angel; and indeed he himself jocularly allowed that he could not have endured Venus herself if she had been announced in a drawing-room by the name of Miss Mac-Jupiter.

Waverley, it may easily be believed, looked upon these young ladies with very different eyes. During the period of the siege he paid them almost daily visits, although he observed with regret that his suit made as little progress in the affections of the former as the arms of the Chevalier in subduing the fortress. She maintained with rigour the rule she had laid down of treating him with indifference, without either affecting to avoid him or to shun intercourse with him. Every word, every look, was strictly regulated to accord with her system, and neither the dejection of Waverley, nor the anger which Fergus scarcely suppressed, could extend Flora's attention to Edward beyond that which the most ordinary politeness demanded. On the other hand, Rose Bradwardine gradually rose in Waverley's opinion. He had several opportunities of remarking that as her extreme timidity wore

185

off, her manners assumed a higher character; that the agitating circumstances of the stormy time seemed to call forth a certain dignity of feeling and expression which he had not formerly observed; and that she omitted no opportunity within her reach to extend her knowledge and refine her taste.

Flora Mac-Ivor called Rose her pupil, and was attentive to assist her in her studies and to fashion both her taste and understanding. It might have been remarked by a very close observer that in the presence of Waverley she was much more desirous to exhibit her friend's excellences than her own. But I must request of the reader to suppose that this kind and disinterested purpose was concealed by the most cautious delicacy, studiously shunning the most distant approach to affectation; so that it was as unlike the usual exhibition of one pretty woman affecting to *proner* another, as the friendship of David and Jonathan might be to the intimacy of two Bond Street loungers. The fact is, that though the effect was felt, the cause could hardly be observed. Each of the ladies, like two excellent actresses, were perfect in their parts, and performed them to the delight of the audience; and such being the case, it was almost impossible to discover that the elder constantly ceded to her friend that which was most suitable to her talents.

But to Waverley, Rose Bradwardine possessed an attraction which few men can resist, from the marked interest which she took in everything that affected him. She was too young and too inexperienced to estimate the full force of the constant attention which she paid to him. Her father was too abstractedly immersed in learned and military discussions to observe her partiality, and Flora

Mac-Ivor did not alarm her by remonstrance, because she saw in this line of conduct the most probable chance of her friend securing at length a return of affection.

The truth is, that in her first conversation after their meeting, Rose had discovered the state of her mind to that acute and intelligent friend, although she was not herself aware of it. From that time, Flora was not only determined upon the final rejection of Waverley's addresses, but became anxious that they should, if possible, be transferred to her friend. Nor was she less interested in this plan, though her brother had from time to time talked, as between jest and earnest, of paying his suit to Miss Bradwardine. She knew that Fergus had the true Continental latitude of opinion respecting the institution of marriage, and would not have given his hand to an angel unless for the purpose of strengthening his alliances and increasing his influence and wealth; the Baron's whim of transferring his estate to the distant heir male, instead of his own daughter, was therefore likely to be an insurmountable obstacle to his entertaining any serious thoughts of Rose Bradwardine. Indeed, Fergus's brain was a perpetual workshop of scheme and intrigue of every possible kind and description; while, like many a mechanic of more ingenuity than steadiness, he would often unexpectedly, and without any apparent motive, abandon one plan, and go earnestly to work upon another, which was either fresh from the forge of his imagination, or had at some former period been flung aside half finished. It was therefore often difficult to guess what line of conduct he might finally adopt upon any given occasion.

187

Although Flora was sincerely attached to her brother, whose high energies might indeed have commanded her admiration even without the ties which bound them together, she was by no means blind to his faults, which she considered as dangerous to the hopes of any woman who should found her ideas of a happy marriage in the peaceful enjoyment of domestic society and the exchange of mutual and engrossing affection. The real disposition of Waverley, on the other hand, notwithstanding his dreams of tented fields and military honour, seemed exclusively domestic. He asked and received no share in the busy scenes which were constantly going on around him, and was rather annoyed than interested by the discussion of contending claims, rights, and interests, which often passed in his presence. All this pointed him out as the person formed to make happy a spirit like that of Rose, which corresponded with his own.

She remarked this point in Waverley's character one day while she sat with Miss Bradwardine. "His genius and elegant taste," answered Rose, "cannot be interested in such trifling discussions. What is it to him, for example, whether the Chief of the Macindallaghers, who has brought out only fifty men, should be a colonel or a captain? and how could Mr. Waverley be supposed to interest himself in the violent altercation between your brother and young Corrinaschian, whether the post of honour is due to the eldest cadet of a clan, or the youngest?"

"My dear Rose, if he were the hero you suppose him, he would interest himself in these matters, not indeed as important in themselves, but for the purpose of mediating between the ardent spirits who actually do make them the subject of discord. You saw when Corrinaschian raised his voice in great passion, and laid his hand upon his sword, Waverley lifted his head as if he had just awaked from a dream, and asked, with great composure, what the matter was."

"Well, and did not the laughter they fell into at his absence of mind, serve better to break off the dispute than anything he could have said to them?"

"True, my dear," answered Flora; "but not quite so creditably for Waverley as if he had brought them to their senses by force of reason."

"Would you have him peacemaker general between all the gunpowder Highlanders in the army? I beg your pardon, Flora, — your brother, you know, is out of the question; he has more sense than half of them. But can you think the fierce, hot, furious spirits, of whose brawls we see much and hear more, and who terrify me out of my life every day in the world, are at all to be compared to Waverley?"

"I do not compare him with those uneducated men, my dear Rose. I only lament that, with his talents and genius, he does not assume that place in society for which they eminently fit him, and that he does not lend their full impulse to the noble cause in which he has enlisted. Are there not Lochiel, and P——, and M——, and G——, all men of the highest education, as well as the first talents, — why will he not stoop, like them, to be alive and useful? I often believe his zeal is frozen by that proud, cold-blooded Englishman whom he now lives with so much."

"Colonel Talbot? He is a very disagreeable person, to be sure. He looks as if he thought no Scottish woman worth the trouble of handing her a cup of tea. But Waverley is so gentle, so well informed — ”

“ Yes,” said Flora, smiling, “ he can admire the moon, and quote a stanza from Tasso.”

“ Besides, you know how he fought,” added Miss Bradwardine.

“ For mere fighting,” answered Flora, “ I believe all men (that is, who deserve the name) are pretty much alike ; there is generally more courage required to run away. They have besides, when confronted with each other, a certain instinct for strife, as we see in other male animals, such as dogs, bulls, and so forth. But high and perilous enterprise is not Waverley's forte. He would never have been his celebrated ancestor Sir Nigel, but only Sir Nigel's eulogist and poet. I will tell you where he will be at home, my dear, and in his place, — in the quiet circle of domestic happiness, lettered indolence, and elegant enjoyments of Waverley Honour. And he will refit the old library in the most exquisite Gothic taste, and garnish its shelves with the rarest and most valuable volumes ; and he will draw plans and landscapes, and write verses, and rear temples, and dig grottoes ; and he will stand in a clear summer night in the colonnade before the hall, and gaze on the deer as they stray in the moonlight, or lie shadowed by the boughs of the huge old fantastic oaks ; and he will repeat verses to his beautiful wife, who will hang upon his arm, — and he will be a happy man.”

“ And she will be a happy woman,” thought poor Rose. But she only sighed, and dropped the conversation.

CHAPTER XXIV

WAVERLEY had, indeed, as he looked closer into the
state of the Chevalier's court, less reason to be satisfied with it. It contained, as they say an acorn
includes all the ramifications of the future oak, as
many seeds of *tracasserie* and intrigue as might
have done honour to the court of a large empire.
Every person of consequence had some separate object, which he pursued with a fury that Waverley
considered as altogether disproportioned to its importance. Almost all had their reasons for discontent, although the most legitimate was that of the
worthy old Baron, who was only distressed on account of the common cause.

" We shall hardly," said he one morning to Waverley, when they had been viewing the castle, —
" we shall hardly gain the obsidional crown, which
you wot well was made of the roots or grain which
takes root within the place besieged, or it may be
of the herb woodbind, *paretaria*, or pellitory ; we
shall not, I say, gain it by this same blockade or
leaguer of Edinburgh Castle." For this opinion
he gave most learned and satisfactory reasons, that
the reader may not care to hear repeated.

Having escaped from the old gentleman, Waverley went to Fergus's lodgings by appointment, to

await his return from Holyrood House. "I am to have a particular audience to-morrow," said Fergus to Waverley, overnight, "and you must meet me to wish me joy of the success which I securely anticipate."

The morrow came, and in the chief's apartment he found Ensign Maccombich waiting to make report of his turn of duty in a sort of ditch which they had dug across the Castle Hill and called a trench. In a short time the chief's voice was heard on the stair in a tone of impatient fury : " Callum, why, Callum Beg, — *Diaoul !* " He entered the room with all the marks of a man agitated by a towering passion ; and there were few upon whose features rage produced a more violent effect. The veins of his forehead swelled when he was in such agitation, his nostril became dilated, his cheek and eye inflamed, and his look that of a demoniac. These appearances of half-suppressed rage were the more frightful because they were obviously caused by a strong effort to temper with discretion an almost ungovernable paroxysm of passion, and resulted from an internal conflict of the most dreadful kind, which agitated his whole frame of mortality.

As he entered the apartment he unbuckled his broadsword, and throwing it down with such violence that the weapon rolled to the other end of the room, " I know not what," he exclaimed, " withholds me from taking a solemn oath that I will never more draw it in his cause ! Load my pistols, Callum, and bring them hither instantly, — instantly ! " Callum, whom nothing ever startled, dismayed, or disconcerted, obeyed very coolly. Evan Dhu, upon whose brow the suspicion that his chief had been

192

insulted, called up a corresponding storm, swelled in sullen silence, awaiting to learn where or upon whom vengeance was to descend.

"So, Waverley, you are there," said the chief, after a moment's recollection. "Yes, I remember I asked you to share my triumph, and you have come to witness my — disappointment we shall call it." Evan now presented the written report he had in his hand, which Fergus threw from him with great passion. "I wish to God," he said, "the old den would tumble down upon the heads of the fools who attack, and the knaves who defend it! I see, Waverley, you think I am mad. Leave us, Evan, but be within call."

"The colonel's in an unco kippage," said Mrs. Flockhart to Evan as he descended; "I wish he may be weel, — the very veins on his brent brow are swelled like whipcord. Wad he no tak something?"

"He usually lets blood for these fits," answered the Highland Ancient, with great composure.

When this officer left the room, the chieftain gradually reassumed some degree of composure. "I know, Waverley," he said, "that Colonel Talbot has persuaded you to curse ten times a day your engagement with us, — nay, never deny it, for I am at this moment tempted to curse my own. Would you believe it, I made this very morning two suits to the prince, and he has rejected them both. What do you think of it?"

"What can I think," answered Waverley, "till I know what your requests were?"

"Why, what signifies what they were, man? I tell you it was I that made them, — I, to whom he owes more than to any three who have joined the

193

standard; for I negotiated the whole business, and brought in all the Perthshire men when not one would have stirred. I am not likely, I think, to ask anything very unreasonable, and if I did, they might have stretched a point. Well, but you shall know all, now that I can draw my breath again with some freedom. You remember my earl's patent: it is dated some years back, for services then rendered; and certainly my merit has not been diminished, to say the least, by my subsequent behaviour. Now, sir, I value this bauble of a coronet as little as you can, or any philosopher on earth; for I hold that the chief of such a clan as the Sliochd nan Ivor is superior in rank to any earl in Scotland. But I had a particular reason for assuming this cursed title at this time. You must know that I learned accidentally that the prince has been pressing that old foolish Baron of Bradwardine to disinherit his male heir, or nineteenth or twentieth cousin, who has taken a command in the Elector of Hanover's militia, and to settle his estate upon your pretty little friend Rose; and this, as being the command of his king and overlord, who may alter the destination of a fief at pleasure, the old gentleman seems well reconciled to."

"And what becomes of the homage?"

"Curse the homage! I believe Rose is to pull off the queen's slipper on her coronation-day, or some such trash. Well, sir, as Rose Bradwardine would always have made a suitable match for me, but for this idiotical predilection of her father for the heir-male, it occurred to me there now remained no obstacle, unless that the Baron might expect his daughter's husband to take the name of Bradwardine (which you know would be impossible in my

194

case), and that this might be evaded by my assuming the title to which I had so good a right, and which, of course, would supersede that difficulty. If she was to be also Viscountess Bradwardine in her own right after her father's demise, so much the better; I could have no objection."

"But, Fergus," said Waverley, "I had no idea that you had any affection for Miss Bradwardine, and you are always sneering at her father."

"I have as much affection for Miss Bradwardine, my good friend, as I think it necessary to have for the future mistress of my family and the mother of my children. She is a very pretty, intelligent girl, and is certainly of one of the very first Lowland families, and, with a little of Flora's instructions and forming, will make a very good figure. As to her father, he is an original, it is true, and an absurd one enough; but he has given such severe lessons to Sir Hew Halbert, that dear defunct the Laird of Balmawhapple, and others, that nobody dare laugh at him, so his absurdity goes for nothing. I tell you there could have been no earthly objection, — none. I had settled the thing entirely in my own mind."

"But had you asked the Baron's consent," said Waverley, "or Rose's?"

"To what purpose? To have spoken to the Baron before I had assumed my title would have only provoked a premature and irritating discussion on the subject of the change of name, when, as Earl of Glennaquoich, I had only to propose to him to carry his d—d bear and boot-jack *party per pale*, or in a scutcheon of pretence, or in a separate shield perhaps, — any way that would not blemish my own coat-of-arms. And as to Rose, I don't see what objection she could have made, if her father was satisfied."

"Perhaps the same that your sister makes to me, you being satisfied."

Fergus gave a broad stare at the comparison which this supposition implied, but cautiously suppressed the answer which rose to his tongue. "Oh, we should easily have arranged all that. So, sir, I craved a private interview, and this morning was assigned; and I asked you to meet me here, thinking, like a fool, that I should want your countenance as bride's-man. Well, I state my pretensions,—they are not denied; the promises so repeatedly made, and the patent granted,—they are acknowledged. But I propose, as a natural consequence, to assume the rank which the patent bestowed,—I have the old story of the jealousy of C—— and M—— trumped up against me; I resist this pretext, and offer to procure their written acquiescence, in virtue of the date of my patent as prior to their silly claims,—I assure you I would have had such a consent from them, if it had been at the point of the sword,—and then out comes the real truth; and he dares to tell me, to my face, that my patent must be suppressed for the present, for fear of disgusting that rascally coward and *fainéant*——[naming the rival chief of his own clan], who has no better title to be a chieftain than I to be Emperor of China, and who is pleased to shelter his dastardly reluctance to come out, agreeable to his promise twenty times pledged, under a pretended jealousy of the prince's partiality to me. And to leave this miserable driveller without a pretence for his cowardice, the prince asks it as a personal favour of me, forsooth, not to press my just and reasonable request at this moment. After this, put your faith in princes ! "

" And did your audience end here ? "

" End ? Oh, no ! I was determined to leave him no pretence for his ingratitude, and I therefore stated, with all the composure I could muster, — for I promise you I trembled with passion, — the particular reasons I had for wishing that his Royal Highness would impose upon me any other mode of exhibiting my duty and devotion, as my views in life made, what at any other time would have been a mere trifle, at this crisis a severe sacrifice; and then I explained to him my full plan."

" And what did the prince answer ? "

" Answer ? Why — it is well it is written, ' Curse not the king, no, not in thy thought ! ' — why, he answered that truly he was glad I had made him my confidant, to prevent more grievous disappointment, for he could assure me, upon the word of a prince, that Miss Bradwardine's affections were engaged, and he was under a particular promise to favour them. ' So, my dear Fergus,' said he, with his most gracious cast of smile, ' as the marriage is utterly out of question, there need be no hurry, you know, about the earldom.' And so he glided off, and left me *planté là*."

" And what did you do ? "

" I 'll tell you what I *could* have done at that moment, — sold myself to the devil or the Elector, whichever offered the dearest revenge. However, I am now cool. I know he intends to marry her to some of his rascally Frenchmen or his Irish officers ; but I will watch them close, and let the man that would supplant me look well to himself. *Bisogna coprirsi, Signor.*"

197

After some further conversation, unnecessary to be detailed, Waverley took leave of the chieftain, whose fury had now subsided into a deep and strong desire of vengeance, and returned home, scarce able to analyze the mixture of feelings which the narrative had awakened in his own bosom.

CHAPTER XXV

"I AM the very child of caprice," said Waverley to himself as he bolted the door of his apartment and paced it with hasty steps. "What is it to me that Fergus Mac-Ivor should wish to marry Rose Bradwardine? I love her not, — I might have been loved by her, perhaps; but I rejected her simple, natural, and affecting attachment, instead of cherishing it into tenderness, and dedicated myself to one who will never love mortal man, unless old Warwick the King-maker should arise from the dead. The Baron, too, — I would not have cared about his estate, and so the name would have been no stumbling-block. The devil might have taken the barren moors, and drawn off the royal *caligæ*, for anything I would have minded. But framed as she is for domestic affection and tenderness, for giving and receiving all those kind and quiet attentions which sweeten life to those who pass it together, she is sought by Fergus Mac-Ivor. He will not use her ill, to be sure, — of that he is incapable; but he will neglect her after the first month; he will be too intent on subduing some rival chieftain or circumventing some favourite at court, on gaining some heathy hill and lake, or adding to his bands some new troop of caterans, to inquire what she does, or how she amuses herself.

199

And then will canker sorrow eat her bud,
And chase the native beauty from her cheek ;
And she will look as hollow as a ghost,
And dim and meagre as an ague fit,
And so she 'll die.

And such a catastrophe of the most gentle creature
on earth might have been prevented if Mr. Edward
Waverley had had his eyes ! Upon my word, I cannot understand how I thought Flora so much, that
is so *very* much, handsomer than Rose. She is taller,
indeed, and her manner more formed; but many
people think Miss Bradwardine's more natural, and
she is certainly much younger. I should think
Flora is two years older than I am, — I will look
at them particularly this evening."

And with this resolution Waverley went to drink
tea (as the fashion was Sixty Years since) at the
house of a lady of quality attached to the cause of
the Chevalier, where he found, as he expected, both
the ladies. All rose as he entered, but Flora immediately resumed her place and the conversation
in which she was engaged. Rose, on the contrary,
almost imperceptibly made a little way in the
crowded circle for his advancing the corner of a
chair. "Her manner, upon the whole, is most engaging," said Waverley to himself.

A dispute occurred whether the Gaelic or Italian
language was most liquid, and best adapted for
poetry. The opinion for the Gaelic, which probably might not have found supporters elsewhere,
was here fiercely defended by seven Highland
ladies, who talked at the top of their lungs, and
screamed the company deaf with examples of Celtic
euphonia. Flora, observing the Lowland ladies sneer
at the comparison, produced some reasons to show

that it was not altogether so absurd ; but Rose, when asked for her opinion, gave it with animation in praise of Italian, which she had studied with Waverley's assistance. "She has a more correct ear than Flora, though a less accomplished musician," said Waverley to himself. " I suppose Miss Mac-Ivor will next compare Mac-Murrough nan Fonn to Ariosto ! "

Lastly, it so befell that the company differed whether Fergus should be asked to perform on the flute, at which he was an adept, or Waverley invited to read a play of Shakspeare ; and the lady of the house good-humouredly undertook to collect the votes of the company for poetry or music, under the condition that the gentleman whose talents were not laid under contribution that evening, should contribute them to enliven the next. It chanced that Rose had the casting vote. Now, Flora, who seemed to impose it as a rule upon herself never to countenance any proposal which might seem to encourage Waverley, had voted for music, providing the Baron would take his violin to accompany Fergus. "I wish you joy of your taste, Miss Mac-Ivor," thought Edward, as they sought for his book. "I thought it better when we were at Glennaquoich ; but certainly the Baron is no great performer, and Shakspeare is worth listening to."

"Romeo and Juliet " was selected, and Edward read with taste, feeling, and spirit several scenes from that play. All the company applauded with their hands, and many with their tears. Flora, to whom the drama was well known, was among the former ; Rose, to whom it was altogether new, belonged to the latter class of admirers. "She has more feeling too," said Waverley, internally.

The conversation turning upon the incidents of the play, and upon the characters, Fergus declared that the only one worth naming, as a man of fashion and spirit, was Mercutio. " I could not," he said, " quite follow all his old-fashioned wit, but he must have been a very pretty fellow, according to the ideas of his time."

" And it was a shame," said Ensign Maccombich, who usually followed his colonel everywhere, " for that Tibbert or Taggart, or whatever was his name, to stick him under the other gentleman's arm while he was redding the fray."

The ladies, of course, declared loudly in favour of Romeo ; but this opinion did not go undisputed. The mistress of the house and several other ladies severely reprobated the levity with which the hero transfers his affections from Rosalind to Juliet. Flora remained silent until her opinion was repeatedly requested, and then answered, she thought the circumstance objected to, not only reconcilable to nature, but such as in the highest degree evinced the art of the poet. " Romeo is described," said she, " as a young man, peculiarly susceptible of the softer passions ; his love is at first fixed upon a woman who could afford it no return ; this he repeatedly tells you, —

From love's weak, childish bow she lives unharmed;

and again, —

She hath forsworn to love.

Now, as it was impossible that Romeo's love, supposing him a reasonable being, could continue to subsist without hope, the poet has, with great art, seized the moment when he was reduced actually

to despair, to throw in his way an object more accomplished than her by whom he had been rejected,
and who is disposed to repay his attachment. I
can scarce conceive a situation more calculated to
enhance the ardour of Romeo's affection for Juliet
than his being at once raised by her from the state
of drooping melancholy in which he appears first
upon the scene, to the ecstatic state in which he
exclaims —

> Come what sorrow can,
> It cannot countervail the exchange of joy
> That one short moment gives me in her sight."

" Good, now, Miss Mac-Ivor," said a young lady
of quality, " do you mean to cheat us out of our
prerogative ? Will you persuade us love cannot subsist without hope, or that the lover must become
fickle if the lady is cruel ? Oh, fie ! I did not expect
such an unsentimental conclusion."

" A lover, my dear Lady Betty," said Flora,
" may, I conceive, persevere in his suit under very
discouraging circumstances. Affection can, now
and then, withstand very severe storms of rigour,
but not a long polar frost of downright indifference.
Don't, even with *your* attractions, try the experiment upon any lover whose faith you value. Love
will subsist on wonderfully little hope, but not altogether without it."

" It will be just like Duncan Mac-Girdie's mare,"
said Evan, " if your ladyships please ; he wanted to
use her by degrees to live without meat, and just as
he had put her on a straw a day, the poor thing
died ! "

Evan's illustration set the company a-laughing,
and the discourse took a different turn. Shortly

203

afterwards the party broke up, and Edward returned home, musing on what Flora had said. " I will love my Rosalind no more," said he; "she has given me a broad enough hint for that; and I will speak to her brother and resign my suit. But for a Juliet, would it be handsome to interfere with Fergus's pretensions? — though it is impossible they can ever succeed; and should they miscarry, what then? Why then *alors comme alors.*" And with this resolution, of being guided by circumstances, did our hero commit himself to repose.

CHAPTER XXVI

A BRAVE MAN IN SORROW

IF my fair readers should be of opinion that my hero's levity in love is altogether unpardonable, I must remind them that all his griefs and difficulties did not arise from that sentimental source. Even the lyric poet who complains so feelingly of the pains of love could not forget that at the same time he was " in debt and in drink," — which, doubtless, were great aggravations of his distress. There were, indeed, whole days in which Waverley thought neither of Flora nor Rose Bradwardine, but which were spent in melancholy conjectures on the probable state of matters at Waverley Honour, and the dubious issue of the civil contest in which he was pledged. Colonel Talbot often engaged him in discussions upon the justice of the cause he had espoused. " Not," he said, " that it is possible for you to quit it at this present moment, for, come what will, you must stand by your rash engagement. But I wish you to be aware that the right is not with you ; that you are fighting against the real interests of your country ; and that you ought, as an Englishman and a patriot, to take the first opportunity to leave this unhappy expedition before the snow-ball melts."

In such political disputes Waverley usually opposed the common arguments of his party, with which it is unnecessary to trouble the reader. But he had little to say when the colonel urged him to compare the strength by which they had undertaken to overthrow the government, with that which was now assembling very rapidly for its support. To this statement Waverley had but one answer: "If the cause I have undertaken be perilous, there would be the greater disgrace in abandoning it." And in his turn he generally silenced Colonel Talbot, and succeeded in changing the subject.

One night, when, after a long dispute of this nature, the friends had separated, and our hero had retired to bed, he was awakened about midnight by a suppressed groan. He started up and listened; it came from the apartment of Colonel Talbot, which was divided from his own by a wainscoted partition, with a door of communication. Waverley approached this door, and distinctly heard one or two deep-drawn sighs. What could be the matter? The colonel had parted from him, apparently, in his usual state of spirits. He must have been taken suddenly ill. Under this impression, he opened the door of communication very gently, and perceived the colonel, in his night-gown, seated by a table, on which lay a letter and picture. He raised his head hastily, as Edward stood uncertain whether to advance or retire, and Waverley perceived that his cheeks were stained with tears.

As if ashamed at being found giving way to such emotion, Colonel Talbot rose with apparent displeasure, and said, with some sternness, "I think, Mr. Waverley, my own apartment and the hour might have secured even a prisoner against —"

"Do not say *intrusion*, Colonel Talbot; I heard you breathe hard, and feared you were ill; that alone could have induced me to break in upon you."

"I am well," said the colonel, " perfectly well."

"But you are distressed," said Edward ; "is there anything can be done ? "

"Nothing, Mr. Waverley ; I was only thinking of home, and some unpleasant occurrences there."

"Good God, my uncle ! " exclaimed Waverley.

"No, it is a grief entirely my own. I am ashamed you should have seen it disarm me so much ; but it must have its course at times, that it may be at others more decently supported. I would have kept it secret from you ; for I think it will grieve you, and yet you can administer no consolation. But you have surprised me, — I see you are surprised yourself, — and I hate mystery. Read that letter."

The letter was from Colonel Talbot's sister, and in these words : —

"I received yours, my dearest brother, by Hodges. Sir E. W. and Mr. R. are still at large, but are not permitted to leave London. I wish to Heaven I could give you as good an account of matters in the Square. But the news of the unhappy affair at Preston came upon us, with the dreadful addition that you were among the fallen. You know Lady Emily's state of health when your friendship for Sir E. induced you to leave her. She was much harassed with the sad accounts from Scotland of the rebellion having broken out, but kept up her spirits as, she said, it became your wife, and for the sake of the future heir, so long hoped for in vain. Alas, my dear brother, these hopes are now ended! Notwithstanding all my watchful care, this unhappy rumour reached her without preparation. She was taken ill immediately, and the poor infant scarce survived its birth. Would to God this were all! But although the contradiction of the horrible report by your own letter has greatly revived her spirits, yet Dr. —— apprehends, I grieve to say, serious, and even dangerous, consequences to her health, especially from the uncertainty in which she must necessarily remain for some time, aggravated by the ideas she has formed of the ferocity of those with whom you are a prisoner.

Do therefore, my dear brother, as soon as this reaches you, endeavour to gain your release, by parole, by ransom, or any way that is practicable. I do not exaggerate Lady Emily's state of health, but I must not — dare not — suppress the truth. Ever, my dear Philip, your most affectionate sister,

"Lucy Talbot."

Edward stood motionless when he had perused this letter; for the conclusion was inevitable, that by the colonel's journey in quest of him he had incurred this heavy calamity. It was severe enough, even in its irremediable part; for Colonel Talbot and Lady Emily, long without a family, had fondly exulted in the hopes which were now blasted. But this disappointment was nothing to the extent of the threatened evil; and Edward, with horror, regarded himself as the original cause of both.

Ere he could collect himself sufficiently to speak, Colonel Talbot had recovered his usual composure of manner, though his troubled eye denoted his mental agony.

"She is a woman, my young friend, who may justify even a soldier's tears," — he reached him the miniature, exhibiting features which fully justified the eulogium; "and yet, God knows, what you see of her there is the least of the charms she possesses, — possessed, I should perhaps say; but God's will be done."

"You must fly, you must fly instantly to her relief. It is not, it shall not be, too late."

"Fly? How is it possible? I am a prisoner — upon parole."

"I am your keeper, — I restore your parole; I am to answer for you."

"You cannot do so consistently with your duty, nor can I accept a discharge from you, with due regard to my own honour, — you would be made responsible."

"I will answer it with my head, if necessary," said Waverley, impetuously. "I have been the unhappy cause of the loss of your child, make me not the murderer of your wife."

"No, my dear Edward," said Talbot, taking him kindly by the hand, "you are in no respect to blame; and if I concealed this domestic distress for two days, it was lest your sensibility should view it in that light. You could not think of me, hardly knew of my existence, when I left England in quest of you. It is a responsibility, Heaven knows, sufficiently heavy for mortality that we must answer for the foreseen and direct result of our actions, — for their indirect and consequential operation, the great and good Being, who alone can foresee the dependence of human events on each other, hath not pronounced his frail creatures liable."

"But that you should have left Lady Emily," said Waverley, with much emotion, "in the situation of all others the most interesting to a husband, to seek a — "

"I only did my duty," answered Colonel Talbot, calmly, " and I do not, ought not to regret it. If the path of gratitude and honour were always smooth and easy, there would be little merit in following it; but it moves often in contradiction to our interest and passions, and sometimes to our

209

better affections. These are the trials of life, and this, though not the least bitter" (the tears came unbidden to his eyes), "is not the first which it has been my fate to encounter. But we will talk of this to-morrow," he said, wringing Waverley's hands. "Good-night; strive to forget it for a few hours. It will dawn, I think, by six, and it is now past two. Good-night."

Edward retired, without trusting his voice with a reply.

CHAPTER XXVII

WHEN Colonel Talbot entered the breakfast-parlour next morning, he learned from Waverley's servant that our hero had been abroad at an early hour, and was not yet returned. The morning was well advanced before he again appeared. He arrived out of breath, but with an air of joy that astonished Colonel Talbot.

"There," said he, throwing a paper on the table, "there is my morning's work. Alick, pack up the colonel's clothes. Make haste, make haste!"

The colonel examined the paper with astonishment. It was a pass from the Chevalier to Colonel Talbot to repair to Leith, or any other port in possession of his Royal Highness's troops, and there to embark for England or elsewhere, at his free pleasure; he only giving his parole of honour not to bear arms against the house of Stewart for the space of a twelvemonth.

"In the name of God," said the colonel, his eyes sparkling with eagerness, "how did you obtain this?"

"I was at the Chevalier's levee as soon as he usually rises. He was gone to the camp at Duddingston. I pursued him thither, asked and obtained an audience — But I will tell you not a word more, unless I see you begin to pack."

211

WAVERLEY

"Before I know whether I can avail myself of this passport, or how it was obtained?"

"Oh, you can take out the things again, you know. Now I see you busy, I will go on. When I first mentioned your name, his eyes sparkled almost as bright as yours did two minutes since. 'Had you,' he earnestly asked, 'shown any sentiments favourable to his cause?' 'Not in the least, nor was there any hope you would do so.' His countenance fell. I requested your freedom. Impossible, he said; your importance, as a friend and confidant of such and such personages, made my request altogether extravagant. I told him my own story and yours, and asked him to judge what my feelings must be by his own. He has a heart, and a kind one, Colonel Talbot, you may say what you please. He took a sheet of paper, and wrote the pass with his own hand. 'I will not trust myself with my council,' he said; 'they will argue me out of what is right. I will not endure that a friend, valued as I value you, should be loaded with the painful reflections which must afflict you in case of further misfortune in Colonel Talbot's family, nor will I keep a brave enemy a prisoner under such circumstances. Besides,' said he, 'I think I can justify myself to my prudent advisers by pleading the good effect such lenity will produce on the minds of the great English families with whom Colonel Talbot is connected.'"

"There the politician peeped out," said the colonel.

"Well, at least he concluded like a king's son: 'Take the passport,—I have added a condition for form's sake; but if the colonel objects to it, let him depart without giving any parole whatever. I

212

come here to war with men, but not to distress or endanger women."

"Well, I never thought to have been so much indebted to the Pretend—"

"To the prince," said Waverley, smiling.

"To the Chevalier," said the colonel; "it is a good travelling name, and which we may both freely use. Did he say anything more?"

"Only asked if there was anything else he could oblige me in; and when I replied in the negative, he shook me by the hand, and wished all his followers were as considerate, since some friends of mine not only asked all he had to bestow, but many things which were entirely out of his power, or that of the greatest sovereign upon earth. Indeed, he said, no prince seemed, in the eyes of his followers, so like the Deity as himself, if you were to judge from the extravagant requests which they daily preferred to him."

"Poor young gentleman," said the colonel, "I suppose he begins to feel the difficulties of his situation. Well, dear Waverley, this is more than kind, and shall not be forgotten while Philip Talbot can remember anything. My life — pshaw! let Emily thank you for that; this is a favour worth fifty lives. I cannot hesitate on giving my parole in the circumstances; there it is. [He wrote it out in form.] And now, how am I to get off?"

"All that is settled; your baggage is packed, my horses wait, and a boat has been engaged, by the prince's permission, to put you on board the 'Fox' frigate. I sent a messenger down to Leith on purpose."

"That will do excellently well. Captain Beaver is my particular friend, — he will put me ashore at

Berwick or Shields, from whence I can ride post to London. And you must intrust me with the packet of papers which you recovered by means of your Miss Bean Lean; I may have an opportunity of using them to your advantage. But I see your Highland friend Glen— What do you call his barbarous name? and his orderly with him — I must not call him his orderly cutthroat any more, I suppose. See how he walks as if the world were his own, with the bonnet on one side of his head, and his plaid puffed out across his breast! I should like now to meet that youth where my hands were not tied; I would tame his pride, or he should tame mine."

"For shame, Colonel Talbot! you swell at sight of tartan as the bull is said to do at scarlet. You and Mac-Ivor have some points not much unlike, so far as national prejudice is concerned."

The latter part of this discourse took place in the street. They passed the chief, the colonel and he sternly and punctiliously greeting each other, like two duellists before they take their ground. It was evident the dislike was mutual. " I never see that surly fellow that dogs his heels," said the colonel, after he had mounted his horse, " but he reminds me of lines I have somewhere heard, — upon the stage, I think, —

> Close behind him
> Stalks sullen Bertram, like a sorcerer's fiend,
> Pressing to be employed."

"I assure you, Colonel," said Waverley, "that you judge too harshly of the Highlanders."

"Not a whit, not a whit; I cannot spare them a jot; I cannot bate them an ace. Let them stay

in their own barren mountains, and puff and swell,
and hang their bonnets on the horns of the moon,
if they have a mind; but what business have they
to come where people wear breeches, and speak an
intelligible language ? — I mean intelligible in comparison to their gibberish ; for even the Lowlanders
talk a kind of English little better than the negroes
in Jamaica.   I could pity the Pr—, I mean the
Chevalier himself, for having so many desperadoes
about him.   And they learn their trade so early.
There is a kind of subaltern imp, for example, a
sort of sucking devil, whom your friend Glena—
Glenamuck there, has sometimes in his train.   To
look at him, he is about fifteen years ; but he is a
century old in mischief and villany.   He was play-
ing at quoits the other day in the court ; a gentleman, a decent-looking person enough, came past,
and as a quoit hit his shin, he lifted his cane.   But
my young bravo whips out his pistol, like Beau
Clincher in the 'Trip to the Jubilee,' and had not a
scream of 'Gardez l'eau' from an upper window set
all parties a scampering for fear of the inevitable
consequences, the poor gentleman would have lost
his life by the hands of that little cockatrice."

"A fine character you'll give of Scotland upon
your return, Colonel Talbot."

"Oh, Justice Shallow," said the colonel, "will
save me the trouble, — 'Barren, barren, beggars all,
beggars all.   Marry, good air,' — and that only when
you are fairly out of Edinburgh, and not yet come
to Leith, as is our case at present."

In a short time they arrived at the seaport, —

> The boat rocked at the pier of Leith,
> Full loud the wind blew down the ferry ;
> The ship rode at the Berwick Law —

215

"Farewell, Colonel; may you find all as you would wish it! Perhaps we may meet sooner than you expect; they talk of an immediate route to England."

"Tell me nothing of that," said Talbot; "I wish to carry no news of your motions."

"Simply, then, adieu. Say, with a thousand kind greetings, all that is dutiful and affectionate to Sir Everard and Aunt Rachel. Think of me as kindly as you can; speak of me as indulgently as your conscience will permit; and once more adieu."

"And adieu, my dear Waverley; many, many thanks for your kindness. Unplaid yourself on the first opportunity. I shall ever think on you with gratitude, and the worst of my censure shall be, 'Que diable alloit il faire dans cette galère?'"

And thus they parted, Colonel Talbot going on board of the boat, and Waverley returning to Edinburgh.

CHAPTER XXVIII

It is not our purpose to intrude upon the province of history. We shall therefore only remind our readers that about the beginning of November the Young Chevalier, at the head of about six thousand men at the utmost, resolved to peril his cause on an attempt to penetrate into the centre of England, although aware of the mighty preparations which were made for his reception. They set forward on this crusade in weather which would have rendered any other troops incapable of marching, but which in reality gave these active mountaineers advantages over a less hardy enemy. In defiance of a superior army lying upon the Borders, under Field-Marshal Wade, they besieged and took Carlisle, and soon afterwards prosecuted their daring march to the southward.

As Colonel Mac-Ivor's regiment marched in the van of the clans, he and Waverley, who now equalled any Highlander in the endurance of fatigue, and was become somewhat acquainted with their language, were perpetually at its head. They marked the progress of the army, however, with very different eyes. Fergus, all air and fire, and confident against the world in arms, measured nothing but that every step was a yard nearer London. He neither asked, expected, nor desired any aid,

217

except that of the clans, to place the Stewarts once
more on the throne; and when by chance a few
adherents joined the standard, he always considered them in the light of new claimants upon the
favours of the future monarch, who, he concluded,
must therefore subtract for their gratification so
much of the bounty which ought to be shared
among his Highland followers.

Edward's views were very different. He could
not but observe that in those towns in which they
proclaimed James the Third, "no man cried, God
bless him." The mob stared and listened, heartless, stupefied, and dull, but gave few signs even of
that boisterous spirit which induces them to shout
upon all occasions, for the mere exercise of their
most sweet voices. The Jacobites had been taught
to believe that the northwestern counties abounded
with wealthy squires and hardy yeomen devoted to
the cause of the White Rose. But of the wealthier
Tories they saw little. Some fled from their houses,
some feigned themselves sick, some surrendered
themselves to the government as suspected persons.
Of such as remained, the ignorant gazed with astonishment, mixed with horror and aversion, at the
wild appearance, unknown language, and singular
garb, of the Scottish clans. And to the more prudent, their scanty numbers, apparent deficiency in
discipline, and poverty of equipment, seemed certain
tokens of the calamitous termination of their rash
undertaking. Thus the few who joined them were
such as bigotry of political principle blinded to consequences, or whose broken fortunes induced to
hazard all on a risk so desperate.

The Baron of Bradwardine, being asked what he
thought of these recruits, took a long pinch of snuff,

218

and answered, drily, "that he could not but have an excellent opinion of them, since they resembled precisely the followers who attached themselves to the good King David at the cave of Adullam,—*videlicet*, every one that was in distress, and every one that was in debt, and every one that was discontented, which the Vulgate renders bitter of soul. And doubtless," he said, "they will prove mighty men of their hands, — and there is much need that they should ; for I have seen many a sour look cast upon us."

But none of these considerations moved Fergus. He admired the luxuriant beauty of the country and the situation of many of the seats which they passed. "Is Waverley Honour like that house, Edward ? "

" It is one half larger."

" Is your uncle's park as fine a one as that ? "

" It is three times as extensive, and rather resembles a forest than a mere park."

" Flora will be a happy woman."

" I hope Miss Mac-Ivor will have much reason for happiness, unconnected with Waverley Honour."

" I hope so too ; but to be mistress of such a place will be a pretty addition to the sum total."

" An addition, the want of which, I trust, will be amply supplied by some other means."

" How," said Fergus, stopping short, and turning upon Waverley, — " How am I to understand that, Mr. Waverley ? Had I the pleasure to hear you aright ? "

" Perfectly right, Fergus."

" And I am to understand that you no longer desire my alliance and my sister's hand ? "

" Your sister has refused mine," said Waverley,

"both directly and by all the usual means by which ladies repress undesired attentions."

"I have no idea," answered the chieftain, "of a lady dismissing or a gentleman withdrawing his suit, after it has been approved of by her legal guardian, without giving him an opportunity of talking the matter over with the lady. You did not, I suppose, expect my sister to drop into your mouth like a ripe plum the first moment you chose to open it?"

"As to the lady's title to dismiss her lover, Colonel," replied Edward, "it is a point which you must argue with her, as I am ignorant of the customs of the Highlands in that particular. But as to my title to acquiesce in a rejection from her without an appeal to your interest, I will tell you plainly, without meaning to undervalue Miss Mac-Ivor's admitted beauty and accomplishments, that I would not take the hand of an angel, with an empire for her dowry, if her consent were extorted by the importunity of friends and guardians, and did not flow from her own free inclination."

"An angel with the dowry of an empire," repeated Fergus, in a tone of bitter irony, "is not very likely to be pressed upon a —— shire squire. But, sir," changing his tone, "if Flora Mac-Ivor have not the dowry of an empire, she is *my* sister; and that is sufficient at least to secure her against being treated with anything approaching to levity."

"She is Flora Mac-Ivor, sir," said Waverley, with firmness, "which to me, were I capable of treating *any* woman with levity, would be a more effectual protection."

The brow of the chieftain was now fully clouded, but Edward felt too indignant at the unreasonable

tone which he had adopted, to avert the storm by
the least concession. They both stood still while
this short dialogue passed, and Fergus seemed half
disposed to say something more violent, but by a
strong effort suppressed his passion, and, turning
his face forward, walked sullenly on. As they had
always hitherto walked together, and almost constantly side by side, Waverley pursued his course
silently in the same direction, determined to let the
chief take his own time in recovering the good-
humour which he had so unreasonably discarded,
and firm in his resolution not to bate him an inch
of dignity.

After they had marched on in this sullen manner
about a mile, Fergus resumed the discourse in a
different tone. "I believe I was warm, my dear
Edward, but you provoke me with your want of
knowledge of the world. You have taken pet at
some of Flora's prudery, or high-flying notions of
loyalty, and now, like a child, you quarrel with the
plaything you have been crying for, and beat me,
your faithful keeper, because my arm cannot reach
to Edinburgh to hand it to you. I am sure, if I
was passionate, the mortification of losing the alliance of such a friend, after your arrangement had
been the talk of both Highlands and Lowlands, and
that without so much as knowing why or wherefore, might well provoke calmer blood than mine.
I shall write to Edinburgh and put all to rights, —
that is, if you desire I should do so; as indeed I
cannot suppose that your good opinion of Flora, it
being such as you have often expressed to me, can
be at once laid aside."

"Colonel Mac-Ivor," said Edward, who had no
mind to be hurried farther or faster than he chose,
in a matter which he had already considered as

broken off, " I am fully sensible of the value of
your good offices ; and certainly, by your zeal on
my behalf in such an affair, you do me no small
honour. But as Miss Mac-Ivor has made her elec-
tion freely and voluntarily, and as all my attentions
in Edinburgh were received with more than coldness, I cannot, in justice either to her or myself,
consent that she should again be harassed upon this
topic. I would have mentioned this to you some
time since ; but you saw the footing upon which
we stood together, and must have understood it.
Had I thought otherwise, I would have earlier
spoken ; but I had a natural reluctance to enter
upon a subject so painful to us both."

" Oh, very well, Mr. Waverley," said Fergus,
haughtily, "the thing is at an end. I have no
occasion to press my sister upon any man."

" Nor have I any occasion to court repeated
rejection from the same young lady," answered
Edward, in the same tone.

" I shall make due inquiry, however," said the
chieftain, without noticing the interruption, " and
learn what my sister thinks of all this : we will
then see whether it is to end here."

" Respecting such inquiries, you will of course be
guided by your own judgment," said Waverley.
" It is, I am aware, impossible Miss Mac-Ivor can
change her mind ; and were such an unsupposable
case to happen, it is certain I will not change mine.
I only mention this to prevent any possibility of
future misconstruction."

Gladly at this moment would Mac-Ivor have put
their quarrel to a personal arbitrament ; his eye
flashed fire, and he measured Edward as if to
choose where he might best plant a mortal wound.
But although we do not now quarrel according

to the modes and figures of Caranza or Vincent Saviola, no one knew better than Fergus that there must be some decent pretext for a mortal duel. For instance, you may challenge a man for treading on your corn in a crowd, or for pushing you up to the wall, or for taking your seat in the theatre; but the modern code of honour will not permit you to found a quarrel upon your right of compelling a man to continue addresses to a female relative which the fair lady has already refused. So that Fergus was compelled to stomach this supposed affront, until the whirligig of time, whose motion he promised himself he would watch most sedulously, should bring about an opportunity of revenge.

Waverley's servant always led a saddle-horse for him in the rear of the battalion to which he was attached, though his master seldom rode. But now, incensed at the domineering and unreasonable conduct of his late friend, he fell behind the column and mounted his horse, resolving to seek the Baron of Bradwardine and request permission to volunteer in his troop, instead of the Mac-Ivor regiment.

" A happy time of it I should have had," thought he, after he was mounted, " to have been so closely allied to this superb specimen of pride and self-opinion and passion. A colonel! why, he should have been a generalissimo. A petty chief of three or four hundred men! his pride might suffice for the Cham of Tartary, the Grand Seignior, the Great Mogul! I am well free of him. Were Flora an angel, she would bring with her a second Lucifer of ambition and wrath for a brother-in-law."

The Baron, whose learning (like Sancho's jests while in the Sierra Morena) seemed to grow mouldy for want of exercise, joyfully embraced the opportunity of Waverley's offering his service in his regiment, to bring it into some exertion. The good-natured old gentleman, however, laboured to effect a reconciliation between the two quondam friends. Fergus turned a cold ear to his remonstrances, though he gave them a respectful hearing; and as for Waverley, he saw no reason why he should be the first in courting a renewal of the intimacy which the chieftain had so unreasonably disturbed. The Baron then mentioned the matter to the prince, who, anxious to prevent quarrels in his little army, declared he would himself remonstrate with Colonel Mac-Ivor on the unreasonableness of his conduct. But in the hurry of their march, it was a day or two before he had an opportunity to exert his influence in the manner proposed.

In the meanwhile Waverley turned the instructions he had received while in Gardiner's dragoons to some account, and assisted the Baron in his command as a sort of adjutant. "Parmi les aveugles un borgne est roi," says the French proverb; and the cavalry, which consisted chiefly of Lowland gentlemen, their tenants and servants, formed a high opinion of Waverley's skill, and a great attachment to his person. This was indeed partly owing to the satisfaction which they felt at the distinguished English volunteer's leaving the Highlanders to rank among them; for there was a latent grudge between the horse and foot, not only owing to the difference of the services, but because most of the gentlemen, living near the Highlands, had at one time or other had quarrels with the tribes in their vicinity, and all of them looked with a jealous eye on the Highlanders' avowed pretensions to superior valour, and utility in the prince's service.

CHAPTER XXIX

IT was Waverley's custom sometimes to ride a little apart from the main body to look at any object of curiosity which occurred on the march. They were now in Lancashire, when, attracted by a castellated old hall, he left the squadron for half an hour to take a survey and slight sketch of it. As he returned down the avenue, he was met by Ensign Maccombich. This man had contracted a sort of regard for Edward since the day of his first seeing him at Tully-Veolan and introducing him to the Highlands. He seemed to loiter, as if on purpose to meet with our hero. Yet as he passed him, he only approached his stirrup and pronounced the single word, "Beware!" and then walked swiftly on, shunning all further communication.

Edward, somewhat surprised at this hint, followed with his eyes the course of Evan, who speedily disappeared among the trees. His servant, Alick Polwarth, who was in attendance, also looked after the Highlander, and then riding up close to his master, said, —

"The ne'er be in me, sir, if I think you 're safe amang thae Highland rinthereouts."

"What do you mean, Alick?" said Waverley.

"The Mac-Ivors, sir, hae gotten it into their heads that ye hae affronted their young leddy, Miss

Flora; and I hae heard mae than ane say they
wadna tak muckle to mak a black-cock o' ye; and
ye ken weel eneugh there's mony o' them wadna
mind a bawbee the weising a ball through the
prince himsell, an the chief gae them the wink, —
or whether he did or no, if they thought it a thing
that would please him when it was dune."

Waverley, though confident that Fergus Mac-
Ivor was incapable of such treachery, was by no
means equally sure of the forbearance of his followers. He knew that where the honour of the chief
or his family was supposed to be touched, the happiest man would be he that could first avenge the
stigma; and he had often heard them quote a proverb, that "The best revenge was the most speedy
and most safe." Coupling this with the hint of
Evan, he judged it most prudent to set spurs to his
horse and ride briskly back to the squadron. Ere
he reached the end of the long avenue, however, a
ball whistled past him, and the report of a pistol
was heard.

"It was that deevil's buckie, Callum Beg," said
Alick; "I saw him whisk away through amang the
reises."

Edward, justly incensed at this act of treachery,
galloped out of the avenue, and observed the battalion of Mac-Ivor at some distance moving along
the common, in which it terminated. He also saw
an individual running very fast to join the party;
this he concluded was the intended assassin, who,
by leaping an enclosure, might easily make a much
shorter path to the main body than he could find
on horseback. Unable to contain himself, he commanded Alick to go to the Baron of Bradwardine,
who was at the head of his regiment about half a

mile in front, and acquaint him with what had happened. He himself immediately rode up to Fergus's regiment. The chief himself was in the act of joining them. He was on horseback, having returned from waiting on the prince. On perceiving Edward approaching, he put his horse in motion towards him.

"Colonel Mac-Ivor," said Waverley, without any farther salutation, "I have to inform you that one of your people has this instant fired at me from a lurking-place."

"As that," answered Mac-Ivor, "excepting the circumstance of a lurking-place, is a pleasure which I presently propose to myself, I should be glad to know which of my clansmen dared to anticipate me."

"I shall certainly be at your command whenever you please ; the gentleman who took your office upon himself is your page there, Callum Beg."

"Stand forth from the ranks, Callum ! Did you fire at Mr. Waverley ?"

"No," answered the unblushing Callum.

"You did," said Alick Polwarth, who was already returned, having met a trooper by whom he despatched an account of what was going forward to the Baron of Bradwardine, while he himself returned to his master at full gallop, neither sparing the rowels of his spurs nor the sides of his horse. "You did ; I saw you as plainly as I ever saw the auld kirk at Coudingham."

"You lie," replied Callum, with his usual impenetrable obstinacy. The combat between the knights would certainly, as in the days of chivalry, have been preceded by an encounter between the squires (for Alick was a stout-hearted Merseman, and feared

227

the bow of Cupid far more than a Highlander's dirk
or claymore), but Fergus, with his usual tone of decision, demanded Callum's pistol. The cock was
down, the pan and muzzle were black with the
smoke: it had been that instant fired.

"Take that," said Fergus, striking the boy upon
the head with the heavy pistol-but with his whole
force, — "take that for acting without orders, and
lying to disguise it." Callum received the blow
without appearing to flinch from it, and fell without sign of life. "Stand still, upon your lives!"
said Fergus to the rest of the clan; "I blow out
the brains of the first man who interferes between
Mr. Waverley and me." They stood motionless;
Evan Dhu alone showed symptoms of vexation and
anxiety. Callum lay on the ground bleeding copi-
ously, but no one ventured to give him any assistance. It seemed as if he had gotten his death-blow.

"And now for you, Mr. Waverley. Please to
turn your horse twenty yards with me upon the
common." Waverley complied; and Fergus, con-
fronting him when they were a little way from the
line of march, said, with great affected coolness, "I
could not but wonder, sir, at the fickleness of taste
which you were pleased to express the other day.
But it was not an angel, as you justly observed,
who had charms for you, unless she brought an empire for her fortune. I have now an excellent commentary upon that obscure text."

"I am at a loss even to guess at your meaning,
Colonel Mac-Ivor, unless it seems plain that you
intend to fasten a quarrel upon me."

"Your affected ignorance shall not serve you,
sir. The prince, the prince himself, has acquainted
me with your manœuvres. I little thought that

your engagements with Miss Bradwardine were the reason of your breaking off your intended match with my sister. I suppose the information that the Baron had altered the destination of his estate, was quite a sufficient reason for slighting your friend's sister and carrying off your friend's mistress."

" Did the prince tell you I was engaged to Miss Bradwardine ? " said Waverley. " Impossible."

" He did, sir," answered Mac-Ivor; " so either draw and defend yourself, or resign your pretensions to the lady."

"This is absolute madness," exclaimed Waverley, " or some strange mistake ! "

" Oh, no evasion ; draw your sword ! " said the infuriated chieftain, his own already unsheathed.

" Must I fight in a madman's quarrel ? "

" Then give up now, and for ever, all pretensions to Miss Bradwardine's hand."

" What title have you," cried Waverley, utterly losing command of himself, — " what title have you, or any man living, to dictate such terms to me ? " And he also drew his sword.

At this moment the Baron of Bradwardine, followed by several of his troop, came up on the spur, some from curiosity, others to take part in the quarrel, which they indistinctly understood had broken out between the Mac-Ivors and their corps. The clan, seeing them approach, put themselves in motion to support their chieftain, and a scene of confusion commenced, which seemed likely to terminate in bloodshed. A hundred tongues were in motion at once. The Baron lectured, the chieftain stormed, the Highlanders screamed in Gaelic, the horsemen cursed and swore in Lowland Scotch. At length matters came to such a pass that the Baron threatened to charge the Mac-Ivors unless they resumed their ranks, and many of them, in return, presented their fire-arms at him and the other troopers. The confusion was privately fostered by old Ballenkeiroch, who made no doubt that his own day of vengeance was arrived, when, behold! a cry arose of " Room! make way! *place à Monseigneur! place à Monseigneur!* " This announced the approach of the prince, who came up with a party of Fitz-James's foreign dragoons, that acted as his body guard. His arrival produced some degree of order. The Highlanders reassumed their ranks, the cavalry fell in and formed squadron, and the Baron and chieftain were silent.

The prince called them and Waverley before him. Having heard the original cause of the quarrel through the villany of Callum Beg, he ordered him into custody of the provost-marshal for immediate execution, in the event of his surviving the chastisement inflicted by his chieftain. Fergus, however, in a tone betwixt claiming a right and asking a favour, requested he might be left to his disposal, and promised his punishment should be exemplary. To deny this might have seemed to encroach on the patriarchal authority of the chieftains, of which they were very jealous, and they were not persons to be disobliged. Callum was therefore left to the justice of his own tribe.

The prince next demanded to know the new cause of quarrel between Colonel Mac-Ivor and Waverley. There was a pause. Both gentlemen found the presence of the Baron of Bradwardine (for by this time all three had approached the Chevalier by his command) an insurmountable barrier against entering upon a subject where the name of his daughter must unavoidably be mentioned. They turned their eyes on the ground, with looks in which shame and embarrassment were mingled with displeasure. The prince, who had been educated amongst the discontented and mutinous spirits of the court of St. Germains, where feuds of every kind were the daily subject of solicitude to the dethroned sovereign, had served his apprenticeship, as old Frederick of Prussia would have said, to the trade of royalty. To promote or restore concord among his followers was indispensable. Accordingly he took his measures.

" Monsieur de Beaujeu ! "

" Monseigneur ! " said a very handsome French cavalry officer, who was in attendance.

" Ayez la bonté d'alligner ces montagnards là, ainsi que la cavalerie, s'il vous plaît, et de les remettre à la marche. Vous parlez si bien l'Anglois, cela ne vous donneroit pas beaucoup de peine."

" Ah ! pas de tout, Monseigneur," replied M. le Comte de Beaujeu, his head bending down to the neck of his little prancing, highly managed charger. Accordingly he *piaffed* away, in high spirits and confidence, to the head of Fergus's regiment, although understanding not a word of Gaelic, and very little English.

" Messieurs les sauvages Ecossois, — dat is, gentilmans savages, — have the goodness d' arranger vous."

The clan, comprehending the order more from the gesture than the words, and seeing the prince himself present, hastened to dress their ranks.

" Ah, ver well ! dat is fort bien ! " said the Comte de Beaujeu. " Gentilmans sauvages — mais, très bien. Eh bien! Qu'est-ce que vous appellez visage, Monsieur?" (to a lounging trooper who stood by him.) " Ah, oui! *face*, — je vous remercie, Monsieur. Gentilshommes, have de goodness to make de face to de right par file, dat is, by files. Marsh! Mais très bien; encore, Messieurs; il faut vous mettre à la marche. Marchez, donc, au nom de Dieu, parce que j'ai oublié le mot Anglois; mais vous êtes des braves gens, et me comprenez très bien."

The count next hastened to put the cavalry in motion. "Gentilmans cavalry, you must fall in, — ah! par ma foi, I did not say fall off! I am a fear de little gross fat gentilman is moche hurt. Ah, mon Dieu! c'est le commissaire qui nous a apporté les premières nouvelles de ce maudit fracas. Je suis trop fâché, Monsieur!"

But poor Macwheeble, who, with a sword stuck across him, and a white cockade as large as a pancake, now figured in the character of a commissary, being overturned in the bustle occasioned by the troopers hastening to get themselves in order in the prince's presence, before he could rally his galloway, slunk to the rear amid the unrestrained laughter of the spectators.

"Eh bien, Messieurs, wheel to de right, — ah! dat is it! Eh, Monsieur de Bradwardine, ayez la bonté de vous mettre à la tête de votre régiment, car, par Dieu, je n'en puis plus!"

The Baron of Bradwardine was obliged to go to the assistance of Monsieur de Beaujeu, after he had fairly expended his few English military phrases. One purpose of the Chevalier was thus answered. The other he proposed was, that in the eagerness to hear and comprehend commands issued through such an indistinct medium in his

232

own presence, the thoughts of the soldiers in both corps might get a current different from the angry channel in which they were flowing at the time.

Charles Edward was no sooner left with the chieftain and Waverley, the rest of his attendants being at some distance, than he said, "If I owed less to your disinterested friendship, I could be most seriously angry with both of you for this very extraordinary and causeless broil at a moment when my father's service so decidedly demands the most perfect unanimity. But the worst of my situation is that my very best friends hold they have liberty to ruin themselves, as well as the cause they are engaged in, upon the slightest caprice."

Both the young men protested their resolution to submit every difference to his arbitration. " Indeed," said Edward, " I hardly know of what I am accused. I sought Colonel Mac-Ivor merely to mention to him that I had narrowly escaped assassination at the hand of his immediate dependant, — a dastardly revenge which I knew him to be incapable of authorizing. As to the cause for which he is disposed to fasten a quarrel upon me, I am ignorant of it, unless it be that he accuses me, most unjustly, of having engaged the affections of a young lady in prejudice of his pretensions."

"If there is an error," said the chieftain, "it arises from a conversation which I held this morning with his Royal Highness himself."

" With me ? " said the Chevalier; "how can Colonel Mac-Ivor have so far misunderstood me ? "

He then led Fergus aside, and after five minutes' earnest conversation, spurred his horse towards Edward. "Is it possible — nay, ride up, Colonel, for I desire no secrets — is it possible, Mr. Waverley, that I am mistaken in supposing that you are an accepted lover of Miss Bradwardine? — a fact of which I was by circumstances, though not by communication from you, so absolutely convinced that I alleged it to Vich Ian Vohr this morning as a reason why, without offence to him, you might not continue to be ambitious of an alliance which to an unengaged person, even though once repulsed, holds out too many charms to be lightly laid aside."

"Your Royal Highness," said Waverley, "must have founded on circumstances altogether unknown to me when you did me the distinguished honour of supposing me an accepted lover of Miss Bradwardine. I feel the distinction implied in the supposition, but I have no title to it. For the rest, my confidence in my own merit is too justly slight to admit of my hoping for success in any quarter after positive rejection."

The Chevalier was silent for a moment, looking steadily at them both, and then said : "Upon my word, Mr. Waverley, you are a less happy man than I conceived I had very good reason to believe you. But now, gentlemen, allow me to be umpire in this matter, not as Prince Regent, but as Charles Stewart, — a brother adventurer with you in the same gallant cause. Lay my pretensions to be obeyed by you entirely out of view, and consider your own honour, and how far it is well or becoming to give our enemies the advantage, and our friends the scandal, of showing that, few as we are, we are not united. And forgive me if I add, that the names of the ladies who have been mentioned crave more respect from us all than to be made themes of discord."

He took Fergus a little apart, and spoke to him very earnestly for two or three minutes, and then returning to Waverley, said : " I believe I have satisfied Colonel Mac-Ivor that his resentment was founded upon a misconception, to which, indeed, I myself gave rise ; and I trust Mr. Waverley is too generous to harbour any recollection of what is past, when I assure him that such is the case. You must state this matter properly to your clan, Vich Ian Vohr, to prevent a recurrence of their precipitate violence." Fergus bowed. " And now, gentlemen, let me have the pleasure to see you shake hands."

They advanced coldly, and with measured steps, each apparently reluctant to appear most forward in concession. They did, however, shake hands, and parted, taking a respectful leave of the Chevalier.

Charles Edward [1] then rode to the head of the Mac-Ivors, threw himself from his horse, begged a drink out of old Ballenkeiroch's canteen, and marched about half a mile along with them, inquiring into the history and connections of Sliochd nan Ivor, adroitly using the few words of Gaelic he possessed, and affecting a great desire to learn it more thoroughly. He then mounted his horse once more and galloped to the Baron's cavalry, which was in front, halted them, and examined their accoutrements and state of discipline, took notice of the principal gentlemen, and even of the cadets, inquired after their ladies, and commended their horses, rode about an hour with the Baron of Bradwardine, and endured three long stories about Field-Marshal the Duke of Berwick.

[1] Note VIII. — Prince Charles Edward.

"Ah, Beaujeu, mon cher ami," said he as he returned to his usual place in the line of march, "que mon métier de prince errant est ennuyant, par fois. Mais, courage! c'est le grand jeu, après tout."

CHAPTER XXX

A SKIRMISH

THE reader need hardly be reminded that after a council of war held at Derby on the 5th of December, the Highlanders relinquished their desperate attempt to penetrate farther into England, and, greatly to the dissatisfaction of their young and daring leader, positively determined to return northward. They commenced their retreat accordingly, and by the extreme celerity of their movements outstripped the motions of the Duke of Cumberland, who now pursued them with a very large body of cavalry.

This retreat was a virtual resignation of their towering hopes. None had been so sanguine as Fergus Mac-Ivor; none, consequently, was so cruelly mortified at the change of measures. He argued, or rather remonstrated, with the utmost vehemence at the council of war; and when his opinion was rejected, shed tears of grief and indignation. From that moment his whole manner was so much altered that he could scarcely have been recognized for the same soaring and ardent spirit for whom the whole earth seemed too narrow but a week before. The retreat had continued for several days when Edward, to his surprise, early on the 12th of December, received a visit from the chieftain in his quarters, in a hamlet about half way between Shap and Penrith.

237

Having had no intercourse with the chieftain since their rupture, Edward waited with some anxiety an explanation of this unexpected visit; nor could he help being surprised, and somewhat shocked, with the change in his appearance. His eye had lost much of its fire, his cheek was hollow, his voice was languid, even his gait seemed less firm and elastic than it was wont; and his dress, to which he used to be particularly attentive, was now carelessly flung about him. He invited Edward to walk out with him by the little river in the vicinity, and smiled in a melancholy manner when he observed him take down and buckle on his sword.

As soon as they were in a wild, sequestered path by the side of the stream, the chief broke out: " Our fine adventure is now totally ruined, Waverley, and I wish to know what you intend to do. Nay, never stare at me, man. I tell you I received a packet from my sister yesterday, and had I got the information it contains sooner, it would have prevented a quarrel which I am always vexed when I think of. In a letter written after our dispute, I acquainted her with the cause of it; and she now replies to me that she never had, nor could have, any purpose of giving you encouragement; so that it seems I have acted like a madman. Poor Flora, she writes in high spirits; what a change will the news of this unhappy retreat make in her state of mind ! "

Waverley, who was really much affected by the deep tone of melancholy with which Fergus spoke, affectionately entreated him to banish from his remembrance any unkindness which had arisen between them, and they once more shook hands, but now with sincere cordiality. Fergus again inquired of Waverley what he intended to do. "Had you not better leave this luckless army and get down before us into Scotland, and embark for the Continent from some of the eastern ports that are still in our possession ? When you are out of the kingdom, your friends will easily negotiate your pardon ; and, to tell you the truth, I wish you would carry Rose Bradwardine with you as your wife, and take Flora also under your joint protection." Edward looked surprised. " She loves you, and I believe you love her, though perhaps you have not found it out, for you are not celebrated for knowing your own mind very pointedly." He said this with a sort of smile.

"How," answered Edward, "can you advise me to desert the expedition in which we are all embarked ? "

"Embarked ! " said Fergus. "The vessel is going to pieces, and it is full time for all who can, to get into the long-boat and leave her."

"Why, what will other gentlemen do ? " answered Waverley ; "and why did the Highland chiefs consent to this retreat, if it is so ruinous ? "

"Oh," replied Mac-Ivor, "they think that, as on former occasions, the heading, hanging, and forfeiting will chiefly fall to the lot of the Lowland gentry ; that they will be left secure in their poverty and their fastnesses, there, according to their proverb, ' to listen to the wind upon the hill till the waters abate.' But they will be disappointed ; they have-been too often troublesome to be so repeatedly passed over, and this time John Bull has been too heartily frightened to recover his good-humour for some time. The Hanoverian ministers always de-

239

served to be hanged for rascals; but now, if they get the power in their hands, — as, sooner or later, they must, since there is neither rising in England nor assistance from France, — they will deserve the gallows as fools if they leave a single clan in the Highlands in a situation to be again troublesome to government. Ay, they will make root-and-branch-work, I warrant them."

"And while you recommend flight to me," said Edward, — " a counsel which I would rather die than embrace, — what are your own views ? "

"Oh," answered Fergus, with a melancholy air, "my fate is settled. Dead or captive I must be before to-morrow."

"What do you mean by that, my friend ? " said Edward. "The enemy is still a day's march in our rear, and if he comes up, we are still strong enough to keep him in check. Remember Gladsmuir."

"What I tell you is true notwithstanding, so far as I am individually concerned."

"Upon what authority can you found so melancholy a prediction ? " asked Waverley.

"On one which never failed a person of my house. I have seen," he said, lowering his voice, — " I have seen the Bodach Glas."

"Bodach Glas ? "

"Yes. Have you been so long at Glennaquoich and never heard of the Gray Spectre ? — though indeed there is a certain reluctance among us to mention him."

"No, never."

"Ah, it would have been a tale for poor Flora to have told you. Or if that hill were Benmore, and that long blue lake, which you see just winding towards yon mountainous country, were Loch

Tay, or my own Loch an Ri, the tale would be better suited with scenery. However, let us sit down on this knoll: even Saddleback and Ulswater will suit what I have to say better than the English hedgerows, enclosures, and farm-houses. You must know, then, that when my ancestor, Ian nan Chaistel, wasted Northumberland, there was associated with him in the expedition a sort of Southland chief, or captain of a band of Lowlanders, called Halbert Hall. In their return through the Cheviots, they quarrelled about the division of the great booty they had acquired, and came from words to blows. The Lowlanders were cut off to a man, and their chief fell the last, covered with wounds, by the sword of my ancestor. Since that time, his spirit has crossed the Vich Ian Vohr of the day when any great disaster was impending, but especially before approaching death. My father saw him twice, — once before he was made prisoner at Sheriff-Muir; another time on the morning of the day on which he died."

"How can you, my dear Fergus, tell such nonsense with a grave face ?"

"I do not ask you to believe it ; but I tell you the truth, ascertained by three hundred years' experience at least, and last night by my own eyes."

"The particulars, for Heaven's sake ! " said Waverley, with eagerness.

"I will, on condition you will not attempt a jest on the subject. Since this unhappy retreat commenced, I have scarce ever been able to sleep for thinking of my clan, and of this poor prince, whom they are leading back like a dog in a string, whether he will or no, and of the downfall of my family. Last night I felt so feverish that I left my quarters

241

and walked out, in hopes the keen, frosty air would brace my nerves. — I cannot tell how much I dislike going on, for I know you will hardly believe me; however — I crossed a small footbridge, and kept walking backwards and forwards, when I observed with surprise, by the clear moonlight, a tall figure in a gray plaid, such as shepherds wear in the south of Scotland, which, move at what pace I would, kept regularly about four yards before me."

" You saw a Cumberland peasant in his ordinary dress, probably."

" No ; I thought so at first, and was astonished at the man's audacity in daring to dog me. I called to him, but received no answer. I felt an anxious throbbing at my heart, and to ascertain what I dreaded, I stood still, and turned myself on the same spot successively to the four points of the compass. By Heaven, Edward, turn where I would, the figure was instantly before my eyes, at precisely the same distance ! I was then convinced it was the Bodach Glas. My hair bristled, and my knees shook. I manned myself, however, and determined to return to my quarters. My ghastly visitant glided before me (for I cannot say he walked), until he reached the foot-bridge ; there he stopped, and turned full round. I must either wade the river, or pass him as close as I am to you. A desperate courage, founded on the belief that my death was near, made me resolve to make my way in despite of him. I made the sign of the cross, drew my sword, and uttered, ' In the name of God, Evil Spirit, give place ! ' ' Vich Ian Vohr,' it said, in a voice that made my very blood curdle, ' beware of to-morrow ! ' It seemed at that moment not half a yard from my sword's point ; but the words were

242

no sooner spoken than it was gone, and nothing appeared further to obstruct my passage. I got home, and threw myself on my bed, where I spent a few hours heavily enough ; and this morning, as no enemy was reported to be near us, I took my horse and rode forward to make up matters with you. I would not willingly fall until I am in charity with a wronged friend."

Edward had little doubt that this phantom was the operation of an exhausted frame and depressed spirits working on the belief common to all Highlanders in such superstitions. He did not the less pity Fergus, for whom, in his present distress, he felt all his former regard revive. With the view of diverting his mind from these gloomy images, he offered, with the Baron's permission, which he knew he could readily obtain, to remain in his quarters till Fergus's corps should come up, and then to march with them as usual. The chief seemed much pleased, yet hesitated to accept the offer.

"We are, you know, in the rear, — the post of danger in a retreat."

"And therefore the post of honour."

"Well," replied the chieftain, " let Alick have your horse in readiness, in case we should be overmatched, and I shall be delighted to have your company once more."

The rear-guard were late in making their appearance, having been delayed by various accidents and by the badness of the roads. At length they entered the hamlet. When Waverley joined the clan Mac-Ivor arm-in-arm with their chieftain, all the resentment they had entertained against him seemed blown off at once. Evan Dhu received him with a grin of congratulation; and even Callum, who was running about as active as ever, pale, indeed, and with a great patch on his head, appeared delighted to see him.

"That gallows-bird's skull," said Fergus, "must be harder than marble; the lock of the pistol was actually broken."

"How could you strike so young a lad so hard?" said Waverley, with some interest.

"Why, if I did not strike hard sometimes, the rascals would forget themselves."

They were now in full march, every caution being taken to prevent surprise. Fergus's people, and a fine clan regiment from Badenoch, commanded by Cluny Mac-Pherson, had the rear. They had passed a large open moor, and were entering into the enclosures which surround a small village called Clifton. The winter sun had set, and Edward began to rally Fergus upon the false predictions of the Gray Spirit. "The ides of March are not past," said Mac-Ivor, with a smile; when, suddenly casting his eyes back on the moor, a large body of cavalry was indistinctly seen to hover upon its brown and dark surface. To line the enclosures facing the open ground, and the road by which the enemy must move from it upon the village, was the work of a short time. While these manœuvres were accomplishing, night sunk down, dark and gloomy, though the moon was at full. Sometimes, however, she gleamed forth a dubious light upon the scene of action.

The Highlanders did not long remain undisturbed in the defensive position they had adopted. Favoured by the night, one large body of dismounted dragoons attempted to force the enclosures, while another, equally strong, strove to penetrate by the high-road. Both were received by such a heavy fire as disconcerted their ranks and effectually checked their progress. Unsatisfied with the advantage thus gained, Fergus, to whose ardent spirit the approach of danger seemed to restore all its elasticity, drawing his sword, and calling out "Claymore!" encouraged his men, by voice and example, to break through the hedge which divided them, and rush down upon the enemy. Mingling with the dismounted dragoons, they forced them, at the sword-point, to fly to the open moor, where a considerable number were cut to pieces. But the moon, which suddenly shone out, showed to the English the small number of assailants, disordered by their own success. Two squadrons of horse moving to the support of their companions, the Highlanders endeavoured to recover the enclosures. But several of them, amongst others their brave chieftain, were cut off and surrounded before they could effect their purpose. Waverley, looking eagerly for Fergus, from whom, as well as from the retreating body of his followers, he had been separated in the darkness and tumult, saw him, with Evan Dhu and Callum, defending themselves desperately against a dozen of horsemen, who were hewing at them with their long broadswords. The moon was again at that moment totally overclouded, and Edward, in the obscurity, could neither bring aid to his friends nor discover which way lay his own road to rejoin the rear-guard. After once or twice narrowly escaping being slain or made prisoner by parties of the cavalry whom he encountered in the darkness, he at length reached an enclosure, and clambering over it, concluded himself in safety,

WAVERLEY

and on the way to the Highland forces, whose pipes he heard at some distance. For Fergus hardly a hope remained, unless that he might be made prisoner. Revolving his fate with sorrow and anxiety, the superstition of the Bodach Glas recurred to Edward's recollection, and he said to himself, with internal surprise, " What, can the devil speak truth ? " [1]

[1] The following account of the skirmish at Clifton is extracted from the manuscript memoirs of Evan Mac-Pherson of Cluny, chief of the clan Mac-Pherson, who had the merit of supporting the principal brunt of that spirited affair. The memoirs appear to have been composed about 1755, only ten years after the action had taken place. They were written in France, where that gallant chief resided in exile, — which accounts for some Gallicisms which occur in the narrative.

" In the prince's return from Derby back towards Scotland, my Lord George Murray, Lieutenant-General, cheerfully charg'd himself with the command of the rear, — a post which, altho' honourable, was attended with great danger, many difficulties, and no small fatigue; for the prince being apprehensive that his retreat to Scotland might be cut off by Marischall Wade, who lay to the northward of him with an armie much supperior to what H. R. H. had, while the Duke of Comberland with his whole cavalrie followed hard in the rear, was obliged to hasten his marches. It was not, therefore, possible for the artilirie to march so fast as the prince's army, in the depth of winter, extremely bad weather, and the worst roads in England; so Lord George Murray was obliged often to continue his marches long after it was dark almost every night, while at the same time he had frequent allarms and disturbances from the Duke of Comberland's advanc'd parties. Towards the evening of the twentie-eight December, 1745, the prince entered the town of Penrith, in the Province of Comberland. But as Lord George Murray could not bring up the artilirie so fast as he wou'd have wish'd, he was oblig'd to pass the night six miles short of that town, together with the regiment of Mac-Donel of Glengarrie, which that day happened to have the arrear guard. The prince, in order to refresh his armie and to give My Lord George and the artilirie time to come up, resolved to sejour the 29th at Penrith; so ordered his little army to appear in the morning under arms, in order to be reviewed, and to know in what manner the numbers stood from his haveing entered England. It did not at that time amount to 5000 foot in all, with about 400

246

cavalrie, compos'd of the noblesse who serv'd as volunteers, part of whom form'd a first troop of guards for the prince, under the command of My Lord Elchoe, now Comte de Weems, who, being proscribed, is presently in France. Another part formed a second troup of guards under the command of My Lord Balmirino, who was beheaded at the Tower of London. A third part serv'd under My Lord le Comte de Kilmarnock, who was likewise beheaded at the Tower. A fourth part serv'd under My Lord Pitsligow, who is also proscribed, — which cavalrie, tho' very few in numbers, being all Noblesse, were very brave, and of infinite advantage to the foot, not only in the day of battle, but in serving as advanced guards on the several marches, and in patroling dureing the night on the different roads which led towards the towns where the army happened to quarter.

"While this small army was out in a body on the 29th December, upon a riseing ground to the northward of Penrith, passing review, Mons. de Cluny, with his tribe, was ordered to the Bridge of Clifton, about a mile to southward of Penrith, after having pass'd in review before Mons. Pattullo, who was charged with the inspection of the troops, and was likeways Quarter Master General of the army, and is now in France. They remained under arms at the Bridge, waiting the arrival of My Lord George Murray with the artilirie, whom Mons. de Cluny had orders to cover in passing the bridge. They arrived about sunsett closly pursued by the Duke of Comberland with the whole body of his cavalrie, reckoned upwards of 3000 strong, about a thousand of whom, as near as might be computed, dismounted, in order to cut off the passage of the artilirie towards the bridge, while the Duke and the others remained on horseback in order to attack the rear. My Lord George Murray advanced, and although he found Mons. de Cluny and his tribe in good spirits under arms, yet the circumstance appear'd extremely delicate. The numbers were vastly unequall, and the attack seem'd very dangerous; so My Lord George declin'd giving orders to such time as he ask'd Mons. de Cluny's oppinion. 'I will attack them with all my heart,' says Mons. de Cluny, 'if you order me.' 'I do order it then,' answered my Lord George, and immediately went on himself along with Mons. de Cluny, and fought sword in hand on foot, at the head of the single tribe of Macphersons. They in a moment made their way through a strong hedge of thorns, under the cover whereof the cavalrie had taken their station, in the strugle of passing which hedge my Lord George Murray, being dressd *en montagnard*, as all the army were, lost his bonet and wig; so continued to fight bear-headed during the action. They at first made a brisk discharge of their fire arms on the enemy, then attacked them with their sabres, and made a great slaughter a considerable time, which obliged Comberland

247

and his cavalrie to fly with precipitation and in great confusion; in so much, that if the Prince had been provided in a sufficient number of cavalrie to have taken advantage of the disorder, it is beyond question that the Duke of Comberland and the bulk of his cavalrie had been taken prisoners. By this time it was so dark that it was not possible to view or number the slain who filled all the ditches which happened to be on the ground where they stood. But it was computed that, besides those who went off wounded, upwards of a hundred at least were left on the spot, among whom was Colonel Honywood, who commanded the dismounted cavalrie, whose sabre, of considerable value, Mons. de Cluny brought off and still preserves; and his tribe lykeways brought off many arms. The colonel was afterwards taken up, and, his wounds being dress'd, with great difficultie recovered. Mons. de Cluny lost only in the action twelve men, of whom some haveing been only wounded, fell afterwards into the hands of the enemy, and were sent as slaves to America, whence several of them returned, and one of them is now in France, a sergeant in the Regiment of Royal Scots. How soon the accounts of the enemies approach had reached the Prince, H. R. H. had immediately ordered Mi-Lord le Comte de Nairne, Brigadier, who, being proscribed, is now in France, with the three batalions of the Duke of Athol, the batalion of the Duke of Perth, and some other troups under his command, in order to support Cluny and to bring off the artilirie. But the action was intirely over before the Comte de Nairne, with his command, cou'd reach nigh to the place. They therefore return'd all to Penrith, and the artilirie marched up in good order. Nor did the Duke of Comberland ever afterwards dare to come within a day's march of the prince and his army dureing the course of all that retreat, which was conducted with great prudence and safety when in some manner surrounded by enemies."

CHAPTER XXXI

EDWARD was in a most unpleasant and dangerous situation. He soon lost the sound of the bagpipes, and, what was yet more unpleasant, when, after searching long in vain, and scrambling through many enclosures, he at length approached the high-road, he learned, from the unwelcome noise of kettle-drums and trumpets, that the English cavalry now occupied it, and consequently were between him and the Highlanders. Precluded, therefore, from advancing in a straight direction, he resolved to avoid the English military, and endeavour to join his friends by making a circuit to the left, for which a beaten path, deviating from the main road in that direction, seemed to afford facilities. The path was muddy, and the night dark and cold; but even these inconveniences were hardly felt amidst the apprehensions which falling into the hands of the king's forces reasonably excited in his bosom.

After walking about three miles, he at length reached a hamlet. Conscious that the common people were in general unfavourable to the cause he had espoused, yet desirous, if possible, to procure a horse and guide to Penrith, where he hoped to find the rear, if not the main body, of the Chevalier's army, he approached the alehouse of the place. There was a great noise within: he paused to listen.

A round English oath or two, and the burden of a campaign song, convinced him the hamlet also was occupied by the Duke of Cumberland's soldiers. Endeavouring to retire from it as softly as possible, and blessing the obscurity which hitherto he had murmured against, Waverley groped his way the best he could along a small paling, which seemed the boundary of some cottage garden. As he reached the gate of this little enclosure, his out-stretched hand was grasped by that of a female, whose voice at the same time uttered, " Edward, is 't thou, man ? "

" Here is some unlucky mistake," thought Edward, struggling, but gently, to disengage himself.

" Naen o' thy foun, now, man, or the red-cwoats will hear thee ; they hae been houlerying and poul-erying every ane that past alehouse door this noight to make them drive their waggons and sick loike. Come into feyther's, or they 'll do ho a mischief."

A good hint, thought Waverley, following the girl through the little garden into a brick-paved kitchen, where she set herself to kindle a match at an expiring fire, and with the match to light a candle. She had no sooner looked on Edward than she dropped the light with a shrill scream of " Oh, fey-ther, feyther ! "

The father, thus invoked, speedily appeared, — a sturdy old farmer, in a pair of leather breeches and boots pulled on without stockings, having just started from his bed ; the rest of his dress was only a West-moreland statesman's *robe-de-chambre*, — that is, his shirt. His figure was displayed to advantage, by a candle which he bore in his left hand ; in his right he brandished a poker.

" What hast ho here, wench ? "

" Oh," cried the poor girl, almost going off in hysterics, " I thought it was Ned Williams, and it is one of the plaid-men."

" And what was thee ganging to do wi' Ned Williams at this time o' noight ? " To this, which was perhaps one of the numerous class of questions more easily asked than answered, the rosy-cheeked damsel made no reply, but continued sobbing and wringing her hands.

" And thee, lad, dost ho know that the dragoons be a town ? Dost ho know that, mon ? Ad, they'll sliver thee loike a turnip, mon."

" I know my life is in great danger," said Waverley; " but if you can assist me, I will reward you handsomely. I am no Scotchman, but an unfortunate English gentleman."

" Be ho Scot or no," said the honest farmer, " I wish thou hadst kept the other side of the hallan. But since thou art here, Jacob Jopson will betray no man's bluid ; and the plaids were gay canny, and did not do so much mischief when they were here yesterday." Accordingly, he set seriously about sheltering and refreshing our hero for the night. The fire was speedily rekindled, but with precaution against its light being seen from without. The jolly yeoman cut a rasher of bacon, which Cicely soon broiled, and her father added a swingeing tankard of his best ale. It was settled that Edward should remain there till the troops marched in the morning, then hire or buy a horse from the farmer, and, with the best directions that could be obtained, endeavour to overtake his friends. A clean though coarse bed received him after the fatigues of this unhappy day.

With the morning arrived the news that the

251

Highlanders had evacuated Penrith and marched
off towards Carlisle, that the Duke of Cumberland
was in possession of Penrith, and that detachments
of his army covered the roads in every direction.
To attempt to get through undiscovered would be
an act of the most frantic temerity. Ned Williams
(the right Edward) was now called to council by
Cicely and her father. Ned, who perhaps did not
care that his handsome namesake should remain too
long in the same house with his sweetheart, for fear
of fresh mistakes, proposed that Waverley, exchang-
ing his uniform and plaid for the dress of the country, should go with him to his father's farm near
Ulswater, and remain in that undisturbed retirement until the military movements in the country
should have ceased to render his departure hazardous. A price was also agreed upon, at which the
stranger might board with Farmer Williams, if he
thought proper, till he could depart with safety.
It was of moderate amount, the distress of his situation, among this honest and simple-hearted race,
being considered as no reason for increasing their
demand.

The necessary articles of dress were accordingly
procured, and by following by-paths known to the
young farmer, they hoped to escape any unpleasant
rencontre. A recompense for their hospitality was
refused peremptorily by old Jopson and his cherry-
cheeked daughter: a kiss paid the one, and a hearty
shake of the hand the other. Both seemed anxious
for their guest's safety, and took leave of him with
kind wishes.

In the course of their route, Edward, with his
guide, traversed those fields which the night before
had been the scene of action. A brief gleam of

CHAPTER OF ACCIDENTS

December's sun shone sadly on the broad heath, which, towards the spot where the great northwest road entered the enclosures of Lord Lonsdale's property, exhibited dead bodies of men and horses, and the usual companions of war, a number of carrion-crows, hawks, and ravens.

"And this, then, was thy last field," said Waverley to himself, his eye filling at the recollection of the many splendid points of Fergus's character, and of their former intimacy, all his passions and imperfections forgotten, — "here fell the last Vich Ian Vohr, on a nameless heath; and in an obscure night-skirmish was quenched that ardent spirit who thought it little to cut a way for his master to the British throne! Ambition, policy, bravery, all far beyond their sphere, here learned the fate of mortals. The sole support, too, of a sister whose spirit, as proud and unbending, was even more exalted than thine own, — here ended all thy hopes for Flora, and the long and valued line which it was thy boast to raise yet more highly by thy adventurous valour!"

As these ideas pressed on Waverley's mind, he resolved to go upon the open heath and search if, among the slain, he could discover the body of his friend, with the pious intention of procuring for him the last rites of sepulture. The timorous young man who accompanied him remonstrated upon the danger of the attempt; but Edward was determined. The followers of the camp had already stripped the dead of all they could carry away; but the country people, unused to scenes of blood, had not yet approached the field of action, though some stood fearfully gazing at a distance. About sixty or seventy dragoons lay slain within the first enclosure, upon

253

the high road and on the open moor. Of the Highlanders, not above a dozen had fallen, chiefly those
who, venturing too far on the moor, could not re-
gain the strong ground. He could not find the body
of Fergus among the slain. On a little knoll, separated from the others, lay the carcasses of three
English dragoons, two horses, and the page Callum
Beg, whose hard skull a trooper's broadsword had
at length effectually cloven. It was possible his
clan had carried off the body of Fergus; but it was
also possible he had escaped, especially as Evan
Dhu, who would never leave his chief, was not
found among the dead; or he might be prisoner,
and the less formidable denunciation inferred from
the appearance of the Bodach Glas might have
proved the true one. The approach of a party sent
for the purpose of compelling the country-people
to bury the dead, and who had already assembled
several peasants for that purpose, now obliged Edward to rejoin his guide, who awaited him in great
anxiety and fear under shade of the plantations.

After leaving this field of death, the rest of their
journey was happily accomplished. At the house
of Farmer Williams, Edward passed for a young
kinsman, educated for the Church, who was come
to reside there till the civil tumults permitted him
to pass through the country. This silenced suspicion among the kind and simple yeomanry of Cumberland, and accounted sufficiently for the grave
manners and retired habits of the new guest. The
precaution became more necessary than Waverley
had anticipated, as a variety of incidents prolonged
his stay at Fasthwaite, as the farm was called.

A tremendous fall of snow rendered his departure
impossible for more than ten days. When the

254

roads began to become a little practicable, they successively received news of the retreat of the Chevalier into Scotland; then, that he had abandoned the frontiers, retiring upon Glasgow, and that the Duke of Cumberland had formed the siege of Carlisle. His army, therefore, cut off all possibility of Waverley's escaping into Scotland in that direction. On the eastern border Marshal Wade, with a large force, was advancing upon Edinburgh, and all along the frontier, parties of militia, volunteers, and partisans were in arms to suppress insurrection and apprehend such stragglers from the Highland army as had been left in England. The surrender of Carlisle, and the severity with which the rebel garrison were threatened, soon formed an additional reason against venturing upon a solitary and hopeless journey through a hostile country and a large army, to carry the assistance of a single sword to a cause which seemed altogether desperate.

In this lonely and secluded situation, without the advantage of company or conversation with men of cultivated minds, the arguments of Colonel Talbot often recurred to the mind of our hero. A still more anxious recollection haunted his slumbers. — it was the dying look and gesture of Colonel Gardiner. Most devoutly did he hope, as the rarely occurring post brought news of skirmishes with various success, that it might never again be his lot to draw his sword in civil conflict. Then his mind turned to the supposed death of Fergus, to the desolate situation of Flora, and, with yet more tender recollection, to that of Rose Bradwardine, who was destitute of the devoted enthusiasm of loyalty, which to her friend hallowed and exalted misfortune. These reveries he was permitted to enjoy, undis-

255

turbed by queries or interruption ; and it was in many a winter walk by the shores of Ulswater that he acquired a more complete mastery of a spirit, tamed by adversity, than his former experience had given him, and that he felt himself entitled to say firmly, though perhaps with a sigh, that the romance of his life was ended, and that its real history had now commenced. He was soon called upon to justify his pretensions by reason and philosophy.

CHAPTER XXXII

THE family at Fasthwaite were soon attached to Edward. He had, indeed, that gentleness and urbanity which almost universally attract corresponding kindness; and to their simple ideas his learning gave him consequence, and his sorrows interest. The last he ascribed, evasively, to the loss of a brother in the skirmish near Clifton; and in that primitive state of society, where the ties of affection were highly deemed of, his continued depression excited sympathy, but not surprise.

In the end of January his more lively powers were called out by the happy union of Edward Williams, the son of his host, with Cicely Jopson. Our hero would not cloud with sorrow the festivity attending the wedding of two persons to whom he was so highly obliged. He therefore exerted himself, danced, sung, played at the various games of the day, and was the blithest of the company. The next morning, however, he had more serious matters to think of.

The clergyman who had married the young couple was so much pleased with the supposed student of divinity that he came next day from Penrith on purpose to pay him a visit. This might have been a puzzling chapter had he entered into any examination of our hero's supposed theological studies; but

257

fortunately he loved better to hear and communicate the news of the day. He brought with him two or three old newspapers, in one of which Edward found a piece of intelligence that soon rendered him deaf to every word which the Reverend Mr. Twigtythe was saying upon the news from the North, and the prospect of the duke's speedily overtaking and crushing the rebels. This was an article in these, or nearly these words : —

"Died at his house in Hill Street, Berkeley Square, upon the 10th inst., Richard Waverley, Esq., second son of Sir Giles Waverley, of Waverley Honour, &c., &c. He died of a lingering disorder, augmented by the unpleasant predicament of suspicion in which he stood, having been obliged to find bail to a high amount to meet an impending accusation of high-treason. An accusation of the same grave crime hangs over his elder brother, Sir Everard Waverley, the representative of that ancient family ; and we understand the day of his trial will be fixed early in the next month, unless Edward Waverley, son of the deceased Richard and heir to the baronet, shall surrender himself to justice. In that case, we are assured it is his Majesty's gracious purpose to drop further proceedings upon the charge against Sir Everard. This unfortunate young gentleman is ascertained to have been in arms in the Pretender's service, and to have marched along with the Highland troops into England. But he has not been heard of since the skirmish at Clifton, on the 18th December last."

Such was this distracting paragraph. "Good God !" exclaimed Waverley, "am I then a parricide ? Impossible ! My father, who never showed the affection of a father while he lived, cannot have been so much affected by my supposed death as to hasten his own. No, I will not believe it; it were distraction to entertain for a moment such a horrible idea. But it were, if possible, worse than parricide to suffer any danger to hang over my noble and generous uncle, who has ever been more to me than a father, if such evil can be averted by any sacrifice on my part!"

While these reflections passed like the stings of scorpions through Waverley's sensorium, the worthy divine was startled, in a long disquisition on the battle of Falkirk, by the ghastliness which they communicated to his looks, and asked him if he was ill? Fortunately the bride, all smirk and blush, had just entered the room. Mrs. Williams was none of the brightest of women, but she was good-natured; and readily concluding that Edward had been shocked by disagreeable news in the papers, interfered so judiciously that, without exciting suspicion, she drew off Mr. Twigtythe's attention, and engaged it until he soon after took his leave. Waverley then explained to his friends that he was under the necessity of going to London with as little delay as possible.

One cause of delay, however, did occur to which Waverley had been very little accustomed. His purse, though well stocked when he first went to Tully-Veolan, had not been reinforced since that period; and although his life since had not been of a nature to exhaust it hastily, for he had lived chiefly with his friends or with the army, yet he found that, after settling with his kind landlord, he should be too poor to encounter the expense of travelling post. The best course, therefore, seemed to be to get into the Great North Road about Boroughbridge, and there take a place in the Northern Diligence, a huge, old-fashioned tub drawn by three horses, which completed the journey from Edinburgh to London ("God willing," as the advertisement expressed it) in three weeks. Our hero, therefore, took an affectionate farewell of his Cumberland friends, whose kindness he promised never to forget, and tacitly hoped one day to acknowledge by substantial proofs of gratitude. After some petty difficulties and vexatious delays, and after putting his dress into a shape better befitting his rank, though perfectly plain and simple, he accomplished crossing the country, and found himself in the desired vehicle, *vis-à-vis* to Mrs. Nosebag, the lady of Lieutenant Nosebag, adjutant and riding-master of the —— dragoons, — a jolly woman of about fifty, wearing a blue habit faced with scarlet, and grasping a silver-mounted horsewhip.

This lady was one of those active members of society who take upon them *faire le frais de conversation*. She had just returned from the North, and informed Edward how nearly her regiment had cut the petticoat people into ribbons at Falkirk, — "only somehow there was one of those nasty, awkward marshes that they are never without in Scotland, I think, and so our poor dear little regiment suffered something, as my Nosebag says, in that unsatisfactory affair. You, sir, have served in the dragoons?"

Waverley was taken so much at unawares that he acquiesced.

"Oh, I knew it at once; I saw you were military from your air, and I was sure you could be none of the foot-wobblers, as my Nosebag calls them. What regiment, pray?"

Here was a delightful question. Waverley, however, justly concluded that this good lady had the whole Army List by heart; and to avoid detection by adhering to truth, answered, " Gardiner's dragoons, Ma'am; but I have retired some time."

" Oh, ay, those as won the race at the battle of Preston, as my Nosebag says. Pray, sir, were you there ? "

"I was so unfortunate, Madam," he replied, " as to witness that engagement."

"And that was a misfortune that few of Gardiner's stood to witness, I believe, sir, ha! ha! ha! I beg your pardon; but a soldier's wife loves a joke."

" Devil confound you," thought Waverley; " what infernal luck has penned me up with this inquisitive hag ! "

Fortunately the good lady did not stick long to one subject. " We are coming to Ferrybridge now," she said, " where there was a party of *ours* left to support the beadles and constables and justices, and these sort of creatures that are examining papers and stopping rebels and all that."

They were hardly in the inn before she dragged Waverley to the window, exclaiming, " Yonder comes Corporal Bridoon, of our poor dear troop, — he 's coming with the constable man. Bridoon 's one of my lambs, as Nosebag calls 'em. Come, Mr. —— a — a — Pray, what 's your name, sir ? "

" Butler, Ma'am," said Waverley, resolved rather to make free with the name of a former fellow-officer than run the risk of detection by inventing one not to be found in the regiment.

" Oh, you got a troop lately, when that shabby fellow, Waverley, went over to the rebels ? Lord, I wish our old cross Captain Crump would go over

261

to the rebels, that Nosebag might get the troop!
Lord, what can Bridoon be standing swinging on
the bridge for? I 'll be hanged if he a'nt hazy, as
Nosebag says. Come, sir, as you and I belong to
the service, we 'll go put the rascal in mind of his
duty."

Waverley, with feelings more easily conceived
than described, saw himself obliged to follow this
doughty female commander. The gallant trooper
was as like a lamb as a drunk corporal of dragoons,
about six feet high, with very broad shoulders and
very thin legs, not to mention a great scar across
his nose, could well be. Mrs. Nosebag addressed
him with something which, if not an oath, sounded
very like one, and commanded him to attend to his
duty.

"You be d—d for a —," commenced the gallant
cavalier; but looking up, in order to suit the action
to the words, and also to enforce the epithet which
he meditated, with an adjective applicable to the
party, he recognized the speaker, made his military
salam, and altered his tone. "Lord love your handsome face, Madam Nosebag, is it you? Why, if a
poor fellow does happen to fire a slug of a morning,
I am sure you were never the lady to bring him to
harm."

"Well, you rascallion, go mind your duty, — this
gentleman and I belong to the service; but be sure
you look after that shy cock in the slouched hat
that sits in the corner of the coach. I believe he 's
one of the rebels in disguise."

"D—n her gooseberry wig," said the corporal,
when she was out of hearing; "that gimlet-eyed
jade — mother adjutant, as we call her — is a greater
plague to the regiment than prévôt-marshal, ser-

geant-major, and old Hubble-de-Shuff, the colonel, into the bargain. Come, Master Constable, let's see if this shy cock, as she calls him [who, by the way, was a Quaker from Leeds, with whom Mrs. Nosebag had had some tart argument on the legality of bearing arms], will stand godfather to a sup of brandy; for your Yorkshire ale is cold on my stomach."

The vivacity of this good lady, as it helped Edward out of this scrape, was like to have drawn him into one or two others. In every town where they stopped, she wished to examine the *corps de garde*, if there was one, and once very narrowly missed introducing Waverley to a recruiting-sergeant of his own regiment. Then she Captain'd and Butler'd him till he was almost mad with vexation and anxiety; and never was he more rejoiced in his life at the termination of a journey than when the arrival of the coach in London freed him from the attentions of Madam Nosebag.

CHAPTER XXXIII

WHAT'S TO BE DONE NEXT?

IT was twilight when they arrived in town; and having shaken off his companions, and walked through a good many streets, to avoid the possibility of being traced by them, Edward took a hackney-coach and drove to Colonel Talbot's house, in one of the principal squares at the west end of the town. That gentleman, by the death of relations, had succeeded since his marriage to a large fortune, possessed considerable political interest, and lived in what is called great style.

When Waverley knocked at his door, he found it at first difficult to procure admittance, but at length was shown into an apartment where the colonel was at table. Lady Emily, whose very beautiful features were still pallid from indisposition, sat opposite to him. The instant he heard Waverley's voice, he started up and embraced him. "Frank Stanley, my dear boy, how d'ye do? Emily, my love, this is young Stanley."

The blood started to the lady's cheek as she gave Waverley a reception, in which courtesy was mingled with kindness, while her trembling hand and faltering voice showed how much she was startled and discomposed. Dinner was hastily replaced, and while Waverley was engaged in refreshing himself, the colonel proceeded: "I wonder you have come here, Frank; the doctors tell me the air of London

264

is very bad for your complaints. You should not have risked it. But I am delighted to see you, and so is Emily, though I fear we must not reckon upon your staying long."

"Some particular business brought me up," muttered Waverley.

"I supposed so; but I sha'n't allow you to stay long. Spontoon," to an elderly, military-looking servant out of livery, "take away these things, and answer the bell yourself, if I ring. Don't let any of the other fellows disturb us; my nephew and I have business to talk of."

When the servants had retired, "In the name of God, Waverley, what has brought you here? It may be as much as your life is worth."

"Dear Mr. Waverley," said Lady Emily, "to whom I owe so much more than acknowledgments can ever pay, how could you be so rash?"

"My father—my uncle—this paragraph." He handed the paper to Colonel Talbot.

"I wish to Heaven these scoundrels were condemned to be squeezed to death in their own presses," said Talbot. "I am told there are not less than a dozen of their papers now published in town; and no wonder that they are obliged to invent lies to find sale for their journals. It is true, however, my dear Edward, that you have lost your father; but as to this flourish of his unpleasant situation having grated upon his spirits and hurt his health, the truth is, — for though it is harsh to say so now, yet it will relieve your mind from the idea of weighty responsibility, — the truth then is that Mr. Richard Waverley, through this whole business, showed great want of sensibility both to your situation and that of your uncle; and the last time I saw him, he told me, with great glee, that as I was so good as to take charge of your interests, he had thought it best to patch up a separate negotiation for himself, and make his peace with government through some channels which former connections left still open to him."

"And my uncle, my dear uncle?"

"Is in no danger whatever. It is true [looking at the date of the paper] there was a foolish report some time ago to the purport here quoted, but it is entirely false. Sir Everard is gone down to Waverley Honour freed from all uneasiness, unless upon your own account. But you are in peril yourself; your name is in every proclamation; warrants are out to apprehend you. How and when did you come here?"

Edward told his story at length, suppressing his quarrel with Fergus; for being himself partial to Highlanders, he did not wish to give any advantage to the colonel's national prejudice against them.

"Are you sure it was your friend Glen's foot-boy you saw dead on Clifton Moor?"

"Quite positive."

"Then that little limb of the devil has cheated the gallows, for cutthroat was written in his face; though," turning to Lady Emily, "it was a very handsome face too. But for you, Edward, I wish you would go down again to Cumberland, or rather I wish you had never stirred from thence; for there is an embargo in all the seaports, and a strict search for the adherents of the Pretender; and the tongue of that confounded woman will wag in her head like the clack of a mill, till somehow or other she will detect Captain Butler to be a feigned personage."

"Do you know anything," asked Waverley, "of my fellow-traveller?"

"Her husband was my sergeant-major for six years; she was a buxom widow with a little money. He married her, was steady, and got on by being a good drill. I must send Spontoon to see what she is about; he will find her out among the old regimental connections. To-morrow you must be indisposed, and keep your room from fatigue. Lady Emily is to be your nurse, and Spontoon and I your attendants. You bear the name of a near relation of mine whom none of my present people ever saw, except Spontoon, so there will be no immediate danger. So pray feel your head ache and your eyes grow heavy as soon as possible, that you may be put upon the sick list; and, Emily, do you order an apartment for Frank Stanley, with all the attentions which an invalid may require."

In the morning the colonel visited his guest. "Now," said he, "I have some good news for you. Your reputation as a gentleman and officer is effectually cleared of neglect of duty and accession to the mutiny in Gardiner's regiment. I have had a correspondence on this subject with a very zealous friend of yours, your Scottish parson, Morton. His first letter was addressed to Sir Everard; but I relieved the good baronet of the trouble of answering it. You must know that your freebooting acquaintance, Donald of the Cave, has at length fallen into the hands of the Philistines. He was driving off the cattle of a certain proprietor called Killan — something or other — "

"Killancureit?"

"The same. Now the gentleman being, it seems, a great farmer, and having a special value for his breed of cattle, being, moreover, rather of a timid disposition, had got a party of soldiers to protect his property. So Donald run his head unawares into the lion's mouth, and was defeated and made prisoner. Being ordered for execution, his conscience was assailed on the one hand by a Catholic priest, on the other by your friend Morton. He repulsed the Catholic, chiefly on account of the doctrine of extreme unction, which this economical gentleman considered as an excessive waste of oil. So his conversion from a state of impenitence fell to Mr. Morton's share, who, I daresay, acquitted himself excellently, though, I suppose, Donald made but a queer kind of Christian after all. He confessed, however, before a magistrate, one Major Melville, who seems to have been a correct, friendly sort of person, his full intrigue with Houghton, explaining particularly how it was carried on, and fully acquitting you of the least accession to it. He also mentioned his rescuing you from the hands of the volunteer officer, and sending you, by orders of the Pret— Chevalier, I mean — as a prisoner to Doune, from whence he understood you were carried prisoner to Edinburgh. These are particulars which cannot but tell in your favour. He hinted that he had been employed to deliver and protect you, and rewarded for doing so ; but he would not confess by whom, alleging that though he would not have minded breaking any ordinary oath to satisfy the curiosity of Mr. Morton, to whose pious admonitions he owed so much, yet in the present case he had been sworn to silence upon the edge of his dirk,[1] — which, it seems, constituted, in his opinion, an inviolable obligation."

[1] Note IX. — Oath upon the Dirk

"And what is become of him?"

"Oh, he was hanged at Stirling after the rebels raised the siege, with his lieutenant and four plaids besides, — he having the advantage of a gallows more lofty than his friends."

"Well, I have little cause either to regret or rejoice at his death; and yet he has done me both good and harm to a very considerable extent."

"His confession, at least, will serve you materially, since it wipes from your character all those suspicions which gave the accusation against you a complexion of a nature different from that with which so many unfortunate gentlemen, now or lately in arms against the government, may be justly charged. Their treason — I must give it its name, though you participate in its guilt — is an action arising from mistaken virtue, and therefore cannot be classed as a disgrace, though it be doubtless highly criminal. Where the guilty are so numerous, clemency must be extended to far the greater number; and I have little doubt of procuring a remission for you, providing we can keep you out of the claws of Justice till she has selected and gorged upon her victims; for in this, as in other cases, it will be according to the vulgar proverb, 'First come, first served.' Besides, government are desirous at present to intimidate the English Jacobites, among whom they can find few examples for punishment. This is a vindictive and timid feeling, which will soon wear off, for, of all nations, the English are least bloodthirsty by nature. But it exists at present, and you must therefore be kept out of the way in the mean time."

Now entered Spontoon, with an anxious countenance. By his regimental acquaintances he had

269

traced out Madam Nosebag, and found her full of
ire, fuss, and fidget at discovery of an impostor who
had travelled from the North with her under the
assumed name of Captain Butler, of Gardiner's dragoons. She was going to lodge an information on
the subject, to have him sought for as an emissary
of the Pretender; but Spontoon (an old soldier),
while he pretended to approve, contrived to make
her delay her intention. No time, however, was to
be lost; the accuracy of this good dame's description might probably lead to the discovery that
Waverley was the pretended Captain Butler, — an
identification fraught with danger to Edward, perhaps to his uncle, and even to Colonel Talbot.
Which way to direct his course was now, therefore,
the question.

"To Scotland," said Waverley.

"To Scotland?" said the colonel, — "with what
purpose? Not to engage again with the rebels, I
hope?"

"No, I considered my campaign ended when,
after all my efforts, I could not rejoin them; and
now, by all accounts, they are gone to make a
winter campaign in the Highlands, where such adherents as I am would rather be burdensome than
useful. Indeed, it seems likely that they only pro-
long the war to place the Chevalier's person out of
danger, and then to make some terms for themselves. To burden them with my presence would
merely add another party whom they would not
give up, and could not defend. I understand they
left almost all their English adherents in garrison
at Carlisle for that very reason. And on a more
general view, Colonel, to confess the truth, though
it may lower me in your opinion, I am heartily tired

of the trade of war, and am, as Fletcher's Humorous Lieutenant says, 'even as weary of this fighting'—"

"Fighting! pooh, what have you seen but a skirmish or two? Ah, if you saw war on the grand scale,— sixty or a hundred thousand men in the field on each side!"

"I am not at all curious, Colonel. 'Enough,' says our homely proverb, 'is as good as a feast.' The plumed troops and the big war used to enchant me in poetry; but the night marches, vigils, couches under the wintry sky, and such accompaniments of the glorious trade are not at all to my taste in practice. Then for dry blows, I had *my* fill of fighting at Clifton, where I escaped by a hair's breadth half a dozen times; and you, I should think — " He stopped.

"Had enough of it at Preston? you mean to say," answered the colonel, laughing; "but 't is my vocation, Hal."

"It is not mine, though," said Waverley; "and having honourably got rid of the sword, which I drew only as a volunteer, I am quite satisfied with my military experience, and shall be in no hurry to take it up again."

"I am very glad you are of that mind; but then what would you do in the North?"

"In the first place, there are some seaports on the eastern coast of Scotland still in the hands of the Chevalier's friends: should I gain any of them, I can easily embark for the Continent."

"Good; your second reason?"

"Why, to speak the very truth, there is a person in Scotland upon whom I now find my happiness depends more than I was always aware, and about whose situation I am very anxious."

271

"Then Emily was right, and there is a love affair in the case after all. And which of these two pretty Scotchwomen, whom you insisted upon my admiring, is the distinguished fair? Not Miss Glen— I hope."

" No."

" Ah, pass for the other; simplicity may be improved, but pride and conceit never. Well, I don't discourage you; I think it will please Sir Everard, from what he said when I jested with him about it, — only I hope that intolerable papa, with his brogue, and his snuff, and his Latin, and his insufferable long stories about the Duke of Berwick, will find it necessary hereafter to be an inhabitant of foreign parts. But as to the daughter, though I think you might find as fitting a match in England, yet if your heart be really set upon this Scotch rosebud, why the baronet has a great opinion of her father and of his family, and he wishes much to see you married and settled, both for your own sake and for that of the three ermines passant, which may otherwise pass away altogether. But I will bring you his mind fully upon the subject, since you are debarred correspondence for the present, for I think you will not be long in Scotland before me."

" Indeed, and what can induce you to think of returning to Scotland ? No relenting longings towards the land of mountains and floods, I am afraid."

" None, on my word ; but Emily's health is now, thank God, re-established, and, to tell you the truth, I have little hopes of concluding the business which I have at present most at heart until I can have a personal interview with his Royal Highness the Commander-in-Chief; for, as Fluellen says, 'the duke doth love me well, and I thank Heaven I have deserved some love at his hands.' I am now going out for an hour or two to arrange matters for your departure ; your liberty extends to the next room, Lady Emily's parlour, where you will find her when you are disposed for music, reading, or conversation. We have taken measures to exclude all servants but Spontoon, who is as true as steel."

In about two hours Colonel Talbot returned, and found his young friend conversing with his lady, — she pleased with his manners and information, and he delighted at being restored, though but for a moment, to the society of his own rank, from which he had been for some time excluded.

"And now," said the colonel, " hear my arrangements, for there is little time to lose. This youngster, Edward Waverley, *alias* Williams, *alias* Captain Butler, must continue to pass by his fourth *alias* of Francis Stanley, my nephew. He shall set out to-morrow for the North, and the chariot shall take him the first two stages. Spontoon shall then attend him, and they shall ride post as far as Huntingdon ; and the presence of Spontoon, well known on the road as my servant, will check all disposition to inquiry. At Huntingdon you will meet the real Frank Stanley. He is studying at Cambridge ; but a little while ago, doubtful if Emily's health would permit me to go down to the North myself, I procured him a passport from the Secretary of State's office to go in my stead. As he went chiefly to look after you, his journey is now unnecessary. He knows your story ; you will dine together at Huntingdon, and perhaps your wise heads may hit upon some plan for removing or diminishing the danger of your farther progress northward. And

273

now," taking out a morocco case, " let me put you in funds for the campaign."

" I am ashamed, my dear Colonel, — "

" Nay," said Colonel Talbot, "you should command my purse in any event; but this money is your own. Your father, considering the chance of your being attainted, left me his trustee for your advantage; so that you are worth above £15,000, besides Brerewood Lodge, — a very independent person, I promise you. There are bills here for £200 ; any larger sum you may have, or credit abroad, as soon as your motions require it."

The first use which occurred to Waverley of his newly acquired wealth was to write to honest Farmer Jopson, requesting his acceptance of a silver tankard on the part of his friend Williams, who had not forgotten the night of the 18th December last. He begged him at the same time carefully to preserve for him his Highland garb and accoutrements, particularly the arms, curious in themselves, and to which the friendship of the donors gave additional value. Lady Emily undertook to find some suitable token of remembrance likely to flatter the vanity and please the taste of Mrs. Williams ; and the colonel, who was a kind of farmer, promised to send the Ulswater patriarch an excellent team of horses for cart and plough.

One happy day Waverley spent in London ; and travelling in the manner projected, he met with Frank Stanley at Huntingdon. The two young men were acquainted in a minute.

" I can read my uncle's riddle," said Stanley ; " the cautious old soldier did not care to hint to me that I might hand over to you this passport, which I have no occasion for; but if it should afterwards

274

come out as the rattle-pated trick of a young Cantab, *cela ne tire à rien*. You are therefore to be Francis Stanley, with this passport." This proposal appeared in effect to alleviate a great part of the difficulties which Edward must otherwise have encountered at every turn; and accordingly, he scrupled not to avail himself of it, the more especially as he had discarded all political purposes from his present journey, and could not be accused of furthering machinations against the government while travelling under protection of the Secretary's passport.

The day passed merrily away. The young student was inquisitive about Waverley's campaigns and the manners of the Highlands; and Edward was obliged to satisfy his curiosity by whistling a pibroch, dancing a strathspey, and singing a Highland song. The next morning Stanley rode a stage northward with his new friend, and parted from him with great reluctance, upon the remonstrances of Spontoon, who, accustomed to submit to discipline, was rigid in enforcing it.

CHAPTER XXXIV

DESOLATION

WAVERLEY, riding post, as was the usual fashion of the period, without any adventure save one or two queries, which the talisman of his passport sufficiently answered, reached the borders of Scotland. Here he heard the tidings of the decisive battle of Culloden. It was no more than he had long expected, though the success at Falkirk had thrown a faint and setting gleam over the arms of the Chevalier. Yet it came upon him like a shock, by which he was for a time altogether unmanned. The generous, the courteous, the noble-minded Adventurer was then a fugitive, with a price upon his head; his adherents, so brave, so enthusiastic, so faithful, were dead, imprisoned, or exiled. Where, now, was the exalted and high-souled Fergus, if, indeed, he had survived the night at Clifton? Where the pure-hearted and primitive Baron of Bradwardine, whose foibles seemed foils to set off the disinterestedness of his disposition, the genuine goodness of his heart, and his unshaken courage? Those who clung for support to these fallen columns, Rose and Flora, where were they to be sought, and in what distress must not the loss of their natural protectors have involved them? Of Flora, he thought with the regard of a brother for a sister; of Rose, with a sensation yet more deep and tender. It might be still

his fate to supply the want of those guardians they
had lost. Agitated by these thoughts, he precipitated his journey.

When he arrived in Edinburgh, where his inquiries must necessarily commence, he felt the full
difficulty of his situation. Many inhabitants of that
city had seen and known him as Edward Waverley:
how, then, could he avail himself of a passport as
Francis Stanley? He resolved, therefore, to avoid
all company, and to move northward as soon as possible. He was, however, obliged to wait a day or
two in expectation of a letter from Colonel Talbot,
and he was also to leave his own address, under his
feigned character, at a place agreed upon. With
this latter purpose he sallied out in the dusk
through the well-known streets, carefully shunning
observation; but in vain: one of the first persons
whom he met at once recognized him. It was
Mrs. Flockhart, Fergus Mac Ivor's good humoured
landlady.

"Gude guide us, Mr. Waverley, is this you? Na,
ye needna be feared for me. I wad betray nae
gentleman in your circumstances. Eh, lack-a-day!
lack-a-day! here's a change o' markets; how merry
Colonel Mac-Ivor and you used to be in our
house!" And the good-natured widow shed a few
natural tears.

As there was no resisting her claim of acquaintance, Waverley acknowledged it with a good grace,
as well as the danger of his own situation.

"As it's near the darkening, sir, wad ye just step
in by to our house and tak a dish o' tea? And I
am sure if ye like to sleep in the little room, I wad
tak care ye are no disturbed, and naebody wad ken
ye; for Kate and Matty, the limmers, gaed aff wi'

twa o' Hawley's dragoons, and I hae twa new queans instead o' them."

Waverley accepted her invitation and engaged her lodging for a night or two, satisfied he should be safer in the house of this simple creature than anywhere else. When he entered the parlour, his heart swelled to see Fergus's bonnet, with the white cockade, hanging beside the little mirror.

"Ay," said Mrs. Flockhart, sighing, as she observed the direction of his eyes, "the puir colonel bought a new ane just the day before they marched, and I winna let them tak that ane doun, but just to brush it ilka day mysell; and whiles I look at it till I just think I hear him cry to Callum to bring him his bonnet, as he used to do when he was ganging out. It's unco silly, — the neighbours ca' me a Jacobite; but they may say their say, I am sure it's no for that, — but he was as kind-hearted a gentleman as ever lived, and as weel-fa'rd too. Oh, d' ye ken, sir, when he is to suffer?"

"Suffer! Good Heaven! Why, where is he?"

"Eh, Lord's sake! d' ye no ken? The poor Hieland body, Dugald Mahony, cam here a while syne, wi' ane o' his arms cuttit off, and a sair clour in the head, — ye 'll mind Dugald, he carried aye an axe on his shouther, — and he cam here just begging, as I may say, for something to eat. Aweel, he tauld us the chief, as they ca'd him (but I aye ca' him the colonel), and Ensign Maccombich, that ye mind weel, were ta'en somewhere beside the English border, when it was sae dark that his folk never missed him till it was ower late, and they were like to gang clean daft. And he said that little Callum Beg (he was a bauld, mischievous callant that) and your honour were killed that same night in the tuilzie, and mony mae braw men. But he grat when he spak o' the colonel, ye never saw the like. And now the word gangs the colonel is to be tried, and to suffer wi' them that were ta'en at Carlisle."

" And his sister ? "

" Ay, that they ca'd the Lady Flora, — weel, she's away up to Carlisle to him, and lives wi' some grand Papist lady thereabouts, to be near him."

"And," said Edward, "the other young lady ?"

" Whilk other? I ken only of ae sister the colonel had."

" I mean Miss Bradwardine," said Edward.

" Ou, ay, — the laird's daughter," said his landlady. "She was a very bonny lassie, poor thing, but far shyer than Lady Flora."

" Where is she, for God's sake ? "

" Ou, wha kens where ony o' them is now ? Puir things! they're sair ta'en doun for their white cockades and their white roses; but she gaed north to her father's in Perthshire, when the government troops cam back to Edinbro'. There was some pretty men amang them, and ane Major Whacker was quartered on me, — a very ceevil gentleman ; but oh, Mr. Waverley, he was naething sae weel fa'rd as the puir colonel."

" Do you know what is become of Miss Bradwardine's father ? "

" The auld laird? Na, naebody kens that; but they say he fought very hard in that bluidy battle at Inverness ; and Deacon Clank, the white-iron smith, says that the government folk are sair agane him for having been *out* twice, — and troth he might hae ta'en warning ; but there's nae fule like an auld fule, — the puir colonel was only out ance."

Such conversation contained almost all the good-

natured widow knew of the fate of her late lodgers
and acquaintances ; but it was enough to determine
Edward, at all hazards, to proceed instantly to Tully-
Veolan, where he concluded he should see, or at
least hear, something of Rose. He therefore left a
letter for Colonel Talbot at the place agreed upon,
signed by his assumed name, and giving for his address the post-town next to the Baron's residence.

From Edinburgh to Perth he took post-horses,
resolving to make the rest of his journey on foot, —
a mode of travelling to which he was partial, and
which had the advantage of permitting a deviation
from the road when he saw parties of military at a
distance. His campaign had considerably strengthened his constitution and improved his habits of
enduring fatigue. His baggage he sent before him
as opportunity occurred.

As he advanced northward, the traces of war
became visible. Broken carriages, dead horses, un-
roofed cottages, trees felled for palisades, and
bridges destroyed, or only partially repaired, — all
indicated the movements of hostile armies. In
those places where the gentry were attached to the
Stewart cause, their houses seemed dismantled or
deserted, the usual course of what may be called
ornamental labour was totally interrupted, and the
inhabitants were seen gliding about with fear, sorrow, and dejection on their faces.

It was evening when he approached the village.
of Tully-Veolan, with feelings and sentiments how
different from those which attended his first entrance ! Then, life was so new to him that a dull
or disagreeable day was one of the greatest misfortunes which his imagination anticipated, and it
seemed to him that his time ought only to be con-

secrated to elegant or amusing study, and relieved by social or youthful frolic. Now, how changed, how saddened, yet how elevated was his character, within the course of a very few months! Danger and misfortune are rapid, though severe, teachers. "A sadder and a wiser man," he felt, in internal confidence and mental dignity, a compensation for the gay dreams which, in his case, experience had so rapidly dissolved.

As he approached the village, he saw, with surprise and anxiety, that a party of soldiers were quartered near it, and, what was worse, that they seemed stationary there. This he conjectured from a few tents which he beheld glimmering upon what was called the Common Moor. To avoid the risk of being stopped and questioned in a place where he was so likely to be recognized, he made a large circuit, altogether avoiding the hamlet, and approaching the upper gate of the avenue by a by-path well known to him. A single glance announced that great changes had taken place. One half of the gate, entirely destroyed and split up for firewood, lay in piles, ready to be taken away; the other swung uselessly about upon its loosened hinges. The battlements above the gate were broken and thrown down, and the carved bears, which were said to have done sentinel's duty upon the top for centuries, now, hurled from their posts, lay among the rubbish. The avenue was cruelly wasted. Several large trees were felled, and left lying across the path; and the cattle of the villagers and the more rude hoofs of dragoon horses had poached into black mud the verdant turf which Waverley had so much admired.

Upon entering the court-yard, Edward saw the fears realized which these circumstances had excited. The place had been sacked by the king's troops, who, in wanton mischief, had even attempted to burn it; and though the thickness of the walls had resisted the fire, unless to a partial extent, the stables and out-houses were totally consumed. The towers and pinnacles of the main building were scorched and blackened, the pavement of the court broken and shattered, the doors torn down entirely, or hanging by a single hinge, the windows dashed in and demolished, and the court strewed with articles of furniture broken into fragments. The accessories of ancient distinction, to which the Baron, in the pride of his heart, had attached so much importance and veneration, were treated with peculiar contumely. The fountain was demolished, and the spring which had supplied it now flooded the courtyard. The stone-basin seemed to be destined for a drinking-trough for cattle, from the manner in which it was arranged upon the ground. The whole tribe of bears, large and small, had experienced as little favour as those at the head of the avenue, and one or two of the family pictures, which seemed to have served as targets for the soldiers, lay on the ground in tatters. With an aching heart, as may well be imagined, Edward viewed this wreck of a mansion so respected. But his anxiety to learn the fate of the proprietors, and his fears as to what that fate might be, increased with every step. When he entered upon the terrace, new scenes of desolation were visible. The balustrade was broken down, the walls destroyed, the borders overgrown with weeds, and the fruit-trees cut down or grubbed up. In one copartment of this old-fashioned garden were two immense horse-chestnut trees, of whose size the Baron was particularly vain: too lazy, perhaps, to cut them down, the spoilers, with malevolent ingenuity, had mined them, and placed a quantity of gunpowder in the cavity. One had been shivered to pieces by the explosion, and the fragments lay scattered around, encumbering the ground it had so long shadowed. The other mine had been more partial in its effect. About one fourth of the trunk of the tree was torn from the mass, which, mutilated and defaced on the one side, still spread on the other its ample and undiminished boughs.[1]

Amid these general marks of ravage there were some which more particularly addressed the feelings of Waverley. Viewing the front of the building thus wasted and defaced, his eyes naturally sought the little balcony which more properly belonged to Rose's apartment, — her *troisième*, or rather *cinquième étage*. It was easily discovered, for beneath it lay the stage-flowers and shrubs with which it was her pride to decorate it, and which had been hurled from the bartizan ; several of her books were mingled with broken flower-pots and other remnants. Among these, Waverley distinguished one of his own, a small copy of Ariosto, and gathered it as a treasure, though wasted by the wind and rain.

While, plunged in the sad reflections which the scene excited, he was looking around for some one who might explain the fate of the inhabitants, he heard a voice from the interior of the building singing, in well-remembered accents, an old Scottish song, —

[1] A pair of chestnut-trees, destroyed, the one entirely, and the other in part, by such a mischievous and wanton act of revenge, grew at Invergarry Castle, the fastness of Mac-Donald of Glengarry.

They came upon us in the night,
And brake my bower and slew my knight;
My servants a' for life did flee,
And left us in extremitie.

They slew my knight, to me sae dear;
They slew my knight, and drave his gear:[1]
The moon may set, the sun may rise,
But a deadly sleep has closed his eyes.

" Alas ! " thought Edward, " is it thou ? Poor,
helpless being, art thou alone left, to gibber and
moan, and fill with thy wild and unconnected
scraps of minstrelsy the halls that protected thee ?
He then called, first low, and then louder, " Davie,
Davie Gellatley ! "

The poor simpleton showed himself from among
the ruins of a sort of greenhouse that once terminated what was called the Terrace-walk, but at
first sight of a stranger retreated, as if in terror.
Waverley, remembering his habits, began to whistle
a tune to which he was partial, which Davie had
expressed great pleasure in listening to, and had
picked up from him by the ear. Our hero's minstrelsy no more equalled that of Blondel, than poor
Davie resembled Cœur-de-Lion ; but the melody
had the same effect, — of producing recognition.
Davie again stole from his lurking-place, but tim-
idly, while Waverley, afraid of frightening him,
stood, making the most encouraging signals he
could devise. " It 's his ghaist," muttered Davie ;
yet, coming nearer, he seemed to acknowledge his
living acquaintance. The poor fool himself appeared the ghost of what he had been. The peculiar dress in which he had been attired in better

---

[1] The first three couplets are from an old ballad called "The
Border Widow's Lament."

days, showed only miserable rags of its whimsical finery, the lack of which was oddly supplied by the remnants of tapestried hangings, window-curtains, and shreds of pictures, with which he had bedizened his tatters. His face, too, had lost its vacant and careless air, and the poor creature looked hollow-eyed, meagre, half-starved, and nervous to a pitiable degree. After long hesitation, he at length approached Waverley with some confidence, stared him sadly in the face, and said: "A' dead and gane, a' dead and gane."

"Who are dead?" said Waverley, forgetting the incapacity of Davie to hold any connected discourse.

"Baron, and Bailie, and Saunders Saunderson, and Lady Rose, that sang sae sweet, — a' dead and gane, — dead and gane;

> But follow, follow me;
> While glow-worms light the lea,
> I'll show ye where the dead should be,
>   Each in his shroud,
>   While winds pipe loud,
>   And the red moon peeps dim through the cloud.
> Follow, follow me;
> Brave should he be
> That treads by night the dead man's lea. "

With these words, chanted in a wild and earnest tone, he made a sign to Waverley to follow him, and walked rapidly towards the bottom of the garden, tracing the bank of the stream, which, it may be remembered, was its eastern boundary. Edward, over whom an involuntary shuddering stole at the import of his words, followed him in some hope of an explanation. As the house was evidently deserted, he could not expect to find among the ruins any more rational informer.

285

Davie, walking very fast, soon reached the extremity of the garden, and scrambled over the ruins of the wall that once had divided it from the wooded glen in which the old Tower of Tully-Veolan was situated. He then jumped down into the bed of the stream, and, followed by Waverley, proceeded at a great pace, climbing over some fragments of rock, and turning with difficulty round others. They passed beneath the ruins of the castle; Waverley followed, keeping up with his guide with difficulty, for the twilight began to fall. Following the descent of the stream a little lower, he totally lost him, but a twinkling light, which he now discovered among the tangled copse-wood and bushes, seemed a surer guide. He soon pursued a very uncouth path, and by its guidance at length reached the door of a wretched hut. A fierce barking of dogs was at first heard, but it stilled at his approach. A voice sounded from within, and he held it most prudent to listen before he advanced.

"Wha hast thou brought here, thou unsonsy villain, thou?" said an old woman, apparently in great indignation.

He heard Davie Gellatley, in answer, whistle a part of the tune by which he had recalled himself to the simpleton's memory, and had now no hesitation to knock at the door. There was a dead silence instantly within, except the deep growling of the dogs, and he next heard the mistress of the hut approach the door, not probably for the sake of undoing a latch, but of fastening a bolt. To prevent this, Waverley lifted the latch himself.

In front was an old, wretched-looking woman, exclaiming, "Wha comes into folk's houses in this gate, at this time o' the night?" On one side, two grim and half-starved deer greyhounds laid aside their ferocity at his appearance, and seemed to recognize him. On the other side, half concealed by the open door, yet apparently seeking that conceal-ment reluctantly, with a cocked pistol in his right hand, and his left in the act of drawing another from his belt, stood a tall, bony, gaunt figure in the remnants of a faded uniform and a beard of three weeks' growth.

It was the Baron of Bradwardine. It is unne-cessary to add that he threw aside his weapon, and greeted Waverley with a hearty embrace.

CHAPTER XXXV

THE Baron's story was short, when divested of the
adages and common-places, Latin, English, and
Scotch, with which his erudition garnished it.   He
insisted much upon his grief at the loss of Edward
and of Glennaquoich, fought the fields of Falkirk
and Culloden, and related how, after all was lost in
the last battle, he had returned home, under the
idea of more easily finding shelter among his own
tenants and on his own estate than elsewhere.   A
party of soldiers had been sent to lay waste his
property, for clemency was not the order of the
day.   Their proceedings, however, were checked by
an order from the civil court.   The estate, it was
found, might not be forfeited to the Crown, to the
prejudice of Malcolm Bradwardine of Inch-Grabbit,
the heir-male, whose claim could not be prejudiced
by the Baron's attainder, as deriving no right
through him, and who, therefore, like other heirs
of entail in the same situation, entered upon possession.   But unlike many in similar circumstances,
the new laird speedily showed that he intended
utterly to exclude his predecessor from all benefit
or advantage in the estate, and that it was his purpose to avail himself of the old Baron's evil fortune
to the full extent.   This was the more ungenerous,
as it was generally known, that, from a romantic

288

idea of not prejudicing this young man's right as heir-male, the Baron had refrained from settling his estate on his daughter.

This selfish injustice was resented by the country people, who were partial to their old master, and irritated against his successor. In the Baron's own words, " The matter did not coincide with the feelings of the commons of Bradwardine, Mr. Waverley ; and the tenants were slack and repugnant in payment of their mails and duties ; and when my kinsman came to the village wi' the new factor, Mr. James Howie, to lift the rents, some wanchancy person — I suspect John Heatherblutter, the auld gamekeeper that was out wi' me in the year Fifteen — fired a shot at him in the gloaming, whereby he was so affrighted that I may say, with Tullius in Catilinam, ' Abiit, evasit, erupit, effugit.' He fled, sir, as one may say, incontinent to Stirling. And now he hath advertised the estate for sale, being himself the last substitute in the entail. And if I were to lament about sic matters, this would grieve me mair than its passing from my immediate possession, whilk, by the course of nature, must have happened in a few years. Whereas now it passes from the lineage that should have possessed it in *sæcula sæculorum*. But God's will be done ; *humana perpessi sumus*. Sir John of Bradwardine, — Black Sir John, as he is called, — who was the common ancestor of our house and the Inch-Grabbits, little thought such a person would have sprung from his loins. Meantime, he has accused me to some of the *primates*, the rulers for the time, as if I were a cutthroat and an abettor of bravoes and assassinates and *coupe-jarrets*. And they have sent soldiers here to abide on the estate, and hunt me like a partridge upon the mountains, as Scripture says of good King David, or like our valiant Sir William Wallace, — not that I bring myself into comparison with either. I thought, when I heard you at the door, they had driven the auld deer to his den at last; and so I e'en proposed to die at bay, like a buck of the first head. But now, Janet, canna ye gie us something for supper?"

"Ou ay, sir; I'll brander the moor-fowl that John Heatherblutter brought in this morning; and ye see puir Davie's roasting the black hen's eggs. I daur say, Mr. Wauverley, ye never kend that a' the eggs that were sae weel roasted at supper in the Ha'-house were aye turned by our Davie? There's no the like o' him ony gate for powtering wi' his fingers amang the het peat-ashes, and roasting eggs." Davie all this while lay with his nose almost in the fire, nuzzling among the ashes, kicking his heels, mumbling to himself, turning the eggs as they lay in the hot embers, as if to confute the proverb that "there goes reason to roasting of eggs," and justify the eulogium which poor Janet poured out upon —

> Him whom she loved, her idiot boy.

"Davie's no sae silly as folk tak him for, Mr. Wauverley; he wadna hae brought you here unless he had kend ye was a friend to his Honour, — indeed, the very dogs kend ye, Mr. Wauverley, for ye was aye kind to beast and body. I can tell you a story o' Davie, wi his Honour's leave. His Honour, ye see, being under hiding in thae sair times, — the mair's the pity, — he lies a' day, and whiles a' night, in the cove in the dern hag; but though

it's a bieldy eneugh bit, and the auld gudeman o'
Corse-Cleugh has panged it wi' a kemple o' strae
amaist, yet when the country's quiet, and the
night very cauld, his Honour whiles creeps doun
here to get a warm at the ingle and a sleep amang
the blankets, and gangs awa in the morning. And
so, ae morning, siccan a fright as I got! Twa unlucky red-coats were up for black-fishing, or some
siccan ploy, — for the neb o' them's never out o'
mischief, — and they just got a glisk o' his Honour
as he gaed into the wood, and banged aff a gun
at him. I out like a gerfalcon, and cried, 'Wad
they shoot an honest woman's poor innocent
bairn?' And I fleyt at them, and threepit it was
my son; and they damned and swuir at me that it
was the auld rebel, as the villains ca'd his Honour;
and Davie was in the wood and heard the tuilzie,
and he, just out o' his ain head, got up the auld
gray mantle that his Honour had flung off him to
gang the faster, and he cam out o' the very same
bit o' the wood, majoring and looking about sae
like his Honour that they were clean beguiled, and
thought they had letten aff their gun at crack-
brained Sawney, as they ca' him; and they gae me
saxpence and twa saumon fish to say naething
about it. Na, na, Davie's no just like other folk,
puir fallow; but he's no sae silly as folk tak him
for. But, to be sure, how can we do eneugh for
his Honour, when we and ours have lived on his
ground this twa hundred years; and when he
keepit my puir Jamie at school and college, and
even at the Ha'-house, till he gaed to a better
place; and when he saved me frae being ta'en to
Perth as a witch — Lord forgi'e them that would
touch sic a puir silly auld body! — and has main-

tained puir Davie at heck and manger maist feck o' his life?"

Waverley at length found an opportunity to interrupt Janet's narrative by an inquiry after Miss Bradwardine.

"She's weel and safe, thank God! at the Duchran," answered the Baron; "the laird's distantly related to us, and more nearly to my chaplain, Mr. Rubrick; and though he be of Whig principles, yet he's not forgetful of auld friendship at this time. The bailie's doing what he can to save something out of the wreck for puir Rose; but I doubt, I doubt, I shall never see her again, for I maun lay my banes in some far country."

"Hout na, your Honour," said old Janet; "ye were just as ill aff in the Feifteen, and got the bonnie baronie back, an' a'. And now the eggs is ready, and the muir-cock's brandered, and there's ilk ane a trencher and some saut, and the heel o' the white loaf that cam frae the bailie's; and there's plenty o' brandy in the graybeard that Luckie Maclearie sent doun; and winna ye be suppered like princes?"

"I wish one prince, at least, of our acquaintance, may be no worse off," said the Baron to Waverley, who joined him in cordial hopes for the safety of the unfortunate Chevalier.

They then began to talk of their future prospects. The Baron's plan was very simple. It was to escape to France, where, by the interest of his old friends, he hoped to get some military employment, of which he still conceived himself capable. He invited Waverley to go with him, — a proposal in which he acquiesced, providing the interest of Colonel Talbot should fail in procuring his pardon.

Tacitly he hoped the Baron would sanction his addresses to Rose, and give him a right to assist him in his exile; but he forbore to speak on this subject until his own fate should be decided. They then talked of Glennaquoich, for whom the Baron expressed great anxiety, although, he observed, he was " the very Achilles of Horatius Flaccus, —

> Impiger, iracundus, inexorabilis, acer.

Which," he continued, " has been thus rendered (vernacularly) by Struan Robertson, —

> A fiery etter-cap, a fractious chiel,
> As het as ginger and as stieve as steel. "

Flora had a large and unqualified share of the good old man's sympathy.

It was now wearing late. Old Janet got into some kind of kennel behind the hallan; Davie had been long asleep, and snoring between Ban and Buscar. These dogs had followed him to the hut after the mansion-house was deserted, and there constantly resided; and their ferocity, with the old woman's reputation of being a witch, contributed a good deal to keep visitors from the glen. With this view, Bailie Macwheeble provided Janet underhand with meal for their maintenance, and also with little articles of luxury for his patron's use, in supplying which much precaution was necessarily used. After some compliments, the Baron occupied his usual couch, and Waverley reclined in an easy-chair of tattered velvet, which had once garnished the state bed-room of Tully-Veolan, — for the furniture of this mansion was now scattered through all the cottages in the vicinity, — and went to sleep as comfortably as if he had been in a bed of down.

293

CHAPTER XXXVI

WITH the first dawn of day old Janet was scuttling about the house to wake the Baron, who usually slept sound and heavily.

"I must go back," he said to Waverley, " to my cove ; will you walk down the glen wi' me ? "

They went out together, and followed a narrow and entangled foot-path which the occasional passage of anglers or wood-cutters had traced by the side of the stream. On their way the Baron explained to Waverley that he would be under no danger in remaining a day or two at Tully-Veolan, and even in being seen walking about, if he used the precaution of pretending that he was looking at the estate as agent or surveyor for an English gentleman who designed to be purchaser. With this view, he recommended to him to visit the bailie, who still lived at the factor's house, called Little Veolan, about a mile from the village, though he was to remove at next term. Stanley's passport would be an answer to the officer who commanded the military ; and as to any of the country people who might recognize Waverley, the Baron assured him he was in no danger of being betrayed by them.

294

" I believe," said the old man, " half the people of the barony know that their poor auld laird is somewhere hereabout; for I see they do not suffer a single bairn to come here a bird-nesting, — a practice whilk, when I was in full possession of my power as baron, I was unable totally to inhibit. Nay, I often find bits of things in my way that the poor bodies, God help them! leave there because they think they may be useful to me. I hope they will get a wiser master and as kind a one as I was."

A natural sigh closed the sentence ; but the quiet equanimity with which the Baron endured his misfortunes had something in it venerable and even sublime. There was no fruitless repining, no turbid melancholy ; he bore his lot, and the hardships which it involved, with a good-humoured, though serious composure, and used no violent language against the prevailing party.

" I did what I thought my duty," said the good old man, " and questionless they are doing what they think theirs. It grieves me sometimes to look upon these blackened walls of the house of my ancestors ; but doubtless officers cannot always keep the soldier's hand from depredation and spuilzie ; and Gustavus Adolphus himself, as ye may read in ' Colonel Munro his Expedition with the worthy Scotch Regiment called Mackay's regiment,' did often permit it. Indeed, I have myself seen as sad sights as Tully-Veolan now is, when I served with the Maréchal Duke of Berwick. To be sure, we may say, with Virgilius Maro, ' Fuimus Troes,' — and there 's the end of an auld sang. But houses and families and men have a' stood lang eneugh when they have stood till they fall with honour ; and now I hae gotten a house that is not unlike a

295

domus ultima," — they were now standing below a steep rock. " We poor Jacobites," continued the Baron, looking up, " are now like the coneys in Holy Scripture (which the great traveller Pococke called Jerboa), — a feeble people, that make our abode in the rocks. So fare you well, my good lad, till we meet at Janet's in the even ; for I must get into my Patmos, — which is no easy matter for my auld stiff limbs."

With that he began to ascend the rock, striding, with the help of his hands, from one precarious footstep to another, till he got about half way up, where two or three bushes concealed the mouth of a hole, resembling an oven, into which the Baron insinuated, first his head and shoulders, and then, by slow gradation, the rest of his long body; his legs and feet finally disappearing, coiled up like a huge snake entering his retreat, or a long pedigree introduced with care and difficulty into the narrow pigeon-hole of an old cabinet. Waverley had the curiosity to clamber up and look in upon him in his den, as the lurking-place might well be termed. Upon the whole, he looked not unlike that ingenious puzzle called " a reel in a bottle," the marvel of children (and of some grown people too, myself for one), who can neither comprehend the mystery how it has got in, nor how it is to be taken out. The cave was very narrow, — too low in the roof to admit of his standing, or almost of his sitting up, though he made some awkward attempts at the latter posture. His sole amusement was the perusal of his old friend Titus Livius, varied by occasionally scratching Latin proverbs and texts of Scripture with his knife on the roof and walls of his fortalice, which were of sandstone. As the cave was dry, and filled with clean straw and withered fern, "it made," as he said, coiling himself up with an air of snugness and comfort which contrasted strangely with his situation, "unless when the wind was due north, a very passable *gîte* for an old soldier." Neither, as he observed, was he without sentries for the purpose of reconnoitring. Davie and his mother were constantly on the watch to discover and avert danger; and it was singular what instances of address seemed dictated by the instinctive attachment of the poor simpleton when his patron's safety was concerned.

With Janet, Edward now sought an interview. He had recognized her at first sight as the old woman who had nursed him during his sickness after his delivery from Gifted Gilfillan. The hut also, though a little repaired, and somewhat better furnished, was certainly the place of his confinement; and he now recollected on the common moor of Tully-Veolan the trunk of a large decayed tree, called the "trysting-tree," which he had no doubt was the same at which the Highlanders rendezvoused on that memorable night. All this he had combined in his imagination the night before; but reasons, which may probably occur to the reader, prevented him from catechising Janet in the presence of the Baron.

He now commenced the task in good earnest; and the first question was, Who was the young lady that visited the hut during his illness? Janet paused for a little; and then observed, that to keep the secret now would neither do good nor ill to anybody.

"It was just a leddy that hasna her equal in the world,— Miss Rose Bradwardine!"

"Then Miss Rose was probably also the author of my deliverance," inferred Waverley, delighted at the confirmation of an idea which local circumstances had already induced him to entertain.

"I wot weel, Mr. Wauverley, and that was she e'en; but sair, sair angry and affronted wad she hae been, puir thing, if she had thought ye had been ever to ken a word about the matter; for she gar'd me speak aye Gaelic when ye was in hearing, to mak ye trow we were in the Hielands. I can speak it weil eneugh, for my mother was a Hieland woman."

A few more questions now brought out the whole mystery respecting Waverley's deliverance from the bondage in which he left Cairnvreckan. Never did music sound sweeter to an amateur than the drowsy tautology with which old Janet detailed every circumstance, thrilled upon the ears of Waverley. But my reader is not a lover, and I must spare his patience by attempting to condense within reasonable compass the narrative which old Janet spread through a harangue of nearly two hours.

When Waverley communicated to Fergus the letter he had received from Rose Bradwardine, by Davie Gellatley, giving an account of Tully-Veolan being occupied by a small party of soldiers, that circumstance had struck upon the busy and active mind of the chieftain. Eager to distress and narrow the posts of the enemy, desirous to prevent their establishing a garrison so near him, and willing also to oblige the Baron, — for he often had the idea of marriage with Rose floating through his brain, — he resolved to send some of his people to drive out the red-coats and to bring Rose to Glennaquoich. But just as he had ordered Evan, with a small party, on this duty, the news of Cope's having marched into the Highlands to meet and disperse the forces of the Chevalier ere they came to a head, obliged him to join the standard with his whole forces.

He sent to order Donald Bean to attend him; but that cautious freebooter, who well understood the value of a separate command, instead of joining, sent various apologies which the pressure of the times compelled Fergus to admit as current, though not without the internal resolution of being revenged on him for his procrastination, time and place convenient. However, as he could not amend the matter, he issued orders to Donald to descend into the Low Country, drive the soldiers from Tully-Veolan, and, paying all respect to the mansion of the Baron, to take his abode somewhere near it, for protection of his daughter and family, and to harass and drive away any of the armed volunteers or small parties of military which he might find moving about the vicinity.

As this charge formed a sort of roving commission, which Donald proposed to interpret in the way most advantageous to himself, as he was relieved from the immediate terrors of Fergus, and as he had, from former secret services, some interest in the councils of the Chevalier, he resolved to make hay while the sun shone. He achieved without difficulty the task of driving the soldiers from Tully-Veolan; but although he did not venture to encroach upon the interior of the family, or to disturb Miss Rose, being unwilling to make himself a powerful enemy in the Chevalier's army,—

For well he knew the Baron's wrath was deadly,—

yet he set about to raise contributions and exactions upon the tenantry, and otherwise to turn the war to his own advantage. Meanwhile he mounted the white cockade, and waited upon Rose with a pretext of great devotion for the service in which her father was engaged, and many apologies for the freedom he must necessarily use for the support of his people. It was at this moment that Rose learned, by open-mouthed fame, with all sorts of exaggeration, that Waverley had killed the smith at Cairnvreckan in an attempt to arrest him, had been cast into a dungeon by Major Melville of Cairnvreckan, and was to be executed by martial law within three days. In the agony which these tidings excited, she proposed to Donald Bean the rescue of the prisoner. It was the very sort of service which he was desirous to undertake, judging it might constitute a merit of such a nature as would make amends for any peccadilloes which he might be guilty of in the country. He had the art, however, pleading all the while duty and discipline, to hold off, until poor Rose, in the extremity of her distress, offered to bribe him to the enterprise with some valuable jewels which had been her mother's.

Donald Bean, who had served in France, knew, and perhaps over-estimated, the value of these trinkets. But he also perceived Rose's apprehensions of its being discovered that she had parted with her jewels for Waverley's liberation. Resolved this scruple should not part him and the treasure, he voluntarily offered to take an oath that he would never mention Miss Rose's share in the transaction; and foreseeing convenience in keeping the oath, and no probable advantage in breaking it, he took the engagement — in order, as he told his lieutenant, to deal handsomely by the young lady — in the only mode and form which, by a mental paction with himself, he considered as binding, — he swore secrecy upon his drawn dirk. He was the more especially moved to this act of good faith by some attentions that Miss Bradwardine showed to his daughter Alice, which, while they gained the heart of the mountain damsel, highly gratified the pride of her father. Alice, who could now speak a little English, was very communicative in return for Rose's kindness, readily confided to her the whole papers respecting the intrigue with Gardiner's regiment, of which she was the depositary, and as readily undertook, at her instance, to restore them to Waverley without her father's knowledge. "For they may oblige the bonnie young lady and the handsome young gentleman," said Alice, "and what use has my father for a whin bits o' scarted paper?"

The reader is aware that she took an opportunity of executing this purpose on the eve of Waverley's leaving the glen.

How Donald executed his enterprise, the reader is aware. But the expulsion of the military from Tully-Veolan had given alarm, and while he was lying in wait for Gilfillan, a strong party, such as Donald did not care to face, was sent to drive back the insurgents in their turn, to encamp there, and to protect the country. The officer, a gentleman and a disciplinarian, neither intruded himself on Miss Bradwardine, whose unprotected situation he respected, nor permitted his soldiers to commit any breach of discipline. He formed a little camp upon an eminence near the house of Tully-Veolan, and placed proper guards at the passes in the vicinity.

This unwelcome news reached Donald Bean Lean as he was returning to Tully-Veolan. Determined, however, to obtain the guerdon of his labour, he resolved, since approach to Tully-Veolan was impossible, to deposit his prisoner in Janet's cottage, — a place, the very existence of which could hardly have been suspected even by those who had long lived in the vicinity, unless they had been guided thither, and which was utterly unknown to Waverley himself. This effected, he claimed and received his reward. Waverley's illness was an event which deranged all their calculations. Donald was obliged to leave the neighbourhood with his people, and to seek more free course for his adventures elsewhere. At Rose's earnest entreaty, he left an old man, an herbalist, who was supposed to understand a little of medicine, to attend Waverley during his illness.

In the meanwhile, new and fearful doubts started in Rose's mind. They were suggested by old Janet, who insisted that, a reward having been offered for the apprehension of Waverley, and his own personal effects being so valuable, there was no saying to what breach of faith Donald might be tempted. In an agony of grief and terror, Rose took the daring resolution of explaining to the prince himself the danger in which Mr. Waverley stood, judging that, both as a politician and a man of honour and humanity, Charles Edward would interest himself to prevent his falling into the hands of the opposite party. This letter she at first thought of sending anonymously, but naturally feared it would not, in that case, be credited. She therefore subscribed her name, though with reluctance and terror, and consigned it in charge to a young man, who, at leaving his farm to join the Chevalier's army, made

302

it his petition to her to have some sort of credentials to the adventurer, from whom he hoped to obtain a commission.

The letter reached Charles Edward on his descent to the Lowlands, and aware of the political importance of having it supposed that he was in correspondence with the English Jacobites, he caused the most positive orders to be transmitted to Donald Bean Lean, to transmit Waverley, safe and uninjured, in person or effects, to the governor of Doune Castle. The freebooter durst not disobey, for the army of the prince was now so near him that punishment might have followed; besides, he was a politician as well as a robber, and was unwilling to cancel the interest created through former secret services, by being refractory on this occasion. He therefore made a virtue of necessity, and transmitted orders to his lieutenant to convey Edward to Doune, which was safely accomplished in the mode mentioned in a former chapter. The governor of Doune was directed to send him to Edinburgh as a prisoner, because the prince was apprehensive that Waverley, if set at liberty, might have resumed his purpose of returning to England without affording him an opportunity of a personal interview. In this, indeed, he acted by the advice of the chieftain of Glennaquoich, with whom it may be remembered the Chevalier communicated upon the mode of disposing of Edward, though without telling him how he came to learn the place of his confinement.

This, indeed, Charles Edward considered as a lady's secret; for although Rose's letter was couched in the most cautious and general terms, and professed to be written merely from motives of humanity, and zeal for the prince's service, yet she expressed so anxious a wish that she should not be known to have interfered that the Chevalier was induced to suspect the deep interest which she took in Waverley's safety. This conjecture, which was well founded, led, however, to false inferences; for the emotion which Edward displayed on approaching Flora and Rose at the ball of Holyrood, was placed by the Chevalier to the account of the latter, and he concluded that the Baron's views about the settlement of his property, or some such obstacle, thwarted their mutual inclinations. Common fame, it is true, frequently gave Waverley to Miss Mac-Ivor; but the prince knew that common fame is very prodigal in such gifts; and watching attentively the behaviour of the ladies towards Waverley, he had no doubt that the young Englishman had no interest with Flora, and was beloved by Rose Bradwardine. Desirous to bind Waverley to his service, and wishing also to do a kind and friendly action, the prince next assailed the Baron on the subject of settling his estate upon his daughter. Mr. Bradwardine acquiesced; but the consequence was, that Fergus was immediately induced to prefer his double suit for a wife and an earldom, which the prince rejected in the manner we have seen. The Chevalier, constantly engaged in his own multiplied affairs, had not hitherto sought any explanation with Waverley, though often meaning to do so. But after Fergus's declaration, he saw the necessity of appearing neutral between the rivals, devoutly hoping that the matter, which now seemed fraught with the seeds of strife, might be permitted to lie over till the termination of the expedition. When on the march to Derby, Fergus, being questioned concerning his quarrel with Waverley, alleged as the cause that Edward was desirous of retracting the suit he had made to his sister, the Chevalier

304

plainly told him that he had himself observed Miss Mac-Ivor's behaviour to Waverley, and that he was convinced Fergus was under the influence of a mistake in judging of Waverley's conduct, who, he had every reason to believe, was engaged to Miss Bradwardine. The quarrel which ensued between Edward and the chieftain is, I hope, still in the remembrance of the reader. These circumstances will serve to explain such points of our narrative as, according to the custom of story-tellers, we deemed it fit to leave unexplained, for the purpose of exciting the reader's curiosity.

When Janet had once finished the leading facts of this narrative, Waverley was easily enabled to apply the clew which they afforded, to other mazes of the labyrinth in which he had been engaged. To Rose Bradwardine, then, he owed the life which he now thought he could willingly have laid down to serve her. A little reflection convinced him, however, that to live for her sake was more convenient and agreeable, and that, being possessed of independence, she might share it with him either in foreign countries or in his own. The pleasure of being allied to a man of the Baron's high worth, and who was so much valued by his uncle Sir Everard, was also an agreeable consideration, had anything been wanting to recommend the match. His absurdities, which had appeared grotesquely ludicrous during his prosperity, seemed, in the sunset of his fortune, to be harmonized and assimilated with the noble features of his character, so as to add peculiarity without exciting ridicule. His mind occupied with such projects of future happiness, Edward sought Little Veolan, the habitation of Mr. Duncan Macwheeble.

CHAPTER XXXVII

Now is Cupid a child of conscience, — he makes restitution.
                                        SHAKSPEARE.

MR. DUNCAN MACWHEEBLE, no longer commissary
or bailie, though still enjoying the empty name of
the latter dignity, had escaped proscription by an
early secession from the insurgent party, and by
his insignificance.

Edward found him in his office, immersed among
papers and accounts. Before him was a large bicker
of oatmeal-porridge, and at the side thereof a horn-
spoon and a bottle of twopenny. Eagerly running
his eye over a voluminous law-paper, he from time
to time shovelled an immense spoonful of these
nutritive viands into his capacious mouth. A pot-
bellied Dutch bottle of brandy which stood by, intimated either that this honest limb of the law had
taken his "morning" already, or that he meant to
season his porridge with such digestive; or perhaps
both circumstances might reasonably be inferred.
His nightcap and morning-gown had whilome been
of tartan; but, equally cautious and frugal, the
honest bailie had got them dyed black, lest their
original ill-omened colour might remind his visitors
of his unlucky excursion to Derby. To sum up the
picture, his face was daubed with snuff up to the
eyes, and his fingers with ink up to the knuckles.
He looked dubiously at Waverley as he approached

the little green rail which fenced his desk and stool from the approach of the vulgar. Nothing could give the bailie more annoyance than the idea of his acquaintance being claimed by any of the unfortunate gentlemen who were now so much more likely to need assistance than to afford profit. But this was the rich young Englishman : who knew what might be his situation? He was the Baron's friend, too : what was to be done?

While these reflections gave an air of absurd perplexity to the poor man's visage, Waverley, reflecting on the communication he was about to make to him, of a nature so ridiculously contrasted with the appearance of the individual, could not help bursting out a-laughing as he checked the propensity to exclaim, with Syphax, —

> Cato 's a proper person to intrust
> A love-tale with !

As Mr. Macwheeble had no idea of any person laughing heartily, who was either encircled by peril or oppressed by poverty, the hilarity of Edward's countenance greatly relieved the embarrassment of his own, and, giving him a tolerably hearty welcome to Little Veolan, he asked what he would choose for breakfast. His visitor had, in the first place, something for his private ear, and begged leave to bolt the door. Duncan by no means liked this precaution, which savoured of danger to be apprehended ; but he could not now draw back.

Convinced he might trust this man, as he could make it his interest to be faithful, Edward communicated his present situation and future schemes to Macwheeble. The wily agent listened with apprehension when he found Waverley was still in a

state of proscription, was somewhat comforted by
learning that he had a passport, rubbed his hands
with glee when he mentioned the amount of his
present fortune, opened huge eyes when he heard
the brilliancy of his future expectations; but when
he expressed his intention to share them with Miss
Rose Bradwardine, ecstasy had almost deprived the
honest man of his senses. The bailie started from
his three-footed stool like the Pythoness from her
tripod, flung his best wig out of the window, because the block on which it was placed stood in the
way of his career, chucked his cap to the ceiling,
caught it as it fell, whistled "Tullochgorum," danced
a Highland fling with inimitable grace and agility,
and then threw himself, exhausted, into a chair,
exclaiming, "Lady Wauverley! ten thousand a-
year, the least penny! Lord preserve my poor
understanding!"

"Amen with all my heart," said Waverley; "but
now, Mr. Macwheeble, let us proceed to business."
This word had somewhat a sedative effect, but the
bailie's head, as he expressed himself, was still "in
the bees." He mended his pen, however, marked
half-a-dozen sheets of paper with an ample marginal
fold, whipped down "Dallas of St. Martin's Styles"
from a shelf, where that venerable work roosted
with Stair's "Institutions," Dirleton's "Doubts,"
Balfour's "Practiques," and a parcel of old account-
books, opened the volume at the article "Contract
of Marriage," and prepared to make what he called
a "sma' minute, to prevent parties frae resiling."

With some difficulty, Waverley made him comprehend that he was going a little too fast. He
explained to him that he should want his assistance, in the first place, to make his residence safe

for the time, by writing to the officer at Tully-Veolan that Mr. Stanley, an English gentleman nearly
related to Colonel Talbot, was upon a visit of business at Mr. Macwheeble's, and knowing the state of
the country, had sent his passport for Captain
Foster's inspection. This produced a polite answer
from the officer, with an invitation to Mr. Stanley
to dine with him, which was declined, as may easily
be supposed, under pretence of business.

Waverley's next request was that Mr. Macwheeble would despatch a man and horse to ——, the
post-town at which Colonel Talbot was to address
him, with directions to wait there until the post
should bring a letter for Mr. Stanley, and then to
forward it to Little Veolan with all speed. In a
moment the bailie was in search of his apprentice
(or servitor, as he was called Sixty Years since),
Jock Scriever, and in not much greater space of
time, Jock was on the back of the white pony.

"Tak care ye guide him weel, sir, for he's aye
been short in the wind since — ahem; Lord be
gude to me! [in a low voice] I was gaun to come
out wi' — since I rode whip and spur to fetch the
Chevalier to redd Mr. Wauverley and Vich Ian
Vohr; and an uncanny coup I gat for my pains,
Lord forgie your honour, — I might hae broken
my neck. But troth it was in a venture, mae ways
nor ane; but this maks amends for a'. Lady Wauverley! ten thousand a-year! Lord be gude unto
me!"

"But you forget, Mr. Macwheeble, we want the
Baron's consent; the lady's — "

"Never fear, I 'se be caution for them; I 'se gie
you my personal warrandice. Ten thousand a-year!
It dings Balmawhapple out and out, — a year's rent 's

worth a' Balmawhapple, fee and life-rent! Lord make us thankful!"

To turn the current of his feelings, Edward inquired if he had heard anything lately of the Chieftain of Glennaquoich?

"Not one word," answered Macwheeble, "but that he was still in Carlisle Castle, and was soon to be panelled for his life. I dinna wish the young gentleman ill," he said, "but I hope that they that hae got him will keep him, and no let him back to this Hieland border to plague us wi' blackmail and a' manner o' violent, wrongous, and masterfu' oppression and spoliation, both by himself and others of his causing, sending, and hounding out; and he couldna tak care o' the siller when he had gotten it neither, but flang it a' into yon idle quean's lap at Edinburgh. But light come, light gane. For my part, I never wish to see a kilt in the country again, nor a red-coat, nor a gun, for that matter, unless it were to shoot a paitrick, — they're a' tarred wi' ae stick. And when they have done ye wrang, even when ye hae gotten decreet of spuilzie, oppression, and violent profits against them, what better are ye? They hae na a plack to pay ye; ye need never extract it."

With such discourse, and the intervening topics of business, the time passed until dinner, Macwheeble meanwhile promising to devise some mode of introducing Edward at the Duchran, where Rose at present resided, without risk of danger or suspicion, — which seemed no very easy task, since the laird was a very zealous friend to government. The poultry-yard had been laid under requisition, and cockyleeky and Scotch collops soon reeked in the bailie's little parlour. The landlord's corkscrew

was just introduced into the muzzle of a pint-bottle
of claret (cribbed possibly from the cellars of Tully-
Veolan), when the sight of the gray pony, passing
the window at full trot, induced the bailie, but with
due precaution, to place it aside for the moment.
Enter Jock Scriever with a packet for Mr. Stanley:
it is Colonel Talbot's seal, and Edward's fingers
tremble as he undoes it. Two official papers,
folded, signed, and sealed in all formality, drop out.
They were hastily picked up by the bailie, who
had a natural respect for everything resembling a
deed, and, glancing slyly on their titles, his eyes,
or rather spectacles, are greeted with "Protection
by his Royal Highness to the person of Cosmo
Comyne Bradwardine, Esq., of that ilk, commonly
called Baron of Bradwardine, forfeited for his accession to the late rebellion." The other proves to
be a protection of the same tenor in favour of
Edward Waverley, Esq. Colonel Talbot's letter
was in these words :—

"MY DEAR EDWARD,—I am just arrived here, and
yet I have finished my business; it has cost me some
trouble though, as you shall hear. I waited upon
his Royal Highness immediately on my arrival, and
found him in no very good humour for my purpose.
Three or four Scotch gentlemen were just leaving
his levee. After he had expressed himself to me very
courteously, 'Would you think it,' he said, 'Talbot?
here have been half-a-dozen of the most respectable
gentlemen, and best friends to government north of
the Forth, Major Melville of Cairnvreckan, Rubrick
of Duchran, and others, who have fairly wrung from
me, by their downright importunity, a present protection and the promise of a future pardon for that
stubborn old rebel whom they call Baron of Brad-

wardine. They allege that his high personal character, and the clemency which he showed to such of our
people as fell into the rebels' hands, should weigh
in his favour, especially as the loss of his estate
is likely to be a severe enough punishment. Rubrick
has undertaken to keep him at his own house till
things are settled in the country; but it's a little
hard to be forced in a manner to pardon such a mortal
enemy to the house of Brunswick.' This was no
favourable moment for opening my business; however, I said I was rejoiced to learn that his Royal
Highness was in the course of granting such requests,
as it emboldened me to present one of the like nature
in my own name. He was very angry, but I persisted;
I mentioned the uniform support of our three votes in
the House, touched modestly on services abroad, though
valuable only in his Royal Highness's having been
pleased kindly to accept them, and founded pretty
strongly on his own expressions of friendship and
good-will. He was embarrassed, but obstinate. I
hinted the policy of detaching, on all future occasions,
the heir of such a fortune as your uncle's from the
machinations of the disaffected. But I made no impression. I mentioned the obligations which I lay
under to Sir Everard and to you personally, and
claimed, as the sole reward of my services, that he
would be pleased to afford me the means of evincing
my gratitude. I perceived that he still meditated a
refusal, and taking my commission from my pocket, I
said (as a last resource) that as his Royal Highness
did not, under these pressing circumstances, think me
worthy of a favour which he had not scrupled to grant
to other gentlemen whose services I could hardly judge
more important than my own, I must beg leave to deposit, with all humility, my commission in his Royal
Highness's hands, and to retire from the service. He
was not prepared for this; he told me to take up my
commission, said some handsome things of my services,

312

and granted my request. You are therefore once more a free man, and I have promised for you that you will be a good boy in future, and remember what you owe to the lenity of government. Thus you see *my* prince can be as generous as *yours*. I do not pretend, indeed, that he confers a favour with all the foreign graces and compliments of your Chevalier errant; but he has a plain English manner, and the evident reluctance with which he grants your request, indicates the sacrifice which he makes of his own inclination to your wishes. My friend the adjutant-general has procured me a duplicate of the Baron's protection (the original being in Major Melville's possession), which I send to you, as I know that if you can find him you will have pleasure in being the first to communicate the joyful intelligence. He will of course repair to the Duchran without loss of time, there to ride quarantine for a few weeks. As for you, I give you leave to escort him thither, and to stay a week there, as I understand a certain fair lady is in that quarter. And I have the pleasure to tell you that whatever progress you can make in her good graces will be highly agreeable to Sir Everard and Mrs. Rachel, who will never believe your views and prospects settled, and the three ermines passant in actual safety, until you present them with a Mrs. Edward Waverley. Now, certain love-affairs of my own — a good many years since — interrupted some measures which were then proposed in favour of the three ermines passant, so I am bound in honour to make them amends. Therefore make good use of your time, for when your week is expired it will be necessary that you go to London to plead your pardon in the law courts.

Ever, dear Waverley, yours most truly,

"Philip Talbot.'

CHAPTER XXXVIII

Happy 's the wooing
That 's not long a-doing.

WHEN the first rapturous sensation occasioned by
these excellent tidings had somewhat subsided,
Edward proposed instantly to go down to the glen
to acquaint the Baron with their import. But the
cautious bailie justly observed that if the Baron
were to appear instantly in public, the tenantry and
villagers might become riotous in expressing their
joy, and give offence to "the powers that be," — a
sort of persons for whom the bailie always had
unlimited respect. He therefore proposed that Mr.
Waverley should go to Janet Géllatley's and bring
the Baron up under cloud of night to Little Veolan,
where he might once more enjoy the luxury of a
good bed. In the meanwhile, he said, he himself
would go to Captain Foster and show him the
Baron's protection, and obtain his countenance for
harbouring him that night, and he would have
horses ready on the morrow to set him on his way
to the Duchran along with Mr. Stanley, "whilk
denomination, I apprehend, your Honour will for
the present retain," said the bailie.

"Certainly, Mr. Macwheeble ; but will you not
go down to the glen yourself in the evening to meet
your patron ? "

"That I wad wi' a' my heart; and mickle obliged to your Honour for putting me in mind o' my bounden duty. But it will be past sunset afore I get back frae the captain's, and at these unsonsy hours the glen has a bad name, — there's something no that canny about auld Janet Gellatley. The laird he'll no believe thae things; but he was aye ower rash and venturesome, and feared neither man nor deevil, — and sae's seen o't. But right sure am I Sir George Mackenyie says that no divine can doubt there are witches, since the Bible says thou shalt not suffer them to live, and that no lawyer in Scotland can doubt it, since it is punishable with death by our law. So there's baith law and gospel for it. An his honour winna believe the Leviticus, he might aye believe the Statute-book. But he may tak his ain way o't; it's a' ane to Duncan Macwheeble. However, I shall send to ask up auld Janet this e'en; it's best no to lightly them that have that character, — and we'll want Davie to turn the spit, for I'll gar Eppie put down a fat goose to the fire for your honours to your supper."

When it was near sunset, Waverley hastened to the hut; and he could not but allow that superstition had chosen no improper locality or unfit object for the foundation of her fantastic terrors. It resembled exactly the description of Spenser, —

There, in a gloomy hollow glen, she found
A little cottage, built of sticks and reeds,
In homely wise, and wall'd with sods around,
In which a witch did dwell in loathly weeds
And wilful want, all careless of her needs ;
So choosing solitary to abide
Far from all neighbours, that her devilish deeds
And hellish arts from people she might hide,
And hurt far off, unknown, whomsoever she espied.

315

He entered the cottage with these verses in his memory. Poor old Janet, bent double with age and bleared with peat-smoke, was tottering about the hut with a birch-broom, muttering to herself as she endeavoured to make her hearth and floor a little clean for the reception of her expected guests. Waverley's step made her start, look up, and fall a-trembling, so much had her nerves been on the rack for her patron's safety. With difficulty Waverly made her comprehend that the Baron was now safe from personal danger; and when her mind had admitted that joyful news, it was equally hard to make her believe that he was not to enter again upon possession of his estate. "It behoved to be," she said, "he wad get it back again; naebody wad be sae gripple as to tak his gear after they had gi'en him a pardon. And for that Inch-Grabbit, I could whiles wish mysell a witch for his sake, if I werena feared the Enemy wad tak me at my word." Waverley then gave her some money, and promised that her fidelity should be rewarded. "How can I be rewarded, sir, sae weel as just to see my auld maister and Miss Rose come back and bruik their ain?"

Waverley now took leave of Janet, and soon stood beneath the Baron's Patmos. At a low whistle he observed the veteran peeping out to reconnoitre, like an old badger with his head out of his hole. "Ye hae come rather early, my good lad," said he, descending; "I question if the red-coats hae beat the tattoo yet, and we're not safe till then."

"Good news cannot be told too soon," said Waverley, and with infinite joy communicated to him the happy tidings. The old man stood for a moment in silent devotion, then exclaimed, "Praise be to God! I shall see my bairn again."

"And never, I hope, to part with her more," said Waverley.

"I trust in God not, unless it be to win the means of supporting her; for my things are but in a bruckle state. But what signifies warld's gear?"

"And if," said Waverley, modestly, "there were a situation in life which would put Miss Bradwardine beyond the uncertainty of fortune, and in the rank to which she was born, would you object to it, my dear Baron, because it would make one of your friends the happiest man in the world?" The Baron turned, and looked at him with great earnestness. "Yes," continued Edward, "I shall not consider my sentence of banishment as repealed unless you will give me permission to accompany you to the Duchran, and — "

The Baron seemed collecting all his dignity to make a suitable reply to what, at another time, he would have treated as the propounding a treaty of alliance between the houses of Bradwardine and Waverley. But his efforts were in vain: the father was too mighty for the Baron; the pride of birth and rank was swept away. In the joyful surprise, a slight convulsion passed rapidly over his features as he gave way to the feelings of nature, threw his arms around Waverley's neck, and sobbed out, "My son, my son! if I had been to search the world, I would have made my choice here." Edward returned the embrace with great sympathy of feeling, and for a little while they both kept silence. At length it was broken by Edward. "But Miss Bradwardine?"

"She had never a will but her old father's, — besides, you are a likely youth, of honest principles and high birth. No, she never had any other will

317

than mine, and in my proudest days I could not have wished a mair eligible espousal for her than the nephew of my excellent old friend Sir Everard. But I hope, young man, ye deal na rashly in this matter ? I hope ye hae secured the approbation of your ain friends and allies, particularly of your uncle, who is *in loco parentis?* Ah, we maun tak heed o' that." Edward assured him that Sir Everard would think himself highly honoured in the flattering reception his proposal had met with, and that it had his entire approbation, in evidence of which he put Colonel Talbot's letter into the Baron's hand. The Baron read it with great attention. "Sir Everard," he said, "always despised wealth in comparison of honour and birth ; and indeed he hath no occasion to court the *Diva Pecunia*. Yet I now wish, since this Malcolm turns out such a parricide, — for I can call him no better, as to think of alienating the family inheritance, — I now wish," his eyes fixed on a part of the roof which was visible above the trees, " that I could have left Rose the auld hurley-house, and the riggs belanging to it. And yet," said he, resuming more cheerfully, " it 's maybe as weel as it is ; for as Baron of Bradwardine I might have thought it my duty to insist upon certain compliances respecting name and bearings whilk now, as a landless laird wi' a tocherless daughter, no one can blame me for departing from."

"Now, Heaven be praised," thought Edward, "that Sir Everard does not hear these scruples ! The three ermines passant and rampant bear would certainly have gone together by the ears." He then, with all the ardour of a young lover, assured the Baron, that he sought for his happiness only in

Rose's heart and hand, and thought himself as happy in her father's simple approbation as if he had settled an earldom upon his daughter.

They now reached Little Veolan. The goose was smoking on the table, and the bailie brandished his knife and fork. A joyous greeting took place between him and his patron. The kitchen, too, had its company. Auld Janet was established at the ingle-nook; Davie had turned the spit to his immortal honour; and even Ban and Buscar, in the liberality of Macwheeble's joy, had been stuffed to the throat with food, and now lay snoring on the floor.

The next day conducted the Baron and his young friend to the Duchran, where the former was expected, in consequence of the success of the nearly unanimous application of the Scottish friends of government in his favour. This had been so general and so powerful that it was almost thought his estate might have been saved, had it not passed into the rapacious hands of his unworthy kinsman, whose right, arising out of the Baron's attainder, could not be affected by a pardon from the Crown. The old gentleman, however, said, with his usual spirit, he was more gratified by the hold he possessed in the good opinion of his neighbours than he would have been in being "rehabilitated and restored *in integrum*, had it been found practicable."

We shall not attempt to describe the meeting of the father and daughter, — loving each other so affectionately, and separated under such perilous circumstances. Still less shall we attempt to analyze the deep blush of Rose, at receiving the compliments of Waverley, or stop to inquire whether she had any curiosity respecting the particular

319

cause of his journey to Scotland at that period.
We shall not even trouble the reader with the hum-
drum details of a courtship Sixty Years since. It
is enough to say that, under so strict a martinet as
the Baron, all things were conducted in due form.
He took upon himself, the morning after their
arrival, the task of announcing the proposal of
Waverley to Rose, which she heard with a proper
degree of maiden timidity. Fame does, however, say
that Waverley had, the evening before, found five
minutes to apprise her of what was coming, while
the rest of the company were looking at three twisted
serpents which formed a *jet d'eau* in the garden.

My fair readers will judge for themselves; but
for my part, I cannot conceive how so important an
affair could be communicated in so short a space of
time, — at least, it certainly took a full hour in the
Baron's mode of conveying it.

Waverley was now considered as a received lover
in all the forms. He was made, by dint of smirk-
ing and nodding on the part of the lady of the
house, to sit next Miss Bradwardine at dinner, to
be Miss Bradwardine's partner at cards. If he
came into the room, she of the four Miss Rubricks
who chanced to be next Rose was sure to recollect
that her thimble or her scissors were at the other
end of the room, in order to leave the seat nearest
to Miss Bradwardine vacant for his occupation.
And sometimes, if papa and mamma were not in
the way to keep them on their good behaviour, the
misses would titter a little. The old Laird of
Duchran would also have his occasional jest, and
the old lady her remark. Even the Baron could not
refrain; but here Rose escaped every embarrassment but that of conjecture, for his wit was usually

320

couched in a Latin quotation. The very footmen
sometimes grinned too broadly, the maid-servants
giggled mayhap too loud, and a provoking air of
intelligence seemed to pervade the whole family.
Alice Bean, the pretty maid of the cavern, who,
after her father's "misfortune," as she called it,
had attended Rose as *fille de chambre*, smiled and
smirked with the best of them. Rose and Edward,
however, endured all these little vexatious circumstances as other folks have done before and since,
and probably contrived to obtain some indemnification, since they are not supposed, on the whole,
to have been particularly unhappy during Waverley's six days' stay at the Duchran.

It was finally arranged that Edward should go to
Waverley Honour to make the necessary arrangements for his marriage, thence to London to take
the proper measures for pleading his pardon, and
return as soon as possible to claim the hand of his
plighted bride. He also intended in his journey to
visit Colonel Talbot; but above all it was his most
important object to learn the fate of the unfortunate Chief of Glennaquoich, to visit him at Carlisle, and to try whether anything could be done
for procuring, if not a pardon, a commutation at
least, or alleviation, of the punishment to which he
was almost certain of being condemned, and in case
of the worst, to offer the miserable Flora an asylum
with Rose, or otherwise to assist her views in any
mode which might seem possible. The fate of
Fergus seemed hard to be averted. Edward had
already striven to interest his friend Colonel Talbot
in his behalf, but had been given distinctly to
understand, by his reply, that his credit in matters
of that nature was totally exhausted.

The colonel was still in Edinburgh, and proposed to wait there for some months upon business confided to him by the Duke of Cumberland. He was to be joined by Lady Emily, to whom easy travelling and goat's whey were recommended, and who was to journey northward under the escort of Francis Stanley. Edward, therefore, met the colonel at Edinburgh, who wished him joy in the kindest manner on his approaching happiness, and cheerfully undertook many commissions which our hero was necessarily obliged to delegate to his charge. But on the subject of Fergus he was inexorable. He satisfied Edward, indeed, that his interference would be unavailing; but, besides, Colonel Talbot owned that he could not conscientiously use any influence in favour of that unfortunate gentleman. "Justice," he said, "which demanded some penalty of those who had wrapped the whole nation in fear and in mourning, could not perhaps have selected a fitter victim. He came to the field with the fullest light upon the nature of his attempt. He had studied and understood the subject. His father's fate could not intimidate him; the lenity of the laws which had restored to him his father's property and rights could not melt him. That he was brave, generous, and possessed many good qualities, only rendered him the more dangerous; that he was enlightened and accomplished, made his crime the less excusable; that he was an enthusiast in a wrong cause, only made him the more fit to be its martyr. Above all, he had been the means of bringing many hundreds of men into the field who, without him, would never have broken the peace of the country.

"I repeat it," said the colonel, "though Heaven

322

knows with a heart distressed for him as an individual, that this young gentleman has studied and fully understood the desperate game which he has played. He threw for life or death, a coronet or a coffin; and he cannot now be permitted, with justice to the country, to draw stakes because the dice have gone against him."

Such was the reasoning of those times, held even by brave and humane men towards a vanquished enemy. Let us devoutly hope that, in this respect at least, we shall never see the scenes or hold the sentiments that were general in Britain Sixty Years since.

CHAPTER XXXIX

To-morrow?   Oh, that's sudden!   Spare him, spare him!
                                                SHAKSPEARE.

EDWARD, attended by his former servant, Alick
Polwarth, who had re-entered his service at Edinburgh, reached Carlisle while the commission of
Oyer and Terminer on his unfortunate associates
was yet sitting.   He had pushed forward in haste,
not, alas! with the most distant hope of saving
Fergus, but to see him for the last time.   I ought
to have mentioned that he had furnished funds for
the defence of the prisoners in the most liberal
manner, as soon as he heard that the day of trial
was fixed.   A solicitor and the first counsel accordingly attended; but it was upon the same footing
on which the first physicians are usually summoned
to the bedside of some dying man of rank, — the
doctors to take the advantage of some incalculable
chance of an exertion of nature; the lawyers to
avail themselves of the barely possible occurrence
of some legal flaw.   Edward pressed into the court,
which was extremely crowded; but by his arriving
from the North, and his extreme eagerness and agitation, it was supposed he was a relation of the
prisoners, and people made way for him.   It was
the third sitting of the court, and there were two
men at the bar.   The verdict of "Guilty" was al-

ready pronounced. Edward just glanced at the bar during the momentous pause which ensued. There was no mistaking the stately form and noble features of Fergus Mac-Ivor, although his dress was squalid, and his countenance tinged with the sickly yellow hue of long and close imprisonment. By his side was Evan Maccombich. Edward felt sick and dizzy as he gazed on them; but he was recalled to himself as the Clerk of Arraigns pronounced the solemn words: "Fergus Mac-Ivor of Glennaquoich, otherwise called Vich Ian Vohr, and Evan Mac-Ivor, in the Dhu of Tarrascleugh, otherwise called Evan Dhu, otherwise called Evan Maccombich, or Evan Dhu Maccombich, — you, and each of you, stand attainted of high treason. What have you to say for yourselves why the court should not pronounce judgment against you, that you die according to law?"

Fergus, as the presiding judge was putting on the fatal cap of judgment, placed his own bonnet upon his head, regarded him with a steadfast and stern look, and replied in a firm voice: "I cannot let this numerous audience suppose that to such an appeal I have no answer to make. But what I have to say you would not bear to hear, for my defence would be your condemnation. Proceed, then, in the name of God, to do what is permitted to you. Yesterday and the day before you have condemned loyal and honourable blood to be poured forth like water. Spare not mine. Were that of all my ancestors in my veins, I would have perilled it in this quarrel." He resumed his seat, and refused again to rise.

Evan Maccombich looked at him with great earnestness, and, rising up, seemed anxious to speak; but

325

the confusion of the court and the perplexity arising from thinking in a language different from that in which he was to express himself, kept him silent. There was a murmur of compassion among the spectators, from the idea that the poor fellow intended to plead the influence of his superior as an excuse for his crime. The judge commanded silence, and encouraged Evan to proceed.

" I was only ganging to say, my lord," said Evan, in what he meant to be an insinuating manner, " that if your excellent Honour and the honourable court would let Vich Ian Vohr go free just this once, and let him gae back to France, and no to trouble King George's government again, that ony six o' the very best of his clan will be willing to be justified in his stead; and if you 'll just let me gae down to Glennaquoich, I 'll fetch them up to ye mysell, to head or hang, and you may begin wi' me the very first man."

Notwithstanding the solemnity of the occasion, a sort of laugh was heard in the court at the extraordinary nature of the proposal. The judge checked this indecency, and Evan, looking sternly around, when the murmur abated, " If the Saxon gentlemen are laughing," he said, " because a poor man such as me thinks my life, or the life of six of my degree, is worth that of Vich Ian Vohr, it 's like enough they may be very right; but if they laugh because they think I would not keep my word and come back to redeem him, I can tell them they ken neither the heart of a Hielandman, nor the honour of a gentleman."

There was no farther inclination to laugh among the audience, and a dead silence ensued.

The judge then pronounced upon both prisoners

the sentence of the law of high treason, with all its horrible accompaniments. The execution was appointed for the ensuing day. "For you, Fergus Mac-Ivor," continued the judge, "I can hold out no hope of mercy. You must prepare against to-morrow for your last sufferings here and your great audit hereafter."

"I desire nothing else, my lord," answered Fergus, in the same manly and firm tone.

The hard eyes of Evan, which had been perpetually bent on his chief, were moistened with a tear. "For you, poor ignorant man," continued the judge, "who, following the ideas in which you have been educated, have this day given us a striking example how the loyalty due to the king and state alone, is, from your unhappy ideas of clanship, transferred to some ambitious individual who ends by making you the tool of his crimes, — for you, I say, I feel so much compassion that if you can make up your mind to petition for grace, I will endeavour to procure it for you. Otherwise — "

"Grace me no grace," said Evan; "since you are to shed Vich Ian Vohr's blood, the only favour I would accept from you, is to bid them loose my hands and gie me my claymore, and bide you just a minute sitting where you are!"

"Remove the prisoners," said the judge; "his blood be upon his own head."

Almost stupefied with his feelings, Edward found that the rush of the crowd had conveyed him out into the street ere he knew what he was doing. His immediate wish was to see and speak with Fergus once more. He applied at the castle where his unfortunate friend was confined, but was re-

327

fused admittance. "The high-sheriff," a non-commissioned officer said, "had requested of the governor that none should be admitted to see the prisoner excepting his confessor and his sister."

"And where was Miss Mac-Ivor?" They gave him the direction. It was the house of a respectable Catholic family near Carlisle.

Repulsed from the gate of the castle, and not venturing to make application to the high-sheriff or judges in his own unpopular name, he had recourse to the solicitor who came down in Fergus's behalf. This gentleman told him that it was thought the public mind was in danger of being debauched by the account of the last moments of these persons, as given by the friends of the Pretender; that there had been a resolution, therefore, to exclude all such persons as had not the plea of near kindred for attending upon them. Yet he promised, to oblige the heir of Waverley Honour, to get him an order for admittance to the prisoner the next morning, before his irons were knocked off for execution.

"Is it of Fergus Mac-Ivor they speak thus," thought Waverley, "or do I dream? Of Fergus, the bold, the chivalrous, the free-minded? The lofty chieftain of a tribe devoted to him? Is it he that I have seen lead the chase and head the attack, — the brave, the active, the young, the noble, the love of ladies, and the theme of song; is it he who is ironed like a malefactor, who is to be dragged on a hurdle to the common gallows, to die a lingering and cruel death, and to be mangled by the hand of the most outcast of wretches? Evil indeed was the spectre that boded such a fate as this to the brave Chief of Glennaquoich!"

With a faltering voice he requested the solicitor to find means to warn Fergus of his intended visit, should he obtain permission to make it. He then turned away from him, and returning to the inn, wrote a scarcely intelligible note to Flora Mac-Ivor, intimating his purpose to wait upon her that evening. The messenger brought back a letter in Flora's beautiful Italian hand, which seemed scarce to tremble even under this load of misery. "Miss Flora Mac-Ivor," the letter bore, "could not refuse to see the dearest friend óf her dear brother, even in her present circumstances of unparalleled distress."

When Edward reached Miss Mac-Ivor's present place of abode, he was instantly admitted. In a large and gloomy tapestried apartment Flora was seated by a latticed window, sewing what seemed to be a garment of white flannel. At a little distance sat an elderly woman, apparently a foreigner, and of a religious order. She was reading in a book of Catholic devotion, but when Waverley entered, laid it on the table and left the room. Flora rose to receive him and stretched out her hand; but neither ventured to attempt speech. Her fine complexion was totally gone, her person considerably emaciated, and her face and hands as white as the purest statuary marble, forming a strong contrast with her sable dress and jet-black hair. Yet amid these marks of distress there was nothing negligent or ill-arranged about her attire; even her hair, though totally without ornament, was disposed with her usual attention to neatness. The first words she uttered were, "Have you seen him?"

"Alas! no," answered Waverley; "I have been refused admittance."

"It accords with the rest," she said; "but we

329

must submit. Shall you obtain leave, do you suppose ? "

" For — for — to-morrow," said Waverley ; but muttering the last word so faintly that it was almost unintelligible.

" Ay, then or never," said Flora, " until," she added, looking upward, " the time when, I trust, we shall all meet. But I hope you will see him while earth yet bears him. He always loved you at his heart, though — But it is vain to talk of the past."

" Vain indeed ! " echoed Waverley.

" Or even of the future, my good friend," said Flora, " so far as earthly events are concerned ; for how often have I pictured to myself the strong possibility of this horrid issue, and tasked myself to consider how I could support my part, — and yet how far has all my anticipation fallen short of the unimaginable bitterness of this hour ! "

" Dear Flora, if your strength of mind — "

" Ay, there it is," she answered, somewhat wildly ; " there is, Mr. Waverley, there is a busy devil at my heart that whispers — but it were madness to listen to it — that the strength of mind on which Flora prided herself has murdered her brother ! "

" Good God ! how can you give utterance to a thought so shocking ? "

" Ay, is it not so ? But yet it haunts me like a phantom ; I know it is unsubstantial and vain, but it *will* be present, will intrude its horrors on my mind, will whisper that my brother, as volatile as ardent, would have divided his energies amid a hundred objects. It was I who taught him to concentrate them and to gage all on this dreadful and desperate cast. Oh that I could recollect that I had but once said to him, 'He that striketh with the sword shall die by the sword;' that I had but once said, 'Remain at home; reserve yourself, your vassals, your life, for enterprises within the reach of man.' But oh, Mr. Waverley, I spurred his fiery temper, and half of his ruin at least lies with his sister!"

The horrid idea which she had intimated, Edward endeavoured to combat by every incoherent argument that occurred to him. He recalled to her the principles on which both thought it their duty to act, and in which they had been educated.

"Do not think I have forgotten them," she said, looking up, with eager quickness; "I do not regret his attempt because it was wrong, — oh, no, on that point I am armed, — but because it was impossible it could end otherwise than thus."

"Yet it did not always seem so desperate and hazardous as it was, and it would have been chosen by the bold spirit of Fergus, whether you had approved it or no; your counsels only served to give unity and consistence to his conduct, to dignify, but not to precipitate, his resolution." Flora had soon ceased to listen to Edward, and was again intent upon her needlework.

"Do you remember," she said, looking up with a ghastly smile, "you once found me making Fergus's bride-favours; and now I am sewing his bridal garment. Our friends here," she continued, with suppressed emotion, "are to give hallowed earth in their chapel to the bloody relics of the last Vich Ian Vohr. But they will not all rest together; no, his head! — I shall not have the last miserable consolation of kissing the cold lips of my dear, dear Fergus!"

331

The unfortunate Flora here, after one or two hysterical sobs, fainted in her chair. The lady, who had been attending in the ante-room, now entered hastily, and begged Edward to leave the room, but not the house.

When he was recalled, after the space of nearly half an hour, he found that, by a strong effort, Miss Mac-Ivor had greatly composed herself. It was then he ventured to urge Miss Bradwardine's claim to be considered as an adopted sister, and empowered to assist her plans for the future.

"I have had a letter from my dear Rose," she replied, "to the same purpose. Sorrow is selfish and engrossing, or I would have written to express that, even in my own despair, I felt a gleam of pleasure at learning her happy prospects, and at hearing that the good old Baron has escaped the general wreck. Give this to my dearest Rose, — it is her poor Flora's only ornament of value, and was the gift of a princess." She put into his hands a case containing the chain of diamonds with which she used to decorate her hair. "To me it is in future useless. The kindness of my friends has secured me a retreat in the convent of the Scottish Benedictine nuns in Paris. To-morrow — if indeed I can survive to-morrow — I set forward on my journey with this venerable sister. And now, Mr. Waverley, adieu! May you be as happy with Rose as your amiable dispositions deserve, and think sometimes on the friends you have lost. Do not attempt to see me again; it would be mistaken kindness."

She gave him her hand, on which Edward shed a torrent of tears, and with a faltering step withdrew from the apartment and returned to the town of Carlisle. At the inn he found a letter from his law friend, intimating that he would be admitted to Fergus next morning as soon as the castle gates were opened, and permitted to remain with him till the arrival of the sheriff gave signal for the fatal procession.

CHAPTER XL

A darker departure is near, —
The death-drum is muffled, and sable the bier.

CAMPBELL.

AFTER a sleepless night, the first dawn of morning found Waverley on the esplanade in front of the old Gothic gate of Carlisle Castle. But he paced it long in every direction before the hour when, according to the rules of the garrison, the gates were opened and the drawbridge lowered. He produced his order to the sergeant of the guard, and was admitted.

The place of Fergus's confinement was a gloomy and vaulted apartment in the central part of the castle, — a huge old tower, supposed to be of great antiquity, and surrounded by outworks seemingly of Henry VIII.'s time, or somewhat later. The grating of the large old-fashioned bars and bolts, withdrawn for the purpose of admitting Edward, was answered by the clash of chains as the unfortunate chieftain, strongly and heavily fettered, shuffled along the stone floor of his prison to fling himself into his friend's arms.

"My dear Edward," he said, in a firm and even cheerful voice, "this is truly kind. I heard of your approaching happiness with the highest pleasure. And how does Rose? and how is our old whimsical friend the Baron? Well, I trust, since I see you at freedom. And how will you settle precedence be-

334

tween the three ermines passant and the bear and
boot-jack ? "

" How, oh, how, my dear Fergus, can you talk of
such things at such a moment ? "

" Why, we have entered Carlisle with happier
auspices, to be sure, — on the 16th of November
last, for example, when we marched in, side by side,
and hoisted the white flag on these ancient towers.
But I am no boy to sit down and weep because the
luck has gone against me. I knew the stake which
I risked; we played the game boldly, and the forfeit shall be paid manfully. And now, since my
time is short, let me come to the questions that
interest me most. The Prince, has he escaped the
bloodhounds ? "

" He has, and is in safety."

" Praised be God for that ! Tell me the particulars of his escape."

Waverley communicated that remarkable history so far as it had then transpired, to which
Fergus listened with deep interest. He then asked
after several other friends, and made many minute
inquiries concerning the fate of his own clansmen.
They had suffered less than other tribes who had
been engaged in the affair; for having in a great
measure dispersed and returned home after the captivity of their chieftain, according to the universal
custom of the Highlanders, they were not in arms
when the insurrection was finally suppressed, and
consequently were treated with less rigour. This
Fergus heard with great satisfaction.

" You are rich," he said, " Waverley, and you are
generous. When you hear of these poor Mac-Ivors
being distressed about their miserable possessions
by some harsh overseer or agent of government,

335

remember you have worn their tartan, and are an adopted son of their race. The Baron, who knows our manners and lives near our country, will apprise you of the time and means to be their protector. Will you promise this to the last Vich Ian Vohr?"

Edward, as may well be believed, pledged his word, which he afterwards so amply redeemed that his memory still lives in these glens by the name of the Friend of the Sons of Ivor.

"Would to God," continued the chieftain, " I could bequeath to you my rights to the love and obedience of this primitive and brave race, or at least, as I have striven to do, persuade poor Evan to accept of his life upon their terms, and be to you what he has been to me, — the kindest, the bravest, the most devoted — "

The tears which his own fate could not draw forth, fell fast for that of his foster-brother.

" But," said he, drying them, " that cannot be. You cannot be to them Vich Ian Vohr; and these three magic words," said he, half smiling, " are the only ' Open Sesame ' to their feelings and sympathies, and poor Evan must attend his foster-brother in death, as he has done through his whole life."

" And I am sure," said Maccombich, raising himself from the floor, on which, for fear of interrupting their conversation, he had lain so still that, in the obscurity of the apartment, Edward was not aware of his presence, — " I am sure Evan never desired or deserved a better end than just to die with his chieftain."

" And now," said Fergus, " while we are upon the subject of clanship, what think you now of the prediction of the Bodach Glas?" Then, before Edward could answer, " I saw him again last night,

— he stood in the slip of moonshine which fell from that high and narrow window towards my bed. Why should I fear him, I thought? To-morrow, long ere this time, I shall be as immaterial as he. 'False Spirit,' I said, 'art thou come to close thy walks on earth, and to enjoy thy triumph in the fall of the last descendant of thine enemy?' The spectre seemed to beckon and to smile, as he faded from my sight. What do you think of it? I asked the same question of the priest, who is a good and sensible man. He admitted that the Church allowed that such apparitions were possible, but urged me not to permit my mind to dwell upon it, as imagination plays us such strange tricks. What do you think of it?"

"Much as your confessor," said Waverley, willing to avoid dispute upon such a point at such a moment. A tap at the door now announced that good man, and Edward retired while he administered to both prisoners the last rites of religion, in the mode which the Church of Rome prescribes.

In about an hour he was re-admitted; soon after, a file of soldiers entered with a blacksmith, who struck the fetters from the legs of the prisoners.

"You see the compliment they pay to our Highland strength and courage. We have lain chained here like wild beasts, till our legs are cramped into palsy, and when they free us, they send six soldiers with loaded muskets to prevent our taking the castle by storm!"

Edward afterwards learned that these severe precautions had been taken in consequence of a desperate attempt of the prisoners to escape, in which they had very nearly succeeded.

Shortly afterwards the drums of the garrison beat

to arms. "This is the last turn-out," said Fergus, "that I shall hear and obey. And now, my dear, dear Edward, ere we part let us speak of Flora, — a subject which awakes the tenderest feeling that yet thrills within me."

"We part not *here !*" said Waverley.

"Oh, yes, we do; you must come no farther. Not that I fear what is to follow for myself," he said, proudly. "Nature has her tortures as well as art; and how happy should we think the man who escapes from the throes of a mortal and painful disorder, in the space of a short half-hour? And this matter, spin it out as they will, cannot last longer. But what a dying man can suffer firmly, may kill a living friend to look upon. This same law of high treason," he continued, with astonishing firmness and composure, "is one of the blessings, Edward, with which your free country has accommodated poor old Scotland; her own jurisprudence, as I have heard, was much milder. But I suppose one day or other, — when there are no longer any wild Highlanders to benefit by its tender mercies, — they will blot it from their records, as levelling them with a nation of cannibals. The mummery, too, of exposing the senseless head, — they have not the wit to grace mine with a paper coronet; there would be some satire in that, Edward. I hope they will set it on the Scotch gate, though, that I may look, even after death, to the blue hills of my own country, which I love so dearly. The Baron would have added, —

Moritur, et moriens dulces reminiscitur Argos."

A bustle, and the sound of wheels and horses' feet, was now heard in the court-yard of the castle.

"As I have told you why you must not follow me, and these sounds admonish me that my time flies fast, tell me how you found poor Flora?"

Waverley, with a voice interrupted by suffocating sensations, gave some account of the state of her mind.

"Poor Flora!" answered the chief, "she could have borne her own sentence of death, but not mine. You, Waverley, will soon know the happiness of mutual affection in the married state, — long, long may Rose and you enjoy it! — but you can never know the purity of feeling which combines two orphans, like Flora and me, left alone as it were in the world, and being all in all to each other from our very infancy. But her strong sense of duty, and predominant feeling of loyalty, will give new nerve to her mind after the immediate and acute sensation of this parting has passed away. She will then think of Fergus as of the heroes of our race, upon whose deeds she loved to dwell."

"Shall she not see you, then?" asked Waverley. "She seemed to expect it."

" A necessary deceit will spare her the last dreadful parting. I could not part with her without tears, and I cannot bear that these men should think they have power to extort them. She was made to believe she would see me at a later hour, and this letter, which my confessor will deliver, will apprise her that all is over."

An officer now appeared, and intimated that the high-sheriff and his attendants waited before the gate of the castle, to claim the bodies of Fergus Mac-Ivor and Evan Maccombich. "I come," said Fergus. Accordingly, supporting Edward by the arm, and followed by Evan Dhu and the priest, he

moved down the stairs of the tower, the soldiers
bringing up the rear. The court was occupied by
a squadron of dragoons and a battalion of infantry
drawn up in hollow square. Within their ranks
was the sledge, or hurdle, on which the prisoners
were to be drawn to the place of execution, about
a mile distant from Carlisle. It was painted black,
and drawn by a white horse. At one end of the
vehicle sat the executioner, — a horrid-looking fellow, as beseemed his trade, with the broad axe in
his hand; at the other end, next the horse, was an
empty seat for two persons. Through the deep
and dark Gothic archway that opened on the drawbridge were seen on horseback the high-sheriff and
his attendants, whom the etiquette betwixt the
civil and military powers did not permit to come
farther. "This is well *got up* for a closing scene,"
said Fergus, smiling disdainfully as he gazed around
upon the apparatus of terror. Evan Dhu exclaimed
with some eagerness, after looking at the dragoons:
"These are the very chields that galloped off at
Gladsmuir, before we could kill a dozen o' them.
They look bold enough now, however." The priest
entreated him to be silent.

The sledge now approached, and Fergus, turning
round, embraced Waverley, kissed him on each side
of the face, and stepped nimbly into his place.
Evan sat down by his side. The priest was to
follow in a carriage belonging to his patron, the
Catholic gentleman at whose house Flora resided.
As Fergus waved his hand to Edward, the ranks
closed around the sledge, and the whole procession
began to move forward. There was a momentary
stop at the gateway while the governor of the castle
and the high-sheriff went through a short ceremony,

340

the military officer there delivering over the persons of the criminals to the civil power. " God save King George ! " said the high-sheriff. When the formality concluded, Fergus stood erect in the sledge, and with a firm and steady voice replied, " God save King *James !* " These were the last words which Waverley heard him speak.

The procession resumed its march, and the sledge vanished from beneath the portal, under which it had stopped for an instant. The dead-march was then heard, and its melancholy sounds were mingled with those of a muffled peal, tolled from the neighbouring cathedral. The sound of the military music died away as the procession moved on ; the sullen clang of the bells was soon heard to sound alone.

The last of the soldiers had now disappeared from under the vaulted archway through which they had been filing for several minutes. The court-yard was now totally empty ; but Waverley still stood there as if stupefied, his eyes fixed upon the dark pass where he had so lately seen the last glimpse of his friend. At length a female servant of the governor's, struck with compassion at the stupefied misery which his countenance expressed, asked him if he would not walk into her master's house and sit down ? She was obliged to repeat her question twice ere he comprehended her, but at length it recalled him to himself. Declining the courtesy by a hasty gesture, he pulled his hat over his eyes, and, leaving the castle, walked as swiftly as he could through the empty streets till he regained his inn, then rushed into an apartment and bolted the door.

In about an hour and a half, which seemed an

341

age of unutterable suspense, the sound of the drums and fifes performing a lively air, and the confused murmur of the crowd which now filled the streets, so lately deserted, apprised him that all was finished, and that the military and populace were returning from the dreadful scene. I will not attempt to describe his sensations.

In the evening the priest made him a visit, and informed him that he did so by directions of his deceased friend, to assure him that Fergus Mac-Ivor had died as he lived, and remembered his friendship to the last. He added, he had also seen Flora, whose state of mind seemed more composed since all was over. With her and Sister Theresa, the priest proposed next day to leave Carlisle, for the nearest seaport from which they could embark for France. Waverley forced on this good man a ring of some value and a sum of money to be employed (as he thought might gratify Flora) in the services of the Catholic Church, for the memory of his friend. "Fungarque inani munere," he repeated, as the ecclesiastic retired. "Yet why not class these acts of remembrance with other honours with which affection, in all sects, pursues the memory of the dead?"

The next morning ere daylight he took leave of the town of Carlisle, promising to himself never again to enter its walls. He dared hardly look back towards the Gothic battlements of the fortified gate under which he passed, — for the place is surrounded with an old wall. "They're no there," said Alick Polwarth, who guessed the cause of the dubious look which Waverley cast backward, and who, with the vulgar appetite for the horrible, was master of each detail of the butchery, — " the heads

are ower the Scotch yate, as they ca' it. It's a
great pity of Evan Dhu, who was a very weel-
meaning, good-natured man, to be a Hielandman, —
and indeed so was the Laird o' Glennaquoich too,
for that matter, when he wasna in ane o' his
tirrivies."

CHAPTER XLI

THE impression of horror with which Waverley left Carlisle softened by degrees into melancholy, — a gradation which was accelerated by the painful, yet soothing, task of writing to Rose; and while he could not suppress his own feelings of the calamity, he endeavoured to place it in a light which might grieve her, without shocking her imagination. The picture which he drew for her benefit he gradually familiarized to his own mind, and his next letters were more cheerful, and referred to the prospects of peace and happiness which lay before them. Yet though his first horrible sensations had sunk into melancholy, Edward had reached his native country before he could, as usual on former occasions, look round for enjoyment upon the face of nature.

He then, for the first time since leaving Edinburgh, began to experience that pleasure which almost all feel who return to a verdant, populous, and highly cultivated country, from scenes of waste desolation, or of solitary and melancholy grandeur. But how were those feelings enhanced when he entered on the domain so long possessed by his forefathers, recognized the old oaks of Waverley Chace, thought with what delight he should introduce Rose to all his favourite haunts, beheld at length the towers of the venerable hall arise above

344

the woods which embowered it, and finally threw himself into the arms of the venerable relations to whom he owed so much duty and affection!

The happiness of their meeting was not tarnished by a single word of reproach. On the contrary, whatever pain Sir Everard and Mrs. Rachel had felt during Waverley's perilous engagement with the young Chevalier, it assorted too well with the principles in which they had been brought up to incur reprobation, or even censure. Colonel Talbot also had smoothed the way, with great address, for Edward's favourable reception, by dwelling upon his gallant behaviour in the military character, particularly his bravery and generosity at Preston, until, warmed at the idea of their nephew's engaging in single combat, making prisoner, and saving from slaughter so distinguished an officer as the colonel himself, the imagination of the baronet and his sister ranked the exploits of Edward with those of Wilibert, Hildebrand, and Nigel, the vaunted heroes of their line.

The appearance of Waverley, embrowned by exercise and dignified by the habits of military discipline, had acquired an athletic and hardy character which not only verified the colonel's narration, but surprised and delighted all the inhabitants of Waverley Honour. They crowded to see, to hear him, and to sing his praises. Mr. Pembroke, who secretly extolled his spirit and courage in embracing the genuine cause of the Church of England, censured his pupil gently, nevertheless, for being so careless of his manuscripts, which, indeed, he said, had occasioned him some personal inconvenience, as, upon the baronet's being arrested by a king's messenger, he had deemed it prudent to retire to a

345

concealment called "The Priest's Hole," from the use it had been put to in former days, where, he assured our hero, the butler had thought it safe to venture with food only once in the day, so that he had been repeatedly compelled to dine upon victuals either absolutely cold, or, what was worse, only half warm, not to mention that sometimes his bed had not been arranged for two days together. Waverley's mind involuntarily turned to the Patmos of the Baron of Bradwardine, who was well pleased with Janet's fare and a few bunches of straw stowed in a cleft in the front of a sand-cliff; but he made no remarks upon a contrast which could only mortify his worthy tutor.

All was now in a bustle to prepare for the nuptials of Edward, — an event to which the good old baronet and Mrs. Rachel looked forward as if to the renewal of their own youth. The match, as Colonel Talbot had intimated, had seemed to them in the highest degree eligible, having every recommendation but wealth, of which they themselves had more than enough. Mr. Clippurse was therefore summoned to Waverley Honour, under better auspices than at the commencement of our story. But Mr. Clippurse came not alone; for, being now stricken in years, he had associated with him a nephew, a younger vulture (as our English Juvenal, who tells the tale of Swallow the attorney, might have called him), and they now carried on business as Messrs. Clippurse and Hookem. These worthy gentlemen had directions to make the necessary settlements on the most splendid scale of liberality, as if Edward were to wed a peeress in her own right, with her paternal estate tacked to the fringe of her ermine.

But before entering upon a subject of proverbial delay, I must remind my reader of the progress of a stone rolled down hill by an idle truant boy (a pastime at which I was myself expert in my more juvenile years); it moves at first slowly, avoiding by inflection every obstacle of the least importance; but when it has attained its full impulse, and draws near the conclusion of its career, it smokes and thunders down, taking a rood at every spring, clearing hedge and ditch like a Yorkshire huntsman, and becoming most furiously rapid in its course when it is nearest to being consigned to rest for ever. Even such is the course of a narrative like that which you are perusing. The earlier events are studiously dwelt upon, that you, kind reader, may be introduced to the character rather by narrative than by the duller medium of direct description; but when the story draws near its close, we hurry over the circumstances, however important, which your imagination must have forestalled, and leave you to suppose those things which it would be abusing your patience to relate at length.

We are, therefore, so far from attempting to trace the dull progress of Messrs. Clippurse and Hookem, or that of their worthy official brethren who had the charge of suing out the pardons of Edward Waverley and his intended father-in-law, that we can but touch upon matters more attractive. The mutual epistles, for example, which were exchanged between Sir Everard and the Baron upon this occasion, though matchless specimens of eloquence in their way, must be consigned to merciless oblivion. Nor can I tell you at length how worthy Aunt Rachel, not without a delicate and affectionate allusion to the circumstances which had transferred

347

Rose's maternal diamonds to the hands of Donald
Bean Lean, stocked her casket with a set of jewels
that a duchess might have envied. Moreover, the
reader will have the goodness to imagine that Job
Houghton and his dame were suitably provided for,
although they could never be persuaded that their
son fell otherwise than fighting by the young squire's
side; so that Alick, who, as a lover of truth, had
made many needless attempts to expound the real
circumstances to them, was finally ordered to say
not a word more upon the subject. He indemnified
himself, however, by the liberal allowance of desperate battles, grisly executions, and raw-head and
bloody-bone stories with which he astonished the
servants'-hall.

But although these important matters may be
briefly told in narrative, like a newspaper report of
a chancery suit, yet, with all the urgency which
Waverley could use, the real time which the law
proceedings occupied, joined to the delay occasioned
by the mode of travelling at that period, rendered
it considerably more than two months ere Waverley,
having left England, alighted once more at the mansion of the Laird of Duchran to claim the hand of
his plighted bride.

The day of his marriage was fixed for the sixth
after his arrival. The Baron of Bradwardine, with
whom bridals, christenings, and funerals were festivals of high and solemn import, felt a little hurt
that, including the family of the Duchran and all
the immediate vicinity who had title to be present
on such an occasion, there could not be above thirty
persons collected. "When he was married," he observed, "three hundred horse of gentlemen born,
besides servants and some score or two of Highland

lairds who never got on horseback, were present on the occasion."

But his pride found some consolation in reflecting that he and his son-in-law, having been so lately in arms against government, it might give matter of reasonable fear and offence to the ruling powers if they were to collect together the kith, kin, and allies of their houses, arrayed in effeir of war, as was the ancient custom of Scotland on these occasions. "And, without dubitation," he concluded, with a sigh, "many of those who would have rejoiced most freely upon these joyful espousals are either gone to a better place, or are now exiles from their native land."

The marriage took place on the appointed day. The Reverend Mr. Rubrick, kinsman to the proprietor of the hospitable mansion where it was solemnized, and chaplain to the Baron of Bradwardine, had the satisfaction to unite their hands; and Frank Stanley acted as bridesman, having joined Edward with that view soon after his arrival. Lady Emily and Colonel Talbot had proposed being present; but Lady Emily's health, when the day approached, was found inadequate to the journey. In amends, it was arranged that Edward Waverley and his lady, who, with the Baron, proposed an immediate journey to Waverley Honour, should, in their way, spend a few days at an estate which Colonel Talbot had been tempted to purchase in Scotland as a very great bargain, and at which he proposed to reside for some time.

349

CHAPTER XLII

This is no mine ain house, I ken by the bigging o't.

Old Song.

THE nuptial party travelled in great style. There was a coach-and-six after the newest pattern, which Sir Everard had presented to his nephew, that dazzled with its splendour the eyes of one half of Scotland; there was the family coach of Mr. Rubrick ; both these were crowded with ladies, and there were gentlemen on horseback, with their servants, to the number of a round score. Nevertheless, without having the fear of famine before his eyes, Bailie Macwheeble met them in the road to entreat that they would pass by his house at Little Veolan. The Baron stared, and said his son and he would certainly ride by Little Veolan and pay their compliments to the bailie, but could not think of bringing with them the "haill *comitatus nuptialis,* or matrimonial procession." He added "that, as he understood that the barony had been sold by its unworthy possessor, he was glad to see his old friend Duncan had regained his situation under the new *dominus,* or proprietor." The bailie ducked, bowed, and fidgeted, and then again insisted upon his invitation ; until the Baron, though rather piqued at the pertinacity of his instances, could not nevertheless refuse to consent without making evident sensations which he was anxious to conceal.

He fell into a deep study as they approached the top of the avenue, and was only startled from it by observing that the battlements were replaced, the ruins cleared away, and (most wonderful of all) that the two great stone bears, those mutilated Dagons of his idolatry, had resumed their posts over the gateway. " Now this new proprietor," said he to Edward, " has shown mair *gusto*, as the Italians call it, in the short time he has had this domain, than that hound Malcolm, though I bred him here mysell, has acquired *vita adhuc durante*. And now I talk of hounds, is not yon Ban and Buscar, who come scouping up the avenue with Davie Gellatley ? "

"I vote we should go to meet them, sir," said Waverley; "for I believe the present master of the house is Colonel Talbot, who will expect to see us. We hesitated to mention to you at first that he had purchased your ancient patrimonial property, and even yet, if you do not incline to visit him, we can pass on to the bailie's."

The Baron had occasion for all his magnanimity. However, he drew a long breath, took a long snuff, and observed, since they had brought him so far, he could not pass the colonel's gate, and he would be happy to see the new master of his old tenants. He alighted accordingly, as did the other gentlemen and ladies ; he gave his arm to his daughter, and as they descended the avenue, pointed out to her how speedily the *Diva Pecunia* of the Southron — their tutelary deity, he might call her — had removed the marks of spoliation.

In truth, not only had the felled trees been re-

moved, but, their stumps being grubbed up, and the
earth round them levelled and sown with grass,
every mark of devastation, unless to an eye intimately acquainted with the spot, was already
totally obliterated.   There was a similar reforma-
tion in the outward man of Davie Gellatley, who
met them, every now and then stopping to admire
the new suit which graced his person, in the same
colours as formerly, but bedizened fine enough to
have served Touchstone himself.   He danced up
with his usual ungainly frolics, first to the Baron,
and then to Rose, passing his hands over his clothes,
crying, " Bra', bra' Davie," and scarce able to sing
a bar to an end of his thousand-and-one songs, for
the breathless extravagance of his joy.   The dogs
also acknowledged their old master with a thousand
gambols.   " Upon my conscience, Rose," ejaculated
the Baron, " the gratitude o' thae dumb brutes and
of that puir innocent brings the tears into my auld
een ; while that schellum Malcolm —   But I 'm
obliged to Colonel Talbot for putting my hounds
into such good condition, and likewise for puir
Davie.   But Rose, my dear, we must not permit
them to be a life-rent burden upon the estate."

As he spoke, Lady Emily, leaning upon the arm of
her husband, met the party at the lower gate, with
a thousand welcomes.   After the ceremony of introduction had been gone through, — much abridged
by the ease and excellent breeding of Lady Emily,
— she apologized for having used a little art to
wile them back to a place which might awaken
some painful reflections.   " But as it was to change
masters, we were very desirous that the Baron — "

" Mr. Bradwardine, Madam, if you please," said
the old gentleman.

"Mr. Bradwardine, then, and Mr. Waverley, should see what we have done towards restoring the mansion of your fathers to its former state."

The Baron answered with a low bow. Indeed, when he entered the court, excepting that the heavy stables, which had been burned down, were replaced by buildings of a lighter and more picturesque appearance, all seemed as much as possible restored to the state in which he had left it when he assumed arms some months before. The pigeon-house was replenished, the fountain played with its usual activity, and not only the bear who predominated over its basin, but all the other bears whatsoever were replaced on their several stations, and renewed or repaired with so much care that they bore no tokens of the violence which had so lately descended upon them. While these *minutiæ* had been so heedfully attended to, it is scarce necessary to add that the house itself had been thoroughly repaired, as well as the gardens, with the strictest attention to maintain the original character of both, and to remove, as far as possible, all appearance of the ravage they had sustained. The Baron gazed in silent wonder; at length he addressed Colonel Talbot.

"While I acknowledge my obligation to you, sir, for the restoration of the badge of our family, I cannot but marvel that you have nowhere established your own crest, whilk is, I believe, a mastiff, anciently called a talbot; as the poet has it,

A talbot strong, — a sturdy tyke.

At least such a dog is the crest of the martial and renowned Earls of Shrewsbury, to whom your family are probably blood relations."

353

" I believe," said the colonel, smiling, " our dogs
are whelps of the same litter. For my part, if crests
were to dispute precedence, I should be apt to let
them, as the proverb says, ' fight dog, fight bear.' "

As he made this speech, at which the Baron took
another long pinch of snuff, they had entered the
house, — that is, the Baron, Rose, and Lady Emily,
with young Stanley and the bailie, — for Edward
and the rest of the party remained on the terrace to
examine a new green-house stocked with the finest
plants. The Baron resumed his favourite topic:
" However it may please you to derogate from the
honour of your burganet, Colonel Talbot, — which
is doubtless your humour, as I have seen in other
gentlemen of birth and honour in your country, — I
must again repeat it as a most ancient and distinguished bearing, as well as that of my young friend
Francis Stanley, which is the eagle and child."

"The bird and bantling they call it in Derby-
shire, sir," said Stanley.

" Ye 're a daft callant, sir," said the Baron, who
had a great liking to this young man, perhaps
because he sometimes teased him, — " Ye 're a daft
callant, and I must correct you some of these days,"
shaking his great brown fist at him. " But what
I meant to say, Colonel Talbot, is, that yours is an
ancient *prosapia*, or descent, and since you have
lawfully and justly acquired the estate for you and
yours, which I have lost for me and mine, I wish
it may remain in your name as many centuries as
it has done in that of the late proprietor's."

" That," answered the colonel, " is very handsome, Mr. Bradwardine, indeed."

" And yet, sir, I cannot but marvel that you,
Colonel, whom I noted to have so much of the *amor*

354

patriæ, when we met in Edinburgh, as even to vili-
pend other countries, should have chosen to establish your Lares, or household gods, *procul a patriæ
finibus,* and in a manner to expatriate yourself."

"Why really, Baron, I do not see why, to keep the
secret of these foolish boys, Waverley and Stanley,
and of my wife, who is no wiser, one old soldier
should continue to impose upon another. You
must know, then, that I have so much of that same
prejudice in favour of my native country that the
sum of money which I advanced to the seller of
this extensive barony has only purchased for me a
box in ——shire, called Brerewood Lodge, with
about two hundred and fifty acres of land, the chief
merit of which is that it is within a very few miles
of Waverley Honour."

"And who, then, in the name of Heaven, has
bought this property?"

"That," said the colonel, "it is this gentleman's
profession to explain."

The bailie — whom this reference regarded, and
who had all this while shifted from one foot to another with great impatience, "like a hen," as he
afterwards said, "upon a het girdle," and chuckling,
he might have added, like the said hen in all the
glory of laying an egg — now pushed forward.
"That I can, that I can, your Honour," drawing
from his pocket a budget of papers, and untying
the red tape with a hand trembling with eagerness.
"Here is the disposition and assignation, by Malcolm Bradwardine of Inch-Grabbit, regularly signed
and tested in terms of the statute, whereby, for a
certain sum of sterling money presently contented
and paid to him, he has disponed, alienated, and
conveyed the whole estate and barony of Bradwar-

355

dine, Tully-Veolan, and others, with the fortalice and manor-place — "

"For God's sake, to the point, sir; I have all that by heart," said the colonel.

"To Cosmo Comyne Bradwardine, Esq.," pursued the bailie, "his heirs and assignees, simply and irredeemably, to be held either *a me vel de me* — "

"Pray read short, sir."

"On the conscience of an honest man, Colonel, I read as short as is consistent with style. Under the burden and reservation always — "

"Mr. Macwheeble, this would outlast a Russian winter. Give me leave. In short, Mr. Bradwardine, your family estate is your own once more, in full property and at your absolute disposal, but only burdened with the sum advanced to re-purchase it, which, I understand, is utterly disproportioned to its value."

"An auld sang, an auld sang, if it please your Honours," cried the bailie, rubbing his hands; "look at the rental book."

"Which sum being advanced by Mr. Edward Waverley, chiefly from the price of his father's property which I bought from him, is secured to his lady, your daughter, and her family by this marriage."

"It is a catholic security", shouted the bailie, "to Rose Comyne Bradwardine, *alias* Waverley, in liferent, and the children of the said marriage in fee; and I made up a wee bit minute of an ante-nuptial contract, *intuitu matrimonij*, so it cannot be subject to reduction hereafter, as a donation *inter virum et uxorem.*"

It is difficult to say whether the worthy Baron

was most delighted with the restitution of his family property, or with the delicacy and generosity that left him unfettered to pursue his purpose in disposing of it after his death, and which avoided, as much as possible, even the appearance of laying him under pecuniary obligation. When his first pause of joy and astonishment was over, his thoughts turned to the unworthy heir-male, who, he pronounced, had sold his birthright, like Esau, for a mess o' pottage.

"But wha cookit the parritch for him?" exclaimed the bailie; "I wad like to ken that, — wha but your Honour's to command, Duncan Macwheeble? His Honour young Mr. Wauverley put it a' into my hand frae the beginning, — frae the first calling o' the summons, as I may say. I circumvented them; I played at bogle about the bush wi' them; I cajoled them; and if I havena gien Inch-Grabbit and Jamie Howie a bonnie begunk, they ken themselves. Him a writer! I didna gae slap-dash to them wi' our young bra' bridegroom to gar them haud up the market, — na, na; I scared them wi' our wild tenantry and the Mac-Ivors, that are but ill settled yet, till they durstna on ony errand whatsoever gang ower the door-stane after gloaming, for fear John Heatherblutter, or some siccan dare-the-deil, should tak a baff at them; then, on the other hand, I beflumm'd them wi' Colonel Talbot, — wad they offer to keep up the price again' the duke's friend? did they na ken wha was master? had they na seen eneugh, by the sad example of mony a puir misguided, unhappy body —"

"Who went to Derby, for example, Mr. Macwheeble?" said the colonel to him, aside.

"Oh, whisht, Colonel; for the love o' God let

357

that flee stick i' the wa'. There were mony good folk at Derby, and it's ill speaking of halters," with a sly cast of his eye toward the Baron, who was in a deep reverie.

Starting out of it at once, he took Macwheeble by the button and led him into one of the deep window recesses, whence only fragments of their conversation reached the rest of the party. It certainly related to stamp-paper and parchment; for no other subject, even from the mouth of his patron, and he, once more, an efficient one, could have arrested so deeply the bailie's reverent and absorbed attention.

"I understand your Honour perfectly; it can be dune as easy as taking out a decreet in absence."

"To her and him, after my demise, and to their heirs-male, but preferring the second son, if God shall bless them with two, who is to carry the name and arms of Bradwardine of that ilk, without any other name or armorial bearings whatsoever."

"Tut, your Honour!" whispered the bailie, "I'll mak a slight jotting the morn; it will cost but a charter of resignation *in favorem*, and I'll hae it ready for the next term in Exchequer."

Their private conversation ended, the Baron was now summoned to do the honours of Tully-Veolan to new guests. These were Major Melville of Cairnvreckan, and the Reverend Mr. Morton, followed by two or three others of the Baron's acquaintances who had been made privy to his having again acquired the estate of his fathers. The shouts of the villagers were also heard beneath in the court-yard; for Saunders Saunderson, who had kept the secret for several days with laudable prudence, had unloosed his tongue upon beholding the arrival of the carriages.

But while Edward received Major Melville with politeness, and the clergyman with the most affectionate and grateful kindness, his father-in-law looked a little awkward, as uncertain how he should answer the necessary claims of hospitality to his guests and forward the festivity of his tenants. Lady Emily relieved him by intimating that though she must be an indifferent representative of Mrs. Edward Waverley in many respects, she hoped the Baron would approve of the entertainment she had ordered, in expectation of so many guests, and that they would find such other accommodations provided as might in some degree support the ancient hospitality of Tully-Veolan. It is impossible to describe the pleasure which this assurance gave the Baron, who, with an air of gallantry half appertaining to the stiff Scottish laird, and half to the officer in the French service, offered his arm to the fair speaker, and led the way, in something between a stride and a minuet-step, into the large dining-parlour, followed by all the rest of the good company.

By dint of Saunderson's directions and exertions, all here, as well as in the other apartments, had been disposed as much as possible according to the old arrangement; and where new movables had been necessary, they had been selected in the same character with the old furniture. There was one addition to this fine old apartment, however, which drew tears into the Baron's eyes. It was a large and spirited painting, representing Fergus Mac-Ivor and Waverley in their Highland dress, the scene a wild, rocky, and mountainous pass, down which the clan were descending in the background. It was taken from a spirited sketch, drawn while they were in Edinburgh by a young man of high genius, and had been painted on a full-length scale by an eminent London artist. Raeburn himself (whose Highland chiefs do all but walk out of the canvas) could not have done more justice to the subject; and the ardent, fiery, and impetuous character of the unfortunate Chief of Glennaquoich was finely contrasted with the contemplative, fanciful, and enthusiastic expression of his happier friend. Beside this painting hung the arms which Waverley had borne in the unfortunate civil war. The whole piece was beheld with admiration, and deeper feelings.

Men must, however, eat, in spite both of sentiment and *vertu ;* and the Baron, while he assumed the lower end of the table, insisted that Lady Emily should do the honours of the head, that they might, he said, set a meet example to the *young folk.* After a pause of deliberation, employed in adjusting in his own brain the precedence between the Presbyterian Kirk and Episcopal Church of Scotland, he requested Mr. Morton, as the stranger, would crave a blessing, observing that Mr. Rubrick, who was at *home*, would return thanks for the distinguished mercies it had been his lot to experience. The dinner was excellent. Saunderson attended in full costume, with all the former domestics, who had been collected, excepting one or two that had not been heard of since the affair of Culloden. The cellars were stocked with wine, which was pronounced to be superb, and it had been contrived that the bear of the fountain, in the court-yard, should (for that night only) play excellent brandy punch for the benefit of the lower orders.

When the dinner was over, the Baron, about to propose a toast, cast a somewhat sorrowful look upon the side-board, which, however, exhibited much of his plate that had either been secreted or purchased by neighbouring gentlemen from the soldiery, and by them gladly restored to the original owner.

"In the late times," he said, "those must be thankful who have saved life and land; yet when I am about to pronounce this toast, I cannot but regret an old heir-loom, Lady Emily, — a *poculum potatorium*, Colonel Talbot — "

Here the Baron's elbow was gently touched by his major-domo, and turning round, he beheld, in the hands of Alexander ab Alexandro, the celebrated cup of Saint Duthac, the Blessed Bear of Bradwardine! I question if the recovery of his estate afforded him more rapture. "By my honour," he said, "one might almost believe in brownies and fairies, Lady Emily, when your ladyship is in presence!"

"I am truly happy," said Colonel Talbot, "that, by the recovery of this piece of family antiquity, it has fallen within my power to give you some token of my deep interest in all that concerns my young friend Edward. But that you may not suspect Lady Emily for a sorceress, or me for a conjuror, — which is no joke in Scotland, — I must tell you that Frank Stanley, your friend, who has been seized with a tartan fever ever since he heard Edward's tales of old Scottish manners, happened to describe to us at second hand this remarkable cup. My servant Spontoon, who, like a true old soldier, observes everything and says little, gave me afterwards to understand that he thought he had seen the piece

361

of plate Mr. Stanley mentioned, in the possession of a certain Mrs. Nosebag, who, having been originally the helpmate of a pawnbroker, had found opportunity, during the late unpleasant scenes in Scotland, to trade a little in her old line, and so became the depositary of the more valuable part of the spoil of half the army. You may believe the cup was speedily recovered; and it will give me very great pleasure if you allow me to suppose that its value is not diminished by having been restored through my means."

A tear mingled with the wine which the Baron filled, as he proposed a cup of gratitude to Colonel Talbot and "The Prosperity of the united Houses of Waverley Honour and Bradwardine!"

It only remains for me to say that as no wish was ever uttered with more affectionate sincerity, there are few which, allowing for the necessary mutability of human events, have been, upon the whole, more happily fulfilled.

CHAPTER XLIII

A POSTSCRIPT WHICH SHOULD HAVE BEEN A PREFACE

OUR journey is now finished, gentle reader; and if your patience has accompanied me through these sheets, the contract is, on your part, strictly fulfilled. Yet, like the driver who has received his full hire, I still linger near you, and make, with becoming diffidence, a trifling additional claim upon your bounty and good-nature. You are as free, however, to shut the volume of the one petitioner, as to close your door in the face of the other.

This should have been a prefatory chapter, but for two reasons : first, that most novel readers, as my own conscience reminds me, are apt to be guilty of the sin of omission respecting that same matter of prefaces; secondly, that it is a general custom with that class of students to begin with the last chapter of a work, — so that, after all, these remarks, being introduced last in order, have still the best chance to be read in their proper place.

There is no European nation which, within the course of half a century or little more, has undergone so complete a change as this kingdom of Scotland. The effects of the insurrection of 1745, — the destruction of the patriarchal power of the Highland chiefs, the abolition of the heritable jurisdictions of the Lowland nobility and barons, the total eradication of the Jacobite party, which, averse to intermingle with the English or adopt their customs, long continued to pride themselves upon maintaining ancient Scottish manners and customs, — commenced this innovation. The gradual influx of wealth and extension of commerce have since united to render the present people of Scotland a class of beings as different from their grandfathers as the existing English are from those of Queen Elizabeth's time. The political and economical effects of these changes have been traced by Lord Selkirk with great precision and accuracy. But the change, though steadily and rapidly progressive, has, nevertheless, been gradual; and like those who drift down the stream of a deep and smooth river, we are not aware of the progress we have made until we fix our eye on the now distant point from which we have been drifted. Such of the present generation as can recollect the last twenty or twenty-five years of the eighteenth century will be fully sensible of the truth of this statement, especially if their acquaintance and connections lay among those who, in my younger time, were facetiously called "folks of the old leaven," who still cherished a lingering, though hopeless, attachment to the house of Stewart. This race has now almost entirely vanished from the land, and with it, doubtless, much absurd political prejudice; but also, many living examples of singular and disinterested attachment to the principles of loyalty which they received from their fathers, and of old Scottish faith, hospitality, worth, and honour.

It was my accidental lot, though not born a Highlander (which may be an apology for much bad Gaelic), to reside, during my childhood and youth, among persons of the above description; and now, for the purpose of preserving some idea of the ancient manners of which I have witnessed the almost total extinction, I have embodied in imaginary scenes, and ascribed to fictitious characters, a part of the incidents which I then received from those who were actors in them. Indeed, the most romantic parts of this narrative are precisely those which have a foundation in fact. The exchange of mutual protection between a Highland gentleman and an officer of rank in the king's service, together with the spirited manner in which the latter asserted his right to return the favour he had received, is literally true. The accident by a musket-shot, and the heroic reply imputed to Flora, relate to a lady of rank not long deceased. And scarce a gentleman who was " in hiding " after the battle of Culloden but could tell a tale of strange concealments and of wild and hair's-breadth 'scapes, as extraordinary as any which I have ascribed to my heroes. Of this, the escape of Charles Edward himself, as the most prominent, is the most striking example. The accounts of the battle of Preston and skirmish at Clifton are taken from the narrative of intelligent eye-witnesses, and corrected from the " History of the Rebellion " by the late venerable author of " Douglas." The Lowland Scottish gentlemen and the subordinate characters are not given as individual portraits, but are drawn from the general habits of the period, of which I have witnessed some remnants in my younger days, and partly gathered from tradition.

It has been my object to describe these persons, not by a caricatured and exaggerated use of the national dialect, but by their habits, manners, and feelings, so as in some distant degree to emulate the admirable Irish portraits drawn by Miss Edgeworth, so different from the "Teagues" and "dear joys" who so long, with the most perfect family resemblance to each other, occupied the drama and the novel.

I feel no confidence, however, in the manner in which I have executed my purpose. Indeed, so little was I satisfied with my production that I laid it aside in an unfinished state, and only found it again by mere accident among other waste-papers in an old cabinet, the drawers of which I was rummaging, in order to accommodate a friend with some fishing-tackle, after it had been mislaid for several years. Two works upon similar subjects, by female authors whose genius is highly creditable to their country, have appeared in the interval, — I mean Mrs. Hamilton's "Glenburnie," and the late account of "Highland Superstitions." But the first is confined to the rural habits of Scotland, of which it has given a picture with striking and impressive fidelity; and the traditional records of the respectable and ingenious Mrs. Grant of Laggan are of a nature distinct from the fictitious narrative which I have here attempted.

I would willingly persuade myself that the preceding work will not be found altogether uninteresting. To elder persons it will recall scenes and characters familiar to their youth; and to the rising generation the tale may present some idea of the manners of their forefathers.

Yet I heartily wish that the task of tracing the evanescent manners of his own country had employed the pen of the only man in Scotland who could have done it justice, — of him so eminently distinguished in elegant literature, and whose sketches of Colonel Caustic and Umphraville are perfectly blended with the finer traits of national character. I should in that case have had more pleasure as a reader than I shall ever feel in the pride of a successful author, should these sheets confer upon me that envied distinction. And as I have inverted the usual arrangement, placing these remarks at the end of the work to which they refer, I will venture on a second violation of form by closing the whole with a Dedication, —

THESE VOLUMES

BEING RESPECTFULLY INSCRIBED

TO

OUR SCOTTISH ADDISON,

HENRY MACKENZIE,

BY

AN UNKNOWN ADMIRER

OF

HIS GENIUS.

AUTHOR'S NOTES

Note I. p. 67. — MAC-FARLANE'S LANTERN

The Clan of Mac-Farlane, occupying the fastnesses of the western side of Loch Lomond, were great depredators on the Low Country, and as their excursions were made usually by night, the moon was proverbially called their lantern. Their celebrated pibroch of *Hoggil nam Bo*, which is the name of their gathering tune, intimates similar practices, the sense being, —

> We are bound to drive the bullocks,
> All by hollows, hirsts, and hillocks,
> > Through the sleet and through the rain.
> When the moon is beaming low
> On frozen lake and hills of snow,
> Bold and heartily we go,
> > And all for little gain.

Note II. p. 70. — THE CASTLE OF DOUNE

This noble ruin is dear to my recollection, from associations which have been long and painfully broken. It holds a commanding station on the banks of the river Teith, and has been one of the largest castles in Scotland. Murdock, Duke of Albany, the founder of this stately pile, was beheaded on the Castle-hill of Stirling, from which he might see the towers of Doune, the monument of his fallen greatness.

In 1745–46, as stated in the text, a garrison on the part of the Chevalier was put into the castle, then less ruinous than at present. It was commanded by Mr. Stewart of Balloch, as governor for Prince Charles; he was a man of property near Callander. This castle became at that time the actual scene of a romantic escape made by John Home, the author of " Douglas," and some other prisoners, who, having been taken at the battle of Falkirk, were confined there by the insurgents. The poet, who had in his own mind a large stock of that romantic and enthusiastic spirit of adventure which he has described as animating the youthful hero of his drama, devised and undertook the perilous enterprise of escaping from his prison. He inspired his companions with his sentiments, and when every attempt at open force was deemed hopeless, they resolved to twist their bed-clothes into ropes, and thus to descend. Four persons, with Home himself, reached the ground in safety. But the rope broke with the fifth, who was a tall, lusty man. The sixth was Thomas Barrow, a brave young Englishman, a particular friend of Home's. Determined to take the risk, even in such unfavourable circumstances, Barrow committed himself to the broken rope, slid down on it as far as it could assist him, and then let himself drop. His friends beneath succeeded in breaking his fall. Nevertheless, he dislocated his ankle, and had several of his ribs broken. His companions, however, were able to bear him off in safety.

The Highlanders next morning sought for their prisoners with great activity. An old gentleman told the Author he remembered seeing the commander, Stewart,

> Bloody with spurring, fiery red with haste,

riding furiously through the country in quest of the fugitives.

Note III. p. 127. — FIELD-PIECE IN THE HIGHLAND ARMY

This circumstance, which is historical, as well as the description that precedes it, will remind the reader of the war of La Vendée, in which the royalists, consisting chiefly of insurgent peasantry, attached a prodigious and even superstitious interest to the possession of a piece of brass ordnance, which they called Marie Jeanne.

The Highlanders of an early period were afraid of cannon, with the noise and effect of which they were totally unacquainted. It was by means of three or four small pieces of artillery that the Earls of Huntly and Errol, in James VI.'s time, gained a great victory at Glenlivat over a numerous Highland army commanded by the Earl of Argyle. At the battle of the Bridge of Dee, General Middleton obtained by his artillery a similar success, the Highlanders not being able to stand the discharge of "Musket's-Mother," which was the

name they bestowed on great-guns. In an old ballad on the
battle of the Bridge of Dee, these verses occur : —

> The Highlandmen are pretty men
> For handling sword and shield ;
> But yet they are but simple men
> To stand a stricken field.
>
> The Highlandmen are pretty men
> For target and claymore ;
> But yet they are but naked men
> To face the cannon's roar.
>
> For the cannons roar on a summer night
> Like thunder in the air ;
> Was never man in Highland garb
> Would face the cannon fair.

But the Highlanders of 1745 had got far beyond the simplicity of their forefathers, and showed throughout the whole
war how little they dreaded artillery, although the common
people still attached some consequence to the possession of
the field-piece, which led to this disquisition.

Note IV. p. 144. — ANDERSON OF WHITBURGH

The faithful friend who pointed out the pass by which the
Highlanders moved from Tranent to Seaton, was Robert Anderson, junior, of Whitburgh, a gentleman of property in East
Lothian. He had been interrogated by the Lord George
Murray concerning the possibility of crossing the uncouth and
marshy piece of ground which divided the armies, and which
he described as impracticable. When dismissed, he recollected
that there was a circuitous path leading eastward through the
marsh into the plain, by which the Highlanders might turn
the flank of Sir John Cope's position without being exposed
to the enemy's fire. Having mentioned his opinion to Mr.
Hepburn of Keith, who instantly saw its importance, he was
encouraged by that gentleman to awake Lord George Murray
and communicate the idea to him. Lord George received the
information with grateful thanks, and instantly awakened
Prince Charles, who was sleeping in the field with a bunch of
pease under his head. The Adventurer received with alacrity
the news that there was a possibility of bringing an excellently
provided army to a decisive battle with his own irregular
forces. His joy on the occasion was not very consistent with

371

the charge of cowardice brought against him by Chevalier
Johnstone, a discontented follower, whose Memoirs possess at
least as much of a romantic as an historical character.   Even
by the account of the Chevalier himself, the prince was at the
head of the second line of the Highland army during the battle, of which he says, "It was gained with such rapidity that
in the second line, where I was still by the side of the prince,
we saw no other enemy than those who were lying on the
ground killed and wounded, *though we were not more than fifty
paces behind our first line, running always as fast as we could to
overtake them.*"

This passage in the Chevalier's Memoirs places the prince
within fifty paces of the heat of the battle, — a position which
would never have been the choice of one unwilling to take a
share of its dangers.   Indeed, unless the chiefs had complied
with the young Adventurer's proposal to lead the van in person, it does not appear that he could have been deeper in
the action.

Note V. p. 149. — DEATH OF COLONEL GARDINER

The death of this good Christian and gallant man is thus
given by his affectionate biographer, Dr. Doddridge, from
the evidence of eye-witnesses: —

"He continued all night under arms, wrapped up in his
cloak, and generally sheltered under a rick of barley, which
happened to be in the field.   About three in the morning he
called his domestic servants to him, of which there were four
in waiting.   He dismissed three of them with most affectionate Christian advice, and such solemn charges relating to the
performance of their duty and the care of their souls as
seemed plainly to intimate that he apprehended it was at least
very probable he was taking his last farewell of them.   There is
great reason to believe that he spent the little remainder of
the time, which could not be much above an hour, in those
devout exercises of soul which had been so long habitual to
him, and to which so many circumstances did then concur to
call him.   The army was alarmed by break of day by the noise
of the rebels' approach, and the attack was made before sunrise, yet when it was light enough to discern what passed.   As
soon as the enemy came within gunshot they made a furious
fire ; and it is said that the dragoons, which constituted the
left wing, immediately fled.   The colonel at the beginning of

the onset, which in the whole lasted but a few minutes, received a wound by a bullet in his left breast, which made him give a sudden spring in his saddle; upon which his servant, who led the horse, would have persuaded him to retreat, but he said it was only a wound in the flesh, and fought on, though he presently after received a shot in his right thigh. In the meantime it was discerned that some of the enemy fell by him, and particularly one man, who had made him a treacherous visit but a few days before, with great profession of zeal for the present establishment.

"Events of this kind pass in less time than the description of them can be written, or than it can be read. The colonel was for a few moments supported by his men, and particularly by that worthy person Lieutenant-Colonel Whitney, who was shot through the arm here, and a few months after fell nobly at the battle of Falkirk, and by Lieutenant West, a man of distinguished bravery, as also by about fifteen dragoons, who stood by him to the last. But after a faint fire, the regiment in general was seized with a panic; and though their colonel and some other gallant officers did what they could to rally them once or twice, they at last took a precipitate flight. And just in the moment when Colonel Gardiner seemed to be making a pause to deliberate what duty required him to do in such circumstances, an accident happened which must, I think, in the judgment of every worthy and generous man, be allowed a sufficient apology for exposing his life to so great hazard, when his regiment had left him. He saw a party of the foot, who were then bravely fighting near him, and whom he was ordered to support, had no officer to head them; upon which he said eagerly, in the hearing of the person from whom I had this account, 'These brave fellows will be cut to pieces for want of a commander,' or words to that effect; which while he was speaking, he rode up to them and cried out, 'Fire on, my lads, and fear nothing.' But just as the words were out of his mouth, a Highlander advanced towards him with a scythe fastened to a long pole, with which he gave him so dreadful a wound on his right arm that his sword dropped out of his hand; and at the same time several others coming about him while he was thus dreadfully entangled with that cruel weapon, he was dragged off from his horse. The moment he fell, another Highlander, who, if the king's evidence at Carlisle may be credited (as I

know not why they should not, though the unhappy creature
died denying it), was one Mac-Naught, who was executed about
a year after, gave him a stroke either with a broadsword or a
Lochaber-axe (for my informant could not exactly distinguish) on the hinder part of his head, which was the mortal
blow. All that his faithful attendant saw further at this time
was that as his hat was falling off he took it in his left hand
and waved it as a signal to him to retreat, and added, what
were the last words he ever heard him speak, ' Take care of
yourself ;' upon which the servant retired. (*Some remarkable
Passages in the Life of Colonel James Gardiner, by P. Doddridge,
D.D.* London, 1747, p. 187.)

I may remark on this extract that it confirms the account
given in the text of the resistance offered by some of the English infantry. Surprised by a force of a peculiar and unusual
description, their opposition could not be long or formidable,
especially as they were deserted by the cavalry and those who
undertook to manage the artillery. But although the affair
was soon decided, I have always understood that many of the
infantry showed an inclination to do their duty.

Note VI. p. 150. — THE LAIRD OF BALMAWHAPPLE

It is scarcely necessary to say that the character of this bru-
tal young laird is entirely imaginary. A gentleman, however,
who resembled Balmawhapple in the article of courage only,
fell at Preston in the manner described. A Perthshire gentleman of high honour and respectability, one of the handful of
cavalry who followed the fortunes of Charles Edward, pursued
the fugitive dragoons almost alone till near St. Clement's
Wells, where the efforts of some of the officers had prevailed
on a few of them to make a momentary stand. Perceiving at
this moment that they were pursued by only one man and a
couple of servants, they turned upon him and cut him down
with their swords. I remember, when a child, sitting on his
grave, where the grass long grew rank and green, distinguishing it from the rest of the field. A female of the family then
residing at St. Clement's Wells used to tell me the tragedy, of
which she had been an eye-witness, and showed me in evidence one of the silver clasps of the unfortunate gentleman's
waistcoat.

AUTHOR'S NOTES

Note VII. p. 167. — ANDREA DE FERRARA

The name of Andrea de Ferrara is inscribed on all the Scottish broadswords which are accounted of peculiar excellence. Who this artist was, what were his fortunes, and when he flourished, have hitherto defied the research of antiquaries; only it is in general believed that Andrea de Ferrara was a Spanish or Italian artificer brought over by James IV. or V. to instruct the Scots in the manufacture of sword blades. Most barbarous nations excel in the fabrication of arms; and the Scots had attained great proficiency in forging swords so early as the field of Pinkie, — at which period the historian Patten describes them as " all notably broad and thin, universally made to slice, and of such exceeding good temper that as I never saw any so good, so I think it hard to devise better" (*Account of Somerset's Expedition*).

It may be observed that the best and most genuine Andrea Ferraras have a crown marked on the blades.

Note VIII. p. 235. — PRINCE CHARLES EDWARD

The Author of "Waverley" has been charged with painting the young Adventurer in colours more amiable than his character deserved. But having known many individuals who were near his person, he has been described according to the light in which those eye-witnesses saw his temper and qualifications. Something must be allowed, no doubt, to the natural exaggerations of those who remembered him as the bold and adventurous prince in whose cause they had braved death and ruin; but is their evidence to give place entirely to that of a single malcontent?

I have already noticed the imputations thrown by the Chevalier Johnstone on the prince's courage. But some part at least of that gentleman's tale is purely romantic. It would not, for instance, be supposed that at the time he is favouring us with the highly wrought account of his amour with the adorable Peggie, the Chevalier Johnstone was a married man, whose grandchild is now alive, or that the whole circumstantial story concerning the outrageous vengeance taken by Gordon of Abbachie on a Presbyterian clergyman, is entirely apocryphal. At the same time, it may be admitted that the prince, like others of his family, did not esteem the services done him by his adherents so highly as he ought. Educated in high ideas of his hereditary right, he has been supposed to have held every exertion and sacrifice made in his cause as too much the duty of the person making it, to merit extravagant gratitude on his part. Dr. King's evidence (which his leaving the Jacobite interest renders somewhat doubtful) goes to strengthen this opinion.

The ingenious editor of Johnstone's Memoirs has quoted a story, said to be told by Helvetius, stating that Prince Charles Edward, far from voluntarily embarking on his daring expedition, was literally bound hand and foot, and to which he seems disposed to yield credit. Now, it being a fact as well known as any in his history, and, so far as I know, entirely undisputed, that the prince's personal entreaties and urgency positively forced Boisdale and Lochiel into insurrection, when they were earnestly desirous that he would put off his attempt until he could obtain a sufficient force from France, it will be very difficult to reconcile his alleged reluctance to undertake the expedition, with his desperately insisting on carrying the rising into effect, against the advice and entreaty of his most powerful and most sage partisans. Surely a man who had been carried bound on board the vessel which brought him to so desperate an enterprise, would have taken the opportunity afforded by the reluctance of his partisans, to return to France in safety.

It is averred in Johnstone's Memoirs that Charles Edward left the field of Culloden without doing the utmost to dispute the victory ; and, to give the evidence on both sides, there is in existence the more trustworthy testimony of Lord Elcho, who states that he himself earnestly exhorted the prince to charge at the head of the left wing, which was entire, and retrieve the day or die with honour. And on his counsel being declined, Lord Elcho took leave of him with a bitter execration, swearing he would never look on his face again, and kept his word.

On the other hand, it seems to have been the opinion of almost all the other officers that the day was irretrievably lost, one wing of the Highlanders being entirely routed, the rest of the army out-numbered, out-flanked, and in a condition totally hopeless. In this situation of things, the Irish officers who surrounded Charles's person interfered to force him off the field. A cornet who was close to the prince, left a strong attestation that he had seen Sir Thomas Sheridan seize the bridle of his horse and turn him round. There is some discrepancy of evidence ; but the opinion of Lord Elcho, a man of fiery temper, and desperate at the ruin which he beheld impending, cannot fairly be taken in prejudice of a character for courage which is intimated by the nature of the enterprise itself, by the prince's eagerness to fight on all occasions, by his determination to advance from Derby to London, and by the presence of mind which he manifested during the romantic perils of his escape. The Author is far from claiming for this unfortunate person the praise due to splendid talents ; but he continues to be of opinion that at the period of his enterprise he had a mind capable of facing danger and aspiring to fame.

That Charles Edward had the advantages of a graceful presence, courtesy, and an address and manner becoming his station, the Author never heard disputed by any who approached his person, nor does he conceive that these qualities are overcharged in the present attempt to sketch his portrait. The following extracts corroborative of the general opinion respecting the prince's amiable disposition are taken from a manuscript account of his romantic expedition by James Maxwell of Kirkconnell, of which I possess a copy by the friendship of J. Menzies, Esq., of Pitfoddells. The Author, though partial to the prince, whom he faithfully followed, seems to have been a fair and candid man, and well acquainted with the intrigues among the Adventurer's council :—

" Everybody was mightily taken with the prince's figure and personal behaviour; there was but one voice about them. Those whom interest or prejudice made a runaway to his cause, could not help acknowledging that they wished him well in all other respects, and could hardly blame him for his present undertaking. Sundry things had concurred to raise his character to the highest pitch, besides the greatness of the enterprise, and the conduct that had hitherto appeared in the execution of it. There were several instances of good-nature and humanity that had made a great impression on people's minds. I shall confine myself to two or three. Immediately after the battle, as the prince was riding along the ground that Cope's army had occupied a few minutes before, one of the officers came up to congratulate him, and said, pointing to the killed : ' Sir, there are your enemies at your feet.' The prince, far from exulting, expressed a great deal of compassion for his father's deluded subjects, whom he declared he was heartily

377

sorry to see in that posture. Next day, while the prince was at Pinkie House, a citizen of Edinburgh came to make some representation to Secretary Murray about the tents that city was ordered to furnish against a certain day. Murray happened to be out of the way, which the prince hearing of, called to have the gentleman brought to him, saying he would rather despatch the business, whatever it was, himself, than have the gentleman wait, which he did, by granting everything that was asked. So much affability in a young prince flushed with victory, drew encomiums even from his enemies. But what gave the people the highest idea of him was the negative he gave to a thing that very nearly concerned his interest, and upon which the success of his enterprise perhaps depended. It was proposed to send one of the prisoners to London to demand of that court a cartel for the exchange of prisoners taken, and to be taken, during this war, and to intimate that a refusal would be looked upon as a resolution on their part to give no quarter. It was visible a cartel would be of great advantage to the prince's affairs ; his friends would be more ready to declare for him if they had nothing to fear but the chance of war in the field ; and if the court of London refused to settle a cartel, the prince was authorised to treat his prisoners in the same manner the Elector of Hanover was determined to treat such of the prince's friends as might fall into his hands: it was urged that a few examples would compel the court of London to comply. It was to be presumed that the officers of the English army would make a point of it. They had never engaged in the service but upon such terms as are in use among all civilized nations, and it could be no stain upon their honour to lay down their commissions if these terms were not observed, and that owing to the obstinacy of their own prince. Though this scheme was plausible, and represented as very important, the prince could never be brought into it ; it was below him, he said, to make empty threats, and he would never put such as those into execution : he would never in cold blood take away lives which he had saved in heat of action, at the peril of his own. These were not the only proofs of good-nature the prince gave about this time. Every day produced something new of this kind. These things softened the rigour of a military government, which was only imputed to the necessity of his affairs, and which he endeavoured to make as gentle and easy as possible."

It has been said that the prince sometimes exacted more state and ceremonial than seemed to suit his condition; but, on the other hand, some strictness of etiquette was altogether indispensable where he must otherwise have been exposed to general intrusion. He could also endure with a good grace the retorts which his affectation of ceremony sometimes exposed him to. It is said, for example, that Grant of Glenmoriston, having made a hasty march to join Charles at the head of his clan, rushed into the prince's presence at Holyrood with unceremonious haste, without having attended to the duties of the toilet. The prince received him kindly, but not without a hint that a previous interview with the barber might not have been wholly unnecessary. " It is not beardless boys," answered the displeased chief, " who are to do your Royal Highness's turn." The Chevalier took the rebuke in good part.

On the whole, if Prince Charles had concluded his life soon after his miraculous escape, his character in history must have stood very high. As it was, his station is amongst those, a certain brilliant portion of whose life forms a remarkable contrast to all which precedes and all which follows it.

Note IX. p. 268. — OATH UPON THE DIRK

As the heathen deities contracted an indelible obligation if they swore by Styx, the Scottish Highlanders had usually some peculiar solemnity attached to an oath which they intended should be binding on them. Very frequently it consisted in laying their hand, as they swore, on their own drawn dirk; which dagger, becoming a party to the transaction, was invoked to punish any breach of faith. But by whatever ritual the oath was sanctioned, the party was extremely desirous to keep secret what the special oath was which he considered as irrevocable. This was a matter of great convenience, as he felt no scruple in breaking his asseveration when made in any other form than that which he accounted as peculiarly solemn ; and therefore readily granted any engagement which bound him no longer than he inclined. Whereas, if the oath which he accounted inviolable was once publicly known, no party with whom he might have occasion to contract would have rested satisfied with any other. Louis XI. of France practised the same sophistry, for he also had a peculiar species of oath, the only one which he was ever known to respect, and which, therefore, he was very unwilling to pledge. The only engagement which that wily tyrant accounted binding upon him, was an oath by the Holy Cross of Saint Lo d'Angers, which contained a portion of the True Cross. If he prevaricated after taking this oath, Louis believed he should die within the year. The Constable Saint-Paul, being invited to a personal conference with Louis, refused to meet the king unless he would agree to insure him safe conduct under sanction of this oath. But, says Comines, the king replied he would never again pledge that engagement to mortal man, though he was willing to take any other oath which could be devised. The treaty broke off, therefore, after much chaffering concerning the nature of the vow which Louis was to take. Such is the difference between the dictates of superstition and those of conscience.

GLOSSARY

A', all.
Aboon, abune, above.
Ae, one.
Aff, off.
Afore, before.
Ahint, behind.
Ain, own.
Aits, oats.
Amaist, almost.
Ambry, close cupboard for keeping cold victuals, bread, etc.
An, if.
Assoilzied, acquitted.
Assythment, satisfaction.
Auld, old.
Aye, always.

Baff, blow, bang, heavy thump.
Bagganet, bayonet.
Bailie, alderman or magistrate.
Bairn, child.
Baith, both.
Ban, curse.
Banes, bones.
Barley, barly, (from parley, *Fr.* parler), a truce; used by boys in their boisterous games.
Bauld, bald; also bold.
Bawbee, halfpenny.
Bawty, sly.
"Bees, in the," excited, bewildered.
Beflummit, palavered, flattered, bamboozled.
Begunk, a trick.
Belike, perhaps.
Ben (be-in), the inner apartment, within. "But and

ben," the out and in, — the front and back rooms of a cotter's hut.
Benempt, named.
"Bent, bide the," to endure misfortune.
Bicker, a wooden bowl.
Bide, stay.
Bieldy, sheltered.
Bigging, building.
Birly-man, a peace officer.
Black-fishing, poaching.
Bluid, blood.
Bodle, a copper coin, fraction of an English penny.
"Bogle about the bush," to beat about the bush.
Boune, to prepare.
Brander, to broil; a gridiron.
Bra', braw, brave, fine, beautiful.
"Brent bro," fair forehead.
Brogues, Highland shoes.
Broo, broth or soup.
Bruckle, brickle, brittle, ticklish, infirm.
Bruick, to enjoy.
Bruilzie, brawl, scuffle, disturbance.
Buckie, shell of a sea-snail, or any spiral shell of whatever size; a mischievous fellow who has an evil twist in his character.
Bullsegg, a half-gelded bull.
Buttock-mail, fine imposed on fornication in lieu of sitting on the stool of repentance.
Bydand, awaiting.

381

GLOSSARY

Ca', call.
Cadger, carrier, huckster.
Cailliachs, old women.
Callant, a young lad, a fine fellow.
Cam', came.
Canny, skilful, prudent, lucky; in a superstitious sense, good-conditioned and safe to deal with, trustworthy.
Carle, a churl, a gruff old man.
Cateran, kearn, Highland irregular soldier, freebooter.
Chields, young fellows.
Clachan, a hamlet.
Clamyhewit, a stroke, a hack.
Clash, tittle-tattle, scandal; to jabber.
Clatter, tattle.
Close, a narrow passage-way.
Clour, bump upon the head from a blow.
Cocky-leeky, leek soup in which a cock has been boiled.
Coronach, dirge.
Corrie, a mountain hollow.
Coup, to turn over.
"Cow yer cracks," hold your tongues.
Cracks, boasts.
Craig, neck, throat.
Crames, booths.
Curragh, a Highland boat or skiff.
Cut-lugged, crop-eared.

Daft, meddlesome, silly.
Daur, dare.
Deaving, deafening.
Decreet, order of decree.
Deil, the devil.
"Deil's buckie," devil's scamp.
Deliver, active, free in motion.
Diaoul, the devil.
Ding, to strike, to subdue.
Dinnle, tingle, thrill.
Doer, a steward.
Doiled, dazed, stupid, doating.
Doited, stupid, confused.
Dorlach, a bundle, a valise.
Dow (pronounced doo), a dove. A term of endearment.
Dowf, stupid, inactive, dull.

Drap, drop; drappie, little drop.
Drave, drove.
"Droghling and coghling," wheezing and blowing.
Dunniewassal, a Highland gentleman.

E'en, evening.
"Effeir of war," warlike guise.
Eneugh, enough.
Etter-cap, a cantankerous person.
Evite, to escape.
Ewast, nearest, contiguous.

Fa'ard, favoured.
Factory, stewardship.
Fallow, fellow.
"Far ben," in particular favour, very intimate.
Fauld, fold.
"Feal and divot," turf and thatch.
Feared, affected with fear.
Feck, a part of a thing.
Feifteen, the Jacobite rebellion of 1715.
Flemit, frightened.
Fleyt, chid.
Forbears, forefathers.
Foun, fun.
Frae, from.
Fule, fool.

Gad, an iron bar.
"Gaed aff," went off.
Gane, gone.
Gang, go.
Gar, to compel.
Garring, compelling.
Gaun, going.
Gear, property.
Ghaist, ghost.
Gin, if, suppose.
Gite, a noodle.
Gled, a kite.
Gleg, sharp, on the alert.
Glisk, a glimpse.
Gloaming, twilight.
Gowd, gold, money.
Graning, groaning.
"Graning carles," crop-eared, groaning humbugs.

Grat, cried, wept.
Gree, agree.
Grice, a sucking pig.
Gripple, greedy, griping, avaricious.
Gude, good.
Gudeman, husband.
Gulpin, a simpleton.

Ha', hall.
" **Hack and manger**," to live in prodigality and unconcern, reckless.
Hae, have.
Haggis, the national dish of Scotland, composed of the pluck, etc. of a sheep, with oatmeal, suet, onions, etc. boiled inside.
Hail, whole.
Hallan, the partition between the door and the fireplace.
Her, the Highland term for *my*.
Het, hot.
Hill-folk, name given to the Covenanters, who worshipped on the hills.
Hog, a sheep from six to fifteen months old.
Horning, enforcing payment of a debt.
Horse-cowper, horse-dealer.
" **Houlerying and poulerying**," hustling and pulling.
Houts, tuts.
Hurdies, buttocks.
Hurley-house; literally, last house, as the house now stands, or as it was last built.

Ilk, the same name. "Bradwardine of that ilk " = Bradwardine of Bradwardine.
Ilka, each.
Ingle, fire; **ingle-nook**, corner by the fire.
" **In the bees**," stupefied.
Intromit, to meddle with.

Justified, died in a good cause.

Keepit, kept.
Kemple, a quantity of straw.

Ken, know.
Kenn'd, cognizant of.
Kilt, the Highlander's short petticoat.
Kippage, a violent passion, disorder, confusion.
Kirk, church.
Kittle, tickle, ticklish.

Laird, lord of a manor, squire.
Landlouper, a tramp, an adventurer.
Leddy, lady.
" **Lee land**," grass or meadow land.
Lifted, to make a prey of, to capture.
Limmers, jades.
Loon, an idle fellow.
Loup, to leap.
Luckie, dame.
Lug, the ear; (*verb*), to carry about with one.
Lunzie, waist.

Mae, more.
Mains, demesne, farmhouse.
" **Mair tint at Sheriffmuir**," more men lost at the battle of Sheriffmuir.
Maist, most, almost.
" **Malt abune the meal**," the drink above the food, half-seas over.
Mask, to mash, to infuse.
Maun, must.
Mearns, Kincardineshire.
Merk = 13⅓ *d*. English money.
Merse, Berwickshire.
Mickle, much, great, large.
Mind, remember.
Morn, "the morn," to-morrow.
Morning, morning dram, or draught.
Mousted, powdered.
Munt, mount.
Mutchkin, an English pint.

Na, nae, no, not.
Naig, nag.
Nan, of.
Nane, none.
Natheless, nevertheless.

GLOSSARY

Neb, nose.
Needna, need not.
Nolt, oxen, black cattle.

"Old to do," more than enough to do.
"Ow ay," oh, yes.
Ower, over.
"Oyer and Terminer," hearing and determining a cause. A legal phrase.

Paitrick, a partridge.
Panged, crammed, stuffed.
Paunie, a peacock.
Pingle, a fuss.
Pinner, a cap with lappets, formerly worn by women of rank.
Plack, a small copper coin.
Plenish, to provide.
Ploy, employment.
Pottinger, an apothecary.
Powney, pony.
Powtering, dabbling.
Pratty, pretty.
Public, public-house, or inn.
Pund Scots = 1s. 8d. English money.

Quean, a young woman, a wench. Sometimes used jocularly, but oftener disrespectfully.

Rapscallion, rascal.
Redd, to put to rights.
Redding, clearing, putting to rights.
Reeked, smoked.
Reises, loose brushwood.
Riggs, fields.
Rin, run.
Rinthereout, a vagabond, a cut-throat.
Rowed, rolled.

Sae, so.
Sair, sore, very.
Sall, shall.
Sark, a shirt.
Saumon, salmon.
Saut, salt.
Scart, to scratch.

Schellum, a low, worthless fellow.
Shanks, legs.
She, the Highland term for *I* or *he*.
Sheers, scissors.
Shouther, shoulder.
"Sic a," "siccan a," such a.
"Sidier roy," red-coated soldiers.
Siller, money.
Sliver, slit, slice.
Sma', small.
Smoky, suspicious, doubtful.
Sneck, a latch.
Sorted, accommodated.
Sowens, a sort of gruel.
Speerings, askings; answers to questions asked, information.
Spence, a dispensary, a parlour.
Sprack, sprightly, lively.
Sprechery, small plunder.
Spuilzie, spoil.
Stieve, firm, stiff.
Stoor, stern, stubborn.
Strae, straw.
Streak, to stroke down.
Swuir, swore.
Syne, since, then, after that, in that case.

Tauld, told.
Thae, these.
Thir, these.
Thraw, a twist.
Threepit, averred, insisted.
Throstle, the thrush.
Till, to; till 't, to it.
Tirrievies, tantrums.
Tocher, a dowry.
Tocherless, portionless.
Toun, hamlet, precincts of a manor.
Trindling, trundling.
Trow, believe.
Tuilzie, a squabble, a skirmish.
Twa, two.
Tyke, a dog, a snarling fellow.

Umquhile, whilom, ci-devant, late.
Unco, very, particularly.
Unsonsy, saucy, dangerous.
Usquebaugh, whisky.

GLOSSARY

Vivers, food, victuals.

Wa', wall.
Wad, wald, would.
Wadset, pledge.
Walise, saddle-bag, portmanteau.
Wan. got, won.
Wanchancy, unlucky.
Ware, to expend, to waste.
Warrandice, security.
Wee, little.
Weel, weil, well.
Weel-far'd, handsome.
Weising, whisking, putting in the way.

Wha, who.
Whar, where.
"What for," why.
Wheen, a few.
"While syne," some time ago.
Whiles, sometimes.
Whilk, which.
Whinge, to whine.
Whingeing, fawning and whining like a dog.
Wi', with.
Winna, will not.
Wiske, a quick stroke or motion.
Wot, to know.

Yate, gate.

*This book, designed
by William B. Taylor,
is a production
of Heron Books, London*

Printed in Switzerland

THE CAMBRIDGE BIBLE COMMENTARY
NEW ENGLISH BIBLE

GENERAL EDITORS
P. R. ACKROYD, A. R. C. LEANEY, J. W. PACKER

1 AND 2 ESDRAS

THE FIRST AND
SECOND BOOKS OF
ESDRAS

COMMENTARY ON I ESDRAS BY

R. J. COGGINS

AND

COMMENTARY ON 2 ESDRAS BY

M. A. KNIBB

Lecturers in Old Testament Studies, King's College, London

CAMBRIDGE UNIVERSITY PRESS

CAMBRIDGE

LONDON · NEW YORK · MELBOURNE

Published by the Syndics of the Cambridge University Press
The Pitt Building, Trumpington Street, Cambridge CB2 1RP
Bentley House, 200 Euston Road, London NW1 2DB
32 East 57th Street, New York, NY 10022, USA
296 Beaconsfield Parade, Middle Park, Melbourne 3206, Australia

First published 1979

Printed in Great Britain at the
University Press, Cambridge

Library of Congress cataloguing in publication data
Bible. O.T. Apocrypha. 1 Edras. English. New English. 1978. The first
and second books of Esdras.
(The Cambridge Bible commentary, New English Bible)
Includes index.
1. Bible. O.T. Apocrypha. 1 Esdras – Commentaries. 2. Bible. O.T.
Apocrypha. 2 Esdras – Commentaries. I. Bible. O.T. Apocrypha.
2 Esdras. English. New English. 1978. II. Coggins, R. J., 1929–. III.
Knibb, M. A., 1938–. IV. Series.
BS1713 1978 229'.1'077 78-16420
ISBN 0 521 08656 6   hard covers
ISBN 0 521 09757 6   paperback

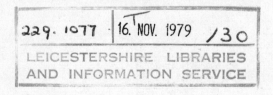

GENERAL EDITORS' PREFACE

The aim of this series is to provide the text of the New English Bible closely linked to a commentary in which the results of modern scholarship are made available to the general reader. Teachers and young people have been especially kept in mind. The commentators have been asked to assume no specialized theological knowledge, and no knowledge of Greek, Latin and Hebrew. Bare references to other literature and multiple references to other parts of the Bible have been avoided. Actual quotations have been given as often as possible.

The completion of the New Testament part of the series in 1967 provided the basis upon which the production of the much larger Old Testament and Apocrypha series could be undertaken. With the publication of this volume and its companion (*Genesis 12–50*), the whole series is complete. The welcome accorded to the series in its earlier stages was an encouragement to the editors to follow the same general pattern throughout, and an attempt has been made to take account of criticisms which have been offered. The Old Testament and Apocrypha volumes have included the full footnotes provided by the translators, since these are essential for the understanding of the text.

Within the severe limits imposed by the size and scope of the series, each commentator has attempted to set out the main findings of recent biblical scholarship and to describe the historical background to the text.

The main theological issues have also been critically discussed.

Much attention has been given to the form of the volumes. The aim is to produce books each of which will be read consecutively from first to last page. The introductory material leads naturally into the text, which itself leads into the alternating sections of the commentary.

The series is accompanied by three volumes of a more general character. *Understanding the Old Testament* sets out to provide the larger historical and archaeological background, to say something about the life and thought of the people of the Old Testament, and to answer the question 'Why should we study the Old Testament?' *The Making of the Old Testament* is concerned with the formation of the books of the Old Testament and Apocrypha in the context of the ancient Near Eastern world, and with the ways in which these books have come down to us in the life of the Jewish and Christian communities. *Old Testament Illustrations* contains maps, diagrams and photographs with an explanatory text. These three volumes are designed to provide material helpful to the understanding of the individual books and their commentaries, but they are also prepared so as to be of use quite independently.

With the completion of this project, there are many whom the General Editors wish to thank. The contributors who have produced their manuscripts and co-operated willingly in revisions suggested to them must clearly be mentioned first. With them we thank the succession of members of the staff of the Cambridge University Press, but above all Mr Michael H. Black, now Publisher at the Press, who has joined so fully in the planning and development of the series and who has been present at all the editorial meetings from the initiation of the project to its conclusion.

P.R.A.
A.R.C.L.
J.W.P.

CONTENTS

CONTENTS

THE FOOTNOTES TO THE
N.E.B. TEXT

The footnotes to the N.E.B. text are designed to help the reader either to understand particular points of detail – the meaning of a name, the presence of a play upon words – or to give information about the actual text. Where the Hebrew (Greek or Latin) text appears to be erroneous, or there is doubt about its precise meaning, it may be necessary to turn to manuscripts which offer a different wording, or to ancient translations of the text which may suggest a better reading, or to offer a new explanation based upon conjecture. In such cases, the footnotes supply very briefly an indication of the evidence, and whether the solution proposed is one that is regarded as possible or as probable. Various abbreviations are used in the footnotes:

(1) Some abbreviations are simply of terms used in explaining a point: *ch(s)*., chapter(s); *cp*., compare; *lit*., literally; *mng*., meaning; *MS(S)*., manuscript(s), i.e. Hebrew manuscript(s), unless otherwise stated; *om*., omit(s); *or*, indicating an alternative interpretation; *poss*., possible; *prob*., probable; *rdg*., reading; *Vs(s)*., Version(s).

(2) Other abbreviations indicate sources of information from which better interpretations or readings may be obtained.

Aq.   Aquila, a Greek translator of the Old Testament (perhaps about A.D. 130) characterized by great literalness.

Aram.   Aramaic – may refer to the text in this language (used in parts of Ezra and Daniel), or to the meaning of an Aramaic word. Aramaic belongs to the same language family as Hebrew, and is known from about 1000 B.C. over a wide area of the Middle East, including Palestine.

Heb.   Hebrew – may refer to the Hebrew text or may indicate the literal meaning of the Hebrew word.

Josephus   Flavius Josephus (A.D. 37/8–about 100), author of the *Jewish Antiquities*, a survey of the whole history of his people, directed partly at least to a non-Jewish audience, and of various other works, notably one on the *Jewish War* (that of A.D. 66–73) and a defence of Judaism (*Against Apion*).

Luc. Sept.   Lucian's recension of the Septuagint, an important edition made in Antioch in Syria about the end of the third century A.D.

Pesh.   Peshitta or Peshitto, the Syriac version of the Old Testament. Syriac is the name given chiefly to a form of Eastern Aramaic used by the Christian community. The translation varies in quality, and is at many points influenced by the Septuagint or the Targums.

Sam.   Samaritan Pentateuch – the form of the first five books of the Old Testament as used by the Samaritan community. It is written in Hebrew in a special form of the Old Hebrew script, and preserves an important form of the text, somewhat influenced by Samaritan ideas.

Scroll(s)   Scroll(s), commonly called the Dead Sea Scrolls, found at or near Qumran from 1947 onwards. These important manuscripts shed light on the state of the Hebrew text as it was developing in the last centuries B.C. and the first century A.D.

Sept.   Septuagint (meaning 'seventy'; often abbreviated as the Roman numeral LXX), the name given to the main Greek version of the Old Testament. According to tradition, the Pentateuch was translated in Egypt in the third century B.C. by 70 (or 72) translators, six from each tribe, but the precise nature of its origin and development is not fully known. It was intended to provide Greek-speaking Jews with a convenient translation. Subsequently it came to be much revered by the Christian community.

Symm.   Symmachus, another Greek translator of the Old Testament (beginning of the third century A.D.), who tried to combine literalness with good style. Both Lucian and Jerome viewed his version with favour.

Targ.   Targum, a name given to various Aramaic versions of the Old Testament, produced over a long period and eventually standardized, for the use of Aramaic-speaking Jews.

Theod.   Theodotion, the author of a revision of the Septuagint (probably second century A.D.), very dependent on the Hebrew text.

Vulg.   Vulgate, the most important Latin version of the Old Testament, produced by Jerome about A.D. 400, and the text most used throughout the Middle Ages in western Christianity.

[. . .]   In the text itself square brackets are used to indicate probably late additions to the Hebrew text.

(Fuller discussion of a number of these points may be found in *The Making of the Old Testament* in this series.)

THE FIRST AND SECOND BOOKS OF

ESDRAS

✳ ✳ ✳ ✳ ✳ ✳ ✳ ✳ ✳ ✳ ✳ ✳ ✳

THE EZRA WRITINGS

To the modern reader, one of the most perplexing pheno-
mena which confront him when he begins any study of the
Bible concerns the authorship of books. There are two basic
difficulties which affect many parts of the Old and New
Testaments, and a third which is more characteristic of,
though not peculiar to, the Apocrypha. The two more
general problems are, first, the fact that many biblical books –
prophetic collections, wisdom writings, gospels – have gone
through a long stage of oral transmission, with resultant
modifications, before being set down in writing; and secondly,
the ancient world differed from modern ideas of authenticity
or 'copyright'. Additions might be made to existing collections in the belief that if the 'founding father' of such a
collection were still alive, the addition now being made
would have been his message for a new situation. The later
chapters of the book of Isaiah, especially chs. 40–66, or some
of the letters attributed to Paul but probably written by a
later writer (for example, Ephesians) can best be explained
in this way.

In the last centuries B.C., however, another custom became common, and this represents the third point to which
reference has been made. New writings were issued under a
pseudonym, usually some famous figure from Israel's past.
Many suggestions have been put forward to explain this
custom, ranging from a fear of being punished by authority
if the writer's real identity was discovered, to a simple
desire for secrecy and mystification. Perhaps the established

custom that existing writings might be added to and up-dated provides at least part of the explanation. In any case, it should be borne in mind that the book of Daniel is usually held to be an example of such pseudonymous writing, and that there are several examples of this practice in the Apocrypha, including the two books of Esdras.

Though many figures from Israel's past – Adam, Abraham, Moses, the prophets – were associated with these pseudonymous writings, certain individuals became particularly prominent in this connection. Among them was Ezra. He lived in the fifth or fourth century B.C., and played a leading part in establishing the Jerusalem community of his time (see Ezra 7–10; Neh. 8). Later tradition came to regard him as the second founder of Judaism, after Moses, and so it is not surprising that he should have given his name to various pseudonymous writings.

Both the books dealt with in this volume are linked with Ezra in this way. ('Esdras' is simply the Greek form of the Hebrew name.) That is, however, virtually all that they have in common. Even the most cursory reading will show that they represent very different kinds of writing. It is essential to remember that 1 and 2 Esdras cannot be regarded in the same way as 1 and 2 Kings, for example, where the second book is simply a continuation of the first. The first and second books of Esdras stand quite apart. Before examining each book separately, however, it is useful to set out in a table the various names which have been given in different traditions to some of the writings associated with Ezra, since they are very liable to cause confusion. From this point on, the two books are treated quite separately.

The titles of the Ezra literature

Title in the N.E.B. (and other English versions)	Title in the Septuagint (Greek Bible)	Title in the Vulgate (Latin Bible)	Original language
Ezra	} Esdras b	I Esdras	Hebrew and Aramaic
Nehemiah	} Esdras b	II Esdras	Hebrew
1 Esdras	Esdras a	III Esdras	Greek (? – see p. 6)
2 Esdras	No equivalent	IV Esdras*	Hebrew (lost; the work is known only from Latin and other translations)

* The custom is also found of dividing this book still further, '4 Ezra' being applied to chs. 3–14, with chs. 1–2 being called '5 Ezra' and chs. 15–16 '6 Ezra': see the commentary on these sections (pp. 76–7, 283–4).

3

THE FIRST BOOK OF
ESDRAS

✳ ✳ ✳ ✳ ✳ ✳ ✳ ✳ ✳ ✳ ✳ ✳ ✳

THE LITERARY PROBLEMS

Biblical scholars have sometimes been accused by general readers of creating problems where none existed. Such a charge could never be justified in regard to 1 Esdras, where the problems are all too obvious. No clear consensus of opinion has emerged concerning the date, the purpose, or the language of the book, nor as to its relation to earlier writings dealing with the same events.

The last difficulty may provide the most convenient starting-point. The period of history dealt with is from the seventh to the fifth or early fourth centuries B.C., from the reign of Josiah, king of Judah, to the time of Ezra. Most of the book bears a close relationship to 2 Chron. 35–6, the book of Ezra, and that part of the book of Nehemiah which deals with the activity of Ezra (7: 73b – 8: 13). But three points are at once noteworthy: (1) the material in Ezra 4: 7–24, which is there arranged on a thematic rather than a chrono-logical basis, is here placed in a different context, in ch. 2; (2) 1 Esdras 3 and 4, entitled in the N.E.B. *A debate at the Persian court*, have no parallel in Ezra; (3) the book apparently breaks off in mid-sentence at 9: 55 (see the N.E.B. footnote at the end of the book). It is noteworthy, however, that at this point in the Old Testament books of Ezra and Nehemiah we have reached the last reference to the work of Ezra (Neh. 8: 13), as the later references (Neh. 12: 26 and 36) are probably later additions to the text. It is therefore not impossible that the conclusion has in fact been reached. It appears that no reference is made to Nehemiah, though the attempt has

4

sometimes been made to find allusions to him (in particular see 5: 40 and the commentary at that point).

Enough has been said to show that 1 Esdras represents a free rendering in Greek of a selected part of the work of the Chronicler. As the table on p. 3 has indicated, it existed alongside another, more literal translation of the books of Ezra and Nehemiah (Esdras b) in the Greek Bible. Broadly speaking, two main views have been held about the relation of 1 Esdras to the corresponding parts of the Old Testament books. One values 1 Esdras highly as providing an ancient and reliable tradition, giving us a better chronology of the events described in so confusing a way in Ezra 4, and avoiding entirely the overlap of the ministries of Ezra and Nehemiah which presents difficulties for the understanding of the Old Testament books. The other view is more sceptical of the independent value of 1 Esdras, on the grounds that a more credible historical presentation is just as likely to come from a late revision as from early and reliable tradition.

It is not possible here to enter into this argument in detail, but, despite a number of recent attempts to establish the reliability of the historical traditions underlying 1 Esdras, it seems more likely that we are here presented with a late attempt, probably from the very last centuries B.C., to set out a less confused account of the traditions relating to Ezra. Thus, the omission of all references to Nehemiah may be due to an early tradition which recognized that his mission was quite separate from that of Ezra, but it may also be due to the fact that the traditions relating to Ezra and Nehemiah developed quite distinctly within Judaism. Thus in 2 Macc. 1: 18 – 2: 13 and Ecclus. 49: 13 Nehemiah is mentioned without reference to Ezra, whereas in the chronicles of the Samaritan community as well as in 1 Esdras, it is Ezra who is the focus of attention without mention of Nehemiah. Ezra was a controversial figure in the Judaism of the last centuries B.C., and the beginning of the Christian era, and part at least of the purpose of 1 Esdras was probably to magnify his achievement in establishing the law as the basis of true Judaism. He is claimed to be the last of those great formative figures in Judaism: Josiah, Zerubbabel and Ezra.

Such a claim might be felt to be especially necessary for Jews who did not speak Hebrew and who lived away from Palestine. As with almost everything else connected with I Esdras, there is dispute about the original language of the book. It has come down to us in Greek, and it is usually held that this was its original language. The suggestion has also been made, however, that underlying our present work is a now lost original in either Hebrew or Aramaic. Again, certainty is impossible, but it seems unnecessary to envisage any Semitic original other than our books of Ezra and Nehemiah, perhaps with some textual variations from the form familiar to us. It is also disputed whether the section found only in I Esdras, *A debate at the Persian court* (chs. 3–4), was first written in Greek, or is a translation from Aramaic.

As for the date of I Esdras, general reference has already been made to the last centuries B.C., and it is hardly possible to be more specific than this. It is virtually certain that it was available to the Jewish historian Josephus, writing in the last third of the first century A.D., so it is possible that it was not written until the beginning of the Christian era; linguistic similarities with books written at a slightly earlier date have, however, persuaded many scholars that the most probable date is the late second or early first century B.C.

In the commentary which follows, special attention will be paid to those sections of I Esdras which either have no parallel in the earlier writings, or differ significantly from them. Though it is hoped that sufficient background information is provided to make the work intelligible as it stands, any fuller exposition of passages paralleled in Chronicles, Ezra or Nehemiah should be sought in the volumes in this series that comment on those books.

✻   ✻   ✻   ✻   ✻   ✻   ✻   ✻   ✻   ✻   ✻   ✻   ✻

Parallels between Chronicles–Ezra–Nehemiah and 1 Esdras

1 Esdras	Chronicles–Ezra–Nehemiah
1: 1–33	2 Chron. 35
1: 34–58	2 Chron. 36
2: 1–15	Ezra 1
2: 16–30	Ezra 4: 7–24a
3: 1 – 5: 6	*No parallel*
5: 7–46	Ezra 2 (and Neh. 7: 6–73a)
5: 47–65	Ezra 3
5: 66–73	Ezra 4: 1–5
6: 1–22	Ezra 4: 24b – 5: 17
6: 23–34	Ezra 6: 1–12
7	Ezra 6: 13–22
8: 1–27	Ezra 7
8: 28–67	Ezra 8
8: 68–90	Ezra 9
8: 91–6	Ezra 10: 1–5
9: 1–36	Ezra 10: 6–44
9: 37–55	Neh. 7: 73b – 8: 13

As is explained in the commentary, 1 Esdras is not simply a translation of parts of certain Old Testament books, so that the equivalences noted above are not always exact. Some of the events described are also referred to in other Old Testament books (notably 2 Kings, Jeremiah, Haggai and Zechariah).

Exile and return

✳ The historical period covered by 1 Esdras is from 622 B.C., (Josiah's Passover) to a date in the fifth or early fourth century which cannot be precisely determined (Ezra's mission). Since these events are described partly in 2 Chronicles and partly in Ezra, and since they include the time of exile, our natural inclination is to think of two different 'ages' being involved. But any such division of history into clearly defined periods is always a dangerous and somewhat subjective exercise, and it is in itself perfectly legitimate both to stress the continuity of Israel's history despite the exile of some of her leading citizens to Babylon, and also to see a measure of correspondence between the reforms carried out by Josiah and those of Ezra. To a later age, this was one of the great formative periods of Judaism, and we need not be surprised that special attention was paid to it.

From the point of view of world history, the period covered was a time of very great changes. Josiah ruled at the time of the break-up of the Assyrian Empire, which had dominated Judah and the neighbouring states for a century. After a brief Egyptian domination, the Babylonian Empire of Nebuchad-nezzar became supreme, and overran Judah, destroying Jerusalem and its temple, and taking many of the leading citizens into exile. All these events took place in little more than a generation (609–587 B.C.). Then, in the years between 550 and 539, the rise of Cyrus led to the Persians replacing Babylon as the dominant power, and under Persian rule, the fortunes of Judah greatly improved. At Jerusalem, the city itself and its temple were restored; some exiles may have been allowed to return; and the work of restoration was brought to a climax by the work of Ezra. At the very least, the period between Cyrus and Ezra was one of nearly a century, and it may have been a good deal more, but from the later viewpoint of the writer of 1 Esdras, as already in the book of Ezra itself, the perspective is shortened, and Ezra's work is seen as part of the one great task of restoration.✷

JOSIAH

1 JOSIAH KEPT the Passover at Jerusalem in honour of his Lord and sacrificed the Passover victims on the
2 fourteenth day of the first month. The priests, duly robed in their vestments, he stationed in the temple of the Lord

according to the order of daily service. He commanded 3
the Levites, who served the temple in Israel, to purify
themselves for the Lord, in order to place the holy Ark
of the Lord in the house which was built by King Solomon, son of David. Josiah said to them, 'You are no 4
longer to carry it on your shoulders. Make yourselves
ready now, family by family and clan by clan, to do
service to the Lord your God and to minister to his
people Israel in the manner prescribed by King David 5
and provided for so magnificently by his son Solomon.
Take your places in the temple as Levites in the prescribed order of your families in the presence of your
brother Israelites; sacrifice the Passover victims, and pre- 6
pare the sacrifices for your brothers. Observe the Passover
according to the ordinance of the Lord which was given
to Moses.'

To those who were present Josiah made a gift of thirty 7
thousand lambs and kids and three thousand calves. These
he gave from the royal estates in fulfilment of his promise
to the people and to the priests and Levites. The temple- 8
wardens, Chelkias, Zacharias, and Esyelus, gave the
priests two thousand six hundred sheep and three hundred calves for the Passover. Jechonias, Samaeas, his 9
brother Nathanael, Sabias, Ozielus, and Joram, army
officers of high rank, gave the Levites five thousand sheep
and seven hundred calves for the Passover.

This was the procedure. The priests and the Levites, 10
bearing the unleavened bread, stood in all their splendour
before the people, in the order of their clans and families,
to make offerings to the Lord as is laid down in the book 11
of Moses. This took place in the morning. They roasted 12

9

the Passover victims over the fire in the prescribed way
and boiled the sacrifices in the vessels and cauldrons, and
13 a pleasant smell went up; then they carried portions
round to the whole assembly. After this they made preparations both for themselves and for their brothers the
14 priests, the sons of Aaron. The priests went on offering
the fat until nightfall, while the Levites made the preparations both for themselves and for their brothers the
15–16 priests, the sons of Aaron. The sons of Asaph, the temple
singers, with Asaph, Zacharias, and Eddinous of the royal
court, and the door-keepers at each gateway remained at
their station according to the ordinances of David, which
prescribe that no one may lawfully default in his daily
duty; their brothers the Levites made the preparations for
17 them. All that pertained to the Lord's sacrifice was com-
18 pleted that day: the keeping of the Passover and the
offering of the sacrifices on the altar of the Lord according
19 to the command of King Josiah. The Israelites who were
present on this occasion kept the Passover and the Feast
20 of Unleavened Bread for seven days. Such a Passover had
not been kept in Israel since the time of the prophet
21 Samuel; none of the kings of Israel had kept such a Passover as was kept by Josiah, the priests and the Levites,
the men of Judah, and those Israelites who happened to
22 be resident in Jerusalem. It was in the eighteenth year of
Josiah's reign that this Passover was celebrated.

23   All that Josiah did he did rightly and in whole-hearted
24 devotion to his Lord. The events of his reign are to be
found in ancient records which tell a story of sin and
rebellion against the Lord graver than that of any other

nation or kingdom, and of offences against him which
brought down his judgement upon Israel.

After all these doings of Josiah's it happened that 25
Pharaoh king of Egypt was advancing to attack Car-
chemish on the Euphrates, and Josiah took the field
against him. The king of Egypt sent him this message: 26
'What is your business with me, king of Judah? It is not 27
against you that the Lord God has sent me to fight; my
campaign is on the Euphrates. The Lord is with me, the
Lord, I say, is with me, driving me on. Withdraw, and
do not oppose the Lord.' Josiah did not turn his chariot 28
but went forward to the attack. He disregarded what the
Lord had said through the prophet Jeremiah and joined 29
battle with Pharaoh in the plain of Megiddo. Pharaoh's
captains swept down upon King Josiah. The king said to 30
his servants, 'Take me out of the battle, for I am badly
hurt.' At once his servants took him out of the line and
lifted him into his second chariot. He was brought back 31
to Jerusalem, and there he died and was buried in his
ancestral tomb.

All Judah mourned Josiah, and the prophet Jeremiah 32
lamented him. The lamentation for Josiah has been observed by the chief men and their wives from that day
to this; it was proclaimed that it should be a custom for
ever for the whole people of Israel. These things are 33
recorded in the book of the histories of the kings of
Judah; every deed that Josiah did which won him fame
and showed his understanding of the law of the Lord,
both what he did earlier and what is told of him here,
is related in the book of the kings of Israel and Judah.

✻ The account of Josiah's reign is parallel to that in 2 Chron. 35, and the impression created is similar. Though we commonly regard Josiah's reign (640–609 B.C.) as the last flicker of life before the final collapse of Judah, coming as it did shortly before the Babylonian invasion, it is also possible to see the appropriateness of taking this period as a beginning. Josiah's religious reform meant a return to the standard of earlier times (verses 20–1), and thus the pattern to be followed by the Jerusalem community was laid down. Exile might disrupt, but could not finally destroy, the continuity between Josiah and the writer's own day.

1. The beginning seems abrupt, but is not necessarily an indication of a lost earlier section. Some Old Testament books start in almost as direct a fashion (cp. Ezra 1: 1).

5. *so magnificently:* this addition, one of several minor changes from the Chronicles' text which is the author's source, is aimed at stressing the importance of the temple.

7. The *gift* was to enable *those who were present* to offer sacrifice, not, as the text might be thought to imply, for their own use.

8. *Chelkias, Zacharias and Esyelus:* Greek proper names were very different from the forms usual in Hebrew. In 2 Chron. 35: 8 these names are found as 'Hilkiah, Zechariah, and Jehiel'. The last in particular would scarcely be recognizable from the Greek form.

10. *in all their splendour:* 2 Chron. 35: 10 has simply 'in their places'. The change may be due to a misunderstanding, or, perhaps more likely, to a deliberate emphasis on the glory of the ministers.

11. *in the morning:* this is unexpected, since the Law required victims to be sacrificed in the evening (Deut. 16: 6). It is doubtful if a variant in liturgical practice is implied here; more probably the translators misunderstood the Hebrew original.

15. *Zacharias and Eddinous:* the latter name is the Greek version of 'Jeduthun' (2 Chron. 35: 15), but *Zacharias* appears

12

to be an error, perhaps influenced by verse 8, for the original 'Heman'. The remainder of this verse and verse 16 go beyond the source in 2 Chronicles in stressing the correct carrying out of the ritual by all concerned.

23–4. The death of Josiah in humiliating circumstances after his great religious reform presented a theological problem for later interpreters. The Chronicler had eased this by representing Josiah as falling away at the last and failing to recognize God's hand in the campaign waged by Pharaoh Necho; this section follows 2 Kings 23: 24–7, in the view that even Josiah's piety could not turn away the punishment made inevitable by the nation's sin.

27. This verse goes even further than 2 Chron. 35: 21, its probable source, in identifying Necho as the messenger of Israel's own God.

28. *through the prophet Jeremiah:* this is not found in 2 Chronicles, and it is not clear that any specific passage of Jeremiah is here in mind. It is an elaboration of the reference to Jeremiah in verse 32, which is already found in 2 Chronicles, and shows how that prophet and the book named after him were associated with the whole complex of events leading up to the fall of the kingdom of Judah.＊

THE FALL OF JERUSALEM

His compatriots took Joachaz the son of Josiah and 34 made him king in succession to his father. He was twenty- 35 three years old, and he reigned over Judah and Jerusalem for three months. Then the king of Egypt deposed him, fined the nation a hundred talents of silver and one talent 36 of gold, and appointed his brother Joakim king of Judah 37 and Jerusalem. Joakim imprisoned the leading men and 38 had his brother Zarius arrested and brought back from Egypt.

Joakim was twenty-five years old when he became 39

13

king of Judah and Jerusalem; he did what was wrong in
40 the eyes of the Lord. Nebuchadnezzar king of Babylon
marched against him; he put him in chains of bronze and
41 took him to Babylon. Nebuchadnezzar also took some
of the sacred vessels of the Lord, carried them off, and
42 put them in his temple in Babylon. The stories about
Joakim, his sacrilegious and godless conduct, are recorded
in the chronicles of the kings.

43   Joakim was succeeded on the throne by his eighteen-
44 year-old son Joakim. He reigned in Jerusalem for three
months and ten days, and did what was wrong in the eyes
of the Lord.

45   A year later Nebuchadnezzar had him deported to
46 Babylon together with the sacred vessels of the Lord. He
made Zedekiah king of Judah and Jerusalem. Zedekiah
47 was twenty-one years old and reigned eleven years. He
did what was wrong in the eyes of the Lord and disregarded what the Lord had said through the prophet
48 Jeremiah. King Nebuchadnezzar had made him take an
oath of allegiance by the Lord, but he broke it and re-
volted. He was stubborn and defiant, and transgressed the
commandments of the Lord, the God of Israel.

49   The leaders of the people and the chief priests committed many wicked and lawless acts, outdoing even the
heathen in sacrilege, and they defiled the holy temple of
50 the Lord in Jerusalem. The God of their fathers sent his
messenger to reclaim them, because he wished to spare
51 them and his dwelling-place. But they derided his messengers, and on the very day when the Lord spoke they
52 were scoffing at his prophets. At last he was roused to
fury against his people for their impieties, and ordained
53 that the kings of the Chaldaeans should attack them. These

put their young men to the sword all round the holy temple, sparing neither old nor young, neither boy nor girl; the Lord handed them all over to their enemies. All the sacred vessels of the Lord, large and small, the 54 furnishings of the Ark of the Lord, and the royal treasures were carried off to Babylon. The house of the Lord was 55 set on fire, the walls of Jerusalem destroyed, its towers burnt, and all its splendours ruined. Nebuchadnezzar 56 carried off to Babylon the survivors from the slaughter, and they remained slaves to him and his sons until the 57 Persians took his empire. This fulfilled the word of the Lord spoken by Jeremiah: 'Until the land has run the full 58 term of its sabbaths, it shall keep sabbath all the time of its desolation till the end of the seventy years.'

* These verses cover the years from 609 to 587/6 B.C. in outline, with a brief concluding reference to the period of the exile. A variety of biblical accounts, together with the presentation of these years in the collection of contemporary clay tablet known as the Babylonian Chronicle, has enabled us to reconstruct the events perhaps more fully than those of any other Old Testament period; it does not seem likely that 1 Esdras preserves any independent sources of information. For the most part it is clearly based on 2 Chron. 36, and conveys a vivid sense of the desperate measures that had to be taken as the political situation steadily worsened for Judah.

34. *His compatriots:* 2 Chron. 36: 1 has 'The people of the land', but by the last pre-Christian centuries this term had come to be one of abuse, denoting the lowest stratum of society, and this may explain the avoidance of it here.

35. *Judah and Jerusalem:* this description, common in the prophets (cp. Isa. 1: 1), brings out the point that Judah was the main body of the land, while Jerusalem stood somewhat apart as the royal city.

38. If these events are correctly described, we have no

other record of them. More probably this is a confused account of the exile of Joachaz to Egypt by Necho (2 Chron. 36: 4). The name *Zarius* is found in various forms in different manuscripts, but it is not easy to identify him with any figure known from other sources.

39-42. The account in 2 Chronicles is followed, both in the otherwise unknown assertion that Joakim was exiled to Babylon, and in its condemnation of his character.

43. *eighteen-year-old:* 2 Chron. 36: 9 has 'eight', and this is followed by some manuscripts of 1 Esdras, but *eighteen* is undoubtedly correct. Some confusion is caused at this point because two very similar Hebrew names, 'Jehoiakim' and 'Jehoiachin' are both rendered *Joakim* in Greek.

45. The actual capture of Jerusalem in 597 B.C. is passed over in silence; it seems as if the author of 1 Esdras envisaged the main damage as having occurred during the time of the first Joakim.

49-58. This sermonic passage, drawing out the moral of the people's wickedness and the inevitability of the fall of Jerusalem, follows the account in 2 Chronicles very closely. At times the emphasis is heightened, as by the reference to a particular 'messenger' (verse 50) and the theme of rejection lasting till 'the very day when the Lord spoke' (verse 51).

54. *the furnishings of the Ark of the Lord:* the N.E.B. translation here is unexpected, and may give too precise an impression; the Greek refers simply to 'treasure-chests'. The fate of the Ark is in fact unknown.

58. The words attributed here to Jeremiah are in fact based partly on Jer. 25: 11 and 29: 10, partly on Lev. 26: 34-5. It is not an exact quotation as we should nowadays understand it. ✻

THE RESTORATION UNDER CYRUS

During the first year of Cyrus king of Persia, the Lord, 1–2 **2**
in order to fulfil his word spoken through Jeremiah,
moved Cyrus king of Persia to make a proclamation
throughout his empire, which he also put in writing:
'This is the decree of Cyrus king of Persia: The Lord of 3
Israel, the most high Lord, has made me king of the
world and has directed me to build him a house at Jeru- 4
salem in Judaea. Whoever among you belongs to his 5
people, may his Lord be with him; let him go up to
Jerusalem in Judaea and build the house of the Lord of
Israel, the Lord who dwells in Jerusalem. Wherever each 6
man lives let his neighbours help him with gold and 7
silver and other gifts, with horses and pack-animals, together with other things set aside as votive offerings for
the Lord's temple in Jerusalem.'

Then the chiefs of the clans of the tribe of Judah and of 8
Benjamin, the priests, the Levites, came forward, and all
whose spirit the Lord had moved to go up to build the
Lord's temple in Jerusalem. Their neighbours helped with 9
everything, with silver and gold, horses and pack-animals;
and many were also moved to help with votive offerings
in great quantity. King Cyrus brought out the sacred 10
vessels of the Lord which Nebuchadnezzar had taken
away from Jerusalem and set up in his idolatrous temple.
Cyrus king of Persia brought them out and delivered 11
them to Mithradates his treasurer, by whom they were 12
delivered to Sanabassar, the governor of Judaea. This is 13
the inventory: a thousand gold cups, a thousand silver
cups, twenty-nine silver censers, thirty gold bowls, two

thousand four hundred and ten silver bowls, and a thou-
14 sand other articles. In all, five thousand four hundred and
15 sixty-nine gold and silver vessels were returned, and taken
from Babylon to Jerusalem by Sanabassar together with
the exiles.

✻ As in 2 Chronicles, the period between the destruction of
Jerusalem and the rise of Cyrus is passed over without
reference to any historical events; as the last verse of the
previous chapter showed, a theological explanation was
regarded as more appropriate. A greater impression of continuity is given here than in the earlier sources, because 1
Esdras bridges the gap between 2 Chronicles and Ezra. The
events described in these verses correspond to Ezra 1 and took
place around 539 B.C.

1–7. These verses follow the general sense of Ezra 1: 1–4
very closely. In particular the double stress in Cyrus' decree
found there is repeated – the permission for the return of
exiles as well as the permission to rebuild the temple, which
is the point stressed in the other forms of the decree (1 Esdras
6: 24–6; cp. Ezra 6: 3–5).

9. *Their neighbours helped with everything:* as originally described in Ezra 1: 6, this was probably an allusion to a theme
in the book of Exodus; what has sometimes been called 'the
spoiling of the Egyptians', that is, the way in which the
Israelites plundered the Egyptians' jewellery and clothing
when they escaped from Pharaoh (Exod. 12: 36). Here it is
treated as the way in which those Jews unable or unwilling to
return to Jerusalem played their part in the enterprise.

12. *Sanabassar, the governor of Judaea:* the role of this figure
is enigmatic. In Ezra he is called 'Sheshbazzar' and his function is not easily distinguished from that of Zerubbabel;
here the difficulties are compounded by the further variation
in his name, and by the more precise description as *governor
of Judaea.* There is no other evidence that he had so specific a
role.

13–14. The total here equals the sum of the parts, which

18

is not the case in Ezra 1 : 9–11. It is more likely that corrections
have been made to bring about this correspondence, than
that this list is original. There are in any case problems of a
historical kind, since according to 2 Kings 24: 13 many of
the vessels of the first temple had been destroyed. ✴

OPPOSITION TO THE REBUILDING

In the time of Artaxerxes king of Persia, Belemus, Mithra- 16
dates, Tabellius, Rathymus, Beeltethmus, Semellius the
secretary, and their colleagues in office in Samaria and
other places, wrote him a letter denouncing the inhabitants of Judaea and Jerusalem in the following terms:

To our Sovereign Lord Artaxerxes your servants 17
Rathymus the recorder, Semellius the secretary, the
other members of their council, and the magistrates in
Coele-syria and Phoenicia:

This is to inform Your Majesty that the Jews who 18
left you to come here have arrived in Jerusalem and are
rebuilding that wicked and rebellious city. They are
repairing its streets and walls and laying the foundation
of the temple. If this city is rebuilt and the walls com- 19
pleted, they will cease paying tribute and will rebel
against the royal house. Since work on the temple is 20
in hand, we have thought it well not to neglect this
important matter but to bring it to Your Majesty's 21
notice, in order that, if it is Your Majesty's pleasure,
search may be made in the records left by your predecessors. You will find in the archives evidence about 22
these matters and will learn that this is a city that has
resisted authority and given trouble to kings and to
other states, and has been a centre of armed rebellion 23
by the Jews from the earliest times. That is why it was

24   laid in ruins. Now we submit to Your Majesty that, if this city be rebuilt and its walls rise again, you will no longer have access to Coele-syria and Phoenicia.

25   Then the king wrote to Rathymus the recorder, Beel-tethmus, Semellius the secretary, and their colleagues in office in Samaria, Syria, and Phoenicia this reply:

26   I have read your letter. I ordered search to be made and it was discovered that this city has always been opposed to its overlords, and its inhabitants have raised

27   rebellions and made wars. There were kings in Jeru-salem, powerful and ruthless men, who in their time controlled Coele-syria and Phoenicia and exacted

28   tribute from them. I therefore command that the men you mention be prevented from rebuilding the city,

29   and that measures be taken to enforce this order and to check the spread of an evil likely to be a nuisance to the royal house.

30   When the letter from King Artaxerxes had been read, Rathymus, Semellius the secretary, and their colleagues set out at once for Jerusalem with cavalry and a large body of other troops and stopped the builders. The building of the temple was broken off until the second year of the reign of Darius king of Persia.

✻ Thus far the order and the details of 2 Chronicles and Ezra have been followed closely; at this point occurs the first major rearrangement, as these verses correspond to Ezra 4: 7–24. It is not difficult to see why such a change was considered necessary, since their placing in Ezra is thematic rather than historical, and if the sequence is understood as historical major problems arise. In Ezra, the passage was relevant to the compiler's theme, but the events recorded are from a different period. The rearrangement here made does not in fact solve the historical problem, since 'Artaxerxes king of Persia' did not become king until 465 B.C., but it is probable that the author of 1 Esdras failed to realize this and took Artaxerxes to be a ruler who reigned between the death of Cyrus (530 B.C.) and the accession of Darius I (522). Further evidence of an attempt at harmonization is found in the references to the temple (verses 18–20), where the passage in Ezra mentions only the rebuilding of the city walls. Here again it seems likely that this reference has been inserted to make it more appropriate to the known circumstances of the sixth century B.C. It is noteworthy that the reconstruction found here is followed very closely by the Jewish historian Josephus, writing in the first century A.D., but for the reasons just given it cannot be regarded as throwing any valuable light on the actual course of events.

16. *In the time of Artaxerxes king of Persia:* assuming, as is likely, that Artaxerxes I is intended, this gives the period 465–424 B.C. *Belemus . . . and their colleagues:* harmonization of what were originally different sources has also taken place here. Ezra 4: 7 mentions a letter sent 'with the agreement of Mithredath, Tabeel and all his colleagues', while 4: 8 introduces a further letter, subsequently set out in full, from 'Rehum the high commissioner and Shimshai the secretary'. Originally these pieces of correspondence appear to have been unrelated, but 1 Esdras has combined the two strands. There are significant changes in the names: the word which the N.E.B. has translated 'with the agreement of' (Ezra 4: 7) was taken as a proper name, *Belemus*; and the Aramaic word translated 'high commissioner' in Ezra 4: 8 is misunderstood as if it were a proper name, *Beeltethmus*. *in Samaria and other places:* it is not known what the original circumstances underlying the opposition may have been, but as represented here they are set out in terms of the rivalry between Jerusalem and her religious and political rivals.

17. The elaborate introduction to the letter in the Aramaic

of Ezra 4: 9–10 is drastically reduced, probable because the various place-names there mentioned were no longer intelligible. The expression *Coele-syria and Phoenicia* is an explanation rather than a translation, denoting the designation of the land in Roman times as against the expression 'the province of Beyond-Euphrates' (Ezra 4: 10), which was the Persian usage.

18. *laying the foundation of the temple:* there is nothing corresponding to this in the original, and it appears to be part of the attempt to give a more plausible historical development. Throughout the letter, the translation is freer than in the narrative passages, possibly in order to make the contents more readily intelligible to readers in very different circumstances from the time when the letter was first written.

26–9. The royal reply is to an even more marked extent a summary of the original rather than a true translation.

30. *Darius king of Persia:* both Ezra 4: 24 (the original of this passage) and this verse illustrate what appears to have been a widespread confusion among the Jews concerning the order in which the Persian kings had ruled. (A comparable confusion seems to underlie part of the book of Daniel, the author of which seems to have thought that the order of rulers at this period was Belshazzar, Darius, Cyrus (Dan. 5: 30; 6: 28).) The reference here must be to Darius I (522–486 B.C.), that is, to a king who reigned long betore Artaxerxes I (465–424), to whom the previous section has referred. ✻

A debate at the Persian court

✻ There now follows, in chs. 3–4, the one extensive section of this book which is without a close parallel in Chronicles–Ezra–Nehemiah. Indeed there is nothing in the first part of the story which is told here to connect it with the context of this book at all. This link only occurs with the quite unexpected announcement in 4: 13 that one of the three young men is the Jewish leader associated with the temple rebuilding, Zerubbabel. Nor should we be led to expect such an identification by the form of the story up to that point. In the discussion as to the strongest power, it might be expected that the one who would be identified as a Jewish hero would suggest a religious answer to the conundrum. Instead all three answers are thoroughly secular: asked who is the strongest, the three youths reply, respectively, wine, the king and women. It seems likely that we have here a popular story, only later elaborated to fit its present context, by identifying the third youth as Zerubbabel and developing his answer to allow a place for truth as well as for women. Various parallels to the story are known to exist in different cultures, but none that can be regarded as a source of this form of it; nor is it certain whether the Greek form in which it has come down to us represents its original language or whether it is a translation from Aramaic. ✻

DARIUS' BANQUET AND THE WAGER

3 KING DARIUS held a great feast for all those under him, his household, the chief men of Media and 2 Persia, and the satraps and commanders and governors of his empire in the hundred and twenty-seven satrapies from India to Ethiopia. When they had eaten and drunk their 3 fill, they went away, and King Darius withdrew to his

4 bedchamber; he went to sleep but woke up again. Then
the three young men of the king's personal bodyguard
5 said to each other: 'Let each one of us name the thing
which he judges the strongest; and to the one whose
opinion seems wisest King Darius will give rich gifts and
6 prizes: he shall be clothed in purple, drink from gold
vessels, and sleep on a golden bed; and he shall have a
chariot with gold-studded bridles, and a fine linen turban,
7 and a chain about his neck. His wisdom shall give him the
right to sit next to Darius and to be given the title Kins-
8 man of Darius.' Then each wrote down his own state-
9 ment, sealed it, and put it under the king's pillow. 'When
the king wakes again,' they said, 'the writing will be
given him. The king and the three chief men of Persia
shall judge whose statement is wisest, and the award will
be made on the merits of the written statement.'

10, 11 One wrote, 'Wine is strongest', the second wrote 'The
12 king is strongest', and the third wrote 'Women are
13 strongest, but truth conquers all'. When the king got up
14 he was presented with what they had written. He read
it, and summoned all the chief men of Persia and Media,
15 satraps, commanders, governors, and chief officers. Then
he took his seat in the council chamber, and what they
16 had written was read out before them. He said, 'Call the
young men and let them expound their statements.' They
17 were called and came in. They were asked, 'Tell us about
what you have written.'

* The general background here is reminiscent of parts of
Esther and Daniel; the great feast is comparable to Xerxes'
(Ahasuerus') banquet (Esther 1), as is also the detail about the
wakefulness of the king (cp. Esther 6: 1). The three young

men in the royal service remind us of the status of Daniel and his three friends under Nebuchadnezzar (Dan. 1). It is possible that these links with other Old Testament books have been added to the present form of the story to give a distinctively Jewish link to a story which was otherwise a traditional Greek theme: what is strongest?

2. *the hundred and twenty-seven satrapies from India to Ethiopia:* this appears to be based on Esther 1: 1, where already historical problems are raised, since there was never anything approaching this number of satrapies (provinces) in the Persian Empire.

5. The theme of the king at a banquet making extravagant promises to those who gain his favour is a well-known one (cp. Herod in Mark 6: 22–3), but it is remarkable to find this generosity being proposed by the aspiring recipients. The Jewish historian Josephus, in his version of the story, also found this improbable, and modified the story so that Darius himself made the promise of rich rewards.

10–12. It seems probable that in the original form of the story, the three contestants each wrote one answer: *Wine, The king, Women,* but in view of the unexpected dénouement regarding the third young man, his answer has been elaborated with its reference to truth. In the end this proves decisive (see 4: 34–42). *

THE FIRST TWO CONTESTANTS

The first, who spoke about the strength of wine, began. 18 'Sirs,' he said, 'how true it is that wine is strongest! It sends astray the wits of all who drink it; king and orphan, 19 slave and free, rich and poor, it has the same effect on them all. It turns all thoughts to revelry and mirth; it brings forgetfulness of grief and debt. It makes all feel 21 rich, cares nothing for king or satrap, and makes men always talk in millions. When they are in their cups, they 22

forget to be friendly to friends and relations, and are
23 quick to draw their swords; when they have recovered
from their wine, they cannot remember what they have
24 done. Sirs, is not wine the strongest, seeing that it forces
men to behave in this way?' With this he ended.

4   Then the second, the one who spoke of the strength of
2 the king, began his speech: 'Sirs, is not man the strongest,
man who masters the earth and the sea and all that is in
3 them? But the strongest of men is the king; he is their
4 lord and master, and they obey all his commands. If he
bids them make war upon one another they do it; if he
dispatches them against his enemies, they march and level
5 mountains and walls and towers. They kill and are killed;
they do not disobey the king's order. If they are victorious they bring everything to the king, their spoils and
6 everything else. Or take those who do not serve as
soldiers or go to war, but work the land: they sow and
reap, and bring their produce to the king. They compel
7 each other to bring him their tribute. Though he is no
more than one man, if he orders them to kill, they kill;
8 if he orders them to release, they release; he orders them
to attack and they attack, to lay waste and they lay waste,
9 to build and they build, to cut down and they cut down,
10 to plant and they plant. So all his people and his troops
obey him. Besides this, while he himself sits at table, eats
and drinks, and goes to sleep, they stand in attendance
11 round about him and none can leave and see to his own
12 affairs; they never disobey him in anything. Sirs, of
course the king must be strongest when he commands
such obedience!' So he stopped speaking.

✳ There are links throughout this section of the book with the traditions of Jewish wisdom literature. In its earlier stages that had been essentially down-to-earth and practical, concerned with the ability to perform one's allotted task successfully; but in the later Old Testament period, possibly under Greek influence, a more speculative note emerged such as is evidenced here.

18–24. There is an ambiguity in the speech praising *wine* which at times has a remarkably modern ring. In part it is praised for itself and for the release from anxiety and care which it provides; in part, the speech is a warning against the danger of succumbing to the strength inherent in wine. There are many descriptions of wine and its effects in the Old Testament which seem to be quite free of any note of condemnation (cp. Ps. 104: 15*a*) and the tradition is carried on in the New Testament (cp. John 2: 1–11), but the dangers of wine and of drunkenness were also fully recognized and warnings against over-indulgence are found in the wisdom literature (cp. Prov. 23: 29–35 for a particularly vivid picture of the dangers of drunkenness). The references in verses 19 and 21 to wine as overcoming even kings suggest the possibility that at one stage this speech followed the one praising the power of kings.

4: 1–12. If the speech on wine has many modern associations, that on the power of *the king* portrays an order of society which is much less familiar. The Persian rulers are often praised, directly or by implication, in the Old Testament, because of their humaneness in comparison with the Assyrians and Babylonians of an earlier period; but all the evidence available shows that they were still absolute rulers whose word was law. The power of the king as here portrayed depends on the unquestioning acceptance of a strictly hierarchical order of society.   ✳

THE SPEECH IN PRAISE OF WOMEN

13   The third, who spoke about women and truth – and
14 this was Zerubbabel – said: 'Sirs, it is true the king is
great, men are many, and wine is strong, but who rules
15 over them? Who is the sovereign power? Women,
surely! The king and all his people who rule land and
sea were born of women, and from them they came.
16 Women brought up the men who planted the vineyards
17 which yield the wine. They make clothes for men and
they bring honour to men; men cannot do without
18 women. If they have amassed gold and silver and all kinds
of beautiful things, and then see a woman with a lovely
19 face and figure, they leave all these things to gape and
stare at her with open mouth, and all choose her in pre-
20 ference to gold or silver or beautiful things. A man will
desert his father who brought him up, desert even his
21 country, and become one with his wife. He forgets father,
mother, and country, and stays with his wife to the end
22 of his days. Here is the proof that women are your
masters: do you not toil and sweat and then bring all you
23 earn and give it to your wives? A man will take his sword
and sally forth to plunder and rob, to sail on sea and
24 river; he faces lions, he travels in the dark; and when he
has robbed and plundered he brings the spoil home to
his beloved.

25   'A man loves his wife more than his father or mother.
26 For women's sakes many men have been driven out of
27 their minds, many have been sold into slavery, many
28 have died or come to grief or ruined their lives. Do you
believe me now? Certainly the king wields great autho-

rity; no country dare lift a finger against him. Yet I 29
watched him with Apame, his favourite concubine,
daughter of the famous Bartacus. She was sitting on the 30
king's right; she took the diadem off his head and put it
on her own, and slapped his face with her left hand; and
the king only gazed at her open-mouthed. When she 31
laughed at him he laughed; when she was cross with him
he coaxed her to make it up. Sirs, if women do as well 32
as this, how can their strength be denied?' The king and 33
the chief men looked at one another.

* It is probable that in the original form of the debate this
speech, like the first two, was anonymous, and was complete
in itself without the elaboration concerning truth which now
follows. The themes here developed are more characteristic of
classical antiquity than of the Old Testament. The Old
Testament has a number of heroines, but the picture given
here of the female as the power behind the throne is not
specially characteristic. (Elijah's opponent, Jezebel (see 1 Kings
19: 1–2; 21: 5–15) may provide an exception.) To some
extent, this speech, like that on wine, brings out the ambiguous
nature of the power it describes (cp. verses 25–6), and this is
reminiscent of the warnings in Proverbs against the seductive
power of women (cp. Prov. 7: 6–23). A similar tension
between the power of the king and that of women is illustrated
by the story in Esther 1 (cp. especially verses 18–20). It is
clear that the themes here discussed were matters for popular
debate in the ancient world.

13. *this was Zerubbabel:* the awkward and unexpected
introduction of the name here has led almost all scholars to
agree that this phrase is a gloss, but it is less clear whether it
was introduced when the rest of the story had already taken
its present form, by way of preparing the reader for the
dénouement, or whether this was part of the basic adaptation
of the story. Only one Zerubbabel is found in the Old

Testament, the figure mentioned in the work of the Chronicler and in the sixth-century prophets Haggai and Zechariah as the leader of the restored community in Jerusalem. The phrase would give the attentive reader his first clue to the significance of the account of the debate.

14-16. These verses take their point from the context. This is a genuine debate, in which the third speaker shows the inadequacies of the views put forward by the first two.

20. There is an obvious comparison with Gen. 2: 24, but whereas there (and in its New Testament citations such as Mark 10: 7) the context is the custom of marriage, as something regarded as desirable, here the stress is on rejection of one's own family and country.

29. *Apame, his favourite concubine, daughter of the famous Bartacus:* presumably the reference is to a concubine of Darius, but there is no other evidence which would enable us to make an identification. *Apame* was certainly a Persian name, and there were at least two prominent women so called in the fourth century B.C. This would scarcely lead us to regard the tale as historical, but it might afford some clue as to a likely date for the original form of the story.

33. It is probable that the original form of the story is here broken off; we should expect this reaction of *The king and the chief men* to lead to their decision, probably the awarding of the prize to the third speaker. Instead, a further speech follows. ✳

IN PRAISE OF TRUTH

34 He then went on to speak about truth: 'Sirs, we have seen that women are strong. The earth is vast, the sky is lofty, the sun swift in his course, for he moves through the
35 circle of the sky and speeds home in a single day. How great is he who does all this! But truth too is great and
36 stronger than all else. The whole earth calls on truth; the sky praises her. All created things shake and tremble; with

her there is no injustice. There is injustice in wine, in 37
kings, in women, in all men, and in all their works, and
so forth. There is no truth in them; they shall perish in
their injustice. But truth abides and is strong for ever; 38
she lives and rules for ever and ever. With her there is 39
no favouritism or partiality; she chooses to do justice
rather than what is unjust and evil. All approve her 40
works; in her judgements there is no injustice. Hers are
strength and royalty, the authority and majesty of all
ages. Praise be to the God of truth!'

So he ended his speech, and all the people shouted and 41
said, 'Great is truth: truth is strongest!' Then the king 42
said to him, 'Ask what you will, even beyond what is
in the writing, and I will grant it you. For you have been
proved the wisest; and you shall sit by me and be called
my Kinsman.'

* No explicitly religious themes have been present in the
first three speeches, and they are not prominent here, but at
least this speech is much closer to the kinds of religious belief
familiar to Jewish readers and those sympathetic to Judaism,
and it will have been inserted at this point to make a more
satisfactory introduction to the triumph of Zerubbabel and
the beneficence of the Persian king.

35-40. There are no close parallels to this speech in the Old
Testament, though a comparison might be made with the
speech in honour of wisdom in Prov. 8: 4-36. Truth is here
not simply the avoidance of error or lying; as in many Old
Testament passages it is closely associated with justice (verse
40). This is similar to such a passage as Ps. 85: 10-11 with its
linking of truth (N.E.B. 'fidelity') and justice. This speech
is therefore susceptible of an orthodox Jewish interpretation,
but some scholars have conjectured that it may once have

been part of a lost hymn in praise of Asha, the Persian god responsible for the right ordering of the universe.

42. The story reverts to the earlier theme of the extravagant generosity of the great king (cp. 3: 5–7). The title of royal *Kinsman* was a regular mark of favour under the Persian and later the Seleucid kings.   ✶

THE REWARD

43 Then he said to the king: 'Remember the vow you made on the day when you came to the throne. You
44 promised to rebuild Jerusalem and to send back all the vessels taken from it which Cyrus set aside. When he vowed to destroy Babylon he also vowed to restore these
45 vessels; and you too made a vow to rebuild the temple which the Edomites burnt when Judaea was ravaged by the Chaldaeans. This is the favour that I now beg of you,
46 my lord king, this is the magnanimity I request: that you should perform the vow which you made to the King of heaven.'

47 King Darius stood up and kissed him, and wrote letters for him to all the treasurers, governors, commanders, and satraps instructing them to give safe conduct to him and to all those who were going up with him to rebuild
48 Jerusalem. To all the governors in Coele-syria and Phoenicia and in Lebanon he wrote letters ordering them to transport cedar-wood from Lebanon to Jerusalem and
49 join with Zerubbabel in building the city. He gave all Jews going up from the kingdom to Judaea letters assuring their liberties; that no officer, satrap, governor, or
50 treasurer should interfere with them, that all land which they should acquire should be immune from taxation, and that the Edomites should surrender the villages they
51 had seized from the Jews. Each year twenty talents were

to be contributed to the building of the temple until it
was finished, and a further ten talents annually for[a] burnt-   52
offerings to be sacrificed daily upon the altar in accordance
with their law. All those who were going from Baby-   53-54
lonia to build the city were to enjoy freedom, and their
descendants after them. He gave written orders that all
the priests going there should also receive maintenance
and the vestments in which they would officiate; that the   55
Levites too should receive maintenance, until the day
when the building of the temple and Jerusalem was completed; and that all who guarded the city should be given   56
land and pay. He sent back all the vessels from Babylon   57
which Cyrus had set aside. All that Cyrus had commanded, he reaffirmed, ordering everything to be restored to Jerusalem.

When the young man, Zerubbabel, went out, he   58
turned his face toward Jerusalem, looked up to heaven,
and praised the King of heaven. 'From thee comes vic-   59
tory,' he said, 'from thee comes wisdom; thine is the
glory and I am thy servant. All praise to thee who hast   60
given me wisdom; to thee I give thanks, O Lord of our
fathers.'

He took the letters and set off for Babylon, where he   61
told his fellow-Jews. They praised the God of their   62
fathers because he had given them full freedom to go and   63
rebuild Jerusalem and the temple called by his name, and
they feasted for a week with music and rejoicing.

٭   The relevance of this episode to the condition of the Jews
is now spelt out. There are details here which do not correspond with other accounts of the restoration, even with what
is said elsewhere in this book. But a concern for exact histo-

[a] *Some witnesses add* seventeen.

rical accuracy is never a major feature of the Chronicler's work, and so it is likely that here the main point is the reward of God for his faithful community. The role of Zerubbabel is here greatly emphasized, and the suggestion has been made that I Esdras originated from a group which understood the important parts in the restoration as having been played by Zerubbabel and Ezra, deliberately omitting Nehemiah, whereas other traditions in Judaism emphasized Nehemiah's part over against that of other leaders. There is not really enough evidence for us to be certain about this kind of reconstruction.

43–6. The allusions in these verses present a number of points which are unattested in any other account of the period. None of the vows mentioned here is known from elsewhere, and to some extent they contradict the picture of the return of the *vessels* 'taken from Babylon to Jerusalem by Sanabassar' (2: 15). *the temple which the Edomites burnt:* again this statement is unsubstantiated, and can be interpreted in two ways. It may be taken as an actual historical event, unrecorded elsewhere, which provides the explanation for the hostility toward Edom shown in the book of Obadiah or in Ps. 137: 7. Alternatively, it may be taken as a comment inspired by those passages and without historical foundation.

47. The problem concerning historicity here becomes even more acute. In the book of Ezra no indication is given of the date of Zerubbabel's arrival in Jerusalem, and in view of his importance and the confusion between his role and that of Sheshbazzar, the issue has been much discussed. Once again, two views are possible for this verse; either that it retains a genuine historical memory and supplies an answer to the problem, or that it is a recognition of the difficulty and an attempt to provide a solution, but does not in fact have any historical worth. If the view that Zerubbabel's role is being deliberately magnified is accepted, then the comparison between this account and the very similar one concerning Nehemiah's return in Neh. 2: 7–9 is noteworthy.

50. Again the reference to the Edomites is without earlier support, and may reflect contemporary rivalries when this book was written. There was great bitterness between the Jews and the Idumaeans, as the later inhabitants of Edom were called, during the last two centuries B.C. The Herod family were Idumaeans, and their power was much resented by many Jews.

51–7. These verses read like a summary of the various decrees by Persian kings mentioned in Ezra and Nehemiah, where great stress is laid on the generosity of the Persian rulers in helping to re-establish the community (cp. Ezra 1: 2–4; 6: 3–12; Neh. 2: 8–9).

59–60. Zerubbabel's prayer is really a psalm, and might have been set out in poetic form. It is characteristic of the literature of the latest Old Testament period to emphasize the importance of prayer.

61. *set off for Babylon:* no indication has been given of where these events are supposed to have taken place. The Persian Empire did not have one fixed capital.

63. This episode ends, as it had begun, with a feast.   *

The temple rebuilt

* After the unparalleled episode described in chs. 3–4, the greater part of the remainder of the book follows its source – mainly the book of Ezra, with a short extract from Nehemiah – very closely. The beginning of this section, however, is without any such close parallel, and appears to be intended as a link between the episode of the three youths and the account of those who returned to Jerusalem.   *

THE RETURN TO JERUSALEM

5 AFTER THIS the heads of families, tribe by tribe, were chosen to go to Jerusalem, with their wives, their sons and daughters, their male and female slaves, and 2 their pack-animals. Darius sent a thousand horsemen to accompany them until they had brought them safely back 3 to Jerusalem, with a band of drums and flutes, and all their brothers dancing. So he sent them off with their escort.

4 These are the names of the men who went to Jerusalem, 5 according to their families, tribes, and allotted duties. The priests, the sons of Phineas son of Aaron, with Jeshua son of Josedek son of Saraeas, and Joakim his son; and[a] Zerubbabel son of Salathiel of the house of David of the 6 line of Phares of the tribe of Judah, who spoke wise words before Darius king of Persia. They went in the second year of his reign, in Nisan the first month.

* These verses serve both to round off the story of the contest and to introduce the list of returning exiles, based on Ezra 2, which follows. Some scholars have regarded this section as a translation of part of the original text of the book of Ezra which has now been lost; but it seems more likely that it was deliberately composed for its present position.

2–3. The picture is of a religious procession rather than of a journey of some 600 miles (965 km).

5. Although the 'hero' of this whole section is Zerubbabel, the dominance of the priesthood in late Judaism is illustrated by the fact that *The priests* are mentioned first. Related to this view of the priesthood was a great concern for the

[a] his son; and: *probable reading (compare Neh. 12: 10).*

36

proper descent of the priestly line, and so we find here the stress on *the sons of Phineas son of Aaron*. Phineas' zeal had been the subject of a story in Num. 25: 6–15, and another book from the Apocrypha, Ecclesiasticus, provides evidence of the esteem with which he and his descendants were regarded (Ecclus. 45: 23–6). *Jeshua*'s name is so spelt in Ezra (3: 2 and elsewhere), whereas the books of Haggai and Zechariah have the form 'Joshua'. The Greek describes Joakim as 'son of Zerubbabel', but the N.E.B. emendation is likely – the reference to Zerubbabel's sons at 1 Chron. 3: 19 does not mention 'Joakim'. *Phares* is the Greek form of 'Perez', from whom David's genealogy is traced in Ruth 4: 18.

6. This very precise dating (March 520 B.C.) has been taken at its face value by some scholars. It is, however, more likely that this is modelled on the detailed dating characteristic of the books of Haggai and Zechariah, which showed that those prophets were active at that time and that Jeshua and Zerubbabel were then in Jerusalem. The parallel with Neh. 2: 1 may also be significant, if part of the purpose of our author is to stress the achievement of Zerubbabel over against that of Nehemiah. ✶

THE RETURNING EXILES

Now these are the men of Judah who came up from 7 amongst the captive exiles, those whom Nebuchadnezzar king of Babylon had transported to Babylon. They re- 8 turned to Jerusalem and the rest of Judaea, each to his own city: they came with Zerubbabel and Jeshua, Nehemiah, Zaraeas, Resaeas, Enenius, Mardochaeus, Beelsarus, Aspharasus, Reelias, Romelius, and Baana, their leaders. The numbers of those from the nation who 9 returned with their leaders were: the line of Phoros two thousand one hundred and seventy-two; the line of 10 Saphat four hundred and seventy-two; the line of Ares

37

11 seven hundred and fifty-six; the line of Phaath-moab, deriving from the line of Jeshua and Joab, two thousand
12 eight hundred and twelve; the line of Elam one thousand two hundred and fifty-four; the line of Zathui nine hundred and forty-five; the line of Chorbe seven hundred and five; the line of Banei six hundred and forty-eight;
13 the line of Bebae six hundred and twenty-three; the line of Astaa one thousand three hundred and twenty-two.
14 The line of Adonikam six hundred and sixty-seven; the line of Bagoi two thousand and sixty-six; the line of
15 Adinus four hundred and fifty-four; the line of Ater son of Hezekias ninety-two; the line of Keilan and Azetas sixty-seven; the line of Azurus four hundred and thirty-
16 two; the line of Annias one hundred and one; the line of Arom and the line of Bassa three hundred and twenty-three; the line of Arsiphurith one hundred and twelve;
17 the line of Baeterus three thousand and five. The line of
18 Bethlomon one hundred and twenty-three; the men of Netophae fifty-five; the men of Anathoth one hundred
19 and fifty-eight; the men of Bethasmoth forty-two; the men of Cariathiarius twenty-five; the men of Caphira
20 and Beroth seven hundred and forty-three; the Chadasians and Ammidaeans four hundred and twenty-two; the men of Kirama and Gabbes six hundred and twenty-
21 one; the men of Macalon one hundred and twenty-two; the men of Betolio fifty-two; the line of Phinis one hun-
22 dred and fifty-six; the line of Calamolalus and Onus seven hundred and twenty-five; the line of Jerechus three
23 hundred and forty-five; the line of Sanaas three thousand three hundred and thirty.
24 The priests: the line of Jeddu son of Jeshua, deriving

from the line of Anasib, nine hundred and seventy-two.
The line of Emmeruth one thousand and fifty-two. The 25
line of Phassurus one thousand two hundred and forty-
seven. The line of Charme one thousand and seventeen.

The Levites: the line of Jesue, Cadmielus, Bannus, and 26
Sudius seventy-four. The temple singers: the line of 27
Asaph one hundred and twenty-eight.

The door-keepers: the line of Salum, of Atar, of 28
Tolman, of Dacubi, of Ateta, of Sabi, in all one hundred
and thirty-nine.

The temple-servitors: the line of Esau, of Asipha, of 29
Taboth, of Keras, of Susa, of Phaleas, of Labana, of 30
Aggaba, of Acud, of Uta, of Ketab, of Gaba, of Subai,
of Anan, of Cathua, of Geddur, of Jairus, of Desan, of 31
Noeba, of Chaseba, of Gazera, of Ozius, of Phinoe,
of Asara, of Basthae, of Asana, of Maani, of Naphisi, of
Acum, of Achipha, of Asur, of Pharakim, of Baaloth, 32
of Meedda, of Coutha, of Charea, of Barchue, of Serar,
of Thomi, of Nasith, of Atepha. The descendants of 33
Solomon's servants: the line of Asapphioth, of Pharida, 34
of Jeeli, of Lozon, of Isdael, of Saphythi, of Hagia, of
Phacareth, of Sabie, of Sarothie, of Masias, of Gas, of
Addus, of Subas, of Apherra, of Barodis, of Saphat, of 35
Adlon. All the temple-servitors and the descendants of
Solomon's servants numbered three hundred and seventy-
two.

The following came from Thermeleth and Thelsas 36
with their leaders Charaathalar and Alar, and could not 37
prove by their families and genealogies that they were
Israelites: the line of Dalan, the line of Ban, and the line
of Necodan six hundred and fifty-two.

38 From among the priests the claimants to the priesthood whose record could not be traced: the line of Obdia, of Accos, of Joddus, who married Augia one of the daughters
39 of Zorzelleas, and took his name; when search was made for their family record in the register it could not be traced, and so they were excluded from priestly service.
40 Nehemiah the governor[a] told them that they should not participate in the sacred offerings until a high priest arose wearing the breastpiece of Revelation and Truth.

41 They were in all: Israelites from twelve years old, not counting slaves male and female, forty-two thousand
42 three hundred and sixty; their slaves seven thousand three hundred and thirty-seven; musicians and singers two
43 hundred and forty-five; camels four hundred and thirty-five, horses seven thousand and thirty-six, mules two hundred and forty-five, donkeys five thousand five hundred and twenty-five.

44 Some of the heads of families, when they arrived at the temple of God in Jerusalem, made a vow to erect the
45 house again on its site as best they could, and to give to the sacred treasury for the fabric fund one thousand minas of gold and five thousand minas of silver and one hundred vestments.

46 The priests, the Levites, and some of the people settled in Jerusalem and the neighbourhood, with the temple musicians and the door-keepers; and all Israel settled in their villages.

✴ There follows a list of returning exiles substantially similar to those found in Ezra 2 and Neh. 7. There are some differences in the names, mostly to be accounted for by the

[a] the governor: *probable meaning; Gk*. and Attharias.

translation into Greek, and frequent disparities in the numbers, which are particularly liable to be altered in the course of transmission. A greater difference arises from the fact that the picture of restoration given here places this mass return in the reign of Darius, rather than that of Cyrus as in Ezra 2. This is probably best understood as part of the overall stress on the role of Zerubbabel, whose work is, as we have seen, associated with the time of Darius and the rebuilding of the temple.

8. Twelve leaders are listed here, as in Neh. 7: 7, whereas Ezra 2: 2 has eleven. Some names have been altered out of all recognition, but it is likely that they are to be pictured as leaders of the twelve tribes.

9–39. The categories of those who returned are set out in the same order as in the earlier lists; the details follow Ezra 2 more closely than Neh. 7.

40. *Nehemiah the governor:* as the N.E.B. footnote shows, it appears as if the Greek translator understood this reference as being to two individuals 'Nehemiah and Attharias'. The latter is based on the unusual word *tirshatha*, translated 'governor' in the N.E.B. at Ezra 2: 63, and applied elsewhere only to Nehemiah (Neh. 8: 9; 10: 1). Over and above this misunderstanding our confusion is increased by the fact that Zerubbabel and Nehemiah are taken as contemporaries, whereas it is virtually certain that nearly a hundred years separated them. There is much evidence that later Jews, looking back from a later period at the restoration, foreshortened the perspective very drastically and treated the leading figures as contemporaries and the main events as virtually simultaneous. Ezra 7: 1 is perhaps the first example of this tendency, which is carried further here and in 2 Maccabees. *the breastpiece of Revelation and Truth:* this represents the Hebrew 'The Urim and the Thummim', words which had once designated some kind of sacred lot. That meaning had been forgotten, but the words are paraphrased here in appropriate Greek forms.

41

41. The total of those returning is the same as the figure given in Ezra 2 and Neh. 7 despite the many differences in its detailed composition.

45. *one thousand minas of gold:* the 'sixty-one thousand drachmas' of Ezra 2: 69, the exact nature and value of which are unknown to us and may already have been so in the time of the Greek translation, are set out in more familiar terms. The *mina* was worth 50 or 60 shekels, that is, a weight of approximately 20 oz (600 grammes) or a little more.

46. This verse might seem to imply that Jerusalem had already been rebuilt, but we should probably not see too precise a reference in the terms here used. ✻

WORSHIP RESTORED

47 When the seventh month came and the Israelites were in their homes they gathered as one man in the broad square
48 of the first gateway toward the east. Jeshua son of Josedek and his brother priests and Zerubbabel son of Salathiel and his colleagues came forward and made ready the
49 altar of the God of Israel, to offer on it whole burnt-offerings according to the directions in the book of Moses
50 the man of God. They were joined[a] by men from the other peoples of the land and they set up the altar on its site (for the peoples in the land as a whole were hostile to them and were too strong for them); and they offered sacrifices to the Lord at the proper time, and whole burnt-
51 offerings morning and evening. They observed the Feast of Tabernacles as enjoined in the law, and the proper
52 sacrifices day by day; and thereafter the continual offer-ings, and sacrifices on sabbaths, at new moons, and on all
53 solemn feasts. All who had made a vow to God offered sacrifices to God from the new moon of the seventh

[a] Or attacked; *the clauses are perhaps in a confused order.*

42

month, although the temple of God was not yet built. Money was paid to the stonemasons and carpenters; the 54–55 Sidonians and Tyrians were supplied with food and drink, and with carts to bring cedar-trees from Lebanon, floating them down as rafts to the anchorage at Joppa, as decreed by Cyrus king of Persia.

☆ These verses follow Ezra 3: 1–7 in an idealistic description of the way in which the first act of the returning exiles was to establish the altar and resume the correct round of sacrifices. No attempt is made to avoid the basic inconsistency, that according to Ezra 3 these events took place in the reign of Cyrus, presumably in 538/7 B.C., whereas here they are placed under Darius.

47. *in their homes:* this appears to present a contrast with Ezra 3: 1, 'in their towns', but in fact the Greek is very vague – it refers simply to 'their own places'. The reference to *the broad square of the first gateway* which follows is an elaboration; our knowledge of the topography is insufficient for a precise identification to be possible.

49. *the book of Moses:* in Ezra's time the Hebrew word *torah* could appropriately be translated 'law' (Ezra 3: 2); by the time of 1 Esdras 'the torah' had become a technical description of the first five books of the Hebrew Bible, and so the translation *book* is now the natural one. By this time, too, the tradition that Moses was the author had become a well-established one (cp. Mark 12: 26).

50. As the N.E.B. footnote indicates, there may be some confusion in the text at this point. The reference in Ezra 3 corresponding to *the other peoples of the land* speaks only of the dread they caused, whereas there appear to be two traditions woven together here – one of joining together in worship with others, the other of mutual hostility. Neither in Ezra nor here is it entirely clear what the connection was between these relationships and the establishment of *the altar*.

51. *They observed the Feast of Tabernacles as enjoined in the*

43

law: the structure of 1 Esdras gives special emphasis to the observance of festivals according to the law: it begins with Josiah's Passover and ends with the festival following Ezra's reading of the law, and the emphasis on the role of Zerubbabel makes this a third high point, similarly marked by a festival. ✳

THE FOUNDATIONS OF THE TEMPLE LAID

56 In the second month of the second year, Zerubbabel son of Salathiel came to the temple of God in Jerusalem and started the work. There were with him Jeshua son of
57 Josedek, their kinsmen, the levitical priests, and all who had come to Jerusalem from the exile; and they laid the foundation of the temple of God. This was at the new moon, in the second month of the second year after they
58 had returned to Judaea and Jerusalem. The Levites from the age of twenty and upwards were set over the works of the Lord. Jeshua, his sons, his brothers, his brother Cadoel, the sons of Jeshua Emadabun, and the sons of Joda son of Iliadun with their sons and brothers, all the Levites, supervisors of the work, were active as one man on the works in the house of God. While the builders
59 built the temple of the Lord, the priests in their vestments with musical instruments and trumpets, and the Levites the sons of Asaph with their cymbals, stood singing to the
60 Lord and praising him as David king of Israel had ap-
61 pointed. They sang psalms praising the Lord, 'for his
62 goodness and glory is for ever toward all Israel'. All the people blew their trumpets and gave a loud shout, singing to the Lord as the building rose.

63 The priests, the Levites, and heads of families, the older men who had seen the former house, came to the building

of this one with cries of lamentation; and so, while many 64
were sounding the trumpets loudly for joy – so loudly as
to be heard far away – the people could not hear the 65
trumpets for the noise of lamentation.

✳ These verses are based on Ezra 3: 8–13, and for the most
part follow their source closely, save for the names in verse 58,
where there are changes both in the names themselves and
in the order in which they are listed.

56. *In the second month of the second year:* based on Ezra 3: 8,
where it is placed in the reign of Cyrus. Here we are allegedly
in the reign of Darius, but it seems that this historical difficulty
does not concern our author.

57. *they laid the foundation of the temple of God:* the account
in Ezra appears to be reworded so as to emphasize once again
the importance of the achievement of Zerubbabel. The same
effect is achieved by the addition of details of the date – the
foundation-laying is treated as a solemn ceremony.

60–1. Neither the Greek nor the English translation is free
from ambiguity; it is not clear whether the reference is to
the general worship arrangements laid down by David according to 1 Chron. 15–16, or whether the reference to David is
to his alleged authorship of the Psalms, from one of which a
quotation follows. (The phrase is too generalized for us to be
able to identify a particular psalm with certainty.)

63–5. The weeping may originally have been a formalized
ritual gesture, but here it is presented as being a natural
emotion, on the part of those who remembered the former
temple. Again there is a shortening of historical perspective;
the number of survivors fifty years after the event, in the time
of Cyrus, would have been very few; sixteen years later, in
Darius' reign, as here presented, it seems incredible that there
would have been any sizeable body to make such *cries of
lamentation.* ✳

OPPOSITION

66 The enemies of Judah and Benjamin heard the noise
67 of the trumpets and came to see what it meant. They
found the returned exiles building the temple for the
68 Lord God of Israel; they came to Zerubbabel and Jeshua
69 and the leaders of the families, and said: 'We will build
with you; for like you we obey your Lord and have
sacrificed to him from the time of Asbasareth king of
70 Assyria who transported us here.' But Zerubbabel and
Jeshua and the leaders of the families of Israel replied:
'You can have no share in building the house for the
71 Lord our God; we alone will build for the Lord of Israel,
72 as Cyrus king of Persia decreed.' But the peoples of the
land harassed*a* the men of Judaea, blockaded them, and
73 interrupted the building. Their plots, agitations, and riots
held up the completion of the building all the lifetime of
King Cyrus. They were prevented from building for two
years until Darius became king.

* The theme of opposition, already briefly touched upon
at verse 50, is now elaborated in accordance with Ezra 4.
However, the main part of that chapter (verses 7–24) has
already been used in 1 Esdras 2, and so the account here is
based on verses 1–5 only. Once again there is historical
confusion caused by the taking over of an account dated in
the reign of Cyrus, who is referred to as still being king
(verse 73) despite the earlier stories about Darius.

66. *heard the noise of the trumpets:* this provides a much
closer link between this section and the preceding one than
is found in Ezra 4: 1 where the word 'heard' is used in the
sense of 'hearing about'. This verse pictures the opponents
as other inhabitants of the immediate area of Jerusalem.

[a] *Probable reading; Gk. obscure.*

46

69. *Asbasareth*: Ezra 4: 2 has 'Esarhaddon' who ruled 681–669 B.C.; Josephus (who normally appears to use I Esdras as his source) has Shalmaneser, an earlier Assyrian king. It is not easy to see how the form here can have arisen, as a version of either of these names, or of that of any other foreign ruler known to us.

69–73. Neither here, nor in the source in Ezra, is the exact course of events easy to follow; probably more than one original has been combined, so that one alien group was anxious to help, while another was opposed to the whole venture, rather than, as is pictured here, initial friendliness turning to hostility.

73. This verse is historically very confused. First, we are transported back to the time of *King Cyrus*; secondly, the reference to *two years* appears to arise from a misunderstanding of Ezra 4: 24, which speaks of 'the second year of the reign of Darius'. The interval between the death of Cyrus (530 B.C.) and the accession of Darius (522) was longer than two years. *

CAN THE TEMPLE BE REBUILT?

In the second year of the reign of Darius, the prophets **6** Haggai and Zechariah son of Addo prophesied to the Jews in Judaea and Jerusalem in the name of the Lord the God of Israel. Then Zerubbabel son of Salathiel and **2** Jeshua son of Josedek began to rebuild the house of the Lord in Jerusalem. The prophets of the Lord were at their side to help them. At that time Sisinnes, the gover- **3** nor-general of Syria and Phoenicia, with Sathrabuzanes and their colleagues, came to them and said: 'Who has **4** authorized you to put up this building, complete with roof and everything else? Who are the builders carrying out this work?' But, thanks to the Lord who protected **5** the returned exiles, the elders of the Jews were not pre- **6**

vented from building during the time that Darius was
being informed and directions issued.

7   Here is a copy of the letter written to Darius, and sent
by Sisinnes, the governor-general of Syria and Phoenicia,
with Sathrabuzanes and their colleagues the authorities in
Syria and Phoenicia:

8   To King Darius our humble duty. Be it known to
our lord the king: we visited the district of Judaea and
entered the city of Jerusalem, and there we found the
9   elders of the Jews returned from exile building a great
new house for the Lord with costly hewn stone and
10   with beams set in the walls. This work was being done
with all speed and the undertaking was making good
progress; it was being executed in great splendour and
11   with the utmost care. We then inquired of these elders
by whose authority they were building this house and
12   laying such foundations. We questioned them so that
we could inform you in writing who their leaders
13   were, and asked for a list of their names. They answered
as follows: 'We are servants of the Lord who made
14   heaven and earth. This house was built and completed
many years ago by a great and powerful king of Israel.
15   When our fathers sinned against the heavenly Lord of
Israel and provoked him, he delivered them over to
Nebuchadnezzar, king of Babylon, king of the Chal-
16   daeans; and they pulled down the house, set it on fire,
17   and took the people into exile in Babylon. In the first
year of the reign of King Cyrus over Babylonia, the
18   king decreed that this house should be rebuilt. The
sacred vessels of gold and silver which Nebuchadnezzar
had taken from the house in Jerusalem, and set up in

his own temple, he brought back out of the temple in
Babylon and delivered to Zerubbabel and Sanabassar
the governor, with orders to take all these vessels and 19
to put them in the temple at Jerusalem, and to rebuild
this temple of the Lord on the same site as before. Then 20
Sanabassar came and laid the foundations of the house
of the Lord in Jerusalem. From then till now the
building has continued and is still unfinished.' There- 21
fore, if it is Your Majesty's pleasure, let search be made
in the royal archives in Babylon, and if it is found that 22
the building of the house of the Lord in Jerusalem took
place with the approval of King Cyrus, and if our lord
the king so decide, let directions be issued to us on this
subject.

✶ This section follows its source (Ezra 4: 24*b* – 5: 17) closely,
though the overall effect is different, because in Ezra this
passage is presented as part of a series of accounts describing
opposition; as we have seen, the earlier part of this Ezra
material has been placed elsewhere by the author of 1 Esdras.
The confusion concerning dates and the appropriate Persian
ruler is now at an end; this section is clearly anchored in
the reign of Darius and can be dated about 520 B.C.

1. *Haggai and Zechariah . . . prophesied to the Jews:* the
ministry of these prophets is in all traditions closely linked with
the rebuilding of the temple. In Ezra 5: 1 they are said to
have 'upbraided' the people, in accordance with the traditions
in the prophetic books themselves about the negligence of
the community. A different impression is created here, as if
this was the first signal to begin the work.

3. *Sisinnes, the governor-general of Syria and Phoenicia, with
Sathrabuzanes:* the names and title here well illustrate the
translation problem. The original names 'Tattenai' and

'Shethar-bozenai' of Ezra 5: 3 are almost unrecognizable in their Greek form; while the description of the province is changed from the Persian 'Beyond-Euphrates' to a description which made more sense in the political situation of a later age.

6. None of the accounts of opposition described in 1 Esdras leads to any extended breakdown in the process of restoration; that mentioned in 5: 73 is very brief (since 'two years' need only imply short parts of two successive years), and here no interruption of the work is involved.

8–22. The translation of the official letter is in places a very free rendering of Ezra 5: 8–17, but the sense is identical – the local officials are anxious to ensure that all is being carried out on proper authority. Only at one point is an addition made which may give a significant pointer to the concern of 1 Esdras: the addition of the name of *Zerubbabel* in verse 18 (where the original, Ezra 5: 14, only mentions 'Sheshbazzar' (*Sanabassar*)) is a further indication of the importance attributed to him in the whole enterprise. ✲

OFFICIAL PERMISSION GRANTED

23 Then King Darius ordered the archives in Babylon to be searched, and a scroll was found in the castle at Ecbatana in the province of Media which contained the following record:

24   In the first year of his reign King Cyrus ordered that the house of the Lord in Jerusalem, where they sacrifice

25 with fire continually, should be rebuilt. Its height should be sixty cubits and its breadth sixty cubits, with three courses of hewn stone to one of new local timber; the

26 expenses to be met from the royal treasury. The sacred gold and silver vessels of the house of the Lord which Nebuchadnezzar removed from the house in Jeru-

salem, and took to Babylon, should be restored to the house in Jerusalem and replaced where they formerly were.

Darius therefore instructed Sisinnes, the governor-general of Syria and Phoenicia, with Sathrabuzanes, their colleagues, and the governors in office in Syria and Phoenicia, to be careful not to interfere with the place, but to allow the servant of the Lord, Zerubbabel, governor of Judaea, and the elders of the Jews to build the house of the Lord on its old site. 'I have also given instructions', he continued, 'that it should be completely rebuilt, and that they should not fail to co-operate with the returned exiles in Judaea until the house of the Lord is finished. From the tribute of Coele-syria and Phoenicia let a contribution be duly given to these men for sacrifices to the Lord, payable to Zerubbabel the governor, for bulls, rams, and lambs; and similarly wheat, salt, wine, and oil are to be provided regularly each year without question, as the priests in Jerusalem may require day by day. Let all this be expended in order that sacrifices and libations may be offered to the Most High God for the king and his children, and that intercession may be made on their behalf.' He also gave these orders: 'If anyone disobeys or neglects any of these orders written above or here set down, let a beam be taken from his own house and let him be hanged on it and his estate forfeited to the king. May the Lord himself, therefore, to whom this temple is dedicated, destroy any king or people who shall lift a finger to delay or damage the Lord's house in Jerusalem. I, Darius the king, decree that these orders be obeyed to the letter.'

✻ The source here is Ezra 6: 1–12, which is followed closely with a few distinctive traces of the characteristic features of 1 Esdras. As in the original, the beneficent attitude of the Persian imperial power is stressed.

23. Ezra 6: 1–2 had emphasized the fact that the search for 'the scroll' at Babylon was fruitless, and that the relevant document was in fact found in another royal residence, far away to the east, at Ecbatana; here the geographical knowledge of these distant areas seems very hazy, and it seems as if the author thought that Ecbatana was part of Babylon.

24–6. These verses represent the Aramaic form of Cyrus' decree, which is commonly held to be an authentic rendering of the original form, whereas the genuineness of the Hebrew form underlying 2: 3–7 has been widely questioned.

27. *the servant of the Lord, Zerubbabel:* both the specific mention of Zerubbabel by name here and in verse 29, and the use of the exalted title *servant of the Lord* to describe him provide further evidence of the important role given to him by our author.

32. It seems likely that a Roman form of punishment is here substituted for the Persian form found in Ezra 6: 11. ✻

THE TEMPLE REBUILT

7 Then, in accordance with the orders of King Darius, Sisinnes, governor-general of Coele-syria and Phoenicia,
2 with Sathrabuzanes and their colleagues, carefully supervised the sacred works, co-operating with the elders of
3 the Jews and the temple officers. With the encouragement of the prophets Haggai and Zechariah, good progress was
4 made with the sacred works, and they were finished by the ordinance of the Lord God of Israel and with the approval of Cyrus, Darius, and Artaxerxes, kings of
5 Persia. It was on the twenty-third of Adar in the sixth

year of King Darius that the house was completed. The 6
Israelites, the priests, the Levites, and the rest of the former
exiles who had joined them carried out the directions in
the book of Moses. For the dedication of the temple of 7
the Lord they offered a hundred bulls, two hundred rams,
four hundred lambs, and twelve goats for the sin of all 8
Israel corresponding to the twelve patriarchs of Israel.
The priests and the Levites in their vestments stood 9
family by family to preside over the services of the Lord
God of Israel according to the book of Moses. The door-
keepers took their stand at every gateway.

The Israelites who had returned from exile kept the 10
Passover on the fourteenth day of the first month. The
priests and the Levites were purified together; not all the 11
returned exiles were purified with the priests, but*a* the
Levites were. They slaughtered the Passover victims for 12
all the returned exiles and for their brother priests and for
themselves. All those Israelites participated who had re- 13
turned from exile and had segregated themselves from
the abominations of the peoples of the land to seek the
Lord. They kept the Feast of Unleavened Bread for 14
seven days, rejoicing before the Lord; for he had changed 15
the policy of the Assyrian king towards them and
strengthened them for the service of the Lord the God
of Israel.

✶   The climax of this middle section of the book is reached
with the successful completion of the rebuilding of the
temple, and the solemn celebration of the Passover which

[*a*] not all .... but: *probable meaning; Gk. obscure; some witnesses omit* not.

follows. The original events took place in 516/15 B.C.; the account here follows closely its source in Ezra 6: 13–22.

2. The co-operation between the imperial authorities and the Jews is stressed even more strongly here than in the original. It is possible that one aim of this book is to emphasize the close and fruitful collaboration that took place between the Jewish leaders and the civil authorities of different periods, perhaps at a time when the Jews were held in suspicion by the contemporary authorities.

4. *Artaxerxes:* this reference is anachronistic, since he did not become Persian Emperor until the following century (465–424 B.C.). Curiously the N.E.B. has relegated the word to a footnote at Ezra 6: 14, but has left it in the text here.

5. The probable date of completion was February/March 515 B.C. The day of the month given here differs from that in Ezra, though the N.E.B. has emended the Ezra text to correspond with this.

6. By the time of the composition of 1 Esdras, *the book of Moses*, the Pentateuch, will have been recognized as the guiding principle of the Jewish community's life, and the loyalty of the leaders to its requirements is here emphasized (cp. 5: 49 and the comment there).

11. The text here is very obscure; the N.E.B. may be right, but certainty is impossible. A parallel may be intended with Hezekiah's Passover in 2 Chron. 30 where the participants from the northern tribes 'had not kept themselves ritually clean, and therefore kept the Passover irregularly' (2 Chron. 30: 18). In a similar way *the returned exiles* here (and the northerners of 2 Chronicles were in a sense returned exiles also) had acted in good faith (verse 13), even though they were not ritually *purified*.

12–15. The last verses follow their source very closely, including the stress on separatism and the curious and unexplained reference to *the Assyrian king*. *

Ezra in Jerusalem

* The account in 1 Esdras follows that in the book of Ezra at this point in passing over a considerable intervening period so as to deal with the mission of Ezra himself, and in that sense the introduction here of a new heading by the N.E.B. is entirely justified. It must, however, be borne in mind that it is our superior knowledge of the chronology of the period, together with our developed historical sense, which leads us to stress the gap between the events so far described and the work of Ezra. Probably neither the original writer of Ezra nor our present authors realized the length of the gap at this point; it is furthermore likely that, if they had been aware of it, it would have been of little consequence to them. Both regarded the restoration of Israel as a unified process, of the people's guidance by their God, so that once again they became his truly dedicated community worshipping in the holy city.

It is universally agreed that there is a long gap between Zerubbabel and Ezra; it is much less generally agreed exactly how long that gap was, for we cannot be certain whether the 'Artaxerxes' referred to in this section is Artaxerxes I (465–424 B.C.) or Artaxerxes II (404–358). (For some discussion of the chronological problem, see the commentary on *Ezra and Nehemiah* in this series, especially pp. 6–8.) For the reader of 1 Esdras, however, confusion is less likely to arise, since it is created largely by the uncertainties of the relation between Ezra and Nehemiah, and that problem does not arise here, since Nehemiah is ignored altogether. For 1 Esdras, Zerubbabel and Ezra are the key figures, and the remainder of the book describes Ezra's accomplishment.

Ezra is sometimes called the 'father of Judaism', and the implications of this description are important for our understanding of the way he is presented here. In the last pre-Christian centuries Judaism came to be heavily dependent

55

upon the law and other written traditions handed down in the community, as it reflected upon and interpreted the way God had dealt with his people in the past. This is the pattern which underlies both post-biblical Jewish writings and the New Testament, and it has been widely held among Jews that Ezra played a major role in establishing this pattern – hence the appropriateness of calling him the 'father of Judaism'. In the traditional view, the religion held to have been founded by Moses has now been codified and structured afresh. *

EZRA GOES TO JERUSALEM

8 AFTER THESE EVENTS, in the reign of Artaxerxes king of Persia, came Ezra, son of Saraeas, son of Ezerias, 2 son of Chelkias, son of Salemus, son of Zadok, son of Ahitub, son of Amarias, son of Ezias, son of Mareroth, son of Zaraeas, son of Savia, son of Bocca, son of Abishua, son of Phineas, son of Eleazar, son of Aaron the chief 3 priest. This Ezra came from Babylon as a talented scholar in the law of Moses which had been given by the God of 4 Israel. The king held him in high regard and looked with favour upon all the requests he made. He was accom- 5 panied to Jerusalem by some Israelites, priests, Levites, 6 temple singers, door-keepers, and temple-servitors, in the fifth month of the seventh year of Artaxerxes' reign.[a] They left Babylon at the new moon in the first month and reached Jerusalem at the new moon in the fifth 7 month; for the Lord gave them a safe journey. Ezra's knowledge of the law of the Lord and the command- ments was exact in every detail, so that he could teach all Israel the ordinances and judgements.

[a] *Probable reading; one witness adds* this was the king's second year.

✻ These verses are based on Ezra 7: 1–10. In that passage there is some ambiguity between the presentation of Ezra as part of the Persian imperial service and his essentially religious role within Judaism; here, as we should expect, all the emphasis is on the latter.

1. Though, as we have seen, an interval of at least fifty-eight years (and perhaps much longer) passed before the arrival of Ezra, it seems likely that the author of 1 Esdras thought of Artaxerxes as approximately contemporary with Cyrus and Darius. He has already referred to him in 2: 16–30 and 7: 4 as if this were so.

1–2. In the last centuries before Christ it was regarded as important for all Jews, and especially for the priestly line, to be able to establish their genealogy. Ezra's family tree is given in various places, each with minor differences. As given in the N.E.B. this list corresponds exactly with Ezra 7: 1–5 save for the Greek form of some of the names, but most Greek manuscripts have a shorter form, omitting the names between *Ezias* and *Bocca*. It is surprising that there is no footnote to indicate this.

3. *a talented scholar in the law of Moses:* in Ezra 7: 6 the description of Ezra as 'a scribe' left open the possibility that this might describe his position in the Persian imperial service; here it is without doubt a religious title, corresponding to the 'scribes' who are frequently mentioned in the gospels.

7. The stress on Ezra's *knowledge of the law of the Lord* fits better in its context here, where the climax of his work will be the proclamation of the law, than in Ezra, where that proclamation is dealt with quite separately. ✻

THE KING'S MANDATE

The following is a copy of the mandate from King 8
Artaxerxes to Ezra the priest, doctor of the law of the
Lord:

9   King Artaxerxes to Ezra the priest, doctor of the law of the Lord, greeting.

10   I have graciously decided, and now command, that those of the Jewish nation and of the priests and Levites, in our kingdom, who so choose, shall go with you to
11   Jerusalem. I and my council of seven Friends have decided that all who so desire may accompany you.
12   Let them look to the affairs of Judaea and Jerusalem in
13   pursuance of the law of the Lord, and bring to Jerusalem for the Lord of Israel the gifts which I and my Friends have vowed, all the gold and silver in Babylonia that may be found to belong to the Lord in
14   Jerusalem, together with what has been given by the nation for the temple of the Lord their God in Jerusalem. Let the gold and silver be expended upon[a] bulls,
15   rams, lambs, and so forth, so that sacrifices may be offered upon the altar of the Lord their God in Jeru-
16   salem. Make use of the gold and silver in whatever ways you and your colleagues desire, according to the will of
17   your God, and deliver the sacred vessels of the Lord which have been given you for the use of the temple of your God in Jerusalem.

18   Any other expenses that you may incur for the needs of the temple of your God you shall defray from the
19   royal treasury. I, Artaxerxes the king, direct the treasurers of Syria and Phoenicia to give without fail to Ezra the priest, doctor of the law of the Most High
20   God, whatever he may request up to a hundred talents of silver, and similarly up to a hundred sacks of wheat and a hundred casks of wine, and salt without limit.

[a] *Or* collected for.

58

Let him diligently fulfil in honour of the Most High 21
God all the requirements of God's law, so that divine
displeasure may not befall the kingdom of the king and
of his descendants. You are also informed that no tax 22
or other impost is to be laid on the priests, the Levites,
the temple singers, the door-keepers, the temple-
servitors, and the lay officers of this temple; no one is
permitted to impose any burden on them. You, Ezra, 23
under God's guidance, are to appoint judges and magistrates to judge all who know the law of your God in all
Syria and Phoenicia; you yourself shall see to the instruction of those who do not know it. All who trans- 24
gress the law of your God and of the king shall be
duly punished with death, degradation, fine, or exile.

Then Ezra said: All praise to the Lord alone, who put 25
this into the king's mind, to glorify his house in Jerusalem. He singled me out for honour before the king, 26
his counsellors, and all his Friends and dignitaries. I took 27
courage from the help of the Lord my God and gathered
men of Israel to go up with me.

* This section follows its source, Ezra 7: 11–28, very closely;
in the original the royal decree is in Aramaic, the language
used by the Persian court for official decrees in its western
provinces.

8. *doctor of the law:* the phrase reminds us once again of the
similarity between the usage in 1 Esdras and that of the New
Testament (cp. the Authorized Version of Luke 2: 46).

10–24. The decree itself follows its source very closely,
with the occasional modifications necessary in translation
(e.g. the details of the measures in verse 20). The impression
that this is treated as part of the original return of Jews from

Babylon is strengthened by the references to provisions for the temple and its vessels; taken by itself this decree would certainly most naturally be read as the start of an entirely new venture.

23. If the N.E.B. translation is right, this arrangement is different from that laid down in Ezra 7: 25, where Ezra and those appointed by him are to join together in instructing those ignorant of the law. But it is possible to interpret the Greek text as bearing the same meaning as the Aramaic of Ezra 7: 25.

25–7. This psalm-like interjection of praise follows its source (Ezra 7: 27–8) in its switch to the first person.　✽

THE LEADERS OF THE COMMUNITY

28 These are the leaders according to clans and divisions who went with me from Babylon to Jerusalem in the reign of King Artaxerxes: from the line of Phineas,
29 Gershom; from the line of Ithamar, Gamael; from the
30 line of David, Attus son of Sechenias; from the line of Phoros, Zacharias and a hundred and fifty men with him
31 according to the register; from the line of Phaath-moab, Eliaonias son of Zaraeas and with him two hundred men;
32 from the line of Zathoe, Sechenias son of Jezelus and with him three hundred men; from the line of Adin, Obeth son of Jonathan and with him two hundred and
33 fifty men; from the line of Elam, Jessias son of Gotholias
34 and with him seventy men; from the line of Sophotias,
35 Zaraeas son of Michael and with him seventy men; from the line of Joab, Abadias son of Jezelus and with him
36 two hundred and twelve men; from the line of Bani, Assalimoth son of Josaphias and with him a hundred and
37 sixty men; from the line of Babi, Zacharias son of Bebae

and with him twenty-eight men; from the line of Astath, 38
Joannes son of Hacatan and with him a hundred and ten
men; last came those from the line of Adonikam, by 39
name Eliphalatus, Jeuel, and Samaeas, and with them
seventy men; from the line of Bago, Uthi son of Istal- 40
curus and with him seventy men.

I assembled them at the river called Theras, where we 41
encamped for three days, and I inspected them. As I 42
found no one there who was of priestly or levitical
descent, I sent to Eleazar, Iduelus, Maasmas, Elnathan, 43
Samaeas, Joribus, Nathan, Ennatas, Zacharias, and Mosol- 44
lamus, who were prominent and discerning men. I told 45
them to go to Doldaeus the chief man at the treasury.
I instructed them to speak with Doldaeus, his colleagues, 46
and the treasurers there, and ask them to send us priests
to officiate in the house of our Lord. Under the provi- 47
dence of God they brought us discerning men from the
line of Mooli son of Levi son of Israel, Asebebias and his
sons and brothers, eighteen men in all, also Asebias and 48
Annunus and Hosaeas his brother. Those of the line of
Chanunaeus and their sons amounted to twenty men; and 49
those of the temple-servitors whom David and the leading
men appointed for the service of the Levites amounted
to two hundred and twenty. A register of all these names
was compiled.

* These verses – based on Ezra 8: 1–20 – show a characteristic concern to identify the leaders of the true community,
setting out their genealogy as the appropriate credentials
by which they might be judged. Though there are minor
changes the source is followed closely.

28–40. The only significant change in this list (which is related to that given in ch. 5) concerns some of the numbers of kinsmen listed.

41. *the river called Theras:* the name is given in only one manuscript of the Greek text, and is not in Ezra 8; its whereabouts is unknown.

42. *no one . . . of priestly or levitical descent:* Ezra 8: 15 speaks only of the lack of Levites. The text here may be softening the implied criticism, or it may be a misunderstanding of the original. In any case it scarcely makes sense, since the families of Phineas and Ithamar, mentioned in verse 29, were certainly priestly, as being of Aaronic descent (1 Chron. 6: 3–4).

43–4. Only ten names are listed here, as against the eleven of Ezra 8: 16, and there are several differences in detail.

45. *at the treasury:* this is a good instance of the hazards of translation. In Ezra 8: 17 a place, perhaps a sanctuary, ('Casiphia') is mentioned; here the place-name has been interpreted as a common noun meaning *treasury*.

46. *to send us priests:* as in verse 42, there is a discrepancy with the Ezra text, which refers only to 'servitors' – a menial office by comparison with the priests mentioned here. ✶

THE SOLEMN PROCESSION

50 There I made a vow that the young men should fast before our Lord to beg him to give us a safe journey for ourselves, our children who accompanied us, and our
51 pack-animals. I was ashamed to ask the king for an escort
52 of infantry and cavalry against our enemies; for we had told the king that the strength of our Lord would ensure
53 success for those who looked to him. So once more we laid all these things before our Lord in prayer and found him gracious.
54 I set apart twelve men from among the heads of the

priestly families, and with them Sarabias and Asamias and
ten of their brother priests. I weighed out for them the 55
silver, the gold, and the sacred vessels of the house of our
Lord; these had been presented by the king himself, his
counsellors, the chief men, and all Israel. When I had 56
weighed it all I handed over to them six hundred and
fifty talents of silver, and vessels of silver weighing a
hundred talents, a hundred talents of gold, and twenty 57
pieces of gold plate, and twelve vessels of brass so fine
that it gleamed like gold. I said to them: 'You are conse- 58
crated to the Lord, and so are the vessels; the silver and the
gold are vowed to the Lord, the Lord of our fathers. Be 59
vigilant and keep guard until you hand them over at
Jerusalem, in the priests' rooms in the house of our Lord,
to the heads of the priestly and levitical families and to
the leaders of the clans of Israel.' The priests and the 60
Levites who received the silver, the gold, and the vessels
in Jerusalem brought them to the temple of the Lord.

We left the river Theras on the twelfth day of the first 61
month, and under the powerful protection which our
Lord gave us we reached Jerusalem. He guarded us against
every enemy on our journey, and so we arrived at Jerusalem. Three days passed, and on the fourth the silver and 62
gold were weighed and handed over in the house of our
Lord to the priest Marmathi son of Uri, with whom was 63
Eleazar son of Phineas. With them also were the Levites
Josabdus son of Jeshua and Moeth son of Sabannus. Everything was numbered and weighed and every weight 64
recorded there and then. The returned exiles offered sacri- 65
fices to the Lord the God of Israel, twelve bulls for all
Israel, with ninety-six rams and seventy-two lambs, and 66

also twelve goats for a peace-offering, the whole as a
67 sacrifice to the Lord. They delivered the king's orders to
the royal treasurers and the governors of Coele-syria and
Phoenicia, and so added lustre to the nation and the
temple of the Lord.

✻ This section follows closely its source in Ezra 8: 21–36,
and in each case what may originally have been a journey
carried out as part of the Persian imperial service is described
as if it were essentially a religious procession. Such a formalized mode of description is reminiscent of some of the
accounts of Israel's wandering in the wilderness before the
entry into Canaan (cp. Ps. 105: 43–5).
  50–3. Fasting and prayer as preparation for an important
venture were characteristic practices in Judaism.
  54–67. This whole section follows its source very closely,
with the minor variants in names and numbers that we have
by now come to expect. Only the last phrase of verse 67
appears to be different, but this is ambiguous in the Greek,
where the subject of the verb translated *added lustre* is not
expressed. ✻

EZRA'S PRAYER

68 When these matters had been settled the leaders came to
69 me and said: 'The nation of Israel, the rulers, the priests,
and the Levites, have not kept themselves apart from the
alien population of the land with all their pollutions, that
is to say the Canaanites, Hittites, Perizzites, Jebusites,
70 Moabites, Egyptians, and Edomites. For they and their
sons have intermarried with the daughters of these
peoples, and the holy race has been mingled with the
alien population of the land; and the leaders and principal
men have shared in this violation of the law from the very
beginning.'

As soon as I heard of this I tore my clothes and sacred 71
vestment, plucked out the hair of my head and my beard,
and sat down perplexed and miserable. Those who at 72
that time were moved by the word of the Lord of Israel
gathered round me, while I grieved over this disregard
of the law, and sat in my misery until the evening sacrifice. Then I rose from my fast with my clothes and sacred 73
vestment torn, and knelt down and, stretching out my
hands to the Lord, said: 74

'O Lord, I am covered with shame and confusion in
thy presence. Our sins tower above our heads; from the 75–76
time of our fathers our offences have reached the sky,
and today we are as deep in sin as ever. Because of our 77
sins and the sins of our fathers, we and our brothers, our
kings and our priests, were given over to the kings of
the earth to be killed, taken prisoner, plundered, and
humiliated down to this very day. And now, Lord, how 78
great is the mercy thou hast shown us! We still have a
root and a name in the place of thy sanctuary, and thou 79
hast rekindled our light in the house of our Lord, and
given us food in the time of our servitude. Even when 80
we were slaves we were not deserted by our Lord; for
he secured for us the favour of the kings of Persia, who 81
have provided our food and added lustre to the temple
of our Lord and restored the ruins of Zion, giving us a
firm foothold in Judaea and Jerusalem. And now, Lord, 82
what are we to say, we who have received all this? For
we have broken thy commandments given us through
thy servants the prophets. Thou didst say: "The land 83
which you are to occupy is a land defiled with the pollution of its heathen peoples; they have filled it with their
impurities. Do not marry your daughters to their sons nor 84

85 take their daughters for your sons; never try to make
peace with them if you want to be strong and enjoy the
good things of the land and take possession of it for your
86 children for ever." All our misfortunes have come upon
us through our evil deeds and our great sins. Although
thou, Lord, hast lightened the burden of our sins and given
87 us so firm a root, yet we have fallen away again and
broken thy law by sharing in the impurities of the heathen
88 peoples of this land. But thou wast not so angry with us,
89 Lord, as to destroy us, root, seed, and name; thou keepest
faith, O Lord of Israel; the root is left, we are here today.
90 Behold us, now before thee in our sins; because of all
we have done we can no longer hold up our heads before
thee.'

91 While Ezra prayed and made confession, weeping prostrate on the ground before the temple, a very large crowd
gathered, men, women, and youths of Jerusalem, and
there was widespread lamentation among the people.
92 Jechonias son of Jeel, one of the Israelites, called out to
Ezra: 'We have sinned against the Lord in taking alien
wives from the heathen population of this land; and yet
93 there is still hope for Israel. Let us take an oath to the
Lord to expel all our wives of alien race with their
94 children, in accordance with your judgement and the
judgement of all who are obedient to the law of the Lord.
95 Come now, set about it, it is in your hands; take strong
96 action and we are with you.' Ezra got up and laid an
oath upon the principal priests and Levites of all Israel
that they would act in this way, and they swore to it.

* Ezra's task in Jerusalem is described as twofold: the breaking-up of mixed marriages, and the proclamation of the law. The relation between these two parts of his work is a complex one, but all forms of the tradition are agreed in placing his action in regard to mixed marriages immediately after his arrival in Jerusalem. Here 1 Esdras is following Ezra 9: 1 – 10: 5; the chapter-division between I Esdras 8 and 9 does not correspond with that between Ezra 9 and 10.

68. Both in the book of Ezra and here it is stressed that the initiative came from the community, not from Ezra himself.

69. *Edomites:* at this point it is likely that 1 Esdras has preserved a better text than Ezra, for it is much more natural to find Edomites – against whom many parts of the Old Testament show hostility – than the 'Amorites' (an alternative name for Canaanites) of Ezra 9: 1.

72. In Ezra 9: 4 it is specified that the offence had been committed by those who had been exiled; that point is omitted here.

74–90. Ezra's prayer is also a word of exhortation to the community. As in its source in Ezra 9, the many allusions to earlier biblical passages serve to identify the contemporary community with the Israel of earlier ages. Already in the original a favourable attitude toward the kings of Persia is found, and this is still more emphasized in verse 81.

91–6. This section reverts to a third-person description of Ezra's action, and again emphasizes how his appeal led to an initiative on the part of the community itself. The reaction may not appear attractive to us, but it is motivated by a strong concern to establish the true meaning of being the people of God in the midst of hostile surroundings. This had been important when Ezra was written; it may have been still more important if 1 Esdras came from a Jewish community away from Palestine and surrounded by adherents of other religions who were suspicious of the Jews.   *

THE EXPULSION OF FOREIGN WIVES

9 Ezra left the court of the temple and entered the room
2 of the priest Joanan son of Eliasibus. There he stayed,
eating no food and drinking no water, while he mourned
over the serious violations of the law by the community.
3 A proclamation was made throughout Judaea and in
Jerusalem to all the returned exiles that they should
4 assemble at Jerusalem; those who failed to arrive within
two or three days, according to the decision of the elders
in office, were to have their cattle confiscated for temple
use and would themselves be excluded from the community of the returned exiles.

5 Three days later all Judah and Benjamin had assembled
in Jerusalem; the date was the twentieth of the ninth
6 month. They all sat together in the open space before the
7 temple, shivering because winter had set in. Ezra stood up
and said to them: 'You have broken the law and married
alien wives, bringing a fresh burden of guilt on Israel.
8, 9 Now make confession to the Lord God of our fathers; do
his will and separate yourselves from the heathen population of this land and from your alien wives.'

10 The whole company answered with a shout: 'We will
11 do as you have said!' 'But', they said, 'our numbers are
great, and we cannot stay here in the open in this wintry
weather. Nor is this the work of a day or two only;
12 the offence is widespread among us. Let the leaders of the
community stay here, and let all members of our settle-
13 ments who have alien wives attend at an appointed time
along with the elders and judges of each place, until we
turn away the Lord's anger at what has been done.'

Jonathan son of Azael and Hezekias son of Thocanus 14 took charge on these terms, and Mosollamus, Levi, and Sabbataeus were their assessors. The returned exiles duly 15 carried all this out.

Ezra the priest selected men by name, all chiefs of their 16 clans, and on the new moon of the tenth month they sat to investigate the matter. This affair of the men who had 17 alien wives was settled by the new moon of the first month.

Among the priests some of those who had come to- 18 gether were found to have alien wives; these were 19 Mathelas, Eleazar, Joribus, and Joadanus of the line of Jeshua son of Josedek and his brothers, who undertook 20 to send away their wives and to offer rams in expiation of their error. Of the line of Emmer: Ananias, Zabdaeus, 21 Manes, Samaeus, Jereel, and Azarias; of the line of 22 Phaesus: Elionas, Massias, Ishmael, Nathanael, Okidelus, and Saloas. Of the Levites: Jozabadus, Semis, Colius (this 23 is Calitas), Phathaeus, Judah, and Jonas. Of the temple 24 singers: Eliasibus, Bacchurus. Of the door-keepers: Sallu- 25 mus and Tolbanes.

Of the people of Israel there were, of the line of 26 Phoros: Jermas, Jeddias, Melchias, Maelus, Eleazar, Asibias, and Bannaeas. Of the line of Ela: Matthanias, 27 Zacharias, Jezrielus, Oabdius, Jeremoth, and Aedias. Of 28 the line of Zamoth: Eliadas, Eliasimus, Othonias, Jari- moth, Sabathus, and Zardaeas. Of the line of Bebae: 29 Joannes, Ananias, Ozabadus, and Emathis. Of the line of 30 Mani: Olamus, Mamuchus, Jedaeus, Jasubus, Asaelus, and Jeremoth. Of the line of Addi: Naathus, Moossias, 31 Laccunus, Naidus, Matthanias, Sesthel, Balnuus, and

32 Manasseas. Of the line of Annas: Elionas, Asaeas, Mel-
33 chias, Sabbaeas, and Simon Chosomaeus. Of the line of
Asom: Altannaeus, Mattathias, Bannaeus, Eliphalat,
34 Manasses, and Semi. Of the line of Baani: Jeremias,
Momdis, Ismaerus, Juel, Mandae, Paedias, Anos, Cara-
basion, Enasibus, Mamnitanaemus, Eliasis, Bannus, Eliali,
Somis, Selemias, and Nathanias. Of the line of Ezora:
35 Sessis, Ezril, Azael, Samatus, Zambris, and Josephus. Of
the line of Nooma: Mazitias, Zabadaeas, Edaes, Juel, and
36 Banaeas. All these had married alien wives; they sent
them away with their children.

* The book of Ezra ends with an account of the carrying out
of the measures for the purification of the community. In that
context it appears to be a peculiarly lame conclusion; here the
source is closely followed, but a different impression is created
by the fact that an account of the law-reading immediately
follows. In the present context we are given an account of the
consequences of the action already described.

1. *the priest Joanan son of Eliasibus:* it has often been argued
that this priest should be identified with the 'Jonathan' or
'Johanan' of Neh. 12: 11, 22, and that 'grandson' rather than
son should be read here, as in the N.E.B. of Ezra 10: 6. If both
these suggestions were correct, it would point toward a
dating of Ezra in the time of Artaxerxes II (about 398 B.C.),
but neither can be regarded as established.

4. *cattle confiscated for temple use:* this is more specific than
Ezra 10: 8, and may reflect the custom within the religious
community of the author's day.

5-15. The outlines of the religious ceremony follow the
same pattern as that described in Ezra 10, with one curious
variant. In Ezra 10: 15 'Jonathan ... and Jahzeiah' are
recorded as being opposed to Ezra's plea; here they are those
who *took charge.* It is possible that this is due to misunder-

standing on the part of I Esdras; more probably we see here
a tradition which stressed the unanimity of the community in
all its major decisions.

18–36. The names listed show a number of minor variants
from those in Ezra 10; this has been characteristic of all the
lists of names incorporated in the book.   *

THE READING OF THE LAW

The priests, the Levites, and such Israelites as were in 37
Jerusalem and its vicinity, settled down there on the new
moon of the seventh month; the other Israelites remained
in their settlements. The entire body assembled as one in 38
the open space before the east gateway of the temple and 39
asked Ezra the high priest and doctor of the law to bring
the law of Moses given by the Lord God of Israel. On the 40
new moon of the seventh month he brought the law to
all the multitude of men and women alike, and to the
priests, for them to hear. He read it in the open space 41
before the temple gateway from daybreak until noon, in
the presence of both men and women, and the whole
body listened intently. Ezra the priest and doctor of the 42
law stood upon the wooden platform which had been
prepared. There stood with him, on his right, Mattathias, 43
Sammus, Ananias, Azarias, Urias, Hezekias, and Baal-
samus, and on his left, Phaldaeus, Misael, Melchias, 44
Lothasubus, Nabarias, and Zacharias. Ezra took up the 45
book of the law; everyone could see him, for he was
seated in a conspicuous place in front of them all, and
when he opened it they all stood up. Ezra praised the 46
Lord God the Most High God of hosts, the Almighty.
All the multitude cried 'Amen, Amen', and lifting up 47

their hands fell to the ground and worshipped the Lord.
48 Jeshua, Annus, Sarabias, Jadinus, Jacubus, Sabbataeas,
Autaeas, Maeannas, Calitas, Azarias, Jozabdus, Ananias,
and Phiathas, the Levites, taught the law of the Lord;
they read the law of the Lord to the whole company, at
the same time instilling into their minds what was read.
49   Then the governor*a* said to Ezra the high priest and
doctor of the law and to each of the Levites who taught
50 the multitude: 'This day is holy to the Lord.' All were
51 weeping as they heard the law. 'Go then, refresh yourselves with rich food and sweet wine, and send shares to
52 those who have none; for the day is holy to the Lord.
Let there be no sadness; for the Lord will give you glory.'
53 The Levites issued the command to all the people: 'This
54 day is holy, do not be sad.' So they all departed to eat
and drink and make merry, and to send shares to those
55 who had none, and to hold a great celebration; because
the teaching given them had been instilled into their minds.
    They gathered together.*b*

*   In the book of Ezra the list of names forms the conclusion,
save for an obscure note at the end which the N.E.B. has
corrected from the text of I Esdras. Too much must not be
made of the apparently unsatisfactory nature of this conclusion, for the books of Ezra and Nehemiah were treated
as a unity until well into the Christian era, but it is still unexpected to find the account of one part of Ezra's work separated
from the account of his reading of the law. That problem
does not arise here, for our text passes directly to Neh. 7: 73
and follows closely from that point the account of the reading
of the law.

[a] *Gk.* Attharates.
[b] *Probably the text originally carried on from this point; compare*
Neh. 8: 13.

It is impossible to be certain whether this placing together of the two parts of Ezra's work was a deliberate rearrangement of his material by the compiler of 1 Esdras, or whether he inherited a tradition which did not include the early chapters of Nehemiah, and so presented Ezra's work as a unity. In view of the evidence we have already seen of the creative way in which 1 Esdras develops existing traditions (e.g. with regard to Zerubbabel), the former possibility is more likely.

37. *the new moon of the seventh month:* this date is taken over from Neh. 8: 2, where in turn it appears to be dependent on Ezra 3: 1. Here it is understood as one of the sequence of dates already given in this chapter.

37–8. The N.E.B. translation reads somewhat awkwardly at this point, appearing to state first that some of the community *remained in their settlements*, then that all *assembled as one*. Probably there is no contradiction; the end of verse 37 refers to the fact that various settlements had by now been established.

38. *before the east gateway of the temple:* this differs from its source, and may be a deliberate attempt to link the solemn law-reading ceremony more closely with the temple.

39. *Ezra the high priest:* he is never so described in the books of Ezra and Nehemiah. This is probably one example of the tendency represented by 1 Esdras, to magnify the role of Ezra in establishing the religious community. *the law of Moses:* here, as probably already in Neh. 8, this is understood as being the Pentateuch. Whether the book actually was the Pentateuch as a whole or in part, is much less certain.

43–4. There are thirteen names listed, as in Neh. 8: 4, but there the disposition is six on the right, seven on the left, whereas here the numbers are reversed, and there are changes in detail.

45–8. To an even clearer extent than its source, this passage appears to reflect the pattern of assembly which was normal in the synagogue. This is particularly noteworthy in the piling-up of divine titles in verse 46.

49. *the governor:* in Neh. 8: 9 there is a reference – widely

73

held to be a later gloss – to 'Nehemiah the governor' at this point. It is likely that here, as at 5: 40, the Greek translators understood the rare word 'tirshatha' as a proper name (cp. the N.E.B. footnote). As presented here, his role is to lead a kind of liturgical refrain.

54. No attempt is made here to set out the festival in terms of the main Jewish autumn festival, Tabernacles, or of the Day of Atonement, which became the major observance of that festival.

55. *They gathered together:* both the way in which the N.E.B presents the text, and the accompanying footnote, make its assumption clear that part of the original text has now been lost. This is probably correct, though it is possible that the work could be regarded as complete; the original has no paragraphs, and it might be regarded as quite appropriate to end with a picture of the gathering together of the faithful community. In any case, it is unlikely that a substantial part of the work is missing, since Ezra's achievement has now been described, and there is no further material dealing with him in the original Hebrew. (The Septuagint form of the work (Esdras b in the table on p. 3) attributes the long prayer in Neh. 9 to Ezra and this is followed by some modern translations (not the N.E.B.), but it seems that this was probably a later attribution of an originally anonymous prayer.) The intention of the compiler of 1 Esdras appears to have been to concentrate on the three great moments in the life of the community associated with Josiah, Zerubbabel and Ezra, and his purpose has now been achieved. ✳

✳   ✳   ✳   ✳   ✳   ✳   ✳   ✳   ✳   ✳   ✳   ✳   ✳

✳ 1. Esdras is quite possibly the least-read book in the whole of the Bible and Apocrypha. This is understandable, for so much of it repeats material which has appeared elsewhere, and this is nowadays regarded as a major problem. But the Bible provides plenty of evidence that this was quite acceptable in the ancient world – the inclusion of both Kings and Chronicles in the Old Testament and of the gospels of Matthew, Mark and Luke in the New amply illustrate this. In other words, what is provided here in the way of creative reflection on the events and figures of the past provides an important clue to the self-understanding of the Jewish (and later the Christian) community. We see here a new estimate of the importance of particular individuals, with the role of Zerubbabel emphasized and that of Nehemiah played down. We see a new perspective on history, linking events before and after the Babylonian exile which we often keep separate; other traditions, such as the book of Daniel, elaborated very greatly the importance of the exile, with the idea often being found that the people were still in a sense 'exiled' from their God, but in 1 Esdras the exile is an episode of past history and the continuity of the people's experience is stressed. Above all, therefore, we see a new interpretation, fitted for changing circumstances, of the way in which God had guided his faithful community when they remained loyal to him. ✶

A NOTE ON FURTHER READING

Very few commentaries have been written on 1 Esdras; much the most useful recent one (which also includes 2 Esdras) is by J. M. Myers, Anchor Bible (Garden City, New York, 1974). An outline of the literary problems of the book is provided by J. A. Soggin, *Introduction to the Old Testament* (S.C.M. Press, 1976) and the historical background of the period dealt with is covered by M. Noth, *A History of Israel*, 2nd ed. (A. & C. Black, 1960) or S. Herrmann, *A History of Israel in Old Testament Times* (S.C.M. Press, 1975).

THE SECOND BOOK OF

ESDRAS

✲ ✲ ✲ ✲ ✲ ✲ ✲ ✲ ✲ ✲ ✲ ✲ ✲ ✲

A COMPOSITE BOOK

At the beginning of this volume it was pointed out that it is customary to divide 2 Esdras, and to refer to chs. 1–2 as 5 Ezra, and chs. 15–16 as 6 Ezra (see p. 3). It will be apparent from even a casual reading that chs. 1–2, 3–14, and 15–16 form in fact three quite separate works, and this is confirmed by the evidence of the Latin version, in which language alone the text of 2 Esdras has survived in its entirety. The manuscripts of the Latin version clearly distinguish between the three sections of the composite book, and some even have chs. 1–2 after ch. 16, or place 1 Esdras between 2 Esdras 1–2 and 3–14 + 15–16. Of these three works, the oldest is 2 Esdras 3–14. This is a Jewish apocalypse, probably composed in Hebrew, and dating from towards the end of the reign of the Emperor Domitian (A.D. 81–96). 2 Esdras 1–2 and 15–16 form two quite independent additions to the original Jewish writing. These are Christian works; they were apparently composed in Greek, and date from the second and third centuries respectively. These additions were made when 2 Esdras had been taken over by the Christian Church, but whereas 2 Esdras 15–16 seems to have been written from the outset as an appendix to chs. 3–14 which was intended to make the earlier work relevant to a new situation, chs. 1–2 initially had an independent existence. The fact that these additions were made to 2 Esdras 3–14 is an indication of the high regard in which the name of Ezra was held by Christians as well as Jews (see further pp. 1-2). The practice in the English versions of the Bible of referring to this composite book as

2 Esdras goes back to the Geneva Bible of 1560. The Geneva Bible took the number 2 Esdras from the Latin translation, but the Latin manuscripts in fact vary quite considerably in the numbers which they assign to the Ezra-writings and to the different sections of 2 Esdras 1-16, and because of this there is some confusion in the numbering of the various Ezra-books. In modern publications 2 Esdras 3-14 is often referred to as 4 Ezra, in distinction from 2 Esdras 1-2 (5 Ezra) and 2 Esdras 15-16 (6 Ezra).

*   *   *   *   *   *   *   *   *   *   *   *   *

2 ESDRAS 1-2

Israel's rejection and glory to come

*   The main theme of 2 Esdras 1-2, which forms, as we have seen, a quite independent work, is that the Church has taken the place of Israel. By content these chapters divide into two parts, of which the first (1: 1 – 2: 9) is primarily concerned with Israel, and the reasons for her rejection, and the second (2: 10–48) with the Church, and the glorious future which awaits it. As will become apparent, the author was a Jewish Christian, and his work represents an attempt to resolve the problem of the relationship of the Church to Israel. In form 2 Esdras 1-2 imitates the style of Old Testament prophecy, and, as in chs. 15–16, Ezra is presented as a prophet. The Old Testament traditions about Ezra do not say this at all, but in later interpretation a number of notable Old Testament characters are described as speaking prophetically, e.g. Moses (Deut. 18: 15; 34: 10–11) and David (2 Sam. 23: 2; Acts 2: 30; see also the commentary on 2 Samuel in this series, p. 219). Besides this, the author of 2 Esdras 1-2 draws very heavily on the Old and New Testaments for the language and content of his work which in places has the appearance of being a mosaic of biblical quotations.

The date of 2 Esdras 1–2 can only be fixed approximately. The author reveals an acquaintance with several New Testament writings (notably the gospels of Matthew and Luke, and the book of Revelation), and this brings us down to the end of the first century A.D. On the other hand, the fact that the controversy between Judaism and Christianity was still a live issue suggests that we should not come down too far beyond the end of the first century, and we should probably think in terms of a date about the middle of the second century A.D. This dating is supported by a parallel which exists between 2: 43 and the *Shepherd of Hermas*, a Christian work which is likewise to be dated about the middle of the second century. Going beyond this, it has been suggested that 2 Esdras 1–2 was written as a Christian response to the unsuccessful outcome of the Jewish revolt of A.D. 132–5; this is an attractive, but somewhat uncertain, possibility. The place of composition is completely unknown. There are hints that the author was writing in the western part of the Roman Empire (see the comments on 1: 11 and 38), but these are so uncertain that no reliance can be placed upon them.

2 Esdras 1–2 has survived only in a Latin translation, but it is generally believed that the language of composition was Greek. The Latin manuscripts of 2 Esdras divide into two groups, or families, one French and the other Spanish. In 2 Esdras 1–2 there are some significant differences between these two groups of manuscripts, but it has been thought inappropriate to discuss these here, and almost without exception they have been ignored. However, it may be noted that the N.E.B. follows the French family of manuscripts. *

EZRA'S PROPHETIC CALL

1 THE SECOND BOOK of the prophet Ezra, son of Seraiah, son of Azariah, son of Hilkiah, son of
2 Shallum, son of Zadok, son of Ahitub, son of Ahijah,

son of Phinehas, son of Eli, son of Amariah, son of Aziah,
son of Marimoth, son of Arna, son of Uzzi, son of
Borith, son of Abishua, son of Phinehas, son of Eleazar,
son of Aaron, of the tribe of Levi.   3

I, Ezra, was a captive in Media in the reign of Artaxerxes,
king of Persia, when the word of the Lord came to me: 4
'Go to my people and proclaim their crimes; tell their 5
children how they have sinned against me, and let them
tell their children's children. They have sinned even more 6
than their fathers; they have forgotten me and sacrificed
to alien gods. Was it not I who rescued them from Egypt, 7
the country where they were slaves? And yet they have
provoked me to anger and ignored my warnings.
   'Now, Ezra, pluck out your hair and let calamities 8
loose upon these people who have disobeyed my law.
They are beyond correction. How much longer shall I 9
endure them, I who have lavished on them such benefits?
Many are the kings I have overthrown for their sake; 10
I struck down Pharaoh with his court and all his army.
I destroyed every nation that stood in their way, and in 11
the east I routed the peoples of two provinces, Tyre and
Sidon, and killed all the enemies of Israel.

*   Ezra is summoned as a prophet to denounce Israel for her
sin.
   1–3a. An introduction, lacking in some of the manuscripts,
which gives Ezra's genealogy and establishes his priestly
descent. It is comparable to the genealogies at the beginning
of the account of Ezra's work in the book of Ezra (cp. 7: 1–5)
and in 1 Esdras (cp. 8: 1–2), but differs from these in a number
of respects. *the prophet Ezra:* this description of Ezra (for

which cp. 12: 42) reflects the fact that 2 Esdras 1–2 has the form of a prophecy, but is in striking contrast to Ezra's role in the Old Testament as 'a scribe learned in the law of Moses' (Ezra 7: 6).

3b. *a captive in Media in the reign of Artaxerxes, king of Persia:* cp. Ezra 7: 1. The prophecy is assumed to have been given to the exiles at a time before Ezra made his journey to Jerusalem. *Media:* here used in a very general way to describe the area in which the exiles were living.

4. *the word of the Lord came to me:* the formula which is used frequently in the Old Testament to introduce the revelation of God's word to a prophet; cp. e.g. Jer. 1: 4; 2: 1; Ezek. 7: 1; 12: 1. This formula is not used of Ezra in the Old Testament.

5–11. Despite the many mercies shown to her, Israel has sinned against God to such an extent that her relationship with him has been brought into question. Here and elsewhere in 2 Esdras 1–2 the author draws very heavily on the language and thought of the Old Testament; some examples of this are indicated in the notes.

6. *they have forgotten me and sacrificed to alien gods:* cp. Jer. 2: 32; 5: 19.

7. Cp. Exod. 20: 2.

8. *pluck out your hair:* based on Ezra 9: 3. In the Old Testament tearing the hair was a physical indication of distress; Ezra is commanded to do it here as a sign of God's anger at Israel's sin.

10. *Many are the kings I have overthrown . . . I struck down Pharaoh:* cp. Exod. 14: 27–8; Ps. 135: 9–10.

11. *and in the east I routed the people of two provinces, Tyre and Sidon:* an obscure passage, made more so by uncertainties about the text (the Latin manuscripts differ quite considerably). Tyre and Sidon are cities, not provinces, and in any case lie to the west, not the east, of Media (cp. verse 3). This latter point has led to the suggestion that 2 Esdras 1–2 was written in the west, but there are difficulties about the

reading *in the east*, and it is not clear how much should be read into this phrase. It is also not clear to what historical situation the author was referring. It is possible that he had in mind such events as the siege of Tyre by Alexander the Great and the destruction of Sidon by Artaxerxes III, but he may also have been influenced by the prophecies about Tyre and Sidon in Ezek. 26: 1 – 28: 23.   ✳

ISRAEL'S DISOBEDIENCE AND REJECTION

'Say to them, "These are the words of the Lord: Was 12, 13 it not I who brought you through the sea, and made safe roads for you where no road had been? I gave you Moses as your leader, and Aaron as your priest; I gave you light 14 from a pillar of fire, and performed great miracles among you. And yet you have forgotten me, says the Lord.

'"These are the words of the Lord Almighty: I gave 15 you the quails as a sign; I gave you a camp for your protection. But all you did there was to grumble and complain – instead of celebrating the victory I had given you 16 when I destroyed your enemies. From that day to this you have never stopped complaining. Have you forgotten 17 what benefits I conferred on you? When you were hungry and thirsty in your journey through the desert, you cried out to me, 'Why have you brought us into this 18 desert to kill us? Better to have remained in Egypt as slaves than to die here in the desert!' I was grieved by 19 your complaints, and gave you manna for food; you ate the bread of angels. When you were thirsty, I split open 20 the rock, and out flowed water in plenty. Against the summer heat I gave you the shelter of leafy trees. I gave 21 you fertile lands to divide among your tribes, expelling the Canaanites, Perizzites, and Philistines who opposed you. What more could I do for you? says the Lord.

22 '"These are the words of the Lord Almighty: When you were in the desert, suffering thirst by the stream of
23 bitter water and cursing me, I did not bring down fire upon you for your blasphemy; I cast a tree into the stream
24 and made the water sweet. What am I to do with you, Jacob? Judah, you have refused to obey me. I will turn to other nations; I will give them my name, and they will
25 keep my statutes. Because you have deserted me, I will desert you; when you cry for mercy, I will show you
26 none; when you pray to me, I will not listen. You have stained your hands with blood; you run hot-foot to
27 commit murder. It is not I whom you have deserted, but yourselves, says the Lord.

* The remainder of the chapter, with the exception of verses 38–40, consists of a series of prophecies, each introduced by the formula 'These are the words of the Lord (Almighty)', which Ezra is to proclaim to the exiles. The theme of the chapter is that Israel, because of her disobedience, is to lose her privileged position with God and be replaced by another people, i.e. by the Christian Church. In verses 12–27 the author gives an account of God's dealings with his people from the exodus from Egypt to the entry into the Promised Land. The account is reminiscent of such Old Testament passages as Ps. 78 and Ezek. 20, and, as in these passages, the emphasis falls on Israel's constant ingratitude and sin. The climax is reached in verse 24 with the rhetorical question, 'What am I to do with you, Jacob?' Israel's sin is such that God will reject her and turn to others.

12. *These are the words of the Lord:* the common formula used in the Old Testament to introduce the words which a

82

prophet, acting as God's messenger, is to speak to the people; cp. e.g. Jer. 2: 1–2*a*, 4–5*a*; Amos 1: 3*a*, 6.

13. Cp. Exod. 14: 21–2, 29.

14. *light from a pillar of fire:* cp. Exod. 13: 21. *And yet you have forgotten me:* cp. Jer. 2: 32.

15. *the Lord Almighty:* cp. 2 Cor. 6: 18 (where the N.E.B. translates the same expression as 'the Lord, the Ruler of all being'); the title is not used in the Old Testament. *the quails:* cp. Exod. 16: 13; Ps. 105: 40. *a camp:* cp. Deut. 1: 32–3. *But all you did there was to grumble and complain:* the complaints of the people in the wilderness form a constant theme of Exod. 15: 22 – 17: 7; Num. 14.

18. Based on Exod. 14: 11–12, but cp. Exod. 16: 3. A more obvious allusion to the latter might have been expected.

19. *and gave you manna for food:* cp. Exod. 16: 14–15, 31. *you ate the bread of angels:* cp. Ps. 78: 25; Wisd. of Sol. 16: 20. The similarity between Ps. 78 and 2 Esdras 1: 12–27 has already been mentioned; the thought of Ps. 78: 15–31 is closely comparable to that of 2 Esdras 1: 15–21.

20. *I split open the rock:* cp. Exod. 17: 6; Num. 20: 11. *I gave you the shelter of leafy trees:* there is no Old Testament tradition to this effect, but the passage is perhaps an elaboration of Exod. 15: 27.

21. *the Canaanites, Perizzites:* cp. Judg. 1: 4–5. *and Philistines:* the mention of the Philistines together with the Canaanites and Perizzites is a little unexpected because there is no Old Testament tradition that the Philistines were defeated at the time of the Israelite settlement in Palestine.

22–3. Cp. Exod. 15: 22–25*a*.

24–7. In the Old Testament Israel is frequently condemned for her sin, and threatened with punishment, but never rejected in such final terms as are used here. This passage, in common with others which refer to the replacement of Israel by another people, is a clear indication that 2 Esdras 1–2 is the work of a Christian, and this view is confirmed by the fact that in a number of places the author appears to make direct use of the New Testament; cp. particularly 2: 42–8 with Rev. 7: 9–17. However, the concern with Israel suggests that the author was a Jewish, not a gentile, Christian.

24. *I will turn to other nations; I will give them my name, and they will keep my statutes:* Israel is to be replaced by the Christian Church; cp. Matt. 21: 43, 'the kingdom of God will be taken away from you, and given to a nation that yields the proper fruit'. The parallel with Matthew is even clearer in a variant reading which is preferable to the text adopted in the N.E.B., 'I will turn to another nation ...' Cp. also Acts 13: 46.

25. *Because you have deserted me, I will desert you:* cp. 2 Chron. 15: 2; 24: 20.

26. *when you pray to me, I will not listen. You have stained your hands with blood:* apparently based on Isa. 1: 15:

> 'When you lift your hands outspread in prayer,
> I will hide my eyes from you.
> Though you offer countless prayers,
>   I will not listen.
> There is blood on your hands'

The reference to blood may, however, have been occasioned by Jewish ill-treatment of Christians. *you run hot-foot to commit murder:* cp. Prov. 1: 16; Isa. 59: 7; Rom. 3: 15.   ✳

GOD'S CONCERN FOR ISRAEL

28 '"These are the words of the Lord Almighty: Have I not pleaded with you as a father with his sons, as a mother with her daughters or a nurse with her children?
29 Have I not said, 'Be my people, and I will be your God;
30 be my sons, and I will be your father'? I gathered you as a hen gathers her chickens under her wings. But now
31 what am I to do with you? I will toss you away. When you offer me sacrifice, I will turn from you; I have

rejected your feasts, your new moons, and your circumcisions. I sent you my servants the prophets, but you took 32 them and killed them, and mutilated their dead bodies. For their murder I will call you to account, says the Lord.

✻ The author develops further the points that have been made in verses 24–7. Here he is concerned to emphasize that Israel's rejection was very far from being God's original intention. God had taken the initiative in seeking Israel, and it was Israel's failure to respond (exemplified in her treatment of the prophets) that made her rejection inevitable. The character of this passage, with its concern for Israel, is a further indication that the author was a Jewish, rather than a gentile, Christian.

28–9. The N.E.B. has slightly obscured the force of the original by inserting *Have I not said* at the beginning of verse 29. The text reads literally, 'Have I not pleaded with you as a father . . . , that you should be my people, and I should be your God . . . ?' To say that God *pleaded* that Israel should be his people is an exaggeration of the thought of the Old Testament; the purpose is to make clear the ingratitude of Israel. '*Be my people, and I will be your God; be my sons, and I will be your father*': not an actual quotation, and not presented as such in the Latin. For the first half cp. Exod. 6: 7; Jer. 7: 23. So far as the second half is concerned, the thought that God is Israel's father is reflected in such passages as Jer. 3: 19; 31: 9, but there is nothing in the Old Testament exactly comparable except the saying addressed to David in 2 Sam. 7: 14. Cp., however, 2 Cor. 6: 16–18.

30. *I gathered you as a hen gathers her chickens under her wings*: based on Matt. 23: 37 (cp. Luke 13: 34), 'How often have I longed to gather your children, as a hen gathers her brood under her wings; but you would not let me.'

31. Based on Isa. 1: 13–14.

32. The theme of the rejection of the prophets occurs

frequently in the Old Testament (cp. e.g. 2 Chron. 36: 15–16), but this verse is based directly on Matt. 23: 34–6, and the parallel, Luke 11: 49–51. *I will call you to account:* the use of this expression points to the particular influence of Luke 11: 49–51, '"I will send them prophets and messengers; and some of these they will persecute and kill"; so that this generation will have to answer for the blood of all the prophets . . . this generation will have to answer for it all.' ✵

THE PEOPLE SOON TO COME

33 '"These are the words of the Lord Almighty: Your house is abandoned. I will toss you away like straw before 34 the wind. Your children shall have no posterity, because like you they have ignored my commandments and done 35 what I have condemned. I will hand over your home to a people soon to come; a people who will trust me, though they have not known me; who will do my bidding, 36 though I gave them no signs; who never saw the prophets, and yet will keep in mind what the prophets 37 taught of old. I vow that this people yet to come shall have my favour. Their little ones shall jump for joy. They have not seen me with their eyes, but they shall perceive by the spirit and believe all that I have said."

38 'Now, father Ezra, look with triumph at the nation 39 coming from the east. The leaders I shall give them are Abraham, Isaac, and Jacob, Hosea and Amos, Micah and 40 Joel, Obadiah and Jonah, Nahum, Habakkuk, and Zephaniah, Haggai and Zechariah, and Malachi, who is also called the Lord's Messenger.

✻ After a further statement of the rejection of Israel the author turns his attention for the first time to the group which is to take Israel's place, i.e. the Christian Church.

33. *Your house is abandoned:* apparently a reference to the temple; cp. Matt. 23: 38; Luke 13: 35a. *like straw before the wind:* a common Old Testament simile; cp. e.g. Job 21: 18.

35. *I will hand over your home* (literally 'your houses') *to a people soon to come:* a symbolic statement of the transfer of Israel's privileges to the Christian Church; cp. 2: 10. *a people who will trust me, though they have not known me:* the author is thinking particularly of gentile Christians; cp. Rom. 15: 21.

37. *They have not seen me with their eyes:* cp. John 20: 29; 1 Pet. 1: 8.

38-40. Ezra is told to observe the coming of a nation 'from the east', whose leaders are to be the patriarchs and the twelve minor prophets.

38. *Now, father Ezra:* Ezra is addressed by God as the father of the nation; the title does not occur in the Old Testament, and is used only here and in 2: 5. Perhaps the author's intention was to compare Ezra with Abraham who is more usually called 'father'; cp. Luke 16: 24, 30. *look with triumph at the nation coming from the east:* the Christian Church is meant, but it is not clear why it should be said to come from the east. It is possible that the author has been influenced by Baruch 4: 36-7 ('Jerusalem, look eastwards and see the joy that is coming to you from God. They come, the sons from whom you parted, they come, gathered together at the word of the Holy One from east to west, rejoicing in the glory of God'), and that he has interpreted this text, which pictures the return of the Babylonian exiles to Jerusalem, to refer to the coming of the Church to take the place of Israel. Alternatively, it is possible that the phrase *from the east* reflects the place of composition of 2 Esdras 1-2 (cp. verse 11); on this view the author, writing in the west, describes Jewish Christians coming from Palestine to the west.

39-40. The Church is to take over from Israel her spiritual

leaders, the patriarchs (cp. Matt. 8: 11), and her prophets. The latter are represented here by the twelve minor prophets (arranged in the order in which they occur in the Septuagint). Isaiah and Jeremiah are mentioned in 2: 18. *who is also called the Lord's Messenger:* a play on the name *Malachi* which means 'my messenger'. ✻

GOD'S JUDGEMENT ON ISRAEL

2 'These are the words of the Lord: I freed this people from slavery, and gave them commandments through my servants the prophets; but they shut their ears to the
2 prophets, and let my precepts become a dead letter. The mother who bore them says to them: "Go, my sons; I am
3 widowed and deserted. Joyfully I brought you up; I have lost you with grief and sorrow, because you have sinned against the Lord God and done what I know to be wrong.
4 What can I do for you now, widowed and deserted as
5 I am? Go, my sons, ask the Lord for mercy." Now I call upon you, father Ezra, to add your testimony to hers,
6 that her children have refused to keep my covenant; and let your words bring confusion on them. May their mother be despoiled, and may they themselves have no
7 posterity. Condemn them to be scattered among the nations, and their name to vanish from the earth, because they have spurned my covenant.

8 'Woe to you, Assyria, for harbouring sinners! Remember, you wicked nation, what I did to Sodom and
9 Gomorrah: their land lies buried under lumps of pitch and heaps of ashes. That is how I will deal with those who have disobeyed me, says the Lord Almighty.

✻ 1–7. In a prophetic saying addressed to Ezra the author takes up once more the theme of ch. 1: Israel's response to God's actions on her behalf has been one of disobedience and ingratitude, and because of this the people are to be scattered and lose their identity as a nation.

  1. *I freed this people from slavery:* cp. 1: 7. *and gave them commandments through my servants the prophets:* for the idea that laws were given by the prophets cp. Ezra 9: 10–11; Dan. 9: 10. *but they shut their ears:* cp. 1: 32.

  2–4. *The mother who bore them:* i.e. Jerusalem, personified as the mother of the nation. The personification goes back ultimately to Isa. 49: 14–21; 54: 1–8 (cp. Gal. 4: 26–7), but there are also similarities between this passage of 2 Esdras and Baruch 4: 5–29, especially verses 8–12, 17, 19, 21. In Isaiah the Jerusalem of the period of the exile is depicted as a bereaved and barren woman who, through the return of the exiles, will acquire a family larger than the one she had before (cp. 49: 19–21; 54: 1). In 2 Esdras Jerusalem is likewise pictured as a mother who has lost her children. *widowed and deserted*, she accuses her sons (Israel) of having brought their punishment on themselves; she can do nothing for them and tells them to cast themselves on the mercy of God. However, a deliberate contrast seems to be intended between mother Jerusalem (verses 2–4) and the mother addressed in verses 15, 17 and 30, namely the Church. The former has lost her family, the latter is described as the mother of sons and is told to nurture her children carefully. The use of the mother theme is a further illustration of the idea that the Church has taken the place of Israel.

  5–7. Ezra is to confirm the truth of the mother's accusation (verse 5) and to proclaim God's judgement on her children (verses 6–7).

  5. *father Ezra:* see the comment on 1: 38.

  6–7. The punishment is to consist of the destruction of Jerusalem and the dispersion of the Jews from Palestine. These events were already facts of history at the time at which 2

Esdras 1–2 was written, but the pseudonymous author is able to make Ezra 'foretell' them. *May their mother be despoiled:* an allusion either to the fall of Jerusalem in A.D. 70, or to the capture of Jerusalem by the forces of the Emperor Hadrian in the course of the suppression of the Bar Cochba revolt (A.D. 132–135). *and may they themselves have no posterity:* cp. 1: 34. *Condemn ... their name to vanish from the earth:* Israel is to lose even her identity as a nation; contrast Isa. 66: 22. This bitter curse reflects the hostility between the Jewish and Christian communities.

8–9. The judgement on the Jewish people is extended to include the nation which harbours them. The fate of Sodom and Gomorrah ought to serve as an example of the way God deals with those who disobey him. *Assyria:* here a cryptic name for the Roman Empire; a similar usage is found in the Qumran War Scroll. Cp. the use of Babylon as a symbolic name for Rome (see e.g. 15: 43; Rev. 14: 8). *sinners:* the Jewish people. *wicked nation:* Assyria (Rome). *what I did to Sodom and Gomorrah:* cp. Gen. 19: 24. Sodom and Gomorrah are frequently used as examples; cp. Zeph. 2: 8–9. ✳

ISRAEL'S PRIVILEGES GIVEN TO THE CHURCH

10 'These are the words of the Lord to Ezra: Tell my people that I will give to them the kingdom of Jerusalem
11 which once I offered to Israel. I will withdraw the splendour of my presence from Israel, and the home that was
12 to be theirs for ever I will give to my own people. The tree of life shall spread its fragrance over them; they shall
13 not toil or grow weary. Ask, and you shall receive; so pray that your short time of waiting may be made shorter still. The kingdom is ready for you now; be on the
14 watch! Call heaven, call earth, to witness: I have cancelled the evil and brought the good into being; for I am the Living One, says the Lord.

✻ These verses mark a turning-point in 2 Esdras 1–2. So far the author has been primarily concerned to explain why Israel has been rejected. He now turns his attention to the group which is to take Israel's place.

10–11. Ezra is told to announce to God's people that the kingdom of Jerusalem, which should have belonged to Israel, is to be given to them. *my people:* used frequently in the Old Testament to refer to Israel, but here, in deliberate contrast, to refer to the Church. The author was possibly influenced by Hos. 2: 23. *the kingdom of Jerusalem:* the expression is not found in the Old or New Testament, but is comparable to, and conveys much the same idea as, 'the kingdom of God'. The use of the expression emphasizes the idea that the coming of the kingdom will involve the re-establishment of an earthly kingdom based on Jerusalem; cp. Mark 11: 10, 'the coming kingdom of our father David', which in a similar way envisages the re-establishment of the Davidic Empire; cp. also Matt. 21: 5, in which Jesus is depicted as the messianic king coming to Jerusalem, 'Tell the daughter of Zion, "Here is your king, who comes to you in gentleness."' Participation in this kingdom was a privilege that had been intended for Israel, but this privilege has now been transferred to the Church; cp. verses 35, 41. *and the home that was to be theirs for ever:* in a more literal translation 'and the eternal home that was to be theirs'. The phrase 'the eternal home' is possibly taken from Luke 16: 9; cp. verse 37 'the heavenly realms'.

12. *The tree of life:* cp. 8: 52; Rev. 2: 7; 22: 2, 14.

13. In phrases reminiscent of the New Testament the Christians are urged to pray that the kingdom may come as quickly as possible. *Ask, and you shall receive:* cp. Matt. 7: 7; Luke 11: 9. *so pray that your short time of waiting may be made shorter still:* cp. Matt. 24: 22. *The kingdom is ready for you now:* cp. Matt. 25: 34. *be on the watch:* a frequent command in the gospels; cp. Mark 13: 37; Matt. 24: 42; 25: 13 (where the N.E.B. in all three cases translates 'Keep awake').

14. *Call heaven, call earth, to witness:* cp. Deut. 30: 19. *I have cancelled the evil and brought the good into being:* a statement

referring specifically to the replacement of Israel by the Church. ✳

ADVICE TO THE CHURCH

15   'Mother, cherish your sons. Rear them joyfully as a dove rears her nestlings; teach them to walk without
16 stumbling. You are my chosen one, says the Lord. I will raise up the dead from their resting-places, and bring them out of their tombs, for I have acknowledged that
17 they bear my name. Have no fear, mother of many sons; I have chosen you, says the Lord.

18   'I will send my servants Isaiah and Jeremiah to help you. As they prophesied, I have set you apart to be my people. I have made ready for you twelve trees laden
19 with different kinds of fruit, twelve fountains flowing with milk and honey, and seven great mountains covered with roses and lilies. There will I fill your sons with joy.
20 Champion the widow, defend the cause of the fatherless, give to the poor, protect the orphan, clothe the naked.
21 Care for the weak and the helpless, and do not mock at the cripple; watch over the disabled, and bring the blind
22 to the vision of my brightness. Keep safe within your walls both old and young.

23   'When you find the dead unburied, mark them with the sign and commit them to the tomb; and then, when I cause the dead to rise, I will give you the chief place.
24 Be calm, my people; for your time of rest shall come.
25 Care for your children like a good nurse, and train them
26 to walk without falling. Of my servants whom I have given you not one shall be lost; I will demand them back
27 from among your number. Do not be anxious when the

time of trouble and hardship comes; others shall lament and be sad, but you shall have happiness and plenty. All 28 nations shall envy you, but shall be powerless against you, says the Lord.

'My power shall protect you, and save your sons from 29 hell. Be joyful, mother, you and your sons, for I will 30 come to your rescue. Remember your children who 31 sleep in the grave; I will bring them up from the depths of the earth, and show mercy to them; for I am merciful, says the Lord Almighty. Cherish your children until I 32 come, and proclaim my mercy to them; for my favour flows abundantly from springs that will never run dry.'

✶ God assures the Church, personified as a mother, of his continuing care and protection, and exhorts her to practise good works.

15. *Mother:* probably the Church, personified as the mother of its members. It has sometimes been held that, as in verses 2–4, the reference is to Jerusalem, thought of here as the mother of the Church. It is true that the earliest Christian Church was in Jerusalem, but the exhortation is addressed directly to the Church as a whole. Indeed, a deliberate contrast seems to be intended between Jerusalem as mother and the Church as mother; see the comment on verses 2–4. *my chosen one:* it is a commonplace of the Old Testament that Israel has been chosen by God; here the idea is deliberately transferred to the Church.

16. *I will raise up the dead from their resting-places:* the promise of resurrection is a dominant theme of this passage; cp. verses 23, 29–31. *and bring them out of their tombs:* cp. Ezek. 37: 12–13; Matt. 27: 52–3.

18a. *I will send my servants Isaiah and Jeremiah to help you:* see the comment on 1: 39–40.

18b–19. A description of the paradise prepared by God for

his people. *twelve trees laden with different kinds of fruit:* the
author appears to be dependent on the tree-of-life motif in
Rev. 22: 2 (part of the vision of the New Jerusalem, Rev. 21:
1 – 22: 5), 'On either side of the river stood a tree of life,
which yields twelve crops of fruit, one for each month of the
year; the leaves of the trees serve for the healing of the
nations.' However, the twelve trees are possibly intended to
symbolize the twelve apostles. *twelve fountains flowing with
milk and honey:* the traditional description of the promised
land (cp. e.g. Exod. 3: 8) is here applied to the paradise
prepared by God for Christians. For the fountains cp. 1
Enoch 48: 1 (the introduction to a passage which describes
the naming of the Son of Man in the presence of the Lord
of Spirits in heaven), 'And in that place I saw an inexhaustible
spring of righteousness, and many springs of wisdom surrounded it, and all the thirsty drank from them and were filled
with wisdom.' In traditional interpretation the 'spring of
righteousness' is the law and the 'springs of wisdom' the
prophets. It is possible that in a similar way the twelve fountains in 2 Esdras are meant to symbolize the minor prophets
(cp. 1: 40). (On 1 Enoch see below, p. 108.) *and seven great
mountains covered with roses and lilies:* the author seems to be
drawing on 1 Enoch 24-5, a passage which describes the
paradisial region of seven mountains where the throne of
God is situated, the throne on which he 'will sit when he
comes down to visit the earth for good' (1 Enoch 25: 3).
Further links with this passage of Enoch are evident in the
fact that around the throne are a number of fragrant trees,
amongst which is the tree of life; cp. 24: 4, 'And there was
among them a tree such as I have never smelt, and none of
them nor any others were like it; it smells more fragrant than
any fragrance, and its leaves and its flowers and its wood
never wither; its fruit (is) good, and its fruit (is) like the
bunches of dates on a palm', and 25: 5, 'From its fruit life
will be given to the chosen.'

20-2. An exhortation reflecting some of the basic ethical

demands of the Old and New Testaments and reminiscent in
particular of such passages as Ps. 82: 3–4; Isa. 1: 17; 58: 7;
Matt. 25: 35–6; Jas. 1: 27.

23. *When you find the dead unburied, mark them with the sign
and commit them to the tomb:* this command has apparently
been added under the influence of Tobit 1: 17–19. *the sign:*
probably the sign of the cross; cp. verse 38. *I will give you
the chief place:* cp. Matt. 20: 23.

26. *Of my servants whom I have given you not one shall be lost:*
apparently based on John 17: 12, 'When I was with them, I
protected by the power of thy name those whom thou hast
given me, and kept them safe. Not one of them is lost except
the man who must be lost.'

27. *the time of trouble and hardship:* the troubles that will
immediately precede the end of this age; cp. Mark 13 and
parallels.

29. *hell:* literally 'Gehenna', here the place of final punishment in the next life, cp. 7: [36]; Matt. 5: 22; 18: 9; see
further the comment on 7: [36].

31. *I will bring...the earth:* see the comment on verse 16. ✳

THE REWARDS OF THE KINGDOM

I, Ezra, received on Mount Horeb a commission from 33
the Lord to go to Israel; but when I came, they scorned
me and rejected the Lord's commandment. Therefore I 34
say to you Gentiles, you who hear and understand: 'Look
forward to the coming of your shepherd, and he will give
you everlasting rest; for he who is to come at the end
of the world is close at hand. Be ready to receive the 35
rewards of the kingdom; for light perpetual will shine
upon you for ever and ever. Flee from the shadow of this 36
world, and receive the joy and splendour that await you.
I bear witness openly to my Saviour. It is he whom the 37

Lord has appointed; receive him and be joyful, giving
thanks to the One who has summoned you to the
38 heavenly realms. Rise, stand up, and see the whole company of those who bear the Lord's mark and sit at his
39 table. They have moved out of the shadow of this world
40 and have received shining robes from the Lord. Receive,
O Zion, your full number, and close the roll of those
arrayed in white who have faithfully kept the law of the
41 Lord. The number of your sons whom you so long
desired is now complete. Pray that the Lord's kingdom
may come, so that your people, whom he summoned
when the world began, may be set apart as his own.'

*   The major part of 2 Esdras 1-2 consists of a speech from
God (1: 5 – 2: 32), but in the final verses (2: 33-48) Ezra
himself speaks. In verses 33-41, as a consequence of Israel's
rejection both of himself and of the Lord's commandment,
he addresses the Gentiles. He urges them to await the imminent
coming of their 'shepherd' and describes the blessings that
lie in store for them.

33. *on Mount Horeb:* like Moses; cp. Exod. 3: 1. Implicit
here is the idea that Ezra was a second Moses, an idea developed at much greater length in ch. 14.

34. *your shepherd:* i.e. Jesus; cp. John 10: 11; Heb. 13: 20;
1 Pet. 2: 25; 5: 4 ('when the Head Shepherd appears, you will
receive for your own the unfading garland of glory').
rest: cp. Matt. 11: 28-9.

35. *the kingdom:* cp. verses 10, 13. *for light perpetual will
shine upon you for ever and ever:* cp. Isa. 60: 19-20; Rev. 21:
23; 22: 5.

36-7. In anticipation of what will only become a complete
reality at the end of this age the Gentiles are exhorted to *Flee
from the shadow of this world*, and to accept thankfully both
their salvation and their coming *Saviour. the shadow of this*

world: cp. Wisd. of Sol. 2: 5, 'A passing shadow – such is our life'; cp. also 1 Chron. 29: 15. *the One who has summoned you to the heavenly realms:* cp. 1 Thess. 2: 12.

38–9. As an encouragement to them, the Gentiles are urged to observe the blessings which are enjoyed by those who have already *moved out of the shadow of this world*, i.e. the Christian dead. *the whole company of those who bear the Lord's mark:* there appears to be a link with Rev. 7: 2–8; cp. also Rev. 9: 4; Ezek. 9: 4–6. The mark is a sign of protection. *and sit at his table:* for the idea of the heavenly banquet cp. Isa. 25: 6; Luke 13: 29; 14: 15; Rev. 19: 9. *and have received shining robes from the Lord:* cp. verse 40, 'those arrayed in white who have faithfully kept the law of the Lord'. The shining or white robes symbolize the glorified state of Christians who have died; cp. Rev. 3: 4–5; 6: 11; 7: 9, 13–14.

40–1. Ezra's speech ends with some words addressed to Zion which here represents the Church. *Receive ... your full number, and close the roll ... The number of your sons ... is now complete:* reflected here is the idea that the number of Christians had been determined in advance, an idea which has a fairly close parallel in Rev. 6: 11, 'Each of them was given a white robe; and they were told to rest a little while longer, until the tally should be complete of all their brothers in Christ's service who were to be killed as they had been'; cp. also 2 Esdras 4: 36–7. The deterministic thought which underlies such passages as these was extremely common in Jewish writings of the intertestamental period (2 Esdras 3–14 is a typical example), and finds expression in these writings in a variety of different ways. For the author to say that the predetermined number of Christians was *complete* is an indication that he believed the end of the world was extremely close; cp. verse 34. *those arrayed in white:* see the comment on verses 38–9. *who have faithfully kept the law of the Lord:* the attitude to the law reflected here is a further indication that the author was a Jewish Christian. *Pray that the Lord's kingdom may come* (literally 'Ask for the Lord's kingdom'): cp. verse 13. But the translation is uncertain because the word rendered 'kingdom' is not *regnum* (as in verses 10, 13, 35), but *imperium*, and it is not quite clear what this means in the context. The passage might mean something like 'Pray to the power of the Lord that . . .' *whom he summoned when the world began:* a further indication of the deterministic thought underlying this passage; cp. Rom. 8: 29-30. ✻

EZRA'S VISION

42 I, Ezra, saw on Mount Zion a crowd too large to
43 count, all singing hymns of praise to the Lord. In the middle stood a very tall young man, taller than all the rest, who was setting a crown on the head of each one of them; he stood out above them all. I was enthralled at
44, 45 the sight, and asked the angel, 'Sir, who are these?' He replied, 'They are those who have laid aside their mortal dress and put on the immortal, those who acknowledged the name of God. Now they are being given crowns and
46 palms.' And I asked again, 'Who is the young man setting crowns on their heads and giving them palms?',
47 and the angel replied, 'He is the Son of God, whom they acknowledged in this mortal life.' I began to praise those
48 who had stood so valiantly for the Lord's name. Then the angel said to me: 'Go and tell my people all the great and wonderful acts of the Lord God that you have seen.'

✻ In the final section of 2 Esdras 1-2 Ezra describes how in a vision he saw a countless number of resurrected Christians being crowned. The vision serves as a confirmation of the reality of the blessings promised to the Church in what has preceded.

42. *I, Ezra, saw on Mount Zion:* cp. Rev. 14: 1, 'Then I

looked, and on Mount Zion stood the Lamb.' *Mount Zion* is the heavenly Jerusalem; cp. Heb. 12: 22–3. *a crowd too large to count, all singing hymns of praise to the Lord:* cp. Rev. 7: 9–10:

> 'After this I looked and saw a vast throng, which no one could count...they shouted together:
>> "Victory to our God who sits on the throne, and to the Lamb!"'

In fact the whole vision (2 Esdras 2: 42–8) seems to be based on Rev. 7: 9–17.

43. *a very tall young man:* i.e. Jesus; cp. verse 47. Comparable descriptions of Jesus can be found in a number of early Christian writings; cp. e.g. the *Shepherd of Hermas*, Similitude IX.6.1, 'And lo, after a little time I saw an array of many men coming, and in the middle there was a man so tall, that he overtopped the tower' (Loeb Classical Library translation of the Apostolic Fathers, vol. 2, pp. 231, 233; the *Shepherd of Hermas* dates from the second century A.D.). The description of the crowning also has a parallel in the same work, cp. Similitude VIII.2.1 and 3.6:

> 'And the angel of the Lord commanded crowns to be brought, and crowns were brought, made, as it were, of palm leaves and he crowned the men ... "Who then, Sir," said I, "are they who were crowned and went into the tower?" "All those," said he, "who wrestled with the devil and conquered him, have been crowned. These are they who suffered for the law"' (Loeb translation, pp. 193, 197).

a crown: the crowns, like the palms (verse 45), were symbols of victory; cp. Rev. 2: 10.

44. The dialogue with the angel is apparently modelled on Rev. 7: 13–14.

45. Cp. Rev. 7: 14, 'Then he said to me, "These are the men who have passed through the great ordeal; they have

washed their robes and made them white in the blood of the Lamb."' *laid aside their mortal dress and put on the immortal:* cp. 1 Cor. 15: 53–4. *crowns and palms:* cp. Rev. 2: 10 and 7: 9. Both are symbols of victory, and the implication is that those who were being crowned were martyrs.   *

2 ESDRAS 3–14
THE APOCALYPSE OF EZRA

The main part of 2 Esdras, i.e. chs. 3–14, consists of a Jewish apocalypse which dates from towards the end of the first century A.D. and is quite independent of the additional chapters (1–2, 15–16) which precede and follow it. In modern writings 2 Esdras 3–14 is often referred to as 4 Ezra, or as the Apocalypse of Ezra; for further discussion of the character and relationship of the different parts of 2 Esdras see pp. 76–7.

2 Esdras 3–14 is ostensibly set in Babylon in the sixth century B.C.; it takes as its starting-point the question whether the fate of Israel, with Jerusalem destroyed and her inhabitants taken into captivity, can be reconciled with the promises which God had made to her. But this question, with its purely national concerns, is broadened out (particularly in the section 6: 35 – 9: 25) into a discussion of the much larger problem whether the eternal punishment of sinners can be reconciled with God's love for mankind. This problem remains in the end unresolved, and in the last part of the book the concern is once more primarily national; Ezra experiences a number of visions which provide an assurance that Israel's distress will very shortly be brought to an end.

This summary account of the contents of 2 Esdras 3–14 already gives some indication of the way in which it is divided up. It falls very clearly into seven sections. The first three (3: 1 – 5: 19; 5: 20 – 6: 34; 6: 35 – 9: 25) are dialogues in which the problems that have just been mentioned are discussed. In each of these a characteristic pattern is followed.

Ezra prays to God and attempts to set out the problems which overwhelm him; the angel Uriel comes to him, and the problem is debated between Ezra and Uriel. Sometimes, however, Uriel recedes into the background, and it appears that God himself answers Ezra directly. These dialogues are in some ways similar to (and may have been modelled on) the dialogues in the Book of Job, just as the problems that are discussed in the two books are similar. However, there are also very real differences in the character of the dialogues.

The fourth, fifth and sixth sections of 2 Esdras 3-14 (9: 26 – 10: 59; 11-12; 13) are accounts of visions that are closely similar in form to the visions in Dan. 2, 7, and 8. The characteristic features of these visions are, first, that what is seen is not straightforward but requires to be interpreted by the angel (or, again, God himself), and secondly, that the interpretation is normally given in terms of allegory. As in Daniel, the visions in 2 Esdras 3-14 are used to make clear that the events of history do not occur by chance, but are predetermined by God. More specifically they are used to provide an assurance that the oppression of Israel will shortly be brought to an end, and to give detailed information about how this will happen.

The seventh section of 2 Esdras 3-14 (i.e. ch. 14) is a legend which describes how, just before the end of his life, Ezra was instructed by God to restore the scriptures.

THE HISTORICAL BACKGROUND AND DATE
OF 2 ESDRAS 3-14

As we have already seen, the ostensible setting of 2 Esdras 3-14 is the Babylonian exile. According to 3: 1 the book is an account of Ezra's experiences in Babylon in the thirtieth year after the fall of Jerusalem, and this would give a date of 557 B.C. This supposed date is historically inappropriate because Ezra belongs not to the sixth century, but to the fifth or even the beginning of the fourth century B.C. (see further the comment on 3: 1–3). It is worth noticing in passing that a similar historical inaccuracy is to be found already in the Old Testament; according to the priestly genealogy of Ezra 7: 1–5 Ezra was the son and successor of Seraiah, the last chief priest of the pre-exile temple (cp. 2 Kings 25: 18–21; see also the commentary on Ezra in this series, p. 44). However, the important point to notice here is that 2 Esdras 3–14 is written as if it were a response to the fall of Jerusalem in 587 B.C., and the question with which the work apparently begins in ch. 3 is, why did God allow Jerusalem to fall in 587, and why did he allow his chosen people to be carried into captivity in Babylon? This setting is purely fictitious; 2 Esdras 3–14 actually belongs to the first century A.D. and reflects the troubled events of that much later time.

In the first century A.D. affairs in Palestine were controlled by the Romans. The arrangements under which the Jewish population was governed changed a number of times during the early decades of the century, but from the death of Herod Agrippa I in A.D. 44 the territory known as Judaea was a Roman province under the direct control of a governor who resided at Caesarea. Partly as a result of the corrupt and provocative rule of the governors, and partly because the belief was current in certain sections of Jewish society that submission to Rome was an offence against God, a revolt broke out in A.D. 66. The Romans were unable to put the revolt down immediately, and because of some initial success the entire Jewish population was forced to join in, including those who did not support the revolt and would have liked to reach some settlement with Rome.

The short- and long-term consequences of this revolt were very serious indeed for the Jews. The Emperor Nero appointed Vespasian, an experienced general, to deal with the situation, and he began his campaign in 67 by subduing Galilee. In the spring of 68 he brought under control the areas around Jerusalem and was preparing to concentrate his attack on the city when the news reached him of the death of Nero in

June 68. Vespasian paused in his campaign to await the outcome of events in Rome, and there was a further pause in 69 which was occasioned by continuing uncertainty over the succession to Nero. Three emperors followed in rapid succession, but eventually Vespasian himself was proclaimed emperor by his troops in the summer of 69, and it was he whose cause finally triumphed. Vespasian handed over control of affairs in Palestine to his son Titus, and the latter resumed the campaign against the Jews in the spring of 70. Jerusalem was besieged and taken, the temple burnt and the city destroyed. This was the effective end of the revolt, although it was at least three more years before the last of the rebels was overcome; a group at the fortress of Masada managed to hold out until 73 (or possibly, as has recently been argued, until 74), but finally killed themselves when capture by the Romans became inevitable.

The destruction of Jerusalem, the city chosen by God (cp. 3: 24), and the burning of the temple, which meant that sacrifice could no longer be offered, caused profound anguish to the Jews, and it is these events – not the events of the sixth century B.C. – which lie behind the composition of 2 Esdras 3–14. Ezra's lament in ch. 3, although ostensibly directed towards the circumstances surrounding the fall of Jerusalem in 587 B.C., is in reality concerned with the events of A.D. 66–73 and their aftermath. The question is not, how could God have given his city into the hands of the Babylonians, but how could he have given it into the hands of the Romans, and this perspective needs to be borne in mind throughout 2 Esdras 3–14. Some indication of the profound effect which these events had upon the Jews can be obtained by reading the very vivid account of them in the work of the Jewish historian Josephus entitled the *Jewish War*. Josephus composed his account shortly after the events which he describes, and his history was in any event published before A.D. 79, the year of Vespasian's death. For Josephus see the Note on Further Reading, p. 306.

2 Esdras 3–14 not only has a fictitious setting; it is also pseudonymous in authorship, for it purports to be an auto-biographical account. These facts ought not to cause surprise. A close parallel to the literary procedures which the author has adopted can be found already in the Old Testament Book of Daniel (see the commentary on Daniel in this series, pp. 4–6). This also is set in Babylon in the period of the exile, but in reality it belongs to the second century B.C. and is directed specifically towards the circumstances of the persecution of Antiochus Epiphanes. Furthermore, the authorship of the second half of Daniel (chs. 7–12) is pseudonymous. Both 2 Esdras 3–14 and Daniel are in fact examples of apocalyptic writings the characteristics of which commonly include pseudonymity of authorship and a fictitious setting. Before, however, pursuing this question further it is perhaps useful to say a little about the evidence on which 2 Esdras 3–14 is dated at the end of the first century A.D.

The first point to be made is that 2 Esdras 3–14 is clearly later than the middle of the second century B.C. because it is not merely similar to the Book of Daniel in form, but also draws heavily on Daniel for its content (see e.g. p. 239 and the comments on 11: 1–2). Secondly, the fact that the author takes as his starting-point the fall of Jerusalem in 587 B.C. suggests that we have to think in terms of a comparable situation in the later period, and this points directly to the fall of Jerusalem in A.D. 70. Beyond this, a more precise dating is provided by the vision in chs. 11–12. As we shall see, this vision refers to the events of Roman history in the first century A.D., and although some of the details are obscure, it is clear that the vision reaches its climax in the reigns of Vespasian and his two sons, Titus and Domitian. Of these only Domitian (emperor from 81 to 96) was still alive at the time at which 2 Esdras 3–14 was written, and the author believed that his death would be one of the events of the last days (see the comment on 12: 28). Thus, the composition of 2 Esdras 3–14 is to be placed between A.D. 81 and 96. However, there is one other indication of date which suggests that we should think in terms of the end rather than the beginning of Domitian's reign. According to 3: 1 the events described in the book took place thirty years after the fall of Jerusalem. This date is apparently taken from Ezek. 1: 1 and is hardly to be taken as indicating that 2 Esdras 3–14 was composed exactly thirty years after A.D. 70 (see further the comment on 3: 1–3). But for it to make sense even as a symbolic date a fair interval of time must have elapsed since the fall of Jerusalem, and thus indirectly we are pointed towards the end of the reign of Domitian.

2 ESDRAS 3–14 AS AN APOCALYPSE

2 Esdras 3–14 belongs, as has already been indicated (see p. 100), among the apocalyptic writings, a group which includes such works as 1 Enoch, the Assumption of Moses, 2 Baruch, and the Apocalypse of Abraham, as well as Daniel and the Revelation of John. Few of these writings in the ancient world were actually called apocalypses, and in some respects they form a rather disparate collection. But they have sufficient in common in terms both of literary form and theological outlook to make it helpful, and indeed essential, to consider them together as a group. The adjective applied to them, 'apocalyptic', has not, it must be admitted, always been used in a very precise way. It comes from the Greek verb *apoka-lupto* ('to uncover, reveal'), from which the noun *apokalupsis* ('revelation' – our English word 'apocalypse') is derived. This noun was used, first of all, to refer to a 'revelation' of divine secrets, and it is in this sense that it occurs in Rev. 1: 1 as the title of the Revelation of John. But it was also used to refer to the 'revelation' of Jesus at his second coming at the end of this age; cp. 1 Pet. 1: 7, 13, 'when Jesus Christ is revealed' (literally 'at the revelation of Jesus Christ'). Both these ideas underlie the modern use of the term 'apocalyptic'. To describe the writings listed above as 'apocalyptic' is

primarily an indication that they are to be understood as
works which, like the Revelation of John, provide a revelation of divine secrets. But there is also the implication that
these secrets have to do above all with the end of this age. Both
these ideas are certainly applicable to 2 Esdras 3–14, which
(particularly in 9: 26 – 13: 58, but in a general way throughout the book) is concerned to provide a revelation of the
secret plans of God for the end of this age. There are both
Jewish and Christian apocalypses, but we are here concerned
only with the former. The writings listed above, which date
from the second and first centuries B.C. and the first century
A.D., are all either Jewish or (in the case of Revelation) have
a strong Jewish substratum.

What then are the common features which justify the treatment of these writings as a group? They are, first of all,
united by a common theological attitude. The authors of all
these writings believed that history was nearing its climax,
and that the end of this present age was imminent. They
stress the contrast between this age, which is under the control
of the forces of evil, and the age to come, when evil will have
been swept away and God will rule unchallenged. They were,
furthermore, convinced that God had determined in advance
the whole course of history – including the time of its end.
These ideas are all present in 2 Esdras 3–14, as we shall see.
It has to be said, however, that this kind of theological
emphasis is not unique to the apocalyptic writings, but is
commonplace in Jewish and Christian literature from the
period. What is unique to the apocalyptic writings is that
these theological ideas, with their emphasis on the end of this
age, are presented as if they were revelations that were made –
usually by means of visions or heavenly journeys – to pious
men who lived long before the time at which these writings
were actually composed. The Revelation of John is here the
exception which proves the rule inasmuch as it is not set in
some remote past, but refers explicitly to the circumstances
of the author's own day, and inasmuch as it is quite unlikely

that 'John' is a pseudonym (see the commentary on Revelation in this series, pp. 1–4). The visions which Ezra experiences, as well as the fictitious setting and pseudonymous authorship of 2 Esdras 3–14, are all entirely typical of this genre. It is the combination of distinctive theological emphasis and distinctive literary form which provides the unifying factor for the apocalyptic writings and justifies their treatment as a coherent group.

The use of pseudonymity is not restricted to the apocalyptic writings, and at the beginning of this volume a number of explanations for the occurrence of this phenomenon were mentioned (see pp. 1–2). Apocalyptic pseudonymity has to be seen against the background of the widespread use of pseudonymity in other types of literature. However, it is possible to suggest a particular reason why the authors of the apocalyptic writings should have used this literary device, namely a desire to provide comfort and assurance for their readers. As we have seen, the apocalyptic authors believed that God had predetermined the course of history. Their writings contain a number of what are, in fact, largely historical retrospects (cp. e.g. 2 Esdras 12: 10–34; Dan. 11: 2–12: 4), but by the use of pseudonymity, and of a fictitious setting in the past, they were able to present what had happened in history as if it had been revealed in advance by God. The fact that history had fallen out as it had been 'foretold' provided confirmation that God was indeed the one who determined the course of history, and an assurance that the future would likewise fall out as God had promised. Thus by the device of pseudonymity the authors were able to reassure their readers: even if circumstances seemed black, everything that happened had been determined in advance by God and was part of his plan; he would shortly intervene to put things right.

The names chosen as pseudonyms by the apocalyptic authors seem largely to have been drawn from the early period (e.g. Enoch, Abraham, Moses) or the age of the exile (e.g. Daniel, Baruch, Ezra). It was doubtless the similarity of

An apocalypse

the circumstances in which Israel found herself after A.D. 70 to those which obtained after 587 B.C. which led to the choice of Ezra as the pseudonymous author of 2 Esdras 3–14.

In the course of the commentary which follows reference will be made to a number of the apocalyptic writings in order to illustrate particular points, and it is perhaps convenient to say a little about them here. Of the writings mentioned in this commentary, the most important and influential is perhaps 1 Enoch; this is a composite work the individual sections of which range in date from the beginning of the second century B.C. to (probably) the first century A.D. The Assumption of Moses, which purports to give an account of the last words of Moses to Joshua, can be dated by means of the events which are referred to in it to shortly after the death of Herod the Great in 4 B.C. Very similar in character and purpose to 2 Esdras 3–14 is 2 Baruch; this apocalypse is in fact generally thought to be modelled on 2 Esdras 3–14, and to have been composed at approximately the same time, i.e. at the end of the first century A.D. It is to this same period that we are to attribute the Apocalypse of Abraham, a work which describes the revelations which Abraham received when he was carried up to heaven. On these works, and on the apocalyptic writings in general, see further the volume in this series entitled *The Making of the Old Testament*, pp. 75–82.

This is perhaps the place to mention that reference is also made in the commentary to the writings of the Rabbis, and particularly to the collection of traditional Jewish law known as the Mishnah (see *The Making of the Old Testament*, pp. 96–7, 167–73). In its present form this collection dates from the latter part of the second century A.D., but it contains older materials.

For English translations of all these writings see the Note on Further Reading, pp. 306–7.

THE UNITY OF 2 ESDRAS 3–14

At the beginning of this century the view was held by some scholars that 2 Esdras 3–14 was not a unity. These scholars drew attention to differences and apparent discrepancies in the various sections of the book, and argued that it was a compilation of several different writings which were put together by an editor. Reference will be made to this view in a number of places throughout the following pages, and here it must suffice to say that the evidence on which it was based now appears unconvincing. It is true that the author has not always worked out his ideas with complete consistency, and a number of minor differences can be observed in the various sections of the book. It is also true that in places he appears to have made use of older traditions. But 2 Esdras 3–14 has an essential dramatic unity, and it is clear that we have to do with an author who has stamped his views and his personality on the entire work; this is not a unity which derives its form merely from an editor or compiler.

Related to the question of unity is the question whether the views which the author himself held are to be found in the speeches of Ezra, or of the angel (and God), or of both. It has been argued that the speeches of Ezra represent a pessimism (about the fate of Israel and of mankind) which the author wished to rebut, and that the speeches of the angel (and God) alone represent the views of the author. It is, however, nowhere made clear that what Ezra says is wrong, and it seems more likely that the dialogue form reflects a tension within the author's own mind. In the first three sections (3: 1 – 9: 25) the author struggles with the problems that overwhelm him, and the two sides of the argument reflect this inner tension. In the fourth section (9: 26 – 10: 59) the author manages to come to terms with the problems that face him, and thereafter Ezra and the angel represent essentially the same viewpoint. Ezra does still question the angel, but his questions are intended merely to elicit information, not to challenge what the angel says.

THE TEXT OF 2 ESDRAS 3–14

It is generally held that 2 Esdras 3–14 was composed in Hebrew, that it was subsequently translated into Greek, and that it was from the Greek version that all the existing translations of this work were made. Neither the Hebrew original nor the Greek translation have survived, but the character of the existing translations points very strongly to the view that the language of composition was Hebrew, while the existence at one time of a Greek translation – which in any case is likely on general grounds – is confirmed by the fact that there are quotations from 2 Esdras 3–14 in Greek in early Christian writings. Of the existing translations, the Latin is undoubtedly the most important, and it was primarily from this version that the N.E.B. translation was made. But 2 Esdras 3–14 was also translated into several oriental languages: complete versions exist in Syriac, Ethiopic, Arabic (in fact there are two Arabic versions), and Armenian, but there are also fragments of Coptic and Georgian translations. Reference is occasionally made to these oriental versions in the N.E.B. footnotes; the most important is the Syriac.

The use of Hebrew for the composition of 2 Esdras 3–14 suggests that the author probably wrote his work in Palestine – but this is by no means certain.

The mystery of human destiny

THE FIRST DIALOGUE (3: 1 – 5: 19)

✶ In the prayers with which each of the first four sections of
2 Esdras 3–14 begin (3: 1–36; 5: 20–30; 6: 35–59; 9: 26–37)
the author attempts to set out the problems with which he is
concerned. His starting-point is the difficulty of understanding
Israel's fate in the light of her choice by God. ✶

EZRA'S PRAYER

IN THE THIRTIETH YEAR after the fall of Jerusalem, I, **3**
Salathiel (who am also Ezra), was in Babylon. As I lay
on my bed I was troubled; my mind was filled with
perplexity, as I considered the desolation of Zion and the 2
prosperity of those who lived in Babylon. My spirit was 3
deeply disturbed; and I uttered my fears to the Most
High. 'My Lord, my Master,' I said, 'was it not you, and 4
you alone, who in the beginning spoke the word that
formed the world? You commanded the dust, and Adam
appeared. His body was lifeless; but yours were the hands 5
that had moulded it, and into it you breathed the breath
of life. So you made him a living person. You led him 6
into paradise, which you yourself had planted before the
earth came into being. You gave him your one com- 7
mandment to obey; he disobeyed it, and thereupon you
made him subject to death, him and his descendants.

'From him were born nations and tribes, peoples and
families, too numerous to count. Each nation went its 8
own way, sinning against you and scorning you; and you

9 did not stop them. But then again, in due time, you brought the flood upon the inhabitants of the earth and
10 destroyed them. The same doom came upon all: death
11 upon Adam, and the flood upon that generation. One man you spared – Noah, with his household, and all his righteous descendants.

12 'The population of the earth increased; families and peoples multiplied, nation upon nation. But then once again they began to sin, more wickedly than those before
13 them. When they sinned, you chose for yourself one of
14 them, whose name was Abraham; him you loved, and to him alone, secretly, at dead of night, you showed how
15 the world would end. You made an everlasting covenant with him and promised never to abandon his descendants.
16 You gave him Isaac, and to Isaac you gave Jacob and Esau; of these you chose Jacob for yourself and rejected Esau; and Jacob grew to be a great nation.

17 'You rescued his descendants from Egypt and brought
18 them to Mount Sinai. There you bent the sky, shook[a] the earth, moved the round world, made the depths
19 shudder, and turned creation upside down. Your glory passed through the four gates of fire and earthquake, wind and frost; and you gave the commandments of the
20 law to the Israelites, the race of Jacob. But you did not take away their wicked heart and enable your law to
21 bear fruit in them. For the first man, Adam, was burdened with a wicked heart; he sinned and was overcome,
22 and not only he but all his descendants. So the weakness became inveterate. Although your law was in your

[a] *So some Vss.; Lat.* fixed.

people's hearts, a rooted wickedness was there too; so that the good came to nothing, and what was bad persisted.

'Years went by, and when the time came you raised 23 up a servant for yourself, whose name was David. You 24 told him to build the city that bears your name and there offer to you in sacrifice what was already your own. This 25 was done for many years; until the inhabitants of the city went astray, behaving just like Adam and all his line; 26 for they had the same wicked heart. And so you gave 27 your own city over to your enemies.

'I said to myself: "Perhaps those in Babylon lead 28 better lives, and that is why they have conquered Zion." But when I arrived here, I saw more wickedness than I 29 could reckon, and these thirty years I have seen many evil-doers with my own eyes. My heart sank, because 30 I saw how you tolerate sinners and spare the godless; how you have destroyed your own people, but protected your enemies. You have given no hint whatever to any- 31 one how to understand your ways.[a] Is Babylon more virtuous than Zion? Has any nation except Israel ever 32 known you? What tribes have put their trust in your covenants as the tribes of Jacob have? But they have seen 33 no reward, no fruit for their pains. I have travelled up and down among the nations, and have seen how they pros- per, heedless though they are of your commandments. So weigh our sins in the balance against the sins of the 34 rest of the world; and it will be clear which way the scale tips. Has there ever been a time when the inhabitants of 35

[a] how . . . . ways: *so some Vss.; Lat. obscure.*

the earth did not sin against you? Has any nation ever
36 kept your commandments like Israel? You may find one
man here, one there; but nowhere a whole nation.'

* The recounting of the main events in the history of God's
dealings with his people forms a characteristic feature of a
number of Old Testament passages which have similarities
with Ezra's prayer. Sometimes this occurs within the context
of the praise of God (e.g. Pss. 105; 135), and sometimes
within the context of the reproach of his people (e.g. Ps. 78;
Ezek. 20). By contrast Ezra retells this same history as the
basis of his accusation that God had treated his people unfairly;
his prayer perhaps has its closest parallel in the Old Testament
in Ps. 89, in which the rejection of the Davidic king is the
centre.

In his prayer Ezra acknowledges that God had on numerous
occasions acted graciously on behalf of his people since the
time of creation; he refers to the sparing of Noah, the choice
of Abraham and of the line descended through Isaac and
Jacob, the deliverance from Egypt, the gift of the law, the
covenant with David, and the choice of Jerusalem as the site
of the temple. But at the same time Ezra recognizes that at
each stage in this history the people had failed to respond and
had continued in a state of wickedness, so that in the end God
had handed his own city (Jerusalem) over to his enemies.
So far the presentation is not very different from, e.g., Ps. 78
or Ezek. 20. What is distinctive here is that Ezra blames this
state of affairs on God. It is true that God had given his
people the law which ought to have provided them with the
means of salvation. But he had failed to take their 'wicked
heart' away from them, and this is why the Israelites had
continued in sin and had, in consequence, been punished by
God at the hands of the Babylonians. Ezra had been prepared
to admit that this might be because the Babylonians lived
better lives than the Israelites. But his experiences in Babylon

had shown him that the exact opposite was true. To make matters worse, no other nation had entered into covenant relationship with God or had kept his commandments as well as Israel. The fact that God was punishing his people thus appeared inexplicable to Ezra (verse 30), and implicitly he accuses God of acting unjustly towards his people. Ezra's prayer is directed ostensibly to the situation of the Jews in the sixth century B.C.; in reality, as we have seen (see pp. 102–3), the prayer, like the whole book, reflects the doubt and anguish of the Jews in the period after the war with the Romans in A.D. 66–73.

1–3. Introduction to the prayer. *In the thirtieth year:* the date (cp. verse 29) was perhaps given in order to imitate the opening words of the Book of Ezekiel, which, like 2 Esdras 3–14, is set in the Babylonian exile, and in any event it is unlikely that an exact time-reference is intended. However, a date thirty years after the fall of Jerusalem in 587 B.C. is not out of place for Salathiel (see below), while a date thirty years after A.D. 70 corresponds, at least in very general terms, with the date which on other grounds seems probable for the composition of 2 Esdras 3–14. From the vision recorded in chs. 11–12 it seems clear that this work was composed during the reign of Domitian (A.D. 81–96). Unless the thirty years are totally out of step with reality, the evidence of 3: 1 suggests that we should think in terms of the end, rather than the beginning, of Domitian's reign (see further pp. 104–5). *Salathiel:* the Greek form of the Hebrew name Shealtiel, and not elsewhere mentioned in 2 Esdras 3–14. Shealtiel appears in the Old Testament (1) as the son of Jeconiah (i.e. Jehoiachin) and uncle of Zerubbabel (1 Chron. 3: 17–19) and (2) as the father of Zerubbabel (Ezra 3: 2; Neh. 12: 1). Whether he was the uncle or father of Zerubbabel, Shealtiel is a link between the beginning and the end of the period of the exile, and a date thirty years after 587 B.C. is not inappropriate for him. The rather artificial identification made here between Shealtiel/Salathiel and Ezra was, therefore, perhaps intended to overcome the chronological difficulties involved in making Ezra, who belongs in a much later period, a figure of the exile. *Babylon:* 2 Esdras 3–14 is set in Babylon because that is where the Old Testament places Ezra (cp. Ezra 7). However, it seems clear that in several places in 2 Esdras 3–14, just as in Revelation (cp. e.g. 14: 8), 'Babylon' is meant to be a symbolic name for Rome (see verses 2, 28, 31*b*). But these references do not necessarily mean that 2 Esdras 3–14 was actually composed in Rome, although such a view is not impossible. We do not know where 2 Esdras 3–14 was written, but the use of Hebrew as the language of composition suggests that it may have been in Palestine (cp. p. 110). *As I lay on my bed I was troubled:* the description is reminiscent of that of Daniel (cp. Dan. 7: 1, 15). *the Most High:* this title for God, although found throughout the Old Testament (see e.g. Gen. 14: 18; Num. 24: 16), is used particularly frequently in the writings of the intertestamental period (see also e.g. Dan. 4: 17; Acts 7: 48). It serves to emphasize God's universal sovereignty and his superiority over all other gods.

4–36. The prayer. One of the characteristic features of 2 Esdras 3–14 (as of the apocalyptic literature in general) is the extensive use that is made of Old Testament material. Sometimes this amounts to no more than a general similarity with Old Testament thought and language; in other places the author seems to draw his inspiration from quite specific passages in the Old Testament which he uses as the basis of his own writing. Ezra's prayer is a case in point: verses 3–15 draw heavily on the early chapters of Genesis, and there seems little doubt that these chapters were quite definitely in the mind of the author as he composed the prayer. After verse 15 the account of the history is abbreviated and dependence on the Old Testament text is much less direct.

4–7*b*. The story of Adam. Creation by *the word* (verse 4*a*) recalls Gen. 1, but the account of the creation of Adam (verses 4*b*–5) follows Gen. 2: 4*b*–7 (cp. particularly *and into it you breathed the breath of life. So you made him a living person* with

Gen. 2: 7). Verses 6 and 7*a* draw on Gen. 2: 8, 9, 15–17, while verse 7*b*, death following upon disobedience, summarizes Gen. 3.

7*c*–11. The flood; cp. Gen. 6–9.

12. An allusion to Gen. 10: 32 and the story of the tower of Babel (Gen. 11: 1–9) which follows.

13–15. The choice of Abraham.

14. *to him alone, secretly, at dead of night, you showed how the world would end:* an allusion to Gen. 15, and particularly to verses 12–17. However, the language used (*you showed how the world would end*) suggests that a wider tradition was in mind according to which Abraham was the recipient of apocalyptic mysteries. There does, in fact, exist an Apocalypse of Abraham (cp. p. 108); this work, which dates from the end of the first century A.D., tells how Abraham was carried up to heaven and there received from God revelations concerning heaven, the origins of sin, the fate of Israel, and the coming judgement.

15. *You made an everlasting covenant with him:* cp. Gen. 15: 18–21; 17: 1–8.

16–22. The author passes quickly over the stories of Isaac, Jacob, the period in Egypt and the deliverance from Egypt, but spends some time dealing with the revelation of the law at Sinai because this provided him with an opportunity of dealing with an aspect of the problem with which he was concerned: although God had given his people the law, he had not taken away 'their wicked heart' which caused them to sin; the perplexing result was 'that the good came to nothing, and what was bad persisted'. At the time at which 2 Esdras 3–14 was written there were in Judaism a number of different explanations of why men sin, and two of these have been brought together here. (1) It was believed that each man has an evil and a good inclination, but that the evil inclination is predominant and causes sin. The idea of the evil inclination is comparable to the idea in 2 Esdras 3–14 of the 'wicked heart' (verse 20; cp. 4: 30–2; 7: [48], [92]). This idea has been integrated with (2) the idea that men sin as a result of the fact that Adam sinned (verse 21; cp. 7: [116], [118]; Rom. 5: 12–14).

18–19. According to the Old Testament, disturbances in the world of nature were the regular accompaniment of God's manifestations of himself; for the revelation of Sinai see Exod. 19: 16–18. *four gates:* perhaps the gates of a series of heavens, each containing a different element, through which the glory of God was thought to descend. Three of the elements are mentioned in connection with a self-revelation of God in 1 Kings 19: 11–12.

23–7. In his account of the history of God's dealings with his people the author jumps from the revelation at Sinai to the time of David and the period of the monarchy. He is able now to be very brief because the points he wanted to emphasize (the divine choice of Israel and the gift of the law) have already been made; it only remains for him to refer to the fate which overtook Israel despite the divine choice.

24. The command *to build the city* and to *offer ... sacrifice* does not as such occur in the Old Testament, but perhaps there is in part an allusion to 2 Sam. 5: 9 and 1 Chron. 11: 8. At the time at which 2 Esdras 3–14 was written sacrifice could not be offered in Jerusalem, and for pious Jews this was one of the worst aspects of their position after A.D. 70.

26. *behaving just like Adam and all his line; for they had the same wicked heart:* as in verses 20–2, the author integrates the ideas of the sin of Adam and of the wicked heart in order to explain why the inhabitants of Jerusalem kept on sinning during the period of the monarchy and so brought about the capture of Jerusalem by the Babylonians (cp. 2 Kings 25: 1–21).

27. The capture of Jerusalem, exactly as in the Old Testament (cp. 2 Kings 24: 20; 2 Chron. 36: 15–17), is interpreted as God's judgement and abandonment of his people.

28–36. The author reflects on what had happened. *Perhaps those in Babylon lead better lives:* but this initial reaction that Israel's punishment had been justified was rapidly shown by experience to be wrong. No *nation except Israel* had *ever known* God, and no *nation* had *ever kept* the *commandments like Israel*. God thus appeared to him to be acting contrary to expectation: to be destroying his own people, and to be protecting and prospering his enemies. The problem was to understand how this could be. ✶

URIEL'S RESPONSE

✶ The angel Uriel now appears for the first time. He is introduced somewhat abruptly, but we are to understand that he is sent to Ezra in response to his prayer in order to answer the difficulties that he had raised. In this first dialogue Uriel essentially makes only two points: (1) it is impossible for a mere man to understand the ways of God (4: 1–11, 12–21); (2) the end will in any case make all things clear (4: 22–32). ✶

MAN CANNOT UNDERSTAND THE WAYS OF GOD

The angel who was sent to me, whose name was Uriel, **4** replied: 'You are at a loss to explain this world; do you 2 then expect to understand the ways of the Most High?' 'Yes, my lord', I replied. 3

'I have been sent to propound to you three of the ways of this world,' he continued, 'to give you three illustrations. If you can explain to me any one of them, then 4 I will answer your question about the way of the Most High, and teach you why the heart is wicked.'

I said, 'Speak, my lord.' 'Come then,' he said, 'weigh 5 me a pound of fire, measure me a bushel^a of wind, or call back a day that has passed.'

'How can you ask me to do that?' I replied; 'no man 6

[a] So some Vss.; Lat. the blast.

7 on earth can do it.' He said: 'Suppose I had asked you, "How many dwellings are there in the heart of the sea? or how many streams to feed the deep? or how many watercourses above the vault of heaven? Where are the paths out of the grave, and the roads into[a] paradise?",

8 you might then have replied, "I have never been down into the deep, I have not yet gone down into the grave,

9 I have never gone up into heaven." But, as it is, I have only asked you about fire, about wind, and about yesterday, things you are bound to have met; and yet you have failed to tell me the answers.

10 'If then', he went on, 'you cannot understand things

11 you have grown up with, how can your small capacity comprehend the ways of the Most High? A man corrupted by the corrupt world can never know the way of the incorruptible.'[b]

☆ Uriel challenges Ezra to do various things and answer various questions which, although having to do only with this world, are clearly beyond men's capabilities – as Ezra himself is forced to admit (verse 6). If Ezra cannot understand these essentially simple matters, how, Uriel asks, can he hope to 'comprehend the ways of the Most High' (verses 10–11).

1. The role of Uriel in 2 Esdras 3–14 is similar to his role in 1 Enoch (on which see p. 108); Uriel is one of the seven archangels and frequently acts as Enoch's guide to explain to him the significance of what he sees.

2–3a. *You are at a loss to explain this world:* these words look forward to the point which the angel develops in the following verses.

[a] the grave . . . into: *so some Vss.; Lat. omits.*
[b] A man . . . incorruptible: *reading based on other Vss.; Lat. obscure.*

3b. three . . . ways . . . three illustrations: those described in verse 5.

4. The main thrust of Ezra's prayer concerned the fate of Israel, the chosen people of God, in comparison with that of the other nations (3: 28–36), but Ezra also touched on the problem of why men sin (3: 20–2). In the light of this it is interesting to observe that the angel interprets Ezra's prayer as being really concerned with the second point, i.e. *why the heart is wicked.* These two questions were in fact interrelated for the author, and at different points in 2 Esdras 3–14 one or other aspect of what was essentially the same problem is emphasized.

5–6. measure me a bushel of wind: Job 28: 25 lists the setting of a weight (N.E.B. 'counterpoise') for the wind as one of God's mysterious acts of creation. Although fire, wind and yesterday are all familiar to Ezra (cp. verse 9), the three actions described in verse 5 are ones which only God can carry out, not a mere man.

7–9. The questions which Uriel admits he would expect to be beyond Ezra are strongly reminiscent of the questions put to Job when God answers him out of the tempest; cp. Job 38: 16–18.

7. *paradise:* see the comment on 7: [36].

8. *"I have never been down into the deep . . .I have never gone up into heaven":* cp. John 3: 12–13:

'If you disbelieve me when I talk to you about things on earth, how are you to believe if I should talk about the things of heaven?

'No one ever went up into heaven except the one who came down from heaven, the Son of Man whose home is in heaven.'

Cp. also verse 21.   ✳

A PARABLE

12   When I heard that, I fell[a] prostrate and exclaimed:
'Better never to have come into existence than be born
into a world of wickedness and suffering which we cannot
13   explain!' He replied, 'I went out into a wood, and the
14   trees of the forest were making a plan. They said, "Come,
let us make war on the sea, force it to retreat, and win
15   ground for more woods." The waves of the sea made a
similar plan: they said, "Come, let us attack the trees of
16   the forest, conquer them, and annex their territory." The
plan made by the trees came to nothing, for fire came and
17   burnt them down. The plan made by the waves failed
just as badly, for the sand stood its ground and blocked
18   their way. If you had to judge between the two, which
would you pronounce right, and which wrong?'
19   I answered, 'Both were wrong; their plans were impossible, for the land is assigned to the trees, and to the
sea is allotted a place for its waves.'
20   'Yes,' he replied, 'you have judged rightly. Why then
21   have you failed to do so with your own question? Just
as the land belongs to the trees and the sea to the waves,
so men on earth can understand earthly things and nothing
else; only those who live[b] above the skies can understand
the things above the skies.'

✶ Ezra's inability to understand makes him despair of life
(verse 12), but Uriel, far from sympathizing with him,
reiterates his point by means of a parable (verses 13–17).

[a] When...fell: *so some Vss.; Lat. defective.*
[b] *Or* he who lives.

The question and answer at the end of the story (verses 18–21) emphasizes the moral: 'men on earth can understand earthly things and nothing else' (cp. Isa. 55: 8–9).

13–17. The imagery of the story reminds us in some ways of Jotham's fable (Judges 9: 7–21), and the author of 2 Esdras 3–14 may perhaps have drawn his inspiration from there. But it is also possible that the author has taken over from another source a fable that was already in existence.

19. The idea that a definite place has been assigned to the sea by God occurs more than once in the Old Testament, e.g. Jer. 5: 22, 'who made the shivering sand to bound the sea' (cp. Job 38: 8–11).

21. Cp. John 3: 12–13 (quoted in the comment on verse 8). ✲

THE NEW AGE WILL MAKE ALL THINGS CLEAR

'But tell me, my lord,' I said, 'why then have I been 22 given the faculty of understanding? My question is not 23 about the distant heavens, but about the things which happen every day before our eyes. Why has Israel been made a byword among the Gentiles; why has the people you loved been put at the mercy of godless nations? Why has the law of our fathers been brought to nothing, and the written covenants made a dead letter? We pass like a 24 flight of locusts, our life is but a vapour, and we are not worth the Lord's pity, though we bear his name; what then will he do for us? These are my questions.' 25

He answered: 'If you survive, you will see; if you live 26 long enough, you will marvel.[a] For this present age is quickly passing away; it is full of sorrow and frailties, too 27 full to enjoy what is promised in due time for the godly.

[a] *So one Vs.; Lat.* live, you will often marvel.

28 The evil about which you ask me has been sown, but its
29 reaping has not yet come. Until the crop of evil has been
reaped as well as sown, until the ground where it was
sown has vanished, there will be no room for the field
30 which has been sown with the good. A grain of the evil
seed was sown in the heart of Adam from the first; how
much godlessness has it produced already! How much
31 more will it produce before the harvest! Reckon this
up: if one grain of evil seed has produced so great a crop
32 of godlessness, how vast a harvest will there be when good
seeds beyond number have been sown!'

✢ 22-5. Ezra is not satisfied with Uriel's answer and
reformulates his problem with greater clarity: he is not concerned with things beyond men's experience, but with the
fate that Israel was actually suffering. Why had Israel 'been
put at the mercy of godless nations', and why had the law,
which ought to have provided the means of salvation, 'been
brought to nothing'?

24. Israel's sorry condition is such that their lives appear
completely transient and insignificant; cp. Ps. 109: 23;
Nahum 3: 17; and Pss. 39: 11; 144: 4. To make matters
worse Israel does not seem to be *worth the Lord's pity* (the
thought of unworthiness contrasts to some extent with the
attitude expressed in 3: 28-36). The anguish of the situation
in which the Jews found themselves after the war of A.D. 66-73
here finds vivid expression (see pp. 102-3).

25. The text could also be translated. 'What then will he
do for his name which we bear?'; cp. Josh. 7: 9.

26-32. In his reply the angel now makes a second point:
the new age is coming soon and will make all things clear,
but the evil in the world which began with Adam must first
run its course, and the judgement take place, before the new
age can come. Jews and Christians at the time at which 2

124

Esdras 3–14 was written commonly made a distinction between the 'present age' (verse 26) and the new age, and in the writings of that period we often find the terms 'this age' and 'the age to come' used in a technical sense to refer to the two ages (sometimes the same words are translated 'this world' and 'the world to come'); see e.g. Matt. 12: 32; Eph. 1: 21; or frequently in the Mishnah (see p. 108). The distinction between the two ages forms a key theme in 2 Esdras 3–14 and is used by the author as a means of trying to solve the problems which burdened him.

27. *full of sorrow and frailties:* one of the characteristics of the present age which mean that it cannot serve as the setting for the enjoyment of the good things promised to *the godly*.

28. Ezra had asked specifically about the fate of Israel (verses 22–5), but the angel deals with the much larger question of the existence of evil in general (for this change of emphasis see the note on 4: 4). *evil* is a further characteristic of the present age; it began with Adam's sin (see verse 30), and the judgement which will bring it to an end has yet to come. In talking of these ideas the author uses for the first time imagery which he subsequently re-uses in different ways on more than one occasion, that of sowing and reaping. This kind of symbolism is familiar both from the Old Testament (cp. Joel 3: 13) and the New (cp. e.g. Matt. 13: 24–30, 36–43; Rev. 14: 14–20).

29. The *evil* in the world must run its course, the judgement take place, and the present age (*the ground*) be brought to an end, before the new age (*the field which has been sown with the good*) can come. The deterministic ideas implicit here are further developed in the remainder of the chapter.

30. The imagery of sowing is used to bring together once more the ideas of the wicked heart and of the sin of Adam and its after-effects; see 3: 20–2 and the note on 3: 16–22.

32. *how vast a harvest will there be when good seeds beyond number have been sown:* the N.E.B., probably correctly, has followed the oriental versions in which the thought is that the

blessings of the new age will be incomparably greater than the troubles of the present. However, the Latin version omits the word 'good'; the contrast would then be between the effect of the sin of one man Adam, and the cumulative effect of the sins of all mankind.   *

WHEN WILL THE NEW AGE COME?

33 I asked, 'But when? How long have we to wait? Why
34 are our lives so short and so miserable?' He replied, 'Do not be in a greater hurry than the Most High himself. You are in a hurry for yourself alone; the Most High
35 for many. Are not these the very questions which were asked by the righteous in the storehouse of souls: "How long must we stay here? When will the harvest begin,
36 the time when we get our reward?" And the archangel Jeremiel gave them this answer: "As soon as the number
37 of those like yourselves is complete. For the Lord has weighed the world in a balance, he has measured and numbered the ages; he will move nothing, alter nothing, until the appointed number is achieved."'

38 'But, my lord, my master,' I replied, 'we are all of us
39 sinners through and through. Can it be that because of us, because of the sins of mankind, the harvest and the
40 reward of the just are delayed?' 'Go,' he said, 'ask a pregnant woman whether she can keep the child in her womb
41 any longer after the nine months are complete.' 'No, my lord,' I said, 'she cannot.' He went on: 'The storehouses
42 of souls in the world below are like the womb. As a woman in travail is impatient to see the end of her labour, so they are impatient to give back all the souls com-
43 mitted to them since time began. Then all your questions will be answered.'

I said, 'If it is possible for you to tell and for me to 44
understand, will you be gracious enough to disclose one
thing more: which is the longer – the future still to come, 45
or the past that has gone by? What is past I know, but 46
not what is still to be.' 'Come and stand on my right,' 47
he said; 'you shall see a vision, and I will explain what
it means.'

So I stood and watched, and there passed before my 48
eyes a blazing fire; when the flames had disappeared from
sight, there was still some smoke left. After that a dark 49
rain-cloud passed before me; there was a heavy storm,
and when it had gone over, there were still some raindrops
left. 'Reflect on this,' said the angel. 'The shower of rain 50
filled a far greater space than the drops of water, and the
fire more than the smoke. In the same way, the past far
exceeds the future in length; what remains is but raindrops and smoke.'

* Ezra is by no means satisfied with the answers he has so
far received, but for the time being he gives up his attack and
begins to ask questions which are intended simply to elicit
information, more precisely to find out when the present age
will come to an end and the new age begin. A comparable
change in the character of the dialogue is to be observed also
in the second and third sections of 2 Esdras 3–14 (i.e. 5:
20 – 6: 34; 6: 35 – 9: 25). The answer to Ezra's main question
is developed in three stages: (1) the end will only come at the
time appointed by God, therefore be patient (verses 33–7);
(2) on the other hand the sin of men cannot affect God's
plan and delay the end (verses 38–43); (3) we are nearer the
end of the present age than the beginning (verses 44–50).

33-4. *How long?:* a common formula in psalms of lament
(e.g. Pss. 74: 10; 80: 4). However, Ezra is urged to be patient.

35-6. The souls of the righteous dead had already asked

the same question as Ezra and had been given the answer that *the harvest . . . the time when* they would get their *reward,* would only come when the predetermined number of the righteous was complete; cp. 2: 40–1; Rev. 6: 9–11. *the storehouse of souls:* the fate of the individual after death was a matter of some concern to the author of 2 Esdras 3–14, and his views on this subject are set out at length in 7: [75–115]. For the time being it is enough to observe that a place (here called a *storehouse*) is set apart for the souls of the righteous where they wait until the day of judgement, the day on which they would rise from the dead to enjoy their reward in the life of the new age. There are similar ideas in e.g. 1 Enoch 22; 2 Baruch 21: 23; 30: 2 (on these two apocalypses see p. 108). *Jeremiel:* the name is perhaps the same as the Old Testament name Jerahmeel (cp. e.g. Jer. 36: 26), and the archangel is possibly to be identified with the archangel Remiel who is said in 1 Enoch 20: 8 to be 'in charge of those who rise', i.e. from the dead.

37. The same point is made as in verse 36, but in a slightly different way. The idea that God has exactly determined the course of history, including the time of the end, forms an important element in many writings of the intertestamental period, but receives particular emphasis in 2 Esdras 3–14.

38–43. Ezra is concerned that the sins of mankind may be delaying the day of judgement, but is assured that once the moment fixed by God is reached nothing will hinder the resurrection from the dead, the time when the just will receive their reward.

40. *a pregnant woman:* this was an important image for the author which he used more than once in the development of his argument in much the same way as he used and reused the image of sowing and reaping.

42. *to give back all the souls committed to them:* cp. the description of the resurrection in 1 Enoch 51: 1, 'And in those days the earth will return that which has been entrusted to it, and Sheol will return that which has been entrusted to

it, that which it has received, and destruction will return what it owes.'

43. The new age will solve all Ezra's difficulties, the same point that is made in verse 26.

44–50. Ezra now asks how much of the history of this world remains to run its course and is told by means of a vision that he is much nearer the end of this age than the beginning; *the past far exceeds the future in length*. Many Jews in the intertestamental period, like the early Christians, lived in the expectation that the end of this world would come very quickly, and in the apocalyptic writings there are sometimes attempts to specify exactly when it would be (cp. e.g. Dan. 7: 25*b*; 8: 13–14; 12: 7, 11–12). By contrast it is noticeable that the nature of the reply given here leaves open the question precisely how much time was left before the end. The attitude of reserve reflected here was perhaps partly conditioned by a feeling that heightened expectations of the end were one of the factors which had contributed to the downfall of the Jewish community. ✻

THE SIGNS OF THE END

'Pray tell me,' I said, 'do you think that I shall live to 51 see those days? Or in whose lifetime will they come?' 'If you ask me what signs will herald them,' he said, 52 'I can tell you in part. But the length of your own life I am not commissioned to tell you; of that I know nothing.

'But now to speak of the signs: there will come a time 5 when the inhabitants of the earth will be seized with panic.*a* The way of truth will be hidden from sight, and the land will be barren of faith. There will be a great 2 increase in wickedness, worse than anything you now see

[a] *So some Vss.; Lat. corrupt.*

3 or have ever heard of. The country you now see governing the world will become a trackless desert, laid waste
4 for all to see. After the third period (if the Most High
grants you a long enough life) you will see confusion
everywhere. The sun will suddenly begin to shine in the
middle of the night, and the moon in the day-time.
5 Trees will drip blood, stones will speak, nations will be
in confusion, and the courses of the stars will be changed.
6 A king unwelcome to the inhabitants of earth will suc-
7 ceed to the throne; even the birds will all fly away. The
Dead Sea will cast up fish, and at night a voice will
8 sound, unknown to the many but heard by all.*[a]* Chasms*[b]*
will open in many places and spurt out flames incessantly.
Wild beasts will range far afield, women will give birth
9 to monsters, fresh springs will run with salt water, and
everywhere friends will become enemies. Then understanding will be hidden, and reason withdraw to her
10 secret chamber. Many will seek her, but not find her;
11 the earth will overflow with vice and wickedness. One
country will ask another, "Has justice passed your way,
12 or any just man?", and it will answer, "No." In those
days men will hope, but hope in vain; they will strive,
but never succeed.

13   'These are the signs I am allowed to tell you. But turn
again to prayer, continue to weep and fast for seven days;
and then you shall hear further signs, even greater than
these.'

[a] *Some Vss. read* and at night one whom the many do not know
will utter his voice, and all will hear it.
[b] *So one Vs.; Lat.* Chaos.

✻ 51–2. *do you think that I shall live to see those days? Or in whose lifetime will they come?*: Ezra tries to force the angel to be more precise about when the end of this age will come, but the angel refuses to commit himself, and his answer (which no doubt represents the views of the author) is consistent with the attitude of reserve reflected in verses 48–50 (see above on 44–50). The angel does, however, agree to tell Ezra something about the signs that will precede the end. Descriptions of the signs of the end – the New Testament calls them 'the birth-pangs of the new age' (Matt. 24: 8; Mark 13: 8*b*) – were a conventional feature of apocalyptic and related writings, and it is possible to trace many parallels to the signs described here; cp. e.g. Joel 2: 30–1; Mark 13: 3–27 (and parallels); 2 Baruch 70. The character of 2 Baruch 70 is well illustrated by verses 2–3:

> 'Behold! the days come, and it shall be when the time of
>   the age has ripened,
> And the harvest of its evil and good seeds has come,
> That the Mighty One will bring upon the earth and its
>   inhabitants and upon its rulers
> Perturbation of spirit and stupor of heart.
> And they shall hate one another,
> And provoke one another to fight,
> And the mean shall rule over the honourable,
> And those of low degree shall be extolled above the
>   famous'

(Translation from R. H. Charles, *Apocrypha and Pseudepigrapha*, vol. 2, p. 517.) However, in 2 Esdras 4, because verse 52 introduces the signs very abruptly (the N.E.B. has smoothed over the harshness of the Latin, see below), and because the signs (5: 1–12) at first sight appear to be rather out of character with what has gone before, it has sometimes been argued that the passage about the signs is an interpolation (the same view has also been held about three related passages: 6: 11–28; 7: 26–[44]; 8: 63 – 9: 12). But the fact that this material seems slightly out of character is largely a result of the fact that the author has used traditional motifs in order to fill out his picture of what will happen before the end, and it is very unlikely that this passage about the signs is an interpolation.

52. In the Latin the reply of the angel begins literally 'Concerning the signs about which you ask me', but Ezra has not yet mentioned any signs. It is possible that a sentence or so has dropped out of the text, but the awkwardness of the existing text is not a justification for doubting the originality of the following passage.

5: 1–12. The character of the signs – the spread of panic and confusion, the loss of faith and increase in wickedness, the complete reversal of the natural order of things – is entirely typical of such lists; cp. the examples mentioned above.

3. *The country you now see governing the world:* i.e. Rome. The judgement of Rome for arrogance and cruelty forms the theme of chs. 11 and 12.

4*a*. It is not clear what is meant by *the third period*, but number schemes are a common characteristic of apocalyptic literature; cp. Dan. 7: 17 ('four kingdoms'), Rev. 12: 14 ('three years and a half'). The passage in 2 Esdras may ultimately go back to Dan. 7: 25.

4*b*–5. 1 Enoch 80: 4–6 describes how in the days of the sinners, i.e. the last days before the end, the sun, moon, and stars will all appear at the wrong time; cp. also Joel 2: 10; Amos 8: 9. 'The very stones will cry out from the wall' (Hab. 2: 11) perhaps provided the inspiration for *stones will speak*.

6. *A king:* Jewish belief about the last days, as expressed in such passages as Assumption of Moses 8: 1 (on this work see p. 108) or 2 Baruch 40: 1, included the expectation of a cruel and despotic ruler, and in Christian writings this has developed into the belief in 'Antichrist' (1 John 2: 18, 22) or 'the Enemy' (2 Thess. 2: 4).

7. *fish:* another reversal of the natural order, since nothing can live in the waters of *The Dead Sea.* There is a similar prophecy in Ezek. 47: 7–10, but there it is one of the blessings of the new era, not one of the terrors of the last days. *a voice:* a similar phenomenon is recorded by Josephus (*Jewish War* 6: 299–300): one of the many portents of the fall of Jerusalem was a mysterious voice speaking in the temple.

8–9a. Further horrors of the last days. *Chasms:* the idea is apparently of a series of earthquakes; cp. Zech. 14: 4. The Latin 'Chaos' (see the footnote) probably derives from a confusion in the Greek text underlying our Latin version. *Wild beasts:* probably mentioned here as one of the dangers that will face men; cp. Ezek. 14: 15. *monsters:* cp. 6: 21. But the word used really conveys the idea that the children born will be signs or portents of what is to come.

9b–10. The withdrawal of wisdom also appears as a characteristic of the last days in 2 Baruch 48: 36:

> 'And many shall say to many at that time:
> "Where hath the multitude of intelligence hidden itself,
> And whither hath the multitude of wisdom removed
>   itself?"'

(Translation from R. H. Charles, *Apocrypha and Pseudepi-grapha*, vol. 2, p. 506.)

13. The end of the first dialogue with the angel. On the command to pray and fast see the comment on 5: 20–2. ✲

THE CONCLUSION OF THE FIRST DIALOGUE

I awoke with a start, shuddering; my spirit faltered, and 14 I was near to fainting. But the angel who had come and 15 talked to me gave me support and strength, and set me on my feet.

The next night Phaltiel, the leader of the people, came 16 to me. 'Where have you been?' he asked, 'and why that

17 sad look? Have you forgotten that Israel in exile has been
18 entrusted to your care? Rouse yourself, take nourishment.
Do not abandon us like a shepherd abandoning his flock
19 to savage wolves.' I replied: 'Leave me; for seven days
do not come near me, then you may come again.' When
he heard this, he left me.

✳ 14–15. Ezra's reaction to what he had experienced as he
lay on his bed (cp. 3: 1) was one of terror and consternation.
This is a traditional feature in apocalyptic writings; cp. Dan.
7: 28; 8: 27.

16–19. The dialogue with Phaltiel provides a certain
relaxation of tension in the development of the argument;
there is a comparable interlude in 12: 40–50.

16. *Phaltiel:* the identification is uncertain because no
person with this name is mentioned in the Old Testament as
living in the time of Ezra. It is true that the name Phaltiel is
related to the name Pelatiah, and that Pelatiah is the name
(1) of a grandson of Zerubbabel (1 Chron. 3: 21), and (2) of
a chief of the people in the time of Nehemiah (Neh. 10: 22);
it is possible that one or other of these passages was in the
mind of the author of 2 Esdras 3–14, but we have no idea
whether this is in fact so.

18. *shepherd:* Ezra is presented to us not only as an apocalyptic seer, but also, in a much more limited way, as the leader
and pastor of the people; cp. 12: 40–50; 14: 23–36. Brief as
these passages are, they are important as reminding us that the
author of 2 Esdras 3–14 did not write his book in isolation,
but in order to meet the needs of a community in a troubled
situation. The shepherd imagery is familiar from the Old
Testament; cp. Ezek. 34; Zech. 11: 4–17.   ✳

THE SECOND DIALOGUE (5: 20 – 6: 34)

* This short dialogue has a similar structure to the first and goes over a good deal of the same ground. However, there is a difference of emphasis in that the first part of the dialogue (5: 20–40) concentrates exclusively on Israel's fate and ignores the problems of sin and the fate of the individual (see the comment on 4: 4). The latter part of the dialogue provides further information about the end of this age. *

EZRA'S SECOND PRAYER

For seven days I fasted, with tears and lamentations, as 20 the angel Uriel had told me to do. By the end of the 21 seven days my mind was again deeply disturbed, but I 22 recovered the power of thought and spoke once more to the Most High.

'My Lord, my Master,' I said, 'out of all the forests 23 of the earth, and all their trees, you have chosen one vine; from all the lands in the whole world you have chosen 24 one plot; and out of all the flowers in the whole world you have chosen one lily. From all the depths of the sea 25 you have filled one stream for yourself, and of all the cities ever built you have set Zion apart as your own. From all the birds that were created you have named one 26 dove, and from all the animals that were fashioned you have taken one sheep. Out of all the countless nations, 27 you have adopted one for your own, and to this chosen people you have given the law which all men have approved. Why then, Lord, have you put this one people 28 at the mercy of so many? Why have you humiliated[a]

[a] *So some Vss.; Lat.* prepared.

135

this one stock more than all others, and scattered your
29 own people among the hordes of heathen? Those who
reject your promises have trampled on the people who
30 trust your covenants. If you so hate your people, they
should be punished by your own hand.'

✳ 20–2. The preparation for the prayer. In the apocalyptic
writings prayer and fasting were the regular means of
preparation for a divine revelation; cp. Dan. 9: 3 (and the
following prayer, verses 4–14); 2 Baruch 21: 1 (and the
following prayer, verses 2–26).

23–30. The prayer. This prayer differs in character from
the prayer in 3: 4–36, but has a similar function. The author
uses a variety of images drawn from the Old Testament in
order to describe the choice of Israel (verses 23–7), and then
poses the problem which concerned him: if God had really
chosen Israel, why had he put her at the mercy of the nations
(verses 28–30)? Unlike the prayer in the first dialogue there is
no suggestion here that Israel's fate might be justified because
of her sin, and no concern with the problem of why men sin.

23. *vine:* a common Old Testament symbol for Israel;
cp. e.g. Ps. 80: 8, 'Thou didst bring a vine out of Egypt';
Isa. 5: 1–7; Hos. 14: 7.

24. *plot:* the Latin version is obscure, and although the
other versions support the N.E.B. translation, it is not clear
what word was used in the Hebrew original. It is possible
that in the original the reference to the choice of the land of
Palestine was expressed symbolically, like that of the nation
itself. *lily:* cp. Hos. 14: 5; Song of Songs 2: 1–2 (the Song of
Songs was interpreted allegorically by Jewish commentators
to refer to God's dealings with his beloved people, Israel).

25. *stream:* the Old Testament background to this symbol
is not as certain as in some of the other examples, but there
may be an allusion to the 'waters of Shiloah, which run so
softly and gently' (Isa. 8: 6). Water is a frequent symbol of

life and healing (cp. John 4: 14). *Zion:* the divine choice of
Jerusalem is an important theme in the Old Testament and is
mentioned in several psalms which use the ancient name
Zion; see e.g. Ps. 78: 68:

> 'he chose the tribe of Judah
> and Mount Zion which he loved'

26. *dove:* the same symbol for Israel is used in the Hebrew
version of Ps. 74: 19 (see the footnote in the N.E.B.); cp. also
Song of Songs 2: 14. *sheep:* another very common Old
Testament symbol for Israel; cp. e.g. Ps. 80: 1:

> 'Hear us, O shepherd of Israel,
> who leadest Joseph like a flock of sheep.'

This symbol is also used in 1 Enoch 85–90 in an extended
allegory of the history of Israel.

27. This verse summarizes what has been described
symbolically in verses 23–6 and makes a further point: God
had not only chosen Israel, but had also given them *the law*,
the means intended by God to provide blessing and salvation;
see above 3: 19–22.

28. *Why then, Lord, have you put this one people at the mercy
of so many?:* the divine choice of Israel and the gift of the law
made God's punishment of her at the hands of the nations all
the more inexplicable. Although writing ostensibly in the
sixth or fifth centuries B.C., the author again really has in
mind the situation which faced the Jews at the end of the first
century |A.D.| *humiliated:* the Latin 'prepared' (see the N.E.B.
footnote) derives from a corruption in the Greek text on
which the Latin translation is based. *stock:* for the symbolism
cp. Isa. 60: 21; 1 Enoch 93: 8, 'the whole race of the chosen
root will be scattered' (as in 2 Esdras, the reference is to the
exile). *scattered:* at the time at which 2 Esdras 3–14 was
written many Jews lived away from Palestine in the so-called
Dispersion, and there were Jewish communities throughout
the Roman Empire. Although granted certain privileges by

the Romans, these Jewish communities were at times subject to harassment.

29. This verse repeats in summary form the point made in 3: 28–36.

30. The author believed that if punishment were necessary, it ought to be carried out by God's *own hand* (i.e. by means of some natural disaster), and not by human enemies; cp. 2 Sam. 24: 14. ✳

THE MYSTERY OF GOD'S JUDGEMENTS

31 When I had finished speaking, the angel who had visited me that previous night was sent to me again. 32 'Listen to me,' he said, 'and I will give you instruction. 33 Attend carefully, and I will tell you more.' 'Speak on, my lord', I replied.

He said to me, 'You are in great sorrow of heart for Israel's sake. Do you love Israel more than Israel's Maker 34 does?' 'No, my lord,' I said, 'but sorrow has forced me to speak; my heart is tortured every hour as I try to understand the ways of the Most High and to fathom some part of his judgements.'

35 He said to me, 'You cannot.' 'Why not, my lord?' I asked. 'Why then was I born? Why could not my mother's womb have been my grave? Then I should never have seen Jacob's trials and the weariness of the race of Israel.'

36 He said to me, 'Count me those who are not yet born, collect the scattered drops of rain, and make the withered 37 flowers bloom again; unlock me the storehouses and let loose the winds shut up there; or make visible the shape of a voice. Then I will answer your question about Israel's trials.'

'My Lord, my master,' I said, 'how can there be any- 38
one with such knowledge except the One whose home
is not among men? I am only a fool; how then can I 39
answer your questions?'

He said to me, 'Just as you cannot do any of the things 40
I have put to you, so you will not be able to find out my
judgements or the ultimate purpose of the love I have
promised to my people.'

* In response to the prayer the angel comes to Ezra again
and by means of a series of questions and answers leads Ezra
to accept two points: (1) Ezra does not love Israel more than
God (see verses 33–4); (2) God's judgements and God's love
for Israel are beyond human understanding (see verse 40). It
will be apparent that we have not advanced very far beyond
the first dialogue; cp. 4: 1–21.

32. The reply of the angel is introduced in much the same
way that the instruction of a wisdom teacher is introduced;
cp. e.g. Prov. 4: 1:

> 'Listen, my sons, to a father's instruction,
>   consider attentively how to gain understanding'

A similar stylistic device is used in 2 Esdras 7: [49].

33–4. Ezra readily admits that God's love for Israel is
greater than his own (cp. 8: 47), but the anguish he experiences
as he tries *to understand the ways of the Most High* forces him to
speak.

35. *Why then was I born?*: the angel's blank denial of the
possibility of understanding God's ways evokes a cry of
despair, the language of which is reminiscent of Job 10:
18–19. The same theme is used in Job 3: 11, closely similar
to Jer. 20: 17–18. *Jacob's trials . . . weariness . . . of Israel*: Ezra's
concern at this point is with the nation, not the individual.

36–40. The angel takes up the question posed by Ezra in
verse 35, 'Why not, my lord?', and uses methods similar to

those already used in the first dialogue (cp. 4: 1–21, especially verses 3–11) in order to prove his point: the purposes of God are beyond the powers of human understanding.

36. *collect the scattered drops of rain:* according to Job 36: 26–7, a passage which was very probably in the mind of the author, one of the signs that 'God is so great that we cannot know him' is that

> 'He draws up drops of water from the sea
> and distils rain from the mist he has made'

Ezra is being asked to do things which God does, but which are impossible for a mere man. *withered flowers:* cp. Ezek. 17: 24, God is the one who makes 'the dry tree put forth buds'.

37. *storehouses:* the idea that the wind is kept in a series of storehouses goes back to Job 37: 9 (cp. 38: 22: there is a similar idea in 1 Enoch 41: 4); the wind is thought of as being kept shut up until it is released at the command of God (cp. Job 37: 6).

38. *except the One whose home is not among men:* a comparable idea is expressed in Dan. 2: 11.

40. *so you will not be able to find out my judgements . . . the love I have promised to my people:* the conclusion drawn is the same as in 4: 20–1, but the author temporarily forgets that the angel, not God, is speaking. This kind of transition occurs frequently in 2 Esdras 3–14, possibly because what is said could often quite naturally and appropriately be attributed to God himself. The same kind of transition (from an angel to God) can be found already in the Old Testament: cp. Gen. 18; Judg. 6: 11–24. ✶

WHY GOD'S JUDGEMENT IS DELAYED

41   I said, 'But surely, lord, your promise[a] is to those who are alive at the end. What is to be the fate of those who

[a] *So one Vs.; Lat. obscure.*

lived before us, or of ourselves, or of those who come after us?'

He said to me, 'I will compare the judgement to a 42 circle: the latest will not be too late, nor the earliest too early.'

To this I replied, 'Could you not have made all men, 43 past, present, and future, at one and the same time? Then you could have held your assize with less delay.' But he 44 answered, 'The creation may not go faster than the Creator, nor could the world support at the same time all those created to live on it.'

'But, my lord,' I said, 'you have told me that you will 45 at one and the same time restore to life every creature you have made; how can that be? If it is going to be possible for all of them to be alive at the same time and for the world to support them all, then it could support all of them together now.' 'Put your question in terms 46 of a woman's womb', he replied. 'Say to a woman, "If you give birth to ten children, why do you do so at intervals? Why not give birth to ten at one and the same time?"' 'No, my lord, she cannot do that,' I said, 'the 47 births must take place at intervals.' 'True,' he answered; 48 'and I have made the earth's womb to bring forth at intervals those conceived in it. An infant cannot give 49 birth, nor can a woman who is too old; and I have made the same rule for the world I have created.'

* 41. Ezra refuses to be silenced, but seizes upon the words used by God in order to express his problem in a new way: God's promised love may well be of benefit to those who will be *alive at the end*, but *What is to be the fate* of those who live

before then? Ezra's starting-point remains the same, the difficulty of reconciling God's promises to his people with the situation in which the Jews found themselves after the war of A.D. 66–73, but here the problem is broadened in scope to take account of all the generations who had lived, and would live, before the judgement.

42. God replies by means of the analogy of *a circle* that the judgement will affect all generations; the reason for this, although the point is not made explicit here, is that on the day of judgement all men will rise from the dead; see verse 45; 7: 32, [37].

43–4. Ezra is not satisfied with this and asks why all men could not have been created at the same time, and then it would not have been necessary to wait so long for the judgement. To this the same kind of deterministic answer is given that we have already observed in the first dialogue: God's plan for the world must run its course (cp. 4: 36–7). But the point is also made that *the world* could not *support at the same time all those created to live on it*.

45–9. Ezra argues that there is a contradiction in what God is saying: on the one hand God has stated that he 'will at one and the same time restore to life' all those whom he has created, i.e. so that they can be present at the judgement (cp. verse 42); on the other hand God has argued that the earth could not at the same time support all those who would live on it (cp. verse 44). To Ezra these statements are incompatible: if the first is true, then surely the world 'could support all of them together now'. Underlying this argument is Ezra's concern that the last judgement should not be delayed (cp. verse 43 and 4: 39), but in response a deterministic answer is once more given. Ezra is told, again by means of an analogy, that God has so ordered the earth that the successive generations must live 'at intervals', i.e. in turn, upon it. God's plan for the world cannot be hurried.

46. *Say to a woman:* the analogy of a woman giving birth is already familiar from 4: 40–3 where it is used to make a

different, but not unrelated, point; the author develops the
analogy in verses 50–5 in order to discuss once more the
question of when the end will come.   *

WHEN AND HOW WILL THE END COME?

I continued my questions. 'Since you have opened the 50
way,' I said, 'may I now ask: is our mother that you
speak of still young, or is she already growing old?' He 51
replied, 'Ask any mother why the children she has lately 52
borne are not like those born earlier, but smaller. And 53
she will tell you, "Those who were born in the vigour
of my youth are very different from those born in my
old age, when my womb is beginning to fail." Think of 54
it then like this: if you are smaller than those born before
you, and those who follow you are smaller still, the 55
reason is that creation is growing old and losing the
strength of youth.'

I said to him, 'If I have won your favour, my lord, 56
show me through whom you will visit your creation.'
He said to me, 'Think of the beginning of this earth: the **6**
gates of the world had not yet been set up; no winds
gathered and blew, no thunder pealed, no lightning 2
flashed; the foundations of paradise were not yet laid,
nor were its fair flowers there to see; the powers that 3
move the stars were not established, nor the countless
hosts of angels assembled, nor the vast tracts of air set up 4
on high; the divisions of the firmaments had not received
their names. Zion had not yet been chosen as God's own
footstool; the present age had not been planned; the 5
schemes of its sinners had not yet been outlawed, nor had
God's seal yet been set on those who have stored up a

6 treasure of fidelity. Then did I think my thought; and the whole world was created through me and through me alone. In the same way, through me and through me alone the end shall come.'

7 'Tell me', I went on, 'about the interval that divides the ages. When will the first age end and the next age
8 begin?' He said, 'The interval will be no bigger than that between Abraham and Abraham; for Jacob and Esau were his descendants, and Jacob's hand was grasping Esau's heel
9 at the moment of their birth. Esau represents the end of
10 the first age, and Jacob the beginning of the next age. The beginning of a man is his hand, and the end of a man is his heel.[a] Between the heel and the hand, Ezra, do not look for any interval.'

✻ At this point the character of the dialogue changes in just the same way that the character of the first dialogue changes; see the comment on 4: 33–50. Ezra abandons his argument for the time being and begins instead to ask for information about the end. Three questions are raised: (1) how near are we to the end? (5: 50–5); (2) through whom will the end come? (5: 56 – 6: 6); (3) what interval will there be between this age and the new age? (6: 7–10).

50. *our mother*: Ezra takes up the analogy of the woman in order to ask once more how near we are to the end of this age; cp. 4: 44–5.

51–5. The reply is given by means of a further development of the analogy: children born in later life are inferior ('smaller') to those born to a woman when she is young; the fact that Ezra's generation is inferior to earlier generations is an indication that 'creation is growing old'. This means

[a] The beginning of a man ... heel: *reading based on other Vss.; Lat. defective.*

that the present age is drawing to its close, the point already made in a different way in 4: 50.

54–5. *if you are smaller than those born before you:* the idea that earlier generations were superior to those that have followed is a familiar one. Superiority in size is implied by Gen. 6: 4 according to which there were 'Nephilim' (footnote 'giants') on the earth before the flood. In a similar way the Bible holds that the length of men's lives has progressively declined since the time of the generations before the Flood; cp. the ages of the patriarchs in Gen. 5 with Gen. 6: 3 and Ps. 90: 10.

5: 56 – 6: 6. Ezra's second question, 'show me through whom you will visit your creation' (5: 56), and God's answer, 'through me and through me alone the end shall come' (6: 6), apparently have a polemical purpose, although it is not clear whether the polemic is directed against Jewish or, as seems more likely, Christian expectations that God would use an intermediary in order to bring this age to an end (cp. the Christian belief in the second coming of Jesus to judge the world; see e.g. Matt. 24: 30–1). Whatever the case may be, it is to be observed that the author of 2 Esdras 3–14 did assign some functions to an intermediary in the events before the end; see 7: 28–9; 12: 31–4; 13: 25–52.

56. *If I have won your favour, my lord:* more or less the same formula (in the Latin the expressions are not quite the same) occurs several times in 2 Esdras 3–14, usually, as here, at the beginning of sections which are intended to provide information (cp. 6: 11; 7: [75], [102]; 12: 7; 14: 22; and contrast 8: 42). *visit:* more is conveyed than by our English word 'visit'; in the Old Testament God sometimes 'visits' his people in order to bless them, but much more frequently in order to judge them. However, the N.E.B. has usually paraphrased the passages in which this word occurs; cp. e.g. Gen. 21: 1 ('showed favour to'); Jer. 6: 15 ('on the day of my reckoning'). In a similar way the N.E.B. has used the word 'judge', instead of 'visit', in 2 Esdras 6: 18, although the

Latin word is the same as the one which occurs in 5: 56. What Ezra is asking about in 5: 56 is the final judgement and the end of the present age.

6: 1–6. What will happen at the end of this world is brought into relationship with what happened at its beginning. God states that before the world was created he planned these things ('Then did I think my thought'); just as he 'alone' brought the world into being, so he 'alone' will bring about its 'end'.

1–5. The description of the time before creation is similar to the description in Prov. 8: 24–9 (although the N.E.B. translation does not fully bring out the points of contact), and Prov. 8 may have been in the mind of the author when he wrote this passage.

4. *footstool:* cp. Lam. 2: 1 'Zion was his footstool', and for the choice of Zion cp. 5: 25.

5. *God's seal:* perhaps intended to serve as a protective mark for the righteous at the last judgement; cp. Ezek. 9: 4–6; Rev. 7: 2–4.

7. *the interval that divides the ages:* Ezra's third question is concerned with the nature of the transition from this age to the new age. The answer is given in allegorical language and falls into two parts (verses 8a and 8b–10).

8a. *between Abraham and Abraham:* i.e. between Abraham and his family. There will in effect be no *interval* between the present age and the next age, but the one will follow immediately on the other just as Abraham was followed immediately by Isaac. The point is made explicitly in a less well-attested variant which reads 'between Abraham and Isaac'.

8b–10. The answer is reinforced by the application to the problem of a passage from the Old Testament which, in the light of other evidence, was apparently traditionally interpreted to refer to the transition from this age to the age to come, i.e. Gen. 25: 26, 'Immediately afterwards his brother was born with his hand grasping Esau's heel, and they called

146

him Jacob'. Just as 'Jacob's hand was grasping Esau's heel at
the moment of their birth' (verse 8b), so there will be no
interval between the ages – the same point that is made in
verse 8a. However, it is possible that the argument is carried
a stage further in verse 9.

9. The names *Esau* and *Jacob* are perhaps to be understood
as symbols for Rome and Israel. If this is so, *the end of the first
age* will be the period when Rome rules the world, and *the
beginning of the next age* will be the period when Israel rules
(perhaps the same as the period of the Messiah; see 7: 28).
This interpretation would provide an answer to the second
part of the question raised in verse 7, 'When will the first age
end and the next age begin?', but it is to be observed that
the idea that the next age will begin with the rule of Israel
does not occur elsewhere in 2 Esdras 3–14. Furthermore,
according to 7: 26–[44] the four-hundred-year rule of the
Messiah marks the end of the present age; this will be followed by an interval of silence for seven days, and only then
will the day of judgement take place and the new age begin
(7: 28–33). These ideas seem to be at variance with the ideas
expressed in 6: 7–10, and it would appear that the author of
2 Esdras 3–14 has not completely integrated his thoughts
about what will happen at the end. ✶

MORE SIGNS OF THE END

'My lord, my master,' I said, 'if I have won your 11
favour, make known to me the last of your signs, of 12
which you showed me a part that former night.'

'Rise to your feet,' he replied, 'and you will hear a 13
loud resounding voice. When it speaks, do not be 14-15
frightened if the place where you stand trembles and
shakes; it speaks of the end, and the earth's foundations
will understand that it is speaking of them. They will 16
tremble and shake; for they know that at the end they

17 must be transformed.' On hearing this I rose to my feet and listened; and a voice began to speak. Its sound was 18 like the sound of rushing waters. The voice said:

'The time draws near when I shall come to judge those 19 who live on the earth, the time when I shall inquire into the wickedness of wrong-doers, the time when Zion's 20 humiliation will be over, the time when a seal will be set on the age about to pass away. Then I will perform these signs: the books shall be opened in the sight of heaven, 21 and all shall see them at the same moment. Children only one year old shall be able to talk, and pregnant women shall give birth to premature babes of three and four 22 months, who shall live and leap about. Fields that were sown shall suddenly prove unsown, and barns that were 23 full shall suddenly be found empty. There shall be a loud trumpet-blast and it shall strike terror into all who hear 24 it. At that time friends shall make war on friends as though they were enemies, and the earth and all its inhabitants shall be terrified. Running streams shall stand still; for three hours they shall cease to flow.

25 'Whoever is left after all that I have foretold, he shall be preserved, and shall see the deliverance that I bring 26 and the end of this world of mine. They shall all see the men who were taken up into heaven without ever knowing death. Then shall men on earth feel a change of 27 heart and come to a better mind. Wickedness shall be 28 blotted out and deceit destroyed, but fidelity shall flourish, corruption be overcome, and truth, so long unfruitful, be brought to light.'

148

✻ The dialogue closes with a continuation of the description of the signs that will precede the end; cp. 4: 51 – 5: 13. This passage occupies the same position in the second dialogue as the corresponding description in the first dialogue.

11–12. *make known to me the last of your signs:* Ezra's request for more information follows quite naturally on the questions that immediately precede (cp. 5: 50; 5: 56; 6: 7), and it can hardly be maintained that this passage on the signs is introduced abruptly; contrast 4: 51–2. There is thus even less reason here than in the case of the first dialogue for saying that the description of the signs is an interpolation in its present context (see above, pp. 131–2).

13–18*a*. Ezra is told to prepare to listen to the answer to his question.

13. *Rise to your feet:* cp. Dan. 10: 11; in a very similar situation Daniel is told 'stand up'. *he replied:* the speaker is apparently the angel who now resumes the dialogue, although this is not made clear. But it makes sense to assume that it is the angel who tells Ezra to prepare to hear the voice of God. *a loud resounding voice:* although not stated explicitly, it is clear from the content of the signs (cp. verses 18*b*, 20) that the voice is that of God; cp. the 'loud voice' in Rev. 1: 10.

14–16. According to the Old Testament the shaking of the earth was one of the natural disturbances which regularly accompanied God's manifestation of himself; cp. e.g. Judg. 5: 4–5, and see above on 3: 18–19. In the same way it was also believed that when God comes to carry out his judgement, the earth would once more be shaken; cp. Isa. 13: 13:

> 'Then the heavens shall shudder,
>> and the earth shall be shaken from its place
> at the fury of the LORD of Hosts, on the day of his anger.'

Because *the earth's foundations will understand* what the divine voice is saying, *They will tremble and shake* in anticipation of what will happen *at the end* when God comes to judge the world and bring this age to a conclusion.

17. *the sound of rushing waters:* the author uses traditional language to describe the sound of God's voice; cp. Ezek. 43: 2 (where the N.E.B. translates 'the sound of a mighty torrent'); Rev. 1: 15.

18*b*–28. The divine reply. Ezra's question about the signs is only answered directly in verses 20*b*–24. Before this there is an introduction referring to the time when the signs will occur (verses 18*b*–20*a*), and after this there is a description of the period which will follow the judgement (verses 25–8).

18*b*–20*a*. The performance of the signs will be an indication that the judgement is about to be held and that the present age is about to pass away.

18*b*. *judge:* in the Latin, the same word that is translated 'visit' in 5: 56 (see the comment on that passage).

19. *Zion's humiliation:* the reference to Jerusalem is a reminder that the starting-point of the book is the author's concern at the situation of the Jews in the period after the war of A.D. 66–73. In the view of the author the only escape from this situation would be found in the judgement and the ending of this age.

20*a*. *a seal will be set on the age:* i.e. as an indication that the present age is done with.

20*b*–24. The common characteristic of all but two of the signs is the reversal of what would naturally be expected; see 5: 4*b*–9*a* and the comment on 5: 1–12. For the signs see also Mark 13: 3–27 (and parallels).

20*b*. *the books shall be opened:* in Jewish belief of the inter-testamental period the good and evil deeds of men were recorded in books which were to be opened at the judgement; cp. e.g. Dan. 7: 10; Rev. 20: 12. The opening of the books is not strictly one of the signs that the judgement is about to take place, but forms the beginning of the judgement itself. However, it is a mistake to expect that the signs should be listed in any sort of logical or temporal order. *in the sight of heaven:* i.e., apparently, in the presence of the heavenly host; cp. the situation described in Dan. 7: 10:

'Thousands upon thousands served him
and myriads upon myriads attended his presence.
The court sat, and the books were opened.'

all: the reference is probably to the angels, but it is just possible
that all mankind is intended.

23. *trumpet-blast:* the sounding of the trumpet was a
traditional feature of Jewish and Christian expectations
concerning the end. According to Isa. 27: 13, 'a blast shall
be blown on a great trumpet' to summon the Jews scattered
in Assyria and Egypt to worship the Lord in Jerusalem.
In a similar way the Son of Man sends out the angels 'With
a trumpet blast' to gather the elect (Matt. 24: 31), but in
Christian tradition the sounding of the trumpet came to be
associated particularly with the resurrection of the dead (cp.
e.g. 1 Thess. 4: 16). In 2 Esdras 3–14 the sound of the trumpet
causes *terror* because it is an indication that the judgement
is imminent.

24a. Cp. Matt. 24: 6, 'The time is coming when you will
hear the noise of battle near at hand and the news of battles
far away.'

24b. *three hours:* perhaps intended to denote in symbolic
language the length of time that the signs would last (cp. the
symbolic use of a 'week' to denote an era of history in the
so-called Apocalypse of Weeks, in 1 Enoch 93 + 91: 11–17,
in which world history is divided into ten 'weeks'). It is in
any event difficult to think that literally three hours are
meant.

25–8. The author now transfers his attention from the
signs that will precede the end to the end itself and the period
which will follow.

25. *Whoever is left after all that I have foretold:* only those
who survive the signs described in 6: 20b–24 and 5: 1–12 will
see the *deliverance* which God brings and the end of the
present world.

26. *the men who were taken up into heaven without ever know-*

ing death: i.e. Enoch (Gen. 5: 24) and Elijah (2 Kings 2: 1–12). It is not clear why these two should be mentioned just at this point, although the author appears to regard translation to heaven before death as a particular mark of divine favour, and apparently believed, although there is no Old Testament tradition to this effect, that Ezra himself was translated directly to heaven; see 14: 9 and the comment on that passage.

26b–28. Conditions in the new age will be the exact opposite of conditions in the present evil age because men themselves will have changed.

26b. *Then shall men on earth feel a change of heart and come to a better mind:* literally 'and the heart of the earth's inhabitants shall be changed and converted to a different mind'; cp. Ezek. 36: 26–7. *

THE CONCLUSION OF THE SECOND DIALOGUE

29 While the voice was speaking to me, the ground under
30 me began to quake.[a] Then the angel said to me, 'These, then, are the revelations I have brought you this night.[b]
31 If once again you pray and fast for seven days, then I will
32 return to tell you even greater things.[c] For be sure your voice has been heard by the Most High. The Mighty God has seen your integrity and the chastity you have observed
33 all your life. That is why he has sent me to you with all
34 these revelations, and with this message: "Be confident, and have no fear. Do not rush too quickly into unprofitable thoughts now in the present age; then you will not act hastily when the last age comes."'

[a] the ground . . . quake: *reading based on other Vss.; Lat. obscure.*
[b] *So one Vs.; Lat.* this coming night.
[c] *So other Vss.; Lat. adds* in the day-time.

✳ After the revelation from God the angel now speaks once more and gives Ezra some advice.

29. The fulfilment of what was anticipated in verses 14–16.

30–1. Essentially the same thing that is said in 5: 13 at the end of the first section.

32–3. The fact that Ezra is privileged to receive *these revelations* is attributed to his *integrity* and *chastity*; similar statements are to be found in the concluding verses of some of the other sections; cp. 10: 39, 57; 12: 36; 13: 53–6; see also the comment on 8: 62. Ezra's righteous standing before God is further stressed in other passages; cp. 7: [76–7]; 8: 47–9. Behind these statements we should perhaps see the author's convictions about his own standing before God.

34. Ezra is in effect advised not to be over-inquisitive *now in the present age* so as not to endanger his salvation *when the last age comes.* ✳

THE THIRD DIALOGUE (6: 35 – 9: 25)

✳ The third, and by far the longest, of the dialogues follows the broad pattern that has been established in the first two. It differs from these by its much greater concentration on the problem of sin and its consequences: why do the majority of men sin and thus incur eternal punishment and why are so few saved? In the course of the dialogue the author also tells us a good deal of his beliefs about the after-life and the end of the present age. This is the most important of the three dialogues and contains the heart of the discussion of the problems which concerned the author. ✳

EZRA'S THIRD PRAYER

Thereupon I wept and fasted again for seven days in the 35 same way as before, thus completing the three weeks enjoined on me. On the eighth night I was again dis- 36

37 turbed at heart, and spoke to the Most High. With spirit
38 aflame and in great agony of mind I said:

'O Lord, at the beginning of creation you spoke the
word. On the first day you said, "Let heaven and earth
39 be made!", and your word carried out its work. At that
time the hovering spirit was there, and darkness circled
round; there was silence, no sound as yet of human
40 voice.[a] Then you commanded a ray of light to be
brought out of your store-chambers, to make your works
41 visible from that time onwards. On the second day you
created the angel[b] of the firmament, and commanded
him to make a dividing barrier between the waters, one
part withdrawing upwards and the other remaining
42 below. On the third day you ordered the waters to collect
in a seventh part of the earth; the other six parts you
made into dry land, and from it kept some to be sown
43 and tilled for your service. Your word went forth, and
44 at once the work was done. A vast profusion of fruits
appeared instantly, of every kind and taste that can be
desired, with flowers of the most subtle colours and
mysterious scents. These were made on the third day.
45 On the fourth day by your command you created the
splendour of the sun, the light of the moon, and the stars
46 in their appointed places; and you ordered them to be
at the service of man, whose creation was about to take
47 place. On the fifth day you commanded the seventh
part, where the water was collected, to bring forth living
48 things, birds and fishes. And so, at your command, dumb
lifeless water brought forth living creatures, and gave the
49 nations cause to tell of your wonders. Then you set apart

[a] *So some Vss.; Lat. adds* from you.   [b] *Literally* spirit.

two creatures: one you called Behemoth and the other
Leviathan. You put them in separate places, for the 50
seventh part where the water was collected was not big
enough to hold them both. A part of the land which was 51
made dry on the third day you gave to Behemoth as his
territory, a country of a thousand hills. To Leviathan you 52
gave the seventh part, the water. You have kept them to
be food for whom you will and when you will. On the 53
sixth day you ordered the earth to produce for you
cattle, wild beasts, and creeping things. To crown your 54
work you created Adam, and gave him sovereignty over
everything you had made. It is from Adam that we, your
chosen people, are all descended.

'I have recited the whole story of the creation, O Lord, 55
because you have said that you made this first world for
our sake, and that all the rest of the nations descended 56
from Adam are nothing, that they are no better than
spittle, and, for all their numbers, no more than a drop
from a bucket. And yet, O Lord, those nations which 57
count for nothing are today ruling over us and devouring
us; and we, your people, have been put into their power – 58
your people, whom you have called your first-born, your
only son, your champion, and your best beloved. Was 59
the world really made for us? Why, then, may we not
take possession of our world? How much longer shall
it be so?'

---

* 35–38*a*. The preparation for the prayer. See the comment on 5: 20–2. *thus completing the three weeks*: only two
weeks of fasting have been mentioned so far (here and in
5: 20), and it is therefore possible that the introduction

(3: 1–3) to the first dialogue originally contained a reference to a week of fasting which has disappeared from the book in its present form. Whether this is so or not, the mention here of 'three weeks' suggests a conscious dependence on Dan. 10: 2–3; Daniel, in order to prepare himself for a revelation, was mourning and fasting 'for three whole weeks'.

38b–59. The prayer. The author retells the story of creation (verses 38b-54) in order to state in a new way the problem that concerned him: if the world was created for Israel's sake, why is she ruled over by other nations and unable to enter into possession of the world (verses 55–9)? The prayer is similar in character and purpose to those in the first two dialogues, and the problem remains the same. In contrast to the first dialogue, and in common with the second, there is no suggestion that Israel's fate was the result of her sin.

38b–54. The account of creation closely follows the narrative in Gen. 1: 1 – 2: 4a which was quite clearly in the mind of the author as he wrote this passage.

38b–40. The first day. The creation of heaven and earth and of light; see Gen. 1: 1–5.

40. *store-chambers:* light, like the wind, was thought to be kept in store-chambers from which it was brought out at God's command; see the comment on 5: 37.

41. The second day. The creation of the firmament to separate the waters; see Gen. 1: 6–8. *the angel of the firmament:* in the Genesis account God creates a firmament (the N.E.B. translation 'a vault' perhaps conveys better what was meant by this word) to separate the waters above heaven from the waters below, but in 2 Esdras 3–14 God creates a spirit or angel *to make a dividing barrier between the waters.* This development corresponds to ideas found in other intertestamental writings according to which natural processes were thought to be under the control of spirits; thus e.g. in 1 Enoch 60: 15–21 the thunder and lightning, the sea, the hoar-frost etc. are all controlled by spirits; cp. verse 16, 'And the spirit of the sea is male and strong, and according to the power of its strength (the spirit) turns it back with a rein, and likewise it is driven forward and scattered amongst all the mountains of the earth.'

42-4. The third day. The separation of the waters and the dry land and the creation of plants; see Gen. 1: 9-13. *seventh part ... six parts:* these figures are not mentioned in Genesis, and the origin of this tradition is unknown. But seven has commonly been regarded as a significant number and is used frequently in the apocalyptic writings; cp. e.g. 1 Enoch 77: 4-8 'seven high mountains', 'seven rivers', 'seven great islands'.

45-6. The fourth day. The creation of the sun, moon and stars; see Gen. 1: 14-19.

46. *to be at the service of man:* i.e. by distinguishing day and night; cp. Gen. 1: 18.

47-52. The fifth day. The creation of birds and fishes and of two other creatures; see Gen. 1: 20-3.

47. *commanded ... the water ... to bring forth ... birds and fishes:* it is a little strange to be told that birds as well as fishes came from the water, but the author has apparently compressed and confused what is said in Genesis.

49-52. *two creatures ... Behemoth ... Leviathan:* these are not mentioned in Genesis, but the author is building on the reference to 'the great sea-monsters' in Gen. 1: 21. In the intertestamental period there was an apparently widespread belief that as one of his acts of creation God made two monsters who were to be kept until the end of this world when they would provide food for the righteous at a great banquet which God would hold; cp. 2 Baruch 29: 4, 'And Behemoth shall be revealed from his place and Leviathan shall ascend from the sea, those two great monsters which I created on the fifth day of creation, and shall have kept until that time, and then they shall be food for all that are left' (translation from R. H. Charles, *Apocrypha and Pseudepigrapha*, vol. 2, p. 497); see also 1 Enoch 60:

'And on that day two monsters will be separated from one another: a female monster, whose name (is) Leviathan, to dwell in the depths of the sea above the springs of the waters; and the name of the male (is) Behemoth, who occupies with his breast an immense desert, named Dendayn, on the east of the garden where the chosen and righteous dwell, where my great-grandfather was received, who was the seventh from Adam, the first man whom the Lord of Spirits made. And I asked that other angel to show me the power of those monsters, how they were separated on one day and thrown, one into the depths of the sea, and the other on to the dry ground of the desert' (verses 7–9).

'And the angel of peace who was with me said to me: "These two monsters, prepared for the great day of the Lord, will provide food [possibly 'will be fed'] that the punishment of the Lord of Spirits may rest upon them, that the punishment of the Lord of Spirits may not come in vain"'' (verse 24; the translation of this verse is based on the evidence of a manuscript that has only recently come to light).

For the idea of a banquet at the end of this age see Isa. 25: 6. The tradition about Behemoth and Leviathan makes use of a number of Old Testament motifs, particularly (1) the belief, also found outside the Old Testament, that the act of creation involved the slaying of a monster which was thought to dwell in, or to personify, the sea; cp. e.g. Pss. 74: 12–17; 89: 9–11; eventually this belief was referred to the future and it came to be held that at the day of judgement God would repeat what he had done at creation; see Isa. 27: 1; (2) the passage about Leviathan (N.E.B. 'the whale') in Job 41: 1–6 and Behemoth (N.E.B. 'the crocodile') in Job 40: 15–24 and 41: 7–34 (but see the N.E.B. footnotes and the commentary on Job in this series, pp. 220–7). *a country of a thousand hills:* based on Ps. 50: 10:

'for all the beasts of the forest are mine
and the cattle in thousands on my hills.'

In Jewish tradition 'the cattle' (Hebrew *behemoth*) was taken
as the name of the sea-monster, while the last words of the
verse can be understood as 'on a thousand hills'.

52. *You have kept them to be food for whom you will and when
you will:* cp. 2 Baruch 29: 4 and 1 Enoch 60: 24, quoted above.

53–4. The sixth day. The creation of animals and of Adam;
see Gen. 1: 24–31.

55–9. The author's purpose in retelling the story of creation
is now made clear: it is the prelude to a statement of the
belief that the world was created for Israel's sake. If this is so,
why is Israel controlled and oppressed by other nations and
unable to take possession of the world? The problem is
essentially the same as in the first and second dialogues
(cp. 3: 28–36 and 5: 28–30), but is here made more acute by
being considered within the wider context of God's original
intentions for the nations of the world which he had created.

55. *because you have said that you made this first world for our
sake:* cp. 7: 11. Although not found in the Old Testament,
this belief was current in the first century A.D.; cp. e.g. Assumption of Moses 1: 12, 'For he has created the world on behalf
of his people'; it was based on such passages as Deut. 10:
15–16; 14: 2 which stress Israel's special position among the
nations. *this first world:* the text is uncertain; the Latin, which
may not be in order, has 'the first-born world', one Arabic
version has 'the first world', but the other versions only have
'this (or 'the') world'. If 'first' is original, it serves to emphasize the contrast between this world and the world to come;
see the comment on 4: 26–32.

56. *spittle:* the author was using Isa. 40: 15, but the text
follows the Septuagint version, not the Hebrew. For the end
of the verse the Septuagint has 'and they shall be counted as
spittle', while the Hebrew, in the N.E.B. translation, reads
'coasts and islands weigh as light as specks of dust'. In Hebrew

the words for 'spittle' (*raq*) and 'specks of dust' (*daq*) are very similar. *a drop from a bucket:* cp. Isa. 40: 15*a*:

> 'Why, to him nations are but drops from a bucket,
>   no more than moisture on the scales'

57. *those nations which count for nothing are today ruling over us and devouring us:* the author was no doubt thinking particularly of the Romans.

58. *your first-born:* cp. Exod. 4: 22, 'Israel is my first-born son.' *your only son:* Israel is not so described in the Old Testament, but cp. Psalms of Solomon 18: 4, 'Your discipline is upon us as (upon) a first-born, an only son' (the Psalms of Solomon are a collection of poems belonging in all probability to the mid-first century B.C.; see in this series *The Making of the Old Testament*, pp. 97–8). *your champion:* the meaning of the Latin word (*aemulatorem*) is not clear; it perhaps conveys the idea of being zealous on God's behalf (cp. Num. 25: 10–13; 1 Macc. 2: 24, 26–7). *your best beloved:* the epithet as such is not applied to Israel in the Old Testament, but the thought is commonplace; cp. Hos. 11: 1–4. ✳

THE DIVINE REPLY

7 When I had finished speaking, the same angel was sent
2 to me as on the previous nights. He said to me, 'Rise to your feet, Ezra, and listen to the message I have come to
3 give you.' 'Speak, my lord', I said.

He said to me: 'Imagine a sea set in a vast open space,
4 spreading far*ᵃ* and wide, but the entrance to it narrow like
5 the gorge of a river. If anyone is determined to reach this sea, whether to set eyes on it or to gain command of it, he cannot arrive at its open waters except through the
6 narrow gorge. Or again, imagine a city built in a plain, a

[a] spreading far: *reading based on other Vss.; Lat.* deep.

city full of everything you can desire, but the entrance to 7
it narrow and steep, with fire to the right and deep water
to the left. There is only the one path, between the fire 8
and the water; and that is only wide enough for one man
at a time. If some man has been given this city as a 9
legacy, how can he take possession of his inheritance
except by passing through these dangerous approaches?'
'That is the only way, my lord', I agreed.   10

He said to me: 'Such is the lot of Israel. It was for 11
Israel that I made the world, and when Adam transgressed my decrees the creation came under judgement.
The entrances to this world were made narrow, painful, 12
and arduous, few and evil, full of perils and grinding
hardship. But the entrances to the greater world are 13
broad and safe, and lead to immortality. All men must 14
therefore enter this narrow and futile existence; otherwise they can never attain the blessings in store. Why 15
then, Ezra, are you so deeply disturbed at the thought
that you are mortal and must die? Why have you not 16
turned your mind to the future instead of the present?'

✶ In the reply the author again argues by means of analogy.
The world was indeed made for Israel's sake, but because of
Adam's sin 'creation came under judgement' (verse 11), and
life in this world became full of difficulty. Israel must endure
the difficulties of this world in order to enjoy the blessings of
the world to come.

1. *the same angel was sent to me as on the previous nights:* cp. 4:
1; 5: 31. Although Uriel is sent to Ezra, we again observe in
this dialogue that it is often God who is thought to be speaking to Ezra; cp. e.g. verse 11 and see the comment on 5: 40.

2. *Rise to your feet:* see the comment on 6: 13.

3*b*–10*a*. For the two analogies cp. Matt. 7: 13–14. Both express the same point, that the way to life is narrow and difficult. However, the explanation of the analogies, at least in the text followed by the N.E.B., modifies this theme to some extent; see the comment on verses 12–13.

11. *Such is the lot of Israel:* Ezra's prayer concerned Israel, and the reply refers in the first instance to Israel. But, as we shall see, the debate is very rapidly widened in scope.

12–13. *The entrances to this world . . . But the entrances to the greater world: entrances* hardly seems the right word in either case because the picture suggested by the two analogies (and below in verse 18) is of this world itself as the entrance to the world to come. Possibly *entrances* was copied by mistake because of the occurrence of the word in verses 4 and 7. There is some evidence for a variant reading 'ways', and it would be easier to make sense of this as referring to the life of this world and of the future world.

12. *narrow, painful, and arduous, few and evil, full of perils and grinding hardship:* cp. Gen. 3: 17–19.

14. *All men* (literally 'the living'): it is significant that the author no longer speaks of 'Israel'; contrast verse 11. From this point on in the third dialogue it is the fate, not of Israel, but of mankind in general that is at issue.

15–16. A further change of emphasis can be observed in these verses which have traditionally been seen as marking a turning-point in the structure of 2 Esdras 3–14. Ezra is reproved for occupying himself with *the present* rather than *the future*, and the remainder of 2 Esdras 3–14 is in fact largely concerned with the future – the fate of men, the end of this world, and the transition to the world to come. But it is the problems raised by his beliefs about the future that the author takes up first. ✳

THE JUSTICE OF GOD'S DEALINGS WITH MEN

'My lord, my master,' I replied, 'in your law you have 17 laid it down that the just shall come to enjoy these blessings but the ungodly shall be lost. The just, therefore, 18 can endure this narrow life and look for the spacious life hereafter; but those who have lived a wicked life will have gone through the narrows without ever reaching the open spaces.'

He said to me: 'You are not a better judge than God, 19 nor wiser than the Most High. Better that many now 20 living should be lost, than that the law God has set before them should be despised! God has given clear instructions 21 for all men when they come into this world, telling them how to attain life and how to escape punishment. But the 22 ungodly have refused to obey him; they have set up their own empty ideas, and planned deceit and wickedness; 23 they have even denied the existence of the Most High and have not acknowledged his ways. They have re- 24 jected his law and refused his promises, have neither put faith in his decrees nor done what he commands. There- 25 fore, Ezra, emptiness for the empty, fullness for the full!

* 17–18. Ezra does not dispute what has just been said to him, but uses the language of the analogies to raise a further problem. He argues in effect that the wicked are treated unfairly. It is all very well for *the just* to have to *endure this narrow life*, because they ultimately attain *the spacious life hereafter*. But the wicked suffer the difficulties of this world without receiving any compensation. The underlying concern here, and throughout much of the third dialogue, is whether the punishment of the wicked, for the author of

2 Esdras 3–14 the majority of mankind, can be reconciled with God's justice. *in your law:* the words that follow are not of course a quotation from the Pentateuch, but the idea contained in them reflects a basic principle of the legislation of Deuteronomy.

19–25. The answer is blunt; it is man's own fault. God had given men the law which was the means by which they could have obtained salvation, but the refusal of men to obey the law made their punishment inevitable.

20. *Better that many . . . should be lost, than that the law . . . should be despised:* the uncompromising tone of these words reflects the importance attached by the author to the law.

21. *God has given clear instructions:* i.e. in the law revealed to Moses at Sinai.

23. *they have even denied the existence of the Most High:* cp. 8: 58; Pss. 14: 1; 53: 1.

25. *emptiness for the empty, fullness for the full:* Ezra's sympathy for the wicked (verse 17–18) is sharply rejected; it is quite right that the wicked perish, and the righteous are rewarded. Cp. Mark 4: 25 (and parallels), 'For the man who has will be given more, and the man who has not will forfeit even what he has.' ✳

THE MESSIANIC KINGDOM AND THE JUDGEMENT

26 'Listen! The time shall come when the signs I have foretold will be seen; the city which is now invisible[a] shall appear and the country now concealed be made 27 visible. Everyone who has been delivered from the evils I have foretold shall see for himself my marvellous acts. 28 My son the Messiah[b] shall appear with his companions and bring four hundred years of happiness to all who 29 survive. At the end of that time, my son the Messiah shall

[a] *So some Vss.; Lat.* the city, the bride, which is now seen . . .
[b] *So some Vss.; Lat.* My son Jesus.

die, and so shall all mankind who draw breath. Then the 30
world shall return to its original silence for seven days as
at the beginning of creation, and no one shall be left
alive. After seven days the age which is not yet awake 31
shall be roused and the age which is corruptible shall die.
The earth shall give up those who sleep in it, and the dust 32
those who rest there in silence; and the storehouses shall
give back the souls entrusted to them. Then the Most 33
High shall be seen on the judgement-seat, and there shall
be an end of all pity and patience. Judgement alone shall 34
remain; truth shall stand firm and faithfulness be strong;
requital*a* shall at once begin and open payment be made; 35
good deeds shall awake and wicked deeds shall not be
allowed to sleep.*b* Then the place of torment shall appear, [36]
and over against it the place of rest; the furnace of hell
shall be displayed, and on the opposite side the paradise
of delight.

'Then the Most High shall say to the nations that have [37]
been raised from the dead: "Look and understand who
it is you have denied and refused to serve, and whose
commandment you have despised. Look on this side, [38]
then on that: here are rest and delight, there fire and
torments." That is what he will say to them on the day
of judgement.

'That day will be a day without sun, moon, or stars; [39]
without cloud, thunder, or lightning; wind, water, or [40]
air; darkness, evening, or morning; without summer, [41]
spring, or winter; without heat, frost, or cold; without

---

[a] *Probable meaning; literally* work.
[b] *The passage from verse* [36] *to verse* [105], *missing from the text of the Authorized Version, but found in ancient witnesses, has been restored.*

[42] hail, rain, or dew; without noonday, night, or dawn; without brightness, glow, or light. There shall be only the radiant glory of the Most High, by which all men [43] will see everything that lies before them. It shall last as [44] it were for a week of years. Such is the order that I have appointed for the Judgement. I have given this revelation to you alone.'

* The argument breaks off and is not resumed until verse 45. Instead we are given more information about the end, more precisely about the reign of the Messiah which will mark the end of the present age, and about the judgement which will follow. Like the passages on the signs (see the comment on 4: 51–2) this passage has sometimes been thought to have been interpolated by the final editor of 2 Esdras 3–14. However, it follows fairly naturally on what precedes and is best understood as going some way to explain what 'emptiness for the empty, fullness for the full' means. Throughout the third dialogue argument and information about the end are interwoven, and it seems unlikely that verses 26–[44] are not original in their context.

26–30. *The reign of the Messiah.* Jews of the intertestamental period had no single belief about what would happen when God brought this age to an end. Thus sometimes it was thought that at the end there would be a great battle in which God's enemies would be destroyed (cp. Ezek. 38–9), and sometimes that there would be a trial in which the wicked would be found guilty and condemned to punishment (cp. Dan. 7: 9–12). Again, sometimes it was thought that God would act on his own, and sometimes that he would make use of an agent (here there is the added complication that there was no single idea of what kind of person the agent would be, what he would do, or what he would be called). Finally, sometimes it was thought that the new age would be more or less a continuation of the present age, only conditions

on earth would be perfect, and sometimes that there would
be a radical break between this age and the new age. It is
characteristic of 2 Esdras 3–14 that the author has combined
several of these different ideas to produce a distinctive
pattern of his own. The end of this age will be marked by the
four-hundred-year rule of the Messiah. Then, following the
death of the Messiah and a period of silence for seven days,
there will be the great last judgement. Only after this does
the new age begin. A comparable pattern of expectation,
but adapted to Christian beliefs, occurs in Rev. 20.

26. *the signs:* those described in 5: 1–12 and 6: 18b–28.
More signs are described in 9: 1–6. *the city which is now
invisible:* the heavenly Jerusalem; cp. 8: 52; 10: 27, 38–55;
13: 36. The expectation of a new Jerusalem no doubt reflects
the circumstances in which the book was written, namely
at a time when the city lay in ruins as a result of its destruction
by the Romans (cp. the prophecies concerning the rebuilding
of Jerusalem which followed its earlier destruction by the
Babylonians; see e.g. Isa. 54: 11–17; Zech. 2: 1–5). The text
of the Latin version, given in the N.E.B. footnote, has
possibly been influenced by Rev. 21: 2, 'I saw the holy city,
new Jerusalem, coming down out of heaven from God, made
ready like a bride adorned for her husband.' *the country now
concealed:* the heavenly paradise; see the comment on verse
[36]. It is a little surprising that the heavenly Jerusalem and
paradise should be mentioned just at this point, i.e. as if they
belonged to the period of the reign of the Messiah, since
elsewhere in 2 Esdras 3–14 they clearly belong to the new age
itself, and this latter only begins after the end of the messianic
kingdom. However, inconsistencies of this kind occur elsewhere in 2 Esdras 3–14, and it is a mistake to expect that the
events of the end should always be presented in a strictly
logical order. For the heavenly Jerusalem and the heavenly
paradise in combination cp. 8: 52.

27. *Everyone who has been delivered . . . shall see for himself my
marvellous acts:* cp. 6: 25.

28. *the Messiah:* the term 'Messiah', a transliteration of the Hebrew word meaning 'anointed', is used in the Old Testament in the first instance as a title of the king (cp. e.g. 1 Sam. 24: 6, 'the LORD's anointed'). However, when the monarchy ceased to exist the title was transferred to the high priest (cp. e.g. Lev. 4: 3, 'the anointed priest'), while at the same time passages mentioning the anointed king (cp. e.g. Ps. 2) were interpreted to refer to an ideal ruler of the future who, so it was held, would restore the fortunes of Israel. By the time of the intertestamental period 'Messiah' was used almost in a technical way as a title for this ideal ruler; cp. e.g., apart from 2 Esdras 3-14, 1 Enoch 48: 10, a passage which refers to the wicked, 'for they denied the Lord of Spirits and his Messiah'; 2 Baruch 72: 2, 'After the signs have come, of which thou wast told before, when the nations become turbulent, and the time of My Messiah is come, he shall both summon all the nations, and some of them he shall spare, and some of them he shall slay' (translation from R. H. Charles, *Apocrypha and Pseudepigrapha*, vol. 2, p. 518). As a quasi-technical term, 'Messiah' has to be ranged alongside other titles, e.g. 'Son of David' (see Matt. 12: 23), 'Son of Man' (see Mark 8: 38), which are applied to the agent who, it was believed, would act on God's behalf when this age was brought to an end. The functions assigned to the figures bearing these titles are not precisely defined, but to some extent overlap, and it is important that each writing in which a concept such as that of the Messiah occurs should be considered carefully on its own merits. In the case of 2 Esdras 3-14 the role of the Messiah is described not only here, but also in 12: 31-4 and 13: 25-52 (in this last passage called 'my son'). From these other passages it emerges that one important function of the Messiah in 2 Esdras 3-14 was to judge and destroy the Romans and other nations (cp. Ps. 2: 8-9 which refers to the 'anointed king'). The judgement and destruction of the nations by the Messiah (apparently at the beginning of his reign) is in addition to the judgement of all men by God at the end of this age.

Here the task of the Messiah is to *bring four hundred years of happiness*; this is an allusion to the reign of the Messiah; cp. 12: 34. There is a description of the idyllic conditions that will exist on earth in the reign of the Messiah in 2 Baruch 73–4. In assigning a role to a Messiah the author of 2 Esdras 3–14 has taken over a traditional idea; the fact that he has done so is best understood as a further reaction to the political and physical circumstances in which the Jews in Palestine were living at the time at which he wrote. *My son the Messiah:* the fact that the Messiah is called 'my son' (cp. 13: 32, 37, 52; 14: 9) is possibly because of a deliberate Christian alteration to the text; this is clearly the case in the Latin version which reads 'My son Jesus' (see the N.E.B. footnote). In 1 Enoch 105: 1 'my son' is also used as a messianic title, but again Christian influence cannot be excluded. On the other hand the messianic interpretation of Ps. 2 (see above), in which God says of the anointed king 'You are my son' (verse 7; cp. Acts 13: 33), provides a possible Jewish background for the use of this title, and it may be wrong to suspect Christian influence. *his companions:* cp. 13: 52, 'his company'. Possibly angels are meant (cp. 2 Thess. 1: 7) or the men, such as Enoch and Elijah, 'who were taken up into heaven without ever knowing death' (6: 26). *four hundred years:* it was not only the author of 2 Esdras 3–14 who assigned this length to the reign of the Messiah; the same idea is also found in some rabbinic sayings, where it emerges that the figure is based on a combination of Gen. 15: 13, 'your descendants will be aliens living in a land that is not theirs; they will be slaves, and will be held in oppression there for four hundred years', and Ps. 90: 15:

'Repay us days of gladness for our days of suffering,
for the years thou hast humbled us.'

(The sense is 'as many as the days . . . as many as the years . . .')
In Christian tradition (Rev. 20: 4) Christ is to reign for a thousand years, and one of the Arabic versions of 2 Esdras 3–14, which has been influenced by this Christian view, has

'one thousand' instead of 'four hundred'. *who survive:* i.e. who survive the horrors described in 5: 1–12 and 6: 18*b*–28.

29. *my son the Messiah shall die:* the reign of the Messiah is quite explicitly of limited duration; it is merely the prelude to the last judgement and the new age which the judgement inaugurates.

30. The world will return to the condition of silence that existed at the time of creation; cp. 6: 39. The *seven days* correspond to the week of creation; the end of this world will be the same as its beginning.

31–[44]. The last judgement. This is held by God on all men, who for this purpose will have risen from the dead.

31. *the age which is not yet awake . . . the age which is corruptible:* the new age and the present age.

32. The resurrection of the dead. *the storehouses:* cp. verse [95] and the comment on 4: 35–6. *shall give back the souls entrusted to them:* cp. 4: 42.

33*a. the Most High shall be seen on the judgement-seat:* cp. Dan. 7: 9–10 and the repeated descriptions of judgement in 1 Enoch 37–71, e.g. 47: 3, 'And in those days I saw the Head of Days sit down on the throne of his glory, and the books of the living were opened before him, and all his host, which (dwells) in the heavens above, and his council were standing before him.'

33*b*–34. God's judgement will be in accordance with the strictest standards of impartiality.

35. *good deeds . . . wicked deeds:* the good and wicked deeds of men on which the judgement will be based will be revealed.

[36–105]. This passage was deliberately removed from the Latin manuscript on which nearly all the surviving Latin manuscripts are dependent because it contains a denial of the value of prayers for the dead (cp. verses [102–5]). However, the Latin version of this passage was discovered in the last century, and it has also been preserved in the other versions.

[36]. The places in which men will be finally punished or rewarded are pictured as being opposite each other. The two

halves of the verse are parallel and thus *the place of torment* is
the same as *the furnace of hell*, and *the place of rest* the same as
the paradise of delight. the furnace of hell: literally 'the furnace of
Gehenna'. 'Gehenna' is the Greek and Latin form of the
Hebrew *ge' hinnom* ('Valley of Hinnom'), the name of a
valley to the south of Jerusalem which was also known as
ge' ben-hinnom ('Valley of Ben-hinnom'). In the latter part
of the monarchical period this valley was used for the sacrifice
of children by fire, and because of this it was desecrated by
Josiah (see 2 Kings 23: 10) and condemned by Jeremiah;
see Jer. 7: 31–2:

> '(the men of Judah) have built a shrine of Topheth in the
> Valley of Ben-hinnom, at which to burn their sons and
> daughters; that was no command of mine, nor did it ever
> enter my thought. Therefore a time is coming, says the
> LORD, when it shall no longer be called Topheth or the
> Valley of Ben-hinnom, but the Valley of Slaughter.'

Because of its evil associations, and the reputation it was given
by Jeremiah, the valley later became in Jewish thought the
traditional place of final punishment where the wicked
would burn for ever; cp. e.g. Matt. 5: 22; 18: 9 (where the
N.E.B. translates 'Gehenna' by 'hell'); 1 Enoch 27: 2–3:

> 'This accursed valley is for those who are cursed for ever;
> here will be gathered together all who speak with their
> mouths against the Lord words that are not fitting and say
> hard things about his glory. Here they will gather them
> together, and here (will be) their place of judgement. And
> in the last days there will be the spectacle of the righteous
> judgement upon them before the righteous for ever, for
> evermore.'

In 1 Enoch 90: 26–7, within the context of an allegorical
account of the last judgement (90: 20–7), there is a vivid
description of an abyss of fire to the south of Jerusalem in
which wicked Israelites were punished:

'And I saw at that time how a similar abyss was opened in the middle of the earth which was full of fire, and they brought those blind sheep, and they were all judged and found guilty and thrown into that abyss of fire, and they burned; and that abyss was on the south of that house. And I saw those sheep burning, and their bones were burning' (the 'blind sheep' are wicked Israelites, and the 'house' is Jerusalem).

the paradise of delight: the word *paradise* is derived from *pairidaêza,* a Persian word which simply means 'garden'. In the intertestamental period this word was used to refer both to the garden where Adam and Eve dwelt (cp. 3: 6) and to the place of bliss where the righteous will dwell in the future. But these conceptions overlap, and even where the future reference is predominant, the word is not used with any precision in the different writings where it occurs. In 2 Esdras 3–14 it refers primarily to the place where the righteous will dwell in the world to come, i.e. to the final place of rest of the righteous; cp. verse [123] and 8: 52; cp. also Rev. 2: 7, 'To him who is victorious I will give the right to eat from the tree of life that stands in the Garden (Greek 'paradise'; see above) of God.'

[39–42a]. Cp. Gen. 8:22:

> 'While the earth lasts
> seedtime and harvest, cold and heat,
> summer and winter, day and night,
> shall never cease.'

The day of judgement will bring an end to the conditions that obtain 'while the earth lasts'; instead conditions will be as they were before creation.

[42b]. *the radiant glory of the Most High:* cp. Isa. 60: 19–20; Rev. 21: 23 – but these passages are not concerned with the day of judgement, but with the replacement of ordinary light (sun and moon) by the light of God's presence in the new age.

[43]. *a week of years:* i.e. seven years. The duration of the judgement apparently corresponds to the length of time it took for the world to be created (cp. verse 30), but with each day as the equivalent of one year. This follows the principle of Dan. 9: 2, 24–7 in which the seventy years of Jer. 25: 11–12; 29: 10 are reinterpreted as seventy weeks of years.

[44]. *revelation to you alone:* cp. 12: 36; 13: 53–6. *

THE ARGUMENT RESUMED

I replied: 'My lord, I repeat what I said before: "How [45] blest are the living who obey the decrees you have laid down!" But as for those for whom I have been praying, [46] is there any man alive who has never sinned, any man who has never transgressed your covenant? I see now that [47] there are few to whom the world to come will bring happiness, and many to whom it will bring torment. For [48] the wicked heart has grown up in us, which has estranged us from God's ways,*a* brought us into corruption and the way of death, opened out to us the paths of ruin, and carried us far away from life. It has done this, not merely to a few, but to almost all who have been created.'

The angel replied: 'Listen to me and I will give you [49] further instruction and correction. It is for this reason [50] that the Most High has created not one world but two. There are, you say, not many who are just, but only a [51] few, whereas the wicked are very numerous; well then, hear the answer. Suppose you had a very few precious [52] stones; would you add to their number by putting common lead and clay among them*b*?' 'No,' I said, 'no one [53]

[a] *Literally* from these things.
[b] by putting...them: *probable reading, based on other Vss.; Lat. obscure.*

[54] would do that.' 'Look at it also in this way,' he continued; 'speak to the earth and humbly ask her; she will
[55] give you the answer. Say to her: "You produce gold,
[56] silver, and copper, iron, lead, and clay. There is more silver than gold, more copper than silver, more iron than
[57] copper, more lead than iron, more clay than lead." Then judge for yourself which things are valuable and desirable – those that are common, or those that are rare.'
[58] 'My lord, my master,' I said, 'the common things are
[59] cheaper, and the rarer are more valuable.' He replied, 'Consider then what follows from that: the owner of something hard to get has more cause to be pleased than
[60] the owner of what is common. In the same way, at my promised judgement,[a] I shall have joy in the few who are saved, because it is they who have made my glory prevail, and through them that my name has been made known.
[61] But I shall not grieve for the many who are lost; for they are no more than a vapour, they are like flame or smoke; they catch fire, blaze up, and then die out.'

✶ [45–8]. The argument of verses 17–25 is now resumed, and Ezra takes up once more the point he had made in verses 17–18. It is all very well for those who keep God's laws, but is there anyone who has not sinned? The world to come will bring torment to almost all mankind, and implicitly Ezra asks whether this can be justified.

[45]. *I repeat what I said before:* the allusion is to verse 17, although the following words are not an exact quotation.

[46–8]. Ezra hesitates between the view that all men are doomed to perish because they have sinned, and the view that a very few men may escape this fate to enjoy

[a] *Reading based on other Vss.; Lat.* creation.

the life of the world to come, but elsewhere in his speeches it is the former idea that is predominant (cp. 8: 35). By contrast the angel consistently takes the view that men are capable of earning their own salvation and is quite unconcerned that only a few will do so. The tension between the views of Ezra and the angel appears to represent a tension within the mind of the author himself, a tension that is never completely resolved, and on this matter the debate ends in something of an impasse; cp. 9: 14–16 with 9: 22 and see the comments on both passages.

[48]. *the wicked heart:* see the comment on 3: 16–22.

[49–61]. The angel once more uses an analogy to argue that it corresponds to a 'law of nature' that only a few are saved. A question-and-answer method is used, and the argument is split into three sections: (1) it would be wrong to increase the number of the saved by adding the wicked to them (verses [51–3]); (2) things that are precious are by nature few in number (verses [54–8]); (3) a consequence of this is that it is entirely right to rejoice over the few who will be saved rather than to worry about the many who will perish (verses [59–61]). An argument from nature of this kind has already been used in 5: 45–9. For the attitude reflected in the words of the angel cp. Matt. 22: 14, 'For though many are invited, few are chosen', and contrast the thought of the parables in Luke 15: 1–10 which emphasize God's concern that the very last sinner should be saved; cp. especially verse 7, 'there will be greater joy in heaven over one sinner who repents than over ninety-nine righteous people who do not need to repent'.

[49]. The angel again begins his reply in the manner of a wisdom teacher; see the comment on 5: 32.

[50]. *It is for this reason:* i.e. because the majority of men are wicked. The angel implicitly accepts that Ezra's analysis of the situation (verses [45–8]) is correct, as the words of verse [51] make clear. *the Most High has created not one world but two:* a fundamental statement of the belief in the two

175

ages; cp. 8: 1 and the comment on 4: 26–32. It was because the majority of men were sinners that God had to create not only this world (for the many sinners), but also the world to come (for the few righteous). The creation of the two ages was predetermined by God because of his knowledge of the way men would act in this world (cp. verses [70] and [74]).

[54–8]. For the analogy cp. also 8: 2–3.

[61]. *vapour . . . flame or smoke:* cp. Hos. 13: 3 (with reference to the idolaters in the northern kingdom):

'Therefore they shall be like the morning mist
   or like dew that vanishes early,
like chaff blown from the threshing-floor
   or smoke from a chimney.'   ✶

THE PITIABLE FATE OF MEN

[62] Then I said: 'Mother Earth, what have you brought forth! Is the mind of man, like the rest of creation, a [63] product of the dust? Far better then if the very dust had never been created, and so had never produced man's [64] mind! But, as it is, we grow up with the power of thought and are tortured by it; we are doomed to die [65] and we know it. What sorrow for mankind; what happiness for the wild beasts! What sorrow for every mother's [66] son; what gladness for the cattle and flocks! How much better their lot than ours! They have no judgement to expect, no knowledge of torment or salvation after death. [67] What good to us is the promise of a future life if it is [68] going to be one of torment? For every man alive is burdened and defiled with wickedness, a sinner through [69] and through. Would it not have been better for us if there had been no judgement awaiting us after death?'

176

The angel replied: 'When the Most High was creating [70] the world and Adam and his descendants, he first of all planned the judgement and what goes with it. Your own [71] words, when you said that man grows up with the power of thought, will give you the answer. It was with con- [72] scious knowledge that the people of this world sinned, and that is why torment awaits them; they received the commandments but did not keep them, they accepted the law but violated it. What defence will they be able to [73] make at the judgement, what answer at the last day? How patient the Most High has been with the men of [74] this world, and for how long! – not for their own sake, but for the sake of the destined age to be.'

---

* [62–9]. In the face of the seemingly heartless attitude of the angel, Ezra laments that it would have been better if man had been born without a mind, because he not only has to face the judgement, but to live his life in the conscious expectation of it. The lot of the animals, who have no expectation of a future judgement, appears in these circumstances to be superior to that of men. In any case the whole idea of a future life with the theoretical possibility of reward or punishment seems pointless if, in fact, punishment is to be the fate of all men, and Ezra questions whether it would not have been better if there had been no judgement at all.

[62–3]. *Is the mind of man, like the rest of creation, a product of the dust?*: in the Latin a conditional sentence; the N.E.B. has conveyed the sense by turning it into a rhetorical question expecting the answer Yes. The allusion is to Gen. 2: 7, 'Then the LORD God formed a man from the dust of the ground' and Gen. 2: 19, 'So God formed out of the ground all the wild animals and all the birds of heaven.' Since *the mind of man*, like man himself and the other creatures, is *a product of the dust*, it would have been better *if the very dust had never*

177

been created, and so had never produced man's mind! Cp. 7: [116], where the creation of man himself is despaired of, and 4: 12.

[65–66a]. The idea that the *lot* of animals is superior to that of men is in sharp contrast with Gen. 1: 26–8 where man, whose creation forms the climax of all God's acts of creation, is placed in charge of the animals.

[67–8]. Here Ezra comes down quite definitely on the side of the view that all men have sinned and therefore are doomed to eternal punishment; see the comments on verses [46–8].

[70–4]. The reply of the angel consists largely of a reiteration of the view, already stated in verses 19–25, that it is man's own fault that he faces condemnation and eternal punishment; man had knowingly sinned, although he had been given the law, and would therefore have no defence to offer on the day of judgement.

[70]. *he first of all planned the judgement:* the angel begins by taking up, and bluntly dismissing, the point Ezra had made last of all. There is no question of there not being a judgement; it belongs amongst the things determined by God when he *was creating the world. and what goes with it:* probably a reference to paradise and Gehenna (cp. verse [36]) which, according to rabbinic teaching, were created before the world was made.

[71–2]. *Your own words ... will give you the answer:* as in 8: 37–40 (cp. 8: 26–30) the angel turns Ezra's own words against him. The fact that *man grows up with the power of thought,* far from being a reason for lamenting his fate, is a reason why he deserves to be punished, for he can legitimately be accused of sinning *with conscious knowledge. the commandments ... the law:* cp. 3: 19–22. The law given at Sinai offered the means of salvation, but men had quite consciously not observed it.

[73]. *the last day:* i.e. the day of judgement.

[74]. God had, in fact, so far dealt very patiently with men, but this was *not for their own sake, but for the sake of the destined age to be.* As is emphasized elsewhere in 2 Esdras 3–14,

God's dealings with this world are in accordance with his
predetermined plan (cp. the comment on 4: 37). *

THE FATE OF MEN AFTER DEATH

Then I said: 'If I have won your favour, my lord, make [75]
this plain to me: at death, when every one of us gives
back his soul, shall we be kept at rest until the time when
you begin to create your new world, or does our torment
begin at once?' 'I will tell you that also', he replied. 'But [76]
do not include yourself among those who have despised
my law; do not count yourself with those who are to
be tormented. For you have a treasure of good works [77]
stored up with the Most High, though you will not be
shown it until the last days. But now to speak of death: [78]
when the Most High has given final sentence for a man
to die, the spirit leaves the body to return to the One who
gave it, and first of all to adore the glory of the Most
High. But as for those who have rejected the ways of the [79]
Most High and despised his law, and who hate all that
fear God, their spirits enter no settled abode, but roam [80]
thenceforward in torment, grief, and sorrow. And this
for seven reasons. First, they have despised the law of the [81]
Most High. Secondly, they have lost their last chance of [82]
making a good repentance and so gaining life. Thirdly, [83]
they can see the reward in store for those who have
trusted the covenants of the Most High. Fourthly, they [84]
begin to think of the torment that awaits them at the end.
Fifthly, they see that angels are guarding the abode of the [85]
other souls in deep silence. Sixthly, they see that they are [86]
soon*a* to enter into torment. The seventh cause for grief, [87]

[a] *So some Vss.; Lat. obscure.*

179

the strongest cause of all, is this: at the sight of the Most High in his glory, they break down in shame, waste away in remorse, and shrivel with fear remembering how they sinned against him in their lifetime, and how they are soon to be brought before him for judgement on the last day.

[88]   'As for those who have kept to the way laid down by the Most High, this is what is appointed for them when [89] their time comes to leave their mortal bodies. During their stay on earth they served the Most High in spite of constant hardship and danger, and kept to the last letter [90] the law given them by the lawgiver. Their reward is this: [91] first they shall exult to see the glory of God who will receive them as his own, and then they shall enter into [92] rest in seven appointed stages of joy. Their first joy is their victory in the long fight against their inborn impulses to evil, which have failed to lead them astray from [93] life into death. Their second joy is to see the souls of the wicked wandering ceaselessly, and the punishment in [94] store for them. Their third joy is the good report given of them by their Maker, that throughout their life they [95] kept the law with which they were entrusted. Their fourth joy is to understand the rest which they are now to share in the storehouses, guarded by angels in deep silence, and the glory waiting for them in the next age. [96] Their fifth joy is the contrast between the corruptible world they have escaped and the future life that is to be their possession, between the cramped laborious*a* life from which they have been set free and the spacious life which [97] will soon be theirs to enjoy for ever and ever. Their sixth

[a] *So some Vss.; Lat. obscure.*

180

joy will be the revelation that they are to shine like stars, never to fade or die, with faces radiant as the sun. Their [98] seventh joy, the greatest joy of all, will be the confident and exultant assurance which will be theirs, free from all fear and shame, as they press forward to see face to face the One whom they served in their lifetime, and from whom they are now to receive their reward in glory.

'The joys I have been declaring are the appointed [99] destiny for the souls of the just; the torments I described before are the sufferings appointed for the rebellious.'

Then I asked: 'When souls are separated from their [100] bodies, will they be given the opportunity to see what you have described to me?' 'They will be allowed seven [101] days,' he replied; 'for seven days they will be permitted to see the things I have told you, and after that they will join the other souls in their abodes.'

---

* The argument is once more interrupted, to be resumed this time only in verse [116]. But again, as in the case of verses 26–[44], the digression is not irrelevant to its context. In the previous section (verses [62–74]) the discussion centred on the fact that mankind, considered by Ezra in its totality to be sinful, was destined to suffer torment. Now Ezra asks for more information about this torment, in particular whether it takes effect at the moment of death or only at the beginning of the new age (verse [75]). In a long reply (verses [76–99]) the angel first rejects the implication in the question that Ezra belongs amongst the sinners and then contrasts the differing fates of the wicked and the righteous in the interval between death and the last judgement. The information is supplemented in a further question and answer (verses [100–1]).

[75]. *If I have won your favour, my lord:* see the comment

on 5: 56. *the time when you begin to create your new world* (literally 'to renew the creation'): for the idea cp. Rev. 21: 1, 'Then I saw a new heaven and a new earth, for the first heaven and the first earth had vanished.' The time when the new age begins is, of course, also the time when the last judgement will occur; cp. verses 31–3.

[76]. A comparable injunction not to class himself with the sinners occurs in 8: 47–9. For Ezra's righteous standing before God see also the comment on 6: 32–3.

[77]. *a treasure of good works:* the author of 2 Esdras 3–14, in common with other Jews of his day, believed that by the strict observance of the law it was possible for an individual to acquire, as it were, a credit balance of good works and to earn thereby the reward in the world to come of life; cp. 8: 33, 'For the reward which will be given to the just, who have many good works stored up with thee, will be no more than their own deeds have earned.' One important way in which such a treasure could be acquired was by the giving of alms, as is indicated in the words of Jesus in Luke 12: 33, 'Sell your possessions and give in charity. Provide for yourselves purses that do not wear out, and never-failing treasure in heaven.' But in this matter the author of 2 Esdras 3–14 regarded 'faith' or 'fidelity' (in the Latin the same word is used) as being equally important; cp. 9: 7, 'Whoever comes safely through and escapes destruction, thanks to his good deeds or the faith he has shown', and see also 6: 5; 13: 23 (what is apparently intended in these passages is faithfulness to the law, although this is not made explicit). However, Ezra was one of the very few who would earn salvation in this way. The author struggled to believe that there would be others who would take part in the life of the world to come as a result of God's mercy (cp. 7: [132–40], especially verses [137–40]), but in the end seems to have been unable to accept this; see further the comment on 7: [132] – 8: 3. *until the last days:* i.e. at the judgement; cp. verse 35.

[78]. At death the spirits of all men initially return to God

in order to appear before him for a brief moment to worship
him. Thereafter the fates of the wicked and the righteous
are very different. *the spirit leaves the body to return to the One
who gave it:* cp. Eccles. 12: 7, 'before the dust returns to the
earth as it began and the spirit returns to God who gave it',
and Gen. 2: 7, 'Then the LORD God formed a man from the
dust of the ground and breathed into his nostrils the breath of
life.'

[79–98]. The two passages which set out the fates of the
wicked and the righteous (verses [79–87] and [88–98]) have a
similar form in that the suffering or joy which the individual
experiences after death is in each case described in seven
stages. These seven stages have been taken as a refinement of
an older belief in seven hells and seven heavens (there is a
description of the seven heavens in the Testament of Levi
2: 7 – 3: 10); but seven was in any case regarded as a significant number, and there may be no more to the use of seven
in these descriptions in 2 Esdras 3–14 than this. (The Testament of Levi forms part of the Testaments of the Twelve
Patriarchs, in its present form a Christian work of the second
century A.D., but containing much older Jewish material.)

[79–87]. The wicked. In the interval between death and
the last judgement the spirits of the wicked, unlike those of
the righteous, have 'no settled abode', but wander about
'in torment, grief, and sorrow' (verse [80]). To this extent
the answer to Ezra's question (verse [75]) is that torment
begins at death. However, it is made clear that a far worse torment awaits the wicked after the last judgement; see verses [84]
and [86] and the comment on verse [36]. The reasons for the
anguish which the wicked suffer in the interim are described
in verses [81–7].

[85]. *in deep silence:* see the comment on verse [95].

[87]. *at the sight of the Most High:* cp. verse [78].

[88–98]. The righteous. As we have already learnt (see 4:
35), the righteous spend the interval between death and the
last judgement in 'storehouses' where they are guarded by

angels (see verse [95]); they are in a state of joy and look
forward to the life of glory which awaits them in the world
to come. The seven stages of their joy are described in verses
[92–8].

[88]. *to leave their mortal bodies:* implicit here is the view
that the body is merely the prison of the soul, and nothing
further is said about the body after death. By contrast, in 1 Cor.
15: 53 Paul argues that at the resurrection men's bodies will
undergo transformation: 'This perishable being must be
clothed with the imperishable, and what is mortal must be
clothed with immortality.'

[91]. *first they shall exult to see the glory of God:* cp. verse
[78].

[92]. *their inborn impulses to evil:* another term for the evil
inclination which leads men to commit sin; see the comment
on the 'wicked heart' (3: 20) in the discussion on 3: 16–22.
from life into death: life and death in the world to come are
meant. Those who succeed in the struggle against the inclination to evil are able to rejoice because they have not lost their
place in the new age.

[93]. *Their second joy is to see ... the punishment:* cp. Ps.
118: 7:

'The LORD is on my side, he is my helper,
and I shall gloat over my enemies.'

[95]. *the rest which they are now to share in the storehouses,
guarded by angels in deep silence:* after death the souls of the
righteous wait for the resurrection and the day of judgement
in storehouses; cp. 4: 35, 'the righteous in the storehouse of
souls' ask how long they are to stay there, and 7: 32, on the
day of judgement 'the storehouses shall give back the souls
(i.e. of the righteous) entrusted to them'; cp. also 7: [85],
[101], where this same place is referred to as an 'abode'.
Comparable ideas about the fate of the righteous after death
are to be found in other Jewish writings of the period. Thus
e.g. in 1 Enoch 22, both righteous and wicked wait for the day

of judgement in a special place in the west of the earth; this place is divided into four sections (two for the righteous, and two for the wicked), and, as in Dan. 12: 2, not all rise from the dead. According to 2 Baruch the righteous wait in 'treasuries' in much the same way as in 2 Esdras 3–14; cp. e.g. 30: 2,

'Then (i.e. when the Messiah returns in glory) all who have fallen asleep in hope of Him shall rise again. And it shall come to pass at that time that the treasuries will be opened in which is preserved the number of the souls of the righteous, and they shall come forth'

(translation from R. H. Charles, *Apocrypha and Pseudepigrapha*, vol. 2, p. 498).

in deep silence: 'quietness' rather than 'silence' would better convey the sense, as the Syriac version makes explicit. After death the righteous enjoy their rest undisturbed by the cares and troubles of this life.

[96]. *between the cramped laborious life ... and the spacious life:* cp. 7: 3b–16 and 17–18.

[97]. *to shine like stars:* cp. Dan. 12: 2–3:

'many of those who sleep in the dust ... will wake ...
The wise leaders shall shine like the bright vault of heaven,
    and those who have guided the people in the true path
    shall be like the stars for ever and ever.'

[98]. *to see face to face the One whom they served:* cp. 1 John 3: 2, 'we know that when he appears (see the N.E.B. footnote) we shall be like him, because we shall see him as he is'.
their reward: see 8: 33 and the comment on 7: [77].

[100–1]. Although not made explicit, it is clear that this question and answer refer only to the souls of the righteous because, as we now know, the souls of the wicked have no abode, but wander about continually until the day of judgement (see verse [80]). *They will be allowed seven days:* an old tradition probably underlies this idea. Cp. the Greek version of the

Life of Adam (a Jewish work which apparently dates from
before A.D. 70) 43 : 3, 'You shall not mourn beyond six days,
but on the seventh day rest and be joyful, for on that day God
and we angels rejoice with the righteous soul that has departed
from the earth.' What is implied here is that the righteous
soul only enters God's presence on the seventh day. This is
not an exact parallel, but it does indicate that the seven days
after death was a traditional length of time.   ✻

THE RIGHTEOUS CANNOT INTERCEDE
FOR THE WICKED

[102]   Then I asked: 'If I have won your favour, my lord,
tell me more. On the day of judgement will the just be
able to win pardon for the wicked, or pray for them to
[103] the Most High? Can fathers do so for their sons, or sons
for their parents? Can brothers pray for brothers, relatives
and friends*a* for their nearest and dearest?'

[104]   'You have won my favour,' he replied, 'and I will tell
you. The day of judgement is decisive,*b* and sets its seal
on the truth for all to see. In the present age a father
cannot send his son in his place, nor a son his father, a
master his slave, nor a man his best friend, to be ill*c* for
[105] him, or sleep, or eat, or be cured for him. In the same way
no one shall ever ask pardon for another; when that day
comes, every individual will be held responsible for his
own wickedness or goodness.'

[106] 36   To this I replied: 'But how is it, then, that we read of
intercessions in scripture? First, there is Abraham, who
prayed for the people of Sodom; then Moses, who prayed
[107] 37 for our ancestors when they sinned in the desert. Next,

[a] friends: *so some Vss.; Lat.* the faithful.   [b] *So one Vs.; Lat.* stern.
[c] *So some Vss.; Lat.* to understand.

there is Joshua, who prayed for the Israelites in the time
of Achan, then Samuel in the time of Saul,^a David during   38 [108]
the plague,^b and Solomon at the dedication of the temple.
Elijah prayed for rain for the people, and for a dead man   39 [109]
that he might be brought back to life. Hezekiah prayed   40 [110]
for the nation in the time of Sennacherib; and there are
many more besides. If, then, in the time when corruption   41 [111]
grew and wickedness increased, the just asked pardon for
the wicked, why cannot it be the same on the day of
judgement?'

The angel gave me this answer: 'The present world is   42 [112]
not the end, and the glory of God does not stay in it
continually.^c That is why the strong have prayed for the
weak. But the day of judgement will be the end of the   43 [113]
present world and the beginning of the eternal world to
come, a world in which corruption will be over, all   44 [114]
excess abolished, and unbelief uprooted, in which justice
will be full-grown, and truth will have risen like the sun.
On the day of judgement, therefore, there can be no   45 [115]
mercy for the man who has lost his case, no reversal for
the man who has won it.'

✻ Ezra's concern at the fate that awaits sinners (for Ezra, as
we have seen, this means virtually all mankind) leads him to
ask a further question: on the day of judgement will it be
possible for a righteous man to intercede on behalf of the
wicked? To this the reply is a decisive No; 'when that day
comes, every individual will be held responsible for his own
wickedness or goodness' (verse [105]). Ezra objects that

[a] in the time of Saul: *so some Vss.; Lat. omits.*
[b] during the plague: *so some Vss.; Lat. for the destruction.*
[c] does...continually: *so some Vss.; Lat. regularly stays in it.*

during the course of Israel's history it had not infrequently been the case that 'the just asked pardon for the wicked' (verse [111]) and asks why the same principle cannot apply. But the angel dismisses the parallel. The day of judgement marks the beginning of the new age in which conditions will be transformed. Although in the present age men had been permitted to pray on behalf of others, in the new age the judgement will be strictly according to justice (verses [112–14]). The attitude of the author reflected in these verses is in sharp contrast with the view held by other Jews at that time who did believe that the prayers of the righteous could benefit the wicked at the judgement. Thus, e.g., in the Testament of Abraham (a Jewish work of the first century A.D.) 12–14 a soul whose sins and righteous deeds are found to be equal is saved through the prayers of Abraham.

[102]. *If I have won your favour:* see the comment on 5: 56.

[105]. *every individual will be held responsible for his own wickedness or goodness:* similar statements are to be found already in the Old Testament, but in a rather different theological context. In the Old Testament stress is laid on the individual's responsibility, over against the idea of inherited guilt (cp. Deut. 24: 16), or, particularly in the period of the exile, on both responsibility and the reality of release from the past guilt of the community (cp. Jer. 31: 29–30; Ezek. 18: 20). Here these ideas are reapplied to the final moment of judgement.

[106]. *Abraham, who prayed for the people of Sodom:* see Gen. 18: 16–33. *Moses, who prayed for our ancestors when they sinned in the desert:* see Exod. 32: 11–14.

[107]. *Joshua, who prayed for the Israelites in the time of Achan:* see Josh. 7: 6–9.

[108]. *Samuel in the time of Saul:* the precise allusion is uncertain; see 1 Sam. 7: 9 (but this antedates the appearance of Saul); 12: 19–25; cp. also Ps. 99: 6, 'Samuel among those who call on his name'. *David during the plague:* see 2 Sam. 24: 17. *Solomon at the dedication of the temple:* see 1 Kings 8: 22–3, 30.

[109]. *Elijah prayed for rain for the people:* see 1 Kings 18: 36–7, 42b. *and for a dead man that he might be brought back to life:* see 1 Kings 17: 20–1.

[110]. *Hezekiah prayed for the nation:* see 2 Kings 19: 15–19.

[112]. *The present world is not the end:* the angel explains the fact that righteous men had in the past prayed on behalf of the wicked by stressing the transitory and imperfect character of life in this world. *and the glory of God does not stay in it continually:* the author refers to God's presence in the world in terms familiar from certain parts of the Old Testament according to which God was thought to manifest himself to his people by means of his glory (see e.g. Exod. 24: 15–18; Ezek. 1: 26–8). According to the Old Testament it was believed that sin led to the withdrawal of God's presence (see e.g. Hos. 5: 6, 15; Ezek. 11: 22–3, the climax of the description of the sin of Jerusalem in Ezek. 8–11); for the author of 2 Esdras 3–14 this was an indication of the imperfect character of this world, and the reason *why the strong have prayed for the weak.* In the Latin text of this verse in 2 Esdras (see the N.E.B. footnote) the negative has been omitted by mistake.

[113–14]. *the day of judgement will be the end of the present world and the beginning of the eternal world to come:* cp. verses 31–3. *a world in which corruption will be over . . . truth will have risen like the sun:* conditions in the world to come will be so transformed that all the imperfections of the present world will disappear, and the judgement itself will be according to the strictest standards of justice and impartiality (cp. verses 33b–34). The implication is clear; there will be no place then for one man to pray on behalf of another. ✳

THE ARGUMENT RESUMED ONCE MORE

I replied, 'But this is my point, my first point and my 46 [116] last: how much better it would have been if the earth had never produced Adam at all, or, since it has done so, if he

[117] 47 had been restrained from sinning! For what good does it do us all to live in misery now and have nothing but
[118] 48 punishment to expect after death? O Adam, what have you done? Your sin was not your fall alone; it was ours
[119] 49 also, the fall of all your descendants. What good is the promise of immortality to us, when we have committed
[120] 50 mortal sins; or the hope of eternity, in the wretched and
[121] 51 futile state to which we have come; or the prospect of dwelling in health and safety, when we have lived such
[122] 52 evil lives? The glory of the Most High will guard those who have led a life of purity; but what help is that to us
[123] 53 whose conduct has been so wicked? What good is the revelation of paradise and its imperishable fruit, the
[124] 54 source of perfect satisfaction and healing? For we shall never enter it, since we have made depravity our home.
[125] 55 Those who have practised self-discipline shall shine with faces brighter than the stars; but what good is that to us
[126] 56 whose faces are darker than the night? For during a life-time of wickedness we have never given a thought to the sufferings awaiting us after death.'

[127] 57   The angel replied, 'This is the thought for every man
[128] 58 to keep in mind during his earthly contest: if he loses, he must accept the sufferings you have mentioned, but if he
[129] 59 wins, the rewards I have been describing will be his. For that was the way which Moses in his time urged the people to take, when he said, "Choose life and live!"
[130] 60 But they did not believe him, nor the prophets after him,
[131] 61 nor me when I spoke to them. Over their damnation there will be no sorrow; there will only be joy for the salvation of those who have believed.'[a]

[a] *So some Vss.; Lat.* for those who are convinced of salvation.

✻ [116–26]. The argument of verses 17–25, [45–74] is now
again taken up in a more direct way. Ezra has just learnt
(verses [75–115]) of the fate that awaits sinners after death,
and this leads him to complain bitterly that it would have been
better if Adam had never been born, or at any rate had been
prevented from sinning and thereby implicating all his
descendants in sin. Ezra concedes that 'Those who have practised self-discipline' (verse [125]) will be rewarded, but for the
sinful majority of mankind promises of eternal bliss are empty
and meaningless. In essence what Ezra is arguing is that the
conditions of life imposed on man by God are unfair.

[116]. *how much better it would have been if the earth had never
produced Adam:* cp. verse [63] and 4: 12.

[118]. *Your sin was not your fall alone; it was ours also, the
fall of all your descendants:* the author refers once more to the
idea that men sin as a result of the fact that Adam sinned; cp. 3:
21; Rom. 5: 12–14. As we saw in the comment on 3: 16–22,
this is only one of his explanations for the existence of sin,
the other being the idea of the wicked heart.

[122]. *The glory of the Most High:* see the comment on
verse [112].

[123]. *paradise:* see the comment on verse [36]. *and its
imperishable fruit:* the belief that the fruit of paradise is imperishable has a parallel in Ezekiel's vision of the spring of life-giving
water flowing from the temple; see Ezek. 47: 1–12, especially
verse 12, 'Beside the torrent on either bank all trees good for
food shall spring up. Their leaves shall not wither, their fruit
shall not cease.' Cp. also Rev. 22: 1–5, particularly verse 2.

[125]. *shall shine with faces brighter than the stars:* cp. Dan.
12: 2–3 (see the comment on verse [97]); Matt. 13: 43, 'And
then (i.e. after the wicked have been destroyed) the righteous
will shine as brightly as the sun in the kingdom of their
Father.'

[127–31]. The angel does not respond directly to Ezra's
complaint, but merely continues the line of argument that he
has already developed in verses 19–25, [70–4]: man is respon-

sible for his own destiny, and it lies entirely within his own hands whether his fate in the world to come is damnation or salvation. Thus in direct contrast to Ezra the angel insists that it is perfectly possible for a man to secure his own salvation. Cp. Ecclus. 15: 14–17:

> 'When he made man in the beginning,
> he left him free to take his own decisions;
> if you choose, you can keep the commandments;
> whether or not you keep faith is yours to decide.
> He has set before you fire and water;
> reach out and take which you choose;
> before man lie life and death,
> and whichever he prefers is his.'

[127]. *his earthly contest:* i.e. with the forces of evil, and more particularly with the wicked heart; cp. verse [92] and 3: 20.

[128]. *the sufferings you have mentioned . . . the rewards I have been describing:* no particular passages are in mind, but throughout the preceding dialogue Ezra has consistently taken the side of the sinners (with whom he identifies himself), whereas the angel has taken the side of the righteous.

[129]. *For that was the way which Moses . . . urged the people to take . . . "Choose life, and live!":* cp. Deut. 30: 19, 'I summon heaven and earth to witness against you this day: I offer you the choice of life or death, blessing or curse. Choose life and then you and your descendants will live.' However, by 'life' the author of 2 Esdras 3–14 was thinking of life in the world to come, an idea which is not present in the passage in Deuteronomy.

[130]. *But they did not believe him, nor the prophets after him:* cp. 1: 32. The rejection of the word of God delivered by the prophets forms a frequent theme in the Old Testament; cp. e.g. 2 Chron. 36: 15–16; 'The LORD God of their fathers had warned them betimes through his messengers, for he took pity on his people and on his dwelling-place; but they

never ceased to deride his messengers, scorn his words and
scoff at his prophets'; cp. also Matt. 23: 37, 'O Jerusalem,
Jerusalem, the city that murders the prophets and stones the
messengers sent to her!' *nor me:* the angel speaks as if he were
God; see the comment on 5: 40.

[131]. Cp. verses 25, [60–1]. *for the salvation of those who
have believed:* so the Syriac and Ethiopic versions. The meaning
of the Latin text is not entirely clear; the N.E.B. footnote
gives a possible interpretation, but it may be that the Latin is
corrupt, and that it is based on a misunderstanding of a
Greek text similar to that presupposed by the Syriac and
Ethiopic. *

EZRA APPEALS TO GOD'S MERCY

'My lord,' I replied, 'I know that the Most High is   62 [132]
called "compassionate", because he has compassion on
those yet unborn; and called "merciful", because he   63 [133]
shows mercy to those who repent and live by his law;
and "patient", because he shows patience to those who   64 [134]
have sinned, his own creatures as they are; and "bene-   65 [135]
factor", because he prefers giving to taking; and "rich   66 [136]
in forgiveness", because again and again he forgives sinners, past, present, and to come. For without his con-   67 [137]
tinued forgiveness there could be no hope of life for the
world and its inhabitants. And he is called "generous",   68 [138]
because without his generosity in releasing sinners from
their sins, not one ten-thousandth part of mankind could
hope to be given life; and he is also called "judge", for   69 [139]
unless he grants pardon to those who have been created
by his word, and blots out their countless offences, I   70 [140]
suppose that of the entire human race only very few
would be spared.'

193

8   The angel said to me in reply: 'The Most High has
made this world for many, but the next world for only
2 a few. Let me give you an illustration, Ezra. Ask the
earth, and it will tell you that it can produce plenty of
clay for making earthenware, but very little gold-dust.
3 The same holds good for the present world: many have
been created, but only a few will be saved.'

* In the face of the hard and inflexible attitude of the angel,
Ezra does not attempt to pursue the argument directly, but
instead describes and acknowledges the compassionate mercy
of God apart from which 'only very few would be spared'
(verse [140]). Implicit in his words is the conviction that the
destruction of the great majority of mankind is incompatible
with God's mercy; rather he believes that through the
compassion of God sinners will be pardoned and 'given life'
(verse [138]) in the world to come. But the response of the
angel remains negative; his short reply consists merely of a
restatement of the view that it is in the nature of things that
'only a few will be saved' (8: 3, cp. 7: [49–61]). The conflict
between the attitude of Ezra and the attitude of the angel
doubtless reflects an unresolved tension in the mind of the
author; he attempts here to find an answer to his problems
in an appeal to God's mercy, but in the end cannot accept this
solution.

[132–40]. This passage is probably based directly on Exod.
34: 6–7, 'Then the LORD passed in front of him and called
aloud, "JEHOVAH, the LORD, a god compassionate and
gracious, long-suffering, ever constant and true, maintaining
constancy to thousands, forgiving iniquity, rebellion, and
sin, and not sweeping the guilty clean away"' (some of the
similarities between Exod. 34: 6–7 and the passage in 2 Esdras
are more obvious in the underlying texts and versions than
in the N.E.B. translation itself). Exod. 34: 6–7 had apparently

already been utilized in several passages in the Old Testament which refer to God's mercy (cp. e.g. Neh. 9: 17; Pss. 103: 8; 145: 8–9), and by the time of 2 Esdras the list of attributes had become to a great extent traditional.

[133]. *"merciful"*: in Exod. 34: 6 the word rendered 'gracious'.

[134]. *"patient"*: in Exod. 34: 6 the word rendered 'long-suffering'. *his own creatures as they are:* cp. Ps. 145: 8–9:

> 'The LORD is gracious and compassionate,
>   forbearing, and constant in his love,
> The LORD is good to all men,
>   and his tender care rests upon all his
>   creatures.'

[135]. *"benefactor"*: the origin of this title is unclear (it is not present in Exod. 34: 6–7). *he prefers giving to taking:* cp. Acts 20: 35, 'Happiness lies more in giving than in receiving', but the context suggests that what is particularly in mind in 2 Esdras 3–14 is the idea of granting pardon instead of exacting punishment.

[136]. *"rich in forgiveness"*: in Exod. 34: 6 the words rendered 'ever constant'.

[137–40]. In contrast to the angel Ezra here argues for the view that through God's mercy *sinners* will *be given life*; cp. 8: 36.

[137]. *life:* both here and in the next verse life in the world to come is meant; those who have not been condemned at the last judgement will enjoy the delights of paradise; cp. verses [36], [123–4]; 8: 52.

138. *"generous"*: the origin of this title is also uncertain, but the whole verse seems to go back ultimately to the words in Exod. 34: 7 which the N.E.B. translates 'maintaining constancy to thousands', but which might also be translated 'maintaining steadfast love to thousands'.

[139–40]. *"judge"*: although attested by all the versions, this is not quite the word we expect, and it is possible that the text is in some way corrupt. However, these two verses appear to be based on Exod. 34: 7, 'forgiving iniquity, rebellion, and sin, and not sweeping the guilty clean away'. *created by his word:* cp. Gen. 1: 26–7.

8: 1. *The Most High has made this world for many, but the next world for only a few:* cp. 7: [50–1].

2. *plenty of clay ... very little gold-dust:* cp. 7: [51–61], particularly verses [54–7].

3. *many have been created, but only a few will be saved:* cp. Matt. 22: 14, 'For though many are invited, few are chosen.' ☆

EZRA AGAIN APPEALS TO GOD'S MERCY

4 I said: 'My soul, drink deep of understanding and eat
5 your fill of wisdom! Without your consent[a] you came
here, and unwillingly you go away; only a brief span of
6 life is given you. O Lord above, if I may be allowed to
approach you in prayer, plant a seed in our hearts and
minds, and make it grow until it bears fruit, so that fallen
7 man may obtain life. For you alone are God, and we are
all shaped by you in one mould, as your word declares.
8 The body moulded in the womb receives from you both
life and limbs; that which you create is kept safe amid
fire and water; for nine months the body moulded by
9 you bears what you have created in it. Both the womb
which holds safely and that which is safely held will be
safe only because you keep them so. And after the womb
10 has delivered up what has been created in it, then from
the human body itself, that is from the breasts, milk, the
11 fruit of the breasts, is supplied by your command. For a
certain time what has been made is nourished in that
way; and afterwards it is still cared for by your mercy.

[a] Without your consent: *so one Vs.; Lat.* To obey.

You bring it up to know your justice, train it in your 12
law, and correct it by your wisdom. It is your creature 13
and you made it; you can put it to death or give it life,
as you please. But if you should lightly destroy one who 14
was fashioned by your command with so much labour,
what was the purpose of creating him?

'And now let me say this: about mankind at large, 15
you know best; but it is for your own people that I 16
grieve, for your inheritance that I mourn; my sorrow is
for Israel and my distress for the race of Jacob. For them 17
and for myself, therefore, I will address my prayer to
you, since I perceive how low we have fallen, we dwellers
on earth; and I know well how quickly your judgement 18
will follow. Hear my words then, and consider the prayer 19
which I make to you.'

Here begins the prayer which Ezra made, before he
was taken up to heaven.

'O Lord, who dost inhabit eternity, to whom the sky 20
and the highest heavens belong; whose throne is beyond 21
imagining, and whose glory is past conceiving; who art
attended by the host of angels trembling as they turn 22
themselves into wind and fire at thy bidding; whose word
is true and constant; whose commands are mighty and
terrible; whose glance dries up the deeps, whose anger 23
melts the mountains, and whose truth stands for ever:[a]
hear thy servant's prayer, O Lord, listen to my petition, 24
for thou hast fashioned me, and consider my words.
While I live I will speak; while understanding lasts, I will 25
answer.

'Do not look upon thy people's offences, look on those 26

[a] *So some Vss.; Lat.* bears witness.

27 who have served thee faithfully; pay no heed to the godless and their pursuits, but to those who have observed
28 thy covenant and suffered for it. Do not think of those who all their life have been untrue to thee, but remember those who have acknowledged and feared thee from the
29 heart. Do not destroy those who have lived like animals, but take account of those who have borne shining witness
30 to thy law. Do not be angry with those judged to be worse than beasts; but show love to those who have put
31 unfailing trust in thy glory. For we and our fathers have lived in mortal sin,[a] yet it is on our account that thou art
32 called merciful; for if it is thy desire to have mercy on us sinners, who have no just deeds to our credit, then indeed
33 thou shalt be called merciful. For the reward which will be given to the just, who have many good works stored up with thee, will be no more than their own deeds have earned.

34 'What is man, that thou shouldst be angry with him? or the race of mortals, that thou shouldst treat them so
35 harshly? The truth is, no man was ever born who did
36 not sin; no man alive is innocent of offence. It is through thy mercy towards those with no store of good deeds to their name that thy justice and kindness, O Lord, will be made known'.

37 The angel said to me in reply: 'Much of what you have
38 said is just, and it will be as you say. Be sure that I shall not give any thought to sinners, to their creation, death,
39 judgement, or damnation; but I shall take delight in the just, in their creation, their departure from this world,
40 their salvation, and their final reward. So I have said, and

[a] in mortal sin: *so some Vss.; Lat. obscure.*

so it is. The farmer sows many seeds in the ground and 41
plants many plants, but not all the seeds sown come up
safely in season, nor do all the plants strike root. So too
in the world of men: not all who are sown will be
preserved.'

∗ The debate of the previous section (7: [132]–8: 3) is
here renewed with an explicit appeal by Ezra for God to show
mercy to his people (verses 4–36) and a further negative response from the angel (verses 37–41). Ezra's appeal falls into
three parts, verses 4–14, 15–19*a*, 19*b*–36.

4–14. After a short introduction (verses 4–5) Ezra asks God
to make it possible for 'fallen man' to 'obtain life' (verse 6).
God has created man with infinite care (verses 7–13), and the
destruction of man seems in these circumstances incomprehensible (verse 14).

4–5. Ezra begins by addressing his soul and urging it to
absorb all the 'understanding' and 'wisdom' that it is capable
of absorbing in view of the uncertainty and brevity of life.
Ezra despairs because he feels he lacks the ability to make
sense of the problems which face him, but he seems at the
same time to be complaining that life is not long enough for
him ever to acquire the insight necessary to solve these
problems. The thought that man's ability to understand God's
ways is restricted by the uncertainty and brevity of life is also
found in 2 Baruch 14: 8–11:

'But who, O Lord, my Lord, will comprehend thy
    judgement,
Or who will search out the profoundness of thy way?
Or who will think out the weight (?) of thy path?
Or who will be able to think out thy incomprehensible
    counsel?
Or who of those that are born has ever found
The beginning or end of thy wisdom?
For we have all been made like a breath. For as the breath
ascends involuntarily, and again dies, so it is with the

nature of men, who depart not according to their own will, and know not what will befall them in the end' (translation from R. H. Charles, *Apocrypha and Pseudepigrapha*, vol. 2, p. 490).

4. *drink deep of understanding and eat your fill of wisdom!*: for the imagery cp. the invitation of Wisdom in Prov. 9: 5-6:

> 'Come, dine with me (literally 'eat of my bread')
> and taste the wine that I have spiced.
> Cease to be silly, and you will live,
> you will grow in understanding.'

5. *Without your consent*: so the Syriac version; the Latin 'To obey' (see the footnote) derives from a misreading of the underlying Greek text. *you came here*: the words used imply a belief in the pre-existence of the soul: cp. Wisd. of Sol. 8: 19-20, 'As a child I was born to excellence, and a noble soul fell to my lot; or rather, I myself was noble, and I entered into an unblemished body.' Cp. also the comment on 7: [88].

6. Ezra appeals to God to bring about such a change in *fallen man* that he *may obtain life* in the world to come. *plant a seed in our hearts and minds, and make it grow until it bears fruit*: the transformation of man is described by means of the same imagery as that used in 4: 30 to describe Adam's fall, 'A grain of the evil seed was sown in the heart of Adam from the first; how much godlessness has it produced already!' For the thought of 8: 6 cp. Ezek. 36: 26-7, 'I will give you a new heart and put a new spirit within you; I will take the heart of stone from your body and give you a heart of flesh. I will put my spirit into you and make you conform to my statutes, keep my laws and live by them.' *until it bears fruit*: man is to be transformed so that he will produce the good works (cp. 7: [77]; 8: 33) which will ensure his salvation. *life*: as elsewhere, life in the new age is meant.

7-14. Ezra bases his appeal (verse 6) on the fact that man's creation and continued existence depend entirely on God. It is inconceivable that God should have taken the care that he did to create man only to destroy him; cp. Job 10: 8–12.

7. *For you alone are God, and we are all shaped by you in one mould* (literally 'and we are one work of your hands'), *as your word declares:* not an exact quotation, but cp. e.g. Isa. 44: 6:

'I am the first and I am the last,
and there is no god but me'

and Isa. 45: 11:

'Thus says the LORD . . .
Would you dare question me concerning my children,
or instruct me in my handiwork?'

8. *amid fire and water:* an allusion to two of the elements of which the body was thought to be composed; according to Philo, a Jewish writer who lived in Alexandria in the first century A.D., the human body was formed from earth, water, air and fire (cp. *On the Creation of the World* 146; see the Loeb Classical Library translation of Philo, vol. I, pp. 115, 117). In 2 Esdras 3–14 the thought is that the embryo, consisting of the elements fire and water, is *kept safe* by God.

12. *train it in your law:* God's concern for man is shown not only by the fact that he creates and sustains him, but also by the fact that he instructs him in the law. The implication of this verse is that the law was intended for all men; cp. 7: 21, [72]; in other passages (3: 19; 5: 27) the law is seen as the special gift of Israel.

13. *you can put it to death or give it life, as you please:* in the context the reference is to God's power to destroy or maintain physical life; contrast the many passages, e.g. verse 6, where 'life' means life in the age to come. Cp. 1 Sam. 2: 6:

'The LORD kills and he gives life,
he sends down to Sheol, he can bring the dead up again'

and see the comments on this verse in the commentary on 1 Samuel in this series.

15–29a. Ezra does not pause for a reply to what he has just

said, but states that he will leave in God's hands the fate of 'mankind at large' (verse 15), and that his concern is 'for Israel' (verse 16). He announces that he will pray on Israel's behalf as well as his own.

16. *your own people . . . your inheritance:* the thought that Israel is God's people is commonplace in the Old Testament, but cp. e.g. Deut. 32: 8–9:

> 'When the Most High parcelled out the nations,
> when he dispersed all mankind,
> he laid down the boundaries of every people
> according to the number of the sons of God;
> but the LORD's share was his own people,
> Jacob was his allotted portion'

(The last line could be translated 'Jacob was his allotted inheritance'.)

17. *and for myself:* as in the prayer which follows (cp. verses 31–2) Ezra classes himself with the sinners. Cp. 7: [75] and contrast the rebukes of the angel in 8: 47–9 and 7: [76].

19*b*–36. Ezra's prayer begins with an invocation to God who is asked to hear the words of his servant (verses 20–5). There follows a petition that God will show mercy to his people by ignoring their sins and by paying attention only to those who have served him and kept his law (verses 26–30). The petition is supported by a confession of sin, with which Ezra associates himself, and an appeal to God to treat sinners with mercy even though they have no good deeds to their credit (verses 31–6). The prayer was used independently of 2 Esdras 3–14 for liturgical purposes; as such it was often copied separately, with the title 'the Confession of Esdras', amongst the collections of canticles and hymns which are to be found in manuscripts of the Vulgate (for the Vulgate see above, the Footnotes to the N.E.B. text, p. xi).

19*b*. *Here begins the prayer which Ezra made, before he was taken up to heaven:* these words are not part of the prayer itself, but a title. The occurrence of this title is an indication of the independent use of the prayer for liturgical purposes (see above). According to this title it was believed that Ezra, like Enoch (Gen. 5: 24) and Elijah (2 Kings 2: 1–12), had been translated to heaven; such a belief is indicated in 2 Esdras 14: 9, and stated explicitly in some words at the end of ch. 14 which occur in the oriental versions of 2 Esdras (e.g. the Syriac), but not in the Latin version, and hence not in the N.E.B. which is based on the Latin version. Cp. the comment on 14: 9 and 14: 48.

20–3. Several of the attributes by which God is invoked are reminiscent of descriptions of God in the Old Testament and one (in verse 22) is actually based on a particular Old Testament passage, namely Ps. 104: 4.

20. *to whom the sky and the highest heavens belong:* cp. Deut. 10: 14, 'To the LORD your God belong heaven itself, the highest heaven, the earth and everything in it.'

21. *whose throne is beyond imagining, and whose glory is past conceiving:* cp. the description of God seated upon his throne in Ezek. 1 (particularly verses 22–28*a*) which concludes with the words 'it was like the appearance of the glory of the LORD'. In Ezekiel 'glory' is a technical term used to describe the way in which God manifested himself to his people (cp. the comment above on 7: [112]); it was conceived of as a brilliant light or fire encircling God. In Rev. 21: 23 the glory of God provides the light for the new Jerusalem: 'And the city had no need of sun or moon to shine upon it; for the glory of God gave it light, and its lamp was the Lamb.' *who art attended by the host of angels:* cp. 1 Kings 22: 19; Dan. 7: 10.

22. *as they turn themselves into wind and fire at thy bidding:* based on Ps. 104: 4, but understood in a different way from the N.E.B. translation:

> 'who makest the winds thy messengers
> and flames of fire thy servants'

Ps. 104: 4 is also used in Heb. 1: 7; Hebrews, like the Septuagint version of Ps. 104, understood the passage in the same way as 2 Esdras.

23. *whose glance dries up the deeps:* cp. Isa. 51: 10:

> 'Was it not you
>   who dried up the sea, the waters of the great abyss?'

whose anger melts the mountains: cp. Mic. 1: 4, part of a description of the coming of God to judge his people:

> 'Beneath him mountains dissolve
>   like wax before the fire'

stands for ever: the Latin 'bears witness' (see the footnote) goes back to a misreading of the original Hebrew text.

26–30. Essentially the same point is made in the five petitions which all have an antithetic structure, one clause contrasting with the other in each case. For the thought cp. Gen. 18: 22–33; cp. also 2 Baruch 14: 7, 'And if others did evil, it was due to Zion that on account of the works of those who wrought good works she should be forgiven, and should not be overwhelmed on account of the works of those who wrought unrighteousness' (translation from R. H. Charles, *Apocrypha and Pseudepigrapha*, vol. 2, p. 490).

27. *who have observed thy covenant and suffered for it:* cp. the stories of martyrdom in the Maccabaean period (2 Macc. 6: 10 – 7: 42).

29. *those who have lived like animals:* cp. the Psalmist's description of himself in Ps. 73: 22:

> 'I would not understand, so brutish was I,
>   I was a mere beast in thy sight, O God.'

In 2 Esdras 3–14 the contrast with bearing witness to the law suggests that what is in mind is lack of understanding leading to disregard for the law.

30. *those judged to be worse than beasts:* Jews worse even than those mentioned in the previous verse. *who have put unfailing trust in thy glory:* that is, in the power and might of God. For this use of 'glory' cp. Wisd. of Sol. 9: 11 where Solomon prays that wisdom may guard him 'in her glory'.

31–6. Ezra supports his petition by a twice-repeated confession of sin (verses 31, 35) and a twice-repeated appeal to God to treat sinners with mercy even though they have 'no store of good deeds to their name' (verses 32–3, 36); man is too insignificant for God to be angry with him (verse 34). The appeal made in these verses is essentially a repetition of the appeal made in 7: [132–40], but, as we shall see, it is again rejected.

31. *For we and our fathers have lived in mortal sin:* cp. Ps. 106: 6. Ezra again includes himself amongst the sinners, as he does also in the next verse; see the comment on verse 17. *yet it is on our account that thou art called merciful:* a reminder to God of his past mercies to his people.

32–3. *no just deeds to our credit . . . many good works stored up with thee:* as we have seen (cp. the comment on 7: [77]) the author of 2 Esdras 3–14 believed that a few very righteous men would earn their place in the life of the world to come by means of their good works. Ezra's appeal is for the vast majority of mankind who would not be in this position.

34. Based on Job 7: 17–18:

> 'What is man that thou makest much of him
> and turnest thy thoughts towards him,
> only to punish him morning by morning
> or to test him every hour of the day?'

This in its turn is related to Ps. 8: 4:

> 'what is man that thou shouldst remember him,
> mortal man that thou shouldst care for him?'

35. *no man was ever born who did not sin:* the absolute terms of this confession (cp. 7: [46], [68]) are strictly speaking inconsistent with what is said in the immediate context. In verses 26–30 Ezra has just appealed to God to take account of those who have kept his law, while verses 32–3 and 36 assume the existence of a group of righteous men whose good works will be sufficient to earn their salvation. Ezra is in effect appealing to God to count men as just, although they are in fact sinners; cp. Rom. 4: 6-8.

36. Cp. the comment on verses 32–3.

37–41. In his reply the angel ignores the main point of Ezra's prayer, i.e. the appeal for God to show mercy to his people. Instead he turns Ezra's own words against him to reiterate the point that God is not concerned with the damnation of sinners, but only with the salvation of the just (verses 37–40, cp. 7: 25, [60–1], [131]), and he uses an analogy to reiterate the point that only a few will be saved (verse 41; cp. 7: [51–61]; 8: 1–3).

37–40. *Much of what you have said is just, and it will be as you say:* the words of Ezra's petition in verses 26–30 are used against him in a contrary sense to that intended; the same stylistic device occurs in 7: [71–2]; cp. 7: [64].

38. The author again forgets that the speaker is supposed to be the angel, not God; cp. the comment on 5: 40.

39. *their departure from this world:* literally 'their pilgrimage', but the parallelism with 'death' in verse 38 indicates how 'pilgrimage' is to be understood.

40. *So I have said:* so the Latin and all the other versions except the Ethiopic, the allusion being to such passages as 7: [131]. The Ethiopic 'So you have said' repeats the thought of verse 37, 'and it will be as you say'. The reading of the Ethiopic has sometimes been preferred as being more appropriate in the context, but it is not clear that this is right.

41. *The farmer sows many seeds in the ground:* for the analogy cp. the parable of the sower, Matt. 13: 4–9, 18–23. The author of 2 Esdras 3–14 has already used the analogy of sowing seed, but in a rather different way, in 4: 28–39; see the comment on 4: 28. ✻

EZRA'S FINAL APPEAL FOR MERCY

42 To that I replied: 'If I have won your favour, let me
43 speak. The farmer's seed may never come up because it is given no rain at the right time, or it may rot because
44 of too much rain. But man, who was formed by your

hands and made in your image, and for whose sake you
made everything – will you compare him with seed sown
by a farmer? Surely not, O Lord above! Spare your own 45
people and pity them, for you will be pitying your own
creation.'

He answered: 'The present is for those now alive, the 46
future for those yet to come. You cannot love my 47
creation with a love greater than mine – far from it! But
never again rank yourself among the unjust, as you have
so often done. Yet the Most High approves of the 48, 49
modesty you have rightly shown; you have not sought
great glory by including yourself among the godly. In 50
the last days, then, the inhabitants of the world will be
punished for their arrogant lives by bitter sufferings. But 51
you, Ezra, should direct your thoughts to yourself and
the glory awaiting those like you. For all of you, paradise 52
lies open, the tree of life is planted, the age to come is
made ready, and rich abundance is in store; the city is
already built, rest from toil is assured, goodness and wisdom are brought to perfection. The root of evil has been 53
sealed off from you; for you there is no more illness,
death*a* is abolished, hell has fled, and decay is quite forgotten. All sorrows are at an end, and the treasure of 54
immortality has been finally revealed. Ask no more 55
questions, therefore, about the many who are lost. For 56
they were given freedom and used it to despise the Most
High, to treat his law with contempt and abandon his
ways. Yes, and they trampled on his just servants; they 57, 58
said to themselves, "There is no God", though well
aware that they must die. Yours, then, will be the joys 59

[a] death: *so some Vss.; Lat. omits.*

207

I have predicted; theirs the thirst and torments which are prepared. It is not that the Most High has wanted any 60 man to be lost, but that those he created have themselves brought dishonour on their Creator's name, and shown ingratitude to the One who had put life within their 61, 62 reach. My day of judgement is now close at hand, but I have not made this known to all; only to you and a few like you.'

* 42–5. Ezra protests at the implications of the analogy of verse 41. Many things may happen to prevent a seed coming up, or a plant reaching maturity, but he cannot believe that God treats men with such indifference (verses 42–45a). He makes a final impassioned appeal for God to show mercy to his people (verse 45b).

42. *If I have won your favour:* see the comment on 5: 56.

43. *The farmer's seed may never come up:* cp. Matt. 13: 4–7.

45. Cp. Joel 2: 17, an appeal to God's care for what he has created:

> 'Spare thy people, O LORD, thy own people,
>   expose them not to reproach'

46–62. Ezra's appeal for mercy for God's 'own people' is once more rejected, and he is urged to think about the glorious future which awaits him rather than to concern himself with the fully justified fate of the wicked. The reply falls into three parts (verses 46–47a, 47b–54, 55–62) and seems at times to be spoken by God and at times by the angel; for the alternation see the comment on 5: 40.

46–47a. Ezra's objection to the analogy of the seeds is dismissed.

46. *The present is for those now alive, the future for those yet to come* (or 'Things present are for those now alive, things future for those yet to come'): the meaning is that the analogy only has relevance in the present age; full understanding of

what will apply in the future age will be possible only for those who will participate in the life of that age. Cp. the arguments in 4: 1–32; 5: 31–40.

47a. *You cannot love my creation with a love greater than mine:* Ezra's understanding of the situation is also erroneous, because, whatever he might think, God's love for mankind is still far greater than his own (cp. 5: 33*b*–34).

47*b*–54. Ezra is rebuked for associating himself with the sinners, but at the same time commended for his modesty in so doing (verses 47*b*–49). Those who are arrogant will suffer punishment, but Ezra ought to direct his thoughts to the glorious future which awaits him and those like him (verses 50–4).

47*b*. *But never again rank yourself among the unjust, as you have so often done:* cp. verses 17 and 31–2, and see also 7: [75–6].

48–9. *the modesty you have rightly shown; you have not sought great glory:* the same attitude that is frequently commended in the gospels; cp. e.g. Matt. 23: 12, 'For whoever exalts himself will be humbled; and whoever humbles himself will be exalted.'

50. In contrast to Ezra those who do lead *arrogant lives* will have to endure *bitter sufferings* at the time of judgement.

51. *to yourself and the glory awaiting those like you:* for Ezra and the righteous like him glory lies in store in the new age; the content of this glory is described in detail in verses 52–4, first positively (verse 52), then negatively (verse 53); verse 54 provides a concluding summary.

52. The blessings of the new age are thought of as being already in existence; cp. 1 Pet. 1: 4–5:

'The inheritance to which we are born is one that nothing can destroy or spoil or wither. It is kept for you in heaven, and you, because you put your faith in God, are under the protection of his power until salvation comes – the salvation which is even now in readiness and will be revealed at the end of time.'

paradise: as elsewhere in 2 Esdras 3–14, the place of rest of the righteous in the world to come; cp. 7: [36], [123] and the comment on 7: [36]. *the tree of life:* cp. 7: [123]; Rev. 2: 7 (quoted in the comment on 7: [36]; Rev. 22: 2. *the city:* the new Jerusalem; the expectation of a new Jerusalem forms part of the beliefs associated with the new age (cp. 7: 26; 10: 27, 38–59; 13: 36; Rev. 21: 1–4 and see also the comment on 7: 26).

53. *The root of evil has been sealed off from you:* 'of evil' has been supplied in the translation, but accurately conveys the sense; cp. 3: 22 'a rooted wickedness' (literally 'the wickedness of the root' or 'the wicked root'). *root* is used here almost as a technical term to describe what it is that causes men to sin; in the new age this root will no longer be able to affect men. *for you there is no more illness, death is abolished, hell has fled, and decay is quite forgotten:* not only the cause, but also the consequences of sin will be removed in the new age. In the Latin version *death* has been omitted by mistake (see the N.E.B. footnote); for the thought cp. Isa. 25: 8, 'he will swallow up death for ever'; Rev. 21: 4. Cp. also Rev. 20: 14, at the judgement 'Death and Hades' are destroyed by being thrown 'into the lake of fire' ('Hades' was the name given in the Graeco-Roman world to hell or the underworld and is similar to 'Sheol' in Old Testament thought).

55-62. Contemplation of the future which lies in store for him ought to lead Ezra to put out of his mind the fate of 'the many who are lost'. Their fate is in any case their own fault; they used the freedom they had been given to disobey God and thereby brought their punishment on themselves. Ezra's appeal for mercy (verse 45) is thus dismissed. As we have seen (cp. 7: 19–25, [70–4], [127–31]), the idea that man is entirely responsible for his destiny in the world to come forms a constant theme in the replies of the angel in the third dialogue, and 8: 55–62 does not really advance the argument any further.

56. *For they were given freedom:* for the thought cp. 7: [127–9]. *to treat his law with contempt:* cp. 7: 24, [72].

58. *they said to themselves, "There is no God":* cp. 7: 23; Pss. 14: 1; 53: 1. *though well aware that they must die:* death in the age to come as a punishment for denying the existence of God seems to be what is meant.

59. *the joys I have predicted:* cp. verses 51–4. *the thirst and torments which are prepared:* cp. 7: [36], [84], [86]. *It is not that the Most High has wanted any man to be lost:* cp. Ezek. 18: 23, 'Have I any desire, says the Lord GOD, for the death of a wicked man? Would I not rather that he should mend his ways and live?'; cp. also Matt. 18: 14.

60. *the One who had put life within their reach:* God had provided the opportunity of life in the age to come for all men, but the majority by their own actions had lost this.

61. *My day of judgement is now close at hand:* the idea that the end of this age and the judgement would come quickly is commonplace in Jewish and Christian writings of this period; cp. e.g. Matt. 24: 34, 'I tell you this: the present generation will live to see it all.'

62. *not made this known to all: only to you and a few like you:* these words reflect the author's own understanding of his work; like the authors of the other apocalypses (see pp. 105–8), he regarded himself as the recipient of a secret revelation intended for a very limited circle of readers. Cp. 12: 36–8; 13: 53–6; 14: 26, 46–7. ✻

MORE ABOUT THE SIGNS OF THE END

'My lord,' I replied, 'you have now revealed to me 63 the many signs which you are going to perform in the last days; but you have not told me when that will be.'

The angel answered: 'Keep a careful count yourself; **9** when you see that some of the signs predicted have already happened, then you will understand that the time 2 has come when the Most High will judge the world he has created. When the world becomes the scene of earth- 3

quakes, insurrections, plots among the nations, unstable
4 government, and panic among rulers, then you will recognize these as the events which the Most High has foretold
5 since first the world began. Just as everything that is
done on earth has its beginning and end clearly marked,*a*
6 so it is with the times which the Most High has determined: their beginning is marked by portents and
miracles, their end by manifestations of power.

7 'Whoever comes safely through and escapes destruction, thanks to his good deeds or the faith he has shown,
8 will survive all the dangers I have foretold and witness
the salvation that I shall bring to my land, the country
9 I have marked out from all eternity as my own. Then
those who have misused my law will be taken by surprise; their contempt for it will bring them continual
10 torment. All who in their lifetime failed to acknowledge
11 me in spite of all the good things I had given them, all
who disdained my law while freedom still was theirs, who
scornfully dismissed the thought of penitence while the
12 way was still open – all these will have to learn the truth
13 through torments after death. Do not be curious any
more, Ezra, to know how the godless will be tormented,
but only how and when the just will be saved; the world
is theirs and it exists for their sake.'

* The statement that the 'day of judgement' is 'close at
hand' (8: 61) leads Ezra to ask when the 'signs' preceding the
end of this age will occur (8: 63). He is told to work this out
for himself from the fulfilment of the signs which have been
foretold and about which he is now given further information
(9: 1–6). In the following verses (9: 7–12) the contrasting fates

[a] has . . . marked: *so one Vs.; Lat. defective.*

of the righteous and the wicked in the period after the last days are described. Finally Ezra is again told not to bother about 'how the godless will be tormented, but only how and when the just will be saved' (9: 13).

This passage about the signs occupies a place in the last part of the third dialogue comparable to that occupied by the earlier passages about the signs in the first and second dialogues (cp. 4: 51 – 5: 13; 6: 11–28). As we saw earlier (see on 4: 51–2), it has sometimes been argued that all the passages about the signs were interpolated by the final editor of 2 Esdras 3–14. This view seems, however, unlikely. So far as 8: 63 – 9: 13 is concerned, the passage fits quite naturally into its context – 8: 63 follows naturally on 8: 61, while 9: 13 brings the discussion firmly back to the main theme of the third dialogue – and is hardly to be regarded as an interpolation.

63. *you have now revealed to me the many signs which you are going to perform in the last days:* cp. 5: 1–12; 6: 18b–28. *but you have not told me when that will be:* Ezra had in fact already asked more than once when the end would be, but had been given only rather vague replies; cp. e.g. 4: 44–52. Here also Ezra is not given a direct reply to his question, but on this occasion he is told to work out the answer for himself from his observation of the fulfilment of the signs (9: 1–2); cp. Mark 13: 3–8, but contrast Acts 1: 7, 'It is not for you to know about dates or times, which the Father has set within his own control.'

9: 1. *the signs:* for the significance of the signs see the comment on 4: 51–2.

3. The signs have a conventional character and occur frequently in lists of this kind, e.g. Mark 13: 7–8:

'When you hear the noise of battle near at hand and the news of battles far away, do not be alarmed. Such things are bound to happen; but the end is still to come. For nation will make war upon nation, kingdom upon kingdom; there will be earthquakes in many places; there will be famines. With these things the birth-pangs of the new age begin.'

When the world becomes the scene of earthquakes: cp. 5: 8; 6: 14–16 and see the comments on both passages. *insurrections, plots among the nations:* cp. 5: 5. *unstable government, and panic among rulers:* cp. 5: 1.

4. *the events which the Most High has foretold since first the world began:* the author appears to allude to the revelations that are associated with figures of the primaeval period such as Adam or Enoch; see the comments on the apocalyptic writings above, pp. 105–8.

5–6. The N.E.B. translation follows the Syriac version, although the text is somewhat uncertain. According to the Syriac Ezra is told that the 'last days' (8: 63) have a clearly defined beginning and end just like everything else that takes place on earth; the beginning of the last days will be indicated *by portents and miracles*, and the end *by manifestations of power*; the occurrence of these events, so it is implied, will enable Ezra to recognize the last days for what they are. Verses 5–6 thus appear to continue the thought of verses 1–4 and provide a further answer to the question posed in 8: 63. *the times which the Most High has determined:* i.e. the last days. *portents and miracles:* an alternative way of referring to the 'signs'. *by manifestations of power* (literally 'in act and in signs'): the great act of judgement (cp. 9: 2) by which this age will be brought to an end and the new age inaugurated.

7–8. The righteous who *survive all the dangers* of the last days will *witness* the inauguration of the new age. Here the new age is described in traditional terms as the establishment of a messianic kingdom based on the land of Israel, cp. Ezek. 36: 24–8. *Whoever comes safely through:* cp. 6: 25. *his good deeds or the faith he has shown:* see the comment on 7: [77]. *my land:* for the idea of Israel as God's land cp. e.g. Jer. 2: 7:

> 'I brought you into a fruitful land
>   to enjoy its fruit and the goodness of it;
>   but when you entered upon it you defiled it
>   and made the home I gave you loathsome.'

The last two lines read literally, 'but you entered and defiled my land and made my inheritance loathsome'. Elsewhere in 2 Esdras 3–14 it is indicated that salvation will be restricted to those who are in the land of Israel; cp. 12: 34; 13: 48–9.

9–12. The advent of the last days will make the wicked realize too late the error of their ways, and they will be compelled to suffer 'continual torment'.

9. *my law:* literally 'my ways'.

10. *All who in their lifetime failed to acknowledge me:* cp. Matt. 10: 32–3.

11. *all who disdained my law while freedom still was theirs:* the angel reiterates the view that men had the opportunity of salvation through the observance of the law, and that their failure to make use of this opportunity was entirely their own fault; cp. e.g. 7: [72]; 8: 56–60. *while the way was still open:* i.e. before death.

12. *all these will have to learn the truth through torments after death:* the author does not here make the clear distinction that he does in 7: [75–87] between the torments which face the wicked between death and the last judgement and the torments which face them after the last judgement.

13. The angel brings the discussion back to the main theme of the third dialogue (Ezra's concern at the fate of the sinful majority of mankind) and tells him once more not to worry about the torments of the wicked, but only about the salvation of the righteous; cp. 8: 51, 55. ✶

THE ARGUMENT RECAPITULATED

I answered, 'I repeat what I have said again and again: 14, 15 the lost outnumber the saved as a wave exceeds a drop of 16 water.'

The angel replied: 'The seed to be sown depends on 17 the soil, the colour on the flower, the product on the workman, and the harvest on the farmer. There was once 18

a time before the world had been created for men to
dwell in; at that time I was planning it for the sake of
19 those who now exist. No one then disputed my plan, for
no one existed. I supplied this world with unfailing food
and a mysterious law; but those whom I created turned
20 to a life of corruption. I looked at my world, and there it
lay spoilt, at my earth in danger from men's wicked
21 thoughts; and at the sight I could scarcely bring myself
to spare them. One grape I saved out of a cluster, one
22 tree out of a forest.[a] So then let it be: destruction for the
many who were born in vain, and salvation for my
grape and my tree, which have cost me such labour to
bring to perfection.

* 14–16. *the lost outnumber the saved as a wave exceeds a drop
of water:* despite the injunction of the angel in verse 13, Ezra
refuses to be silenced, but restates in forceful terms the essence
of the problem that occupies the central place in the third
dialogue: why is it that virtually all mankind is doomed to
perish? Ezra still finds it impossible to reconcile the fate of
mankind with his notions of God's justice, and his words
constitute a defiant refusal to accept the arguments that have
been put to him and a demand for a more convincing explanation. *the lost outnumber the saved* (literally, 'those who are lost
are more than those who will be saved'): Ezra's accusation
picks up directly the words of the angel in verse 13, 'how and
when the just will be saved'.

17–22. The angel does not respond to Ezra's demand, but
repeats the view that man is responsible for his own destiny.
It is because of sin and the effects of sin that mankind faces
destruction, and it is only through God's grace that a very
small number will be saved.

17. The reply of the angel begins with a wisdom saying

[a] *So some Vss.; Lat.* tribe.

which illustrates in a striking way the principle of cause and effect. The application of the principle is given in verses 18–21. The use of sayings cast in a striking and pithy form is a characteristic feature of 2 Esdras 3–14; cp. 7: 25; 8: 46. *The seed to be sown depends on the soil* (literally, 'As is the field, so is the seed', and similarly in the following examples): the N.E.B. translation does not really convey the sense; the thought is rather that what a seed produces depends on the soil – as the other three examples indicate.

18–21. The application of the principle stated in verse 17: because the majority of men have sinned, so they will suffer punishment in the world to come. Despite the fact that God provided men 'with unfailing food and a mysterious law' (the means of physical life and the means of salvation), men 'turned to a life of corruption'. They brought ruin to the earth and thereby provoked God's anger, so much so that it was only with difficulty that a small remnant was spared. Man's total responsibility for this state of affairs is underlined by reference to the conditions that existed before the earth was created; 'at that time' God was planning the earth for the sake of men, and there was no opposition to God because man himself did not yet exist.

19b–20a. *but those whom I created turned to a life of corruption. I looked at my world, and there it lay spoilt:* cp. Gen. 6: 11–12, 'Now God saw that the whole world was corrupt and full of violence. In his sight the world had become corrupted, for all men had lived corrupt lives on earth.'

21. *I could scarcely bring myself to spare them. One grape I saved out of a cluster, one tree out of a forest:* these words, as also those of verse 22, imply that the salvation even of the few is only the result of God's grace; elsewhere it is stated that the salvation of the few will be the fully deserved reward of their deeds and their faith; cp. 8: 33; 9: 7. *forest:* the Latin 'tribe' (see the footnote) derives from a corruption in the Greek text which underlies the Latin version.

22. *So then let it be: destruction for the many who were born in*

vain, and salvation for my grape and my tree: the angel reaffirms his view in words as adamant as those of Ezra in verses 14–16; cp. 7: 25, 'Therefore, Ezra, emptiness for the empty, fullness for the full!'; also 7: [60–1]; 7: [131]. *which have cost me such labour to bring to perfection:* see on verse 21. ✳

THE CONCLUSION OF THE THIRD DIALOGUE

23, 24   'You, Ezra, must wait one more week. Do not fast this time, but go to a flowery field where no house stands, and
25   eat only what grows there – no meat or wine – and pray unceasingly to the Most High. Then I will come and talk to you again.'

✳ The conclusion of the third dialogue differs significantly from the corresponding passages in the previous dialogues (cp. 5: 14–19; 6: 29–34). As before Ezra is told to wait seven days for a further revelation and to pray, but this time he is told not to fast. Instead he is to 'go to a flowery field' and to 'eat only what grows there – no meat or wine'. This formal change marks a correspondingly significant change in the character of 2 Esdras. From now on Ezra abandons his complaints and accepts the viewpoint of God; the dialogue form is given up, and Ezra becomes the recipient of revelations in vision form, as is often the case in the so-called apocalyptic writings; see pp. 105–8.

24. The command not to eat meat or drink wine, but to eat only what grows in the field (literally 'of the flowers of the field'), has probably been included by the author under the influence of the story of Daniel and his three companions; cp. Dan 1: 5, 8–16. However, Ezra's diet also corresponds to the diet of man in the period before the flood; see Gen. 1: 29; 9: 3. ✳

Visions of the last days

✻ As we have seen, the debate between Ezra and the angel has reached something of an impasse, with neither side prepared to accept the viewpoint of the other; cp. 9: 14–16 with 9: 22. Now, however, the character of the debate changes, and Ezra, who throughout the three dialogues has accused God of injustice, comes to accept that the ways of God are just (see 10: 15–16). No reason is given for Ezra's change of attitude. Instead, just as in the end Job comes to realize not through argument but through his experience of God that he had been in the wrong, so Ezra comes through experience to acknowledge that God's treatment of man is fair. The transition is marked in the fourth section of 2 Esdras 3–14 (9: 26 – 10: 59). Ezra begins, as before, with complaint (9: 28–37), but confronted by the vision of the woman in distress (9: 38 – 10: 4) his attitude changes, and he urges the woman to 'accept God's decree as just' (10: 16). From this point on Ezra ceases complaining; his questions are no longer intended to accuse, but to elicit information. The change in the content of 2 Esdras 3–14 corresponds to a change in its form. The fourth, fifth, and sixth sections of 2 Esdras 3–14 (9: 26 – 10: 59; 11–12; 13) consist of a series of allegorical visions; in the interpretations of these visions (particularly of the last two) Ezra is given detailed information about the events of the end. The way for this has, however, already been prepared in the dialogues, namely in the sections which provide information, particularly about the signs of the end (cp. 4: 33 – 5: 13; 5: 50 – 6: 28; 7: 26–[44]; 7: [75–115]; 8: 63 – 9: 13). It is to be observed also that from the fourth section onwards the fate of mankind in general recedes into the background, and the concern is primarily with Israel.

The contrast in character between the different parts of

2 Esdras 3–14 (particularly between 3: 1 – 10: 59 and 11–12; 13; 14) led some older scholars to argue that 2 Esdras 3–14 was not a unity, but a compilation of several different writings. This view, however, fails to take account of the links that exist between the different parts of the book. It also fails to take account of its essential dramatic unity. The conflicts within the mind of the author that are revealed in the three dialogues (3: 1 – 9: 25) find their resolution in the crucial fourth section (9: 26 – 10: 59); thereafter the author is able to devote his attention exclusively to the events of the end which alone will provide the final answer to the problems that concern him. To say this is not to deny that the author has made use of older traditions, nor to deny that his ideas are not always consistent. But there are no strong reasons for not regarding 2 Esdras 3–14 as essentially the work of one author. ✳

THE VISION OF THE WOMAN IN
DISTRESS (9: 26 – 10: 59)

EZRA'S PERPLEXITIES

S O I WENT OUT, as the angel told me, to a field called Ardat. There I sat among the flowers; my food was what grew in the field, and I ate to my heart's content.
27 The week ended, and I was lying on the grass, troubled
28 again in mind with all the same perplexities. I broke my
29 silence and addressed the Most High. 'O Lord,' I said, 'you showed yourself to our fathers in the desert at the time of the exodus from Egypt, when they were travelling
30 through the barren and untrodden waste. You said, "Hear
31 me, Israel; listen to my words, race of Jacob. This is my law, which I sow among you to bear fruit and bring you
32 glory for ever." But our fathers who received your law did not keep it; they did not observe your commandments. Not that the fruit of the law perished; that was

impossible, for it was yours. Those who received it 33
perished, because they failed to keep safe the good seed
that had been sown in them. Now the usual way of 34
things is that when seed is put into the earth, or a ship on
the sea, or food or drink into a jar, then if the seed, or the
ship, or the contents of the jar should be destroyed, what 35
held or contained them does not perish with them. But
with us sinners it is different. Destruction will come upon 36
us, the recipients of the law, and upon our hearts, the
vessel that held the law. The law itself is not destroyed, 37
but survives in all its glory.'

✶ The fourth section begins in the same way as the first three
with a prayer in which Ezra, as he lies 'on the grass, troubled
again in mind with all the same perplexities' (verse 27),
attempts once more to set out the problem which concerns
him. Israel had been given the law, but had failed to observe
it; as a result Israel, but not the law, had been destroyed. Ezra
is perplexed by this state of affairs; he argues by analogy from
the natural world that it is contrary to 'the usual way of
things' (verse 34) that those who had received the law should
perish, but the law itself should survive.

26. Ezra fulfils the instructions given him in verses 23-5.
Ardat: the versions provide a number of variants for this
name, and its exact form remains uncertain. However, it is
difficult to identify Ardat with any known locality, and it
seems likely that the name has a symbolic meaning – although
what this is cannot now be ascertained. *my food was what grew
in the field:* see the comments on verses 23-5.

27. *and I was lying on the grass, troubled again in mind with
all the same perplexities:* cp. 3: 1; 5: 21; 6: 36-7.

29. *you showed yourself to our fathers in the desert at the time
of the exodus from Egypt:* cp. Exod. 19: 9; Deut. 4: 12-13.

30-1. Not an actual quotation, although for the opening

words *Hear me, Israel* cp. Deut. 4: 1; 5: 1; 6: 4; cp. also Ps. 50: 7. Verse 31 does, however, sum up in terms of the theology of 2 Esdras 3–14 the basis of the covenant relationship between God and Israel as it is expressed in Deuteronomy (cp. e.g. 7: 12–16) and elsewhere in the Old Testament. In the wilderness God gave Israel the law; obedience to the law would bring Israel *glory for ever*. By *glory* the author probably had in mind participation in the life of the world to come; cp. 7: [95]. For the gift of the law cp. also 3: 17–22; 5: 27; in the present passage the gift of the law is expressed in terms of the imagery of sowing; cp. 3: 20; 8: 6 and contrast 4: 28–32 where the same imagery is used of the 'wicked heart'.

32. *the fruit of the law:* obedience to the law leading to participation in the life of the new age; the existence of the new age was not affected by Israel's failure to keep the law.

36–7. Cp. 2 Baruch 14: 19, 'And now I see that as for the world which was made on account of us, lo! it abides, but we, on account of whom it was made, depart' (from R. H. Charles, *Apocrypha and Pseudepigrapha*, vol. 2, p. 491). ✻

THE VISION

38 While these thoughts were in my mind, I looked round, and on my right I saw a woman in great distress, mourning and loudly lamenting; her dress was torn, and 39 she had ashes on her head. Abandoning my meditations, 40 I turned to her, and said: 'Why are you weeping? What 41 is troubling you?' 'Sir,' she replied, 'please leave me to my tears and my grief; great is my bitterness of heart, 42 great my distress.' 'Tell me,' I asked, 'what has hap- 43 pened to you?' 'Sir,' she replied, 'I was barren and 44 childless through thirty years of marriage. Every hour of every day during those thirty years, day and night alike, 45 I prayed to the Most High. Then after thirty years, my

God answered my prayer and had mercy on my distress;
he took note of my sorrow and granted me a son. What
happiness he brought to my husband and myself and to
all our neighbours! What praise we gave to the Mighty
God! I took great pains over his upbringing. When he 46,47
came of age, I chose a wife for him, and fixed the date
of the wedding.

'But when my son entered his wedding-chamber, he **10**
fell down dead. So we all put out our lamps, and all my 2
neighbours came to comfort me; I controlled my grief
till the evening of the following day. When they had all 3
ceased urging me to take comfort and control my grief,
I rose and stole away in the night, and came here, as you
can see, to this field. I have made up my mind never to 4
go back to the town, but to stay here eating nothing and
drinking nothing, and to continue my mourning and
fasting unbroken till I die.'

At that I interrupted the train of my thoughts, and I 5
spoke sternly to the woman: 'You are the most foolish 6
woman in the world,' I said; 'are you blind to the grief
and sufferings of our nation? It is for the sorrow and 7
humiliation of Zion, the mother of us all, that you should
mourn so deeply; you should share in our common 8
mourning and sorrow. But you are deep in sorrow for 9
your one son. Ask the earth and she will tell you; she
must mourn for the thousands and thousands who come
to birth upon her. From her we all originally sprang, and 10
there are more to come. Almost all her children go to
perdition, and their vast numbers are wiped out. Who 11
then has the better right to be in mourning – the earth,
who has lost such vast numbers, or you, whose sorrow

12 is for one alone? You may say to me, "But my grief is very different from the earth's grief; I have lost the fruit of my own womb, which I brought to birth with pain
13 and travail, but it is only in the course of nature that the vast numbers now alive on earth should depart in the
14 same way as they have come." My answer to that is: at the cost of pain you have been a mother, but in the same way the earth has always been the mother of mankind, bearing fruit to earth's creator.

15 'Keep your sorrow to yourself, therefore, and bear
16 your misfortunes bravely. If you will accept God's decree as just, then in due time you will receive your son back
17 again, and win an honoured name among women. So go back to the town and to your husband.'

18 'No, I will not,' she replied; 'I will not go back to the town; I will stay here to die.'

19, 20 But I continued to argue with her. 'Do not do what you say', I urged; 'be persuaded because of Zion's misfortunes, and take comfort to yourself from the sorrow
21 of Jerusalem. You see how our sanctuary has been laid waste, our altar demolished, and our temple destroyed.
22 Our harps are unstrung, our hymns silenced, our shouts of joy cut short; the light of the sacred lamp is out, and the ark of our covenant has been taken as spoil; the holy vessels are defiled, and the name which God has conferred on us is disgraced; our leading men[a] have been treated shamefully, our priests burnt alive, and the Levites taken off into captivity; our virgins have been raped and our wives ravished, our godfearing men carried off, and our children abandoned; our youths have been enslaved,

[a] *So some Vss.; Lat.* our children.

224

and our strong warriors reduced to weakness. Worst of 23
all, Zion, once sealed with God's own seal, has forfeited
its glory and is in the hands of our enemies. Then throw 24
off your own heavy grief, and lay all your sorrows aside;
may the Mighty God restore you to his favour, may the
Most High give you rest and peace after your troubles!'

Suddenly, while I was still speaking to the woman, I 25
saw her face begin to shine; her countenance flashed like
lightning, and I shrank from her in terror. While I 26
wondered what this meant, she suddenly uttered a loud
and terrible cry, which shook the earth. I looked up and 27
saw no longer a woman but a complete city, built[a] on
massive foundations. I cried aloud in terror, 'Where is 28
the angel Uriel, who visited me before? It is his doing
that I have fallen into this bewilderment, that all my
hopes are shattered,[b] and all my prayers in vain.'

✻ Ezra's prayer is interrupted by his observation on his right
of 'a woman in great distress' (verse 38); we subsequently
learn that this is part of a visionary experience. The woman
tells him that she is mourning her son, born after a period of
thirty years' barrenness and brought up with great care, who
had died on his wedding-night; so great is her distress that
she has resolved to die (9: 38 – 10: 4). Ezra at first reproaches
her; she ought rather to be mourning the fate of Jerusalem
(10: 5–8). But he subsequently attempts to console her by
arguing that her loss is small in comparison with the loss
perpetually suffered by the earth whose children (i.e. mankind) are constantly dying (10: 9–18), and by urging her to
take comfort in her sorrow from the misfortunes which
Jerusalem has suffered (10: 19–24). At this point, while Ezra

[a] *Probable meaning, based on other Vss.; Lat.* but a city was being
built...   [b] *Or* that my destiny turns out to be corruption.

is still talking to her, the woman is suddenly and dramatically transformed into a city. Ezra, overwhelmed by his experiences, appeals once again to Uriel for help (10: 25–8).

The vision of the Woman in Distress, like the two following visions (chs. 11–12; 13), belongs to a distinct group of what may be termed allegorical visions. Visions of this type are to be found in several apocalyptic writings (cp. e.g. Dan. 7 and 8), and it is characteristic of them that the content of the vision is to a great extent interpreted in terms of allegory. One unusual feature of the present passage is that Ezra himself plays a role in the vision he sees.

The interpretation that is given in 10: 40–54 provides an explanation of the main elements of the vision, but it is significant that a number of features are not explained: that the woman prayed ceaselessly for the birth of the child (9: 44); that the neighbours are mentioned as sharing in both the joy at the birth and the grief at the death (9: 45; 10: 2); that it is on his wedding-night that the son dies (10: 1); that the lamps are put out (10: 2); that the woman mourns until the second night and then flees, determined to die (10: 3–4). The presence of these features, which add to the vividness of the story, but are totally ignored in the interpretation, has led to the suggestion that the author took over and adapted to his purposes an old folk-tale similar in some ways to the kind of story we have in the book of Tobit (see chs. 6–8). We lack the conclusion to the story, but it is possible in the light of 10: 16 that it told how in the end the son was miraculously restored to life (cp. 2 Kings 4: 18–37).

The words of Ezra's reply to the woman in 10: 5–8 and 10: 19–24 reveal once again how deeply affected the author of 2 Esdras 3–14 was by the fall of Jerusalem in A.D. 70, and, as we have already seen, it was largely in response to this event that 2 Esdras 3–14 was written. It is important to observe, however, that despite his continued grief, Ezra no longer blames God for these events (contrast 3: 28–36). Instead Ezra advises the woman: 'Keep your sorrow to yourself, therefore, and bear your misfortunes bravely. If you will accept God's decree as just, then in due time you will receive your son back again, and win an honoured name among women' (10: 15–16). Ezra (and behind him we are no doubt to see the author) is now prepared to accept the reality of what has happened and the justice of God's dealings in this matter. The reason for this change is not indicated; rather we are left to understand that through experience the author has overcome his doubts and no longer seeks to accuse God.

38. *her dress was torn, and she had ashes on her head:* the characteristic signs of mourning; cp. 2 Sam. 13: 19; Esther 4: 1.

43. *I was barren and childless through thirty years of marriage:* this is a common motif in a number of stories; cp. Sarah (Gen. 21: 1–7); Rachel (Gen: 30: 22–4); Hannah (1 Sam. 1); Elizabeth (Luke 1).

44. *I prayed to the Most High:* cp. 1 Sam. 1: 9–11.

45. *my distress . . . my sorrow:* so barrenness was regarded in Israel; cp. 1 Sam. 1: 6–8, 11; Luke 1: 25. *What happiness . . . to all our neighbours:* cp. Luke 1: 58.

47. *I chose a wife for him:* the father would be the one normally expected to choose the wife; the fact that the mother does it in this case has probably been dictated by the needs of the story. *the wedding:* the Latin word (*epulum*) is perhaps better translated 'wedding-feast'; for feasts at weddings cp. Judg. 14: 10; Tobit 8: 19–20; Matt. 22: 1–10.

10: 1. *he fell down dead:* cp. the theme of Tobit 6–8.

2. *lamps:* for lamps at a wedding-feast cp. Matt. 25: 1–13.

5–14. The thought of Zion as 'the mother of us all' (verses 7–8; cp. Gal. 4: 26, 'the heavenly Jerusalem . . . is our mother') leads naturally into the thought of the earth as 'the mother of mankind' (verses 8–14, especially verse 14) – although the actual expression 'mother of mankind' is not present in the Latin text.

10. *Almost all her children go to perdition:* the exceptions in the mind of the author were presumably men such as Enoch (Gen. 5: 24) and Elijah (2 Kings 2: 11).

14. Although not stated, the implication of the argument

is that the earth bears her fruit (i.e. gives birth to mankind) *at the cost of pain* in the same way as a mother.

16. *then in due time you will receive your son back again:* either through the restoration to life of the original son, or through the birth of another son; the following words imply the latter (the woman will gain honour through giving birth), but the expression used *you will receive your son back again* is somewhat ambiguous. It is possible, as we have seen, that the folk-tale which appears to have been taken over by the author ended with an account of the restoration to life of the son. *and win an honoured name among women:* cp. the words spoken by 'the women' when a son is born to Ruth (Ruth 4: 14–15).

18. The woman is not persuaded, but merely repeats what she has already stated in verse 4.

21–3. The anguish experienced by the author at the fall of Jerusalem in A.D. 70 and the consequential loss of the temple is revealed clearly in these verses.

22. *Our harps are unstrung, our hymns silenced, our shouts of joy cut short:* the loss of the temple meant the end of the worship of God in the temple. *the light of the sacred lamp is out:* the lamps on the lamp-stand (Exod. 25: 31–7) were supposed to be tended regularly (Exod. 27: 20–1; Lev. 24: 2–4), and their extinction was an indication that the temple services had ceased. In 1 Macc. 4: 50 the relighting of the lamps on the lamp-stand was one of the measures undertaken as part of the restoration of the temple after its desecration in the time of Antiochus Epiphanes (167–164 B.C.). When the temple was destroyed in A.D. 70, the lamp-stand and the other sacred utensils came into the hands of Titus and were subsequently taken to Rome and displayed in his triumphal procession. The scene is depicted on the Arch of Titus in Rome; for a photograph see the volume in this series entitled *New Testament Illustrations*, p. 17. *and the ark of our covenant has been taken as spoil:* the mention of the Ark is an historical allusion appropriate to the supposed setting of 2 Esdras 3–14 in the

sixth century B.C., not to its actual setting at the end of the
first century A.D. The Ark was apparently destroyed at the
time of the destruction of Jerusalem in 587 B.C., if not earlier,
and in any event nothing is known of it after that date.
the holy vessels are defiled: this again is a feature appropriate to
the setting of 2 Esdras 3–14 in the sixth century; see 2 Kings
25: 14–15 which refers to the taking of the temple vessels to
Babylon, and Ezra 1: 7–11 which refers to their return.
The temple vessels also play an important part in the story
of Belshazzar's feast, Dan. 5 (cp. Dan. 1: 2). In the case
of the vessels, however, the author was probably thinking
much more of their seizure by Titus in his own day (see
above). For a list of the sacred vessels see 1 Macc. 4: 49–51.
and the name which God has conferred on us is disgraced (literally,
'and the name which is called over us is disgraced'): i.e. the
name of God. Israel is called by God's name (cp. Deut. 28: 10;
2 Macc. 8: 15), an indication that the nation belongs to him.
our leading men have been treated shamefully: cp. on the one
hand 2 Kings 25: 18–21, on the other Josephus, *Jewish War*
6: 271:

> 'While the temple blazed, the victors plundered everything
> that fell in their way and slaughtered wholesale all who
> were caught. No pity was shown for age, no reverence for
> rank; children and greybeards, laity and priests, alike were
> massacred; every class was pursued and encompassed in the
> grasp of war, whether suppliants for mercy or offering
> resistance' (Loeb Classical Library translation of Josephus,
> vol. 3, p. 455).

In 2 Esdras 3–14 the reading of the Latin 'our children' (see
the footnote; the Latin text could also be translated 'our free
men') probably goes back to the same Hebrew text as that of
the other versions. *our priests burnt alive:* perhaps an exaggeration, but Josephus (*Jewish War* 6: 280) does report that two
leading priests plunged themselves into the fire that was con-
suming the temple rather than give up or face capture.

23. *Worst of all, Zion, once sealed with God's own seal, has forfeited its glory:* the translation and meaning of this passage are a little uncertain; the N.E.B. has paraphrased, and a more literal rendering of the Latin would be 'Worst of all, the seal of Zion, for she has now been unsealed of her glory.' Possibly the 'seal of Zion' is to be understood as a mark of God's protection of Jerusalem which had been withdrawn.

24. *Then throw off your own heavy grief, and lay all your sorrows aside:* repetition of the advice of verse 15.

25–7. The woman is dramatically transformed into a city. For the vision cp. Rev. 21: 9–11:

'Then one of the seven angels ... came and spoke to me and said, "Come, and I will show you the bride, the wife of the Lamb." So in the Spirit he carried me away to a great high mountain, and showed me the holy city of Jerusalem coming down out of heaven from God. It shone with the glory of God; it had the radiance of some priceless jewel, like a jasper, clear as crystal.'

Cp. also the description of the 'man' (probably the angel Gabriel) seen by Daniel in Dan. 10: 5–6.

28. *I cried aloud in terror, 'Where is the angel Uriel ... ?':* cp. verse 25, 'and I shrank from her in terror'. Fear and consternation at the sight of the vision and an appeal for an explanation are characteristic elements in allegorical visions of this kind; cp. e.g. Dan. 7: 15–16; 8: 15–17; in 2 Esdras 3–14 cp. 12: 3b–9; 13: 13b–20. *Uriel:* cp. 4: 1. *that all my hopes are shattered:* the translation given in the footnote is a less convincing interpretation of the same Latin text. Ezra cannot understand the vision and feels that his prayer (9: 29–37) has been ignored; he does not realize that the vision is in fact an answer to his prayer. *

THE INTERPRETATION OF THE VISION

I was still speaking when the angel appeared who had 29
visited me before. When he saw me lying in a dead faint, 30
unconscious on the ground, he grasped me by my right
hand, put strength into me, and raised me to my feet.
'What is the matter?' he asked. 'Why are you over- 31
come? What was it that disturbed your mind and made
you faint?' It was because you deserted me', I replied. 32
'I did what you told me: I came out to the field; and
what I have seen here and can still see is beyond my
power to relate.'

'Stand up like a man,' he said, 'and I will explain it 33
to you.'

'Speak, my lord,' I replied; 'only do not abandon me 34
and leave me to die unsatisfied. For I have seen and I hear 35
things beyond my understanding – unless this is all an 36
illusion and a dream. I beg you to tell me, my lord, the 37
meaning of my vision.'

'Listen to me,' replied the angel, 'while I explain to 38
you the meaning of the things that terrify you; for the
Most High has revealed many secrets to you. He has seen 39
your blameless life, your unceasing grief for your people,
and your deep mourning over Zion. Here then is the 40
meaning of the vision. A little while ago you saw a 41
woman in mourning, and tried to give her comfort;
now you no longer see that woman, but a whole city. 42
She told you she had lost her son, and this is the explana- 43
tion. The woman you saw is Zion, which you now see as 44
a city with all its buildings. She told you she was childless 45
for thirty years; that was because there were three thou-

sand years in which sacrifices were not yet offered in
46 Zion. But then, after the three thousand years, Solomon
built the city and offered the sacrifices; that was the time
47 when the barren woman bore her son. She took great
pains, she said, over his upbringing; that was the period
48 when Jerusalem was inhabited. Then she told you of the
great loss she suffered, how her son died on the day he
entered his wedding-chamber; that was the destruction
49 which overtook Jerusalem. Such then was the vision that
you saw – the woman mourning for her son – and you
tried to comfort her in her sufferings; this was the revela-
50 tion you had to receive. Seeing your sincere grief and
heartfelt sympathy for the woman, the Most High is now
51 showing you her radiant glory and her beauty. That was
why I told you to stay in a field where no house stood,
52 for I knew that the Most High intended to send you this
53 revelation. I told you to come to this field, where no
54 foundation had been laid for any building; for in the
place where the city of the Most High was to be revealed,
no building made by man could stand.

✻ 29–37. In response to his appeal Uriel comes to Ezra and
revives him. Ezra asks to be told the meaning of his vision.

30. Collapse on the ground and revival by an angel are
traditional elements in apocalyptic visions; see on verse 28 and
cp. Dan. 8: 17–18; 10: 8–11; Rev. 1: 17.

32. *and can still see:* the vision of the city remains before
Ezra; cp. verse 55.

33. *Stand up like a man:* see the comment on 6: 13; cp.
also 7: 2.

38–54. The interpretation of the vision given by Uriel is
not completely straightforward, but the main points seem

fairly clear. Since the woman is identified as Zion (verse 44), but the birth and death of the son correspond to the building and destruction of Jerusalem (verses 46, 48), it is now generally argued that the mother is the heavenly Jerusalem and the son the earthly Jerusalem, and it is this view which is followed here. We have seen earlier that the heavenly Jerusalem belongs to the age to come, but is at the same time thought of as being already in existence (see 8: 52 and cp. also 7: 26; 13: 36). Ezra's complaint about the fate of Israel (9: 29-37) is thus answered by a revelation of the new Jerusalem: the earthly Jerusalem had indeed been destroyed, but this was not the end; the heavenly Jerusalem was waiting ready to take its place in the age to come.

38. *the things that terrify you . . . many secrets:* in both cases the things Ezra has seen in the vision.

39. *He has seen your blameless life:* see the comments on 6: 32-3. *your unceasing grief for your people, and your deep mourning over Zion:* as revealed in the dialogues (3: 1 – 9: 25) and in the introductory prayer of the present section (9: 29-37).

44. *The woman you saw is Zion:* i.e. the heavenly Jerusalem.

45. *there were three thousand years in which sacrifices were not yet offered in Zion:* i.e. the period from the creation of the world to the building of the temple. Most Latin manuscripts have 'three years' instead of 'three thousand years' (the reading of the Syriac, Ethiopic and Arabic versions), and the three years have been interpreted literally to refer to the three years between Solomon's accession and the building of the temple (1 Kings 6: 1), and at the same time to refer mystically to three world years of one thousand years each, i.e. three thousand years. This double interpretation of the three years is not convincing, but the reading 'three years' is perhaps not just a mistake, but points to the existence of an alternative understanding of what Uriel's explanation of the vision means. *in Zion:* literally, 'in her', but it is pressing the logic of the symbolism too far to argue that the author is talking

about sacrifice in the heavenly Jerusalem; what he means is that there were three thousand years before regular sacrifices were offered in the place where the earthly Jerusalem and the temple were eventually built (the author ignores the occasional sacrifices that were offered before the building of the temple, e.g. 2 Sam. 24: 25).

46. *after the three thousand years:* so the Syriac, Ethiopic and Arabic versions; the Latin manuscripts again have 'three years' (see on verse 45). *Solomon built the city and offered the sacrifices:* contrast 3: 23-4, 'you raised up ... David. You told him to build the city that bears your name and there offer to you in sacrifice what was already your own.' Neither David nor Solomon actually built Jerusalem, but both made additions to it; see 2 Sam. 5: 9, 11; 1 Kings 6-7; in 2 Esdras 10 the author probably referred to Solomon because he had in mind particularly the building of the temple. *her son:* i.e. the earthly Jerusalem.

48. *the destruction which overtook Jerusalem:* according to the supposed setting of the book the destruction of 587 B.C., but the author really has in mind the events of A.D. 70.

49. *this was the revelation you had to receive:* so the Latin (other versions omit); if the text is correct, the point being made is that the vision is the answer to Ezra's prayer.

50. The revelation of the new Jerusalem was granted to Ezra because of his *sympathy for the woman*; cp. verse 39.

51. *That was why I told you to stay in a field where no house stood:* cp. 9: 24. ✻

THE CONCLUSION OF THE VISION

55 'Have no fear then, Ezra, and set your trembling heart at rest; go into the city, and see the magnificence of the buildings, so far as your eyes have power to see it all.
56 Then, after that, you shall hear as much as your ears have
57 power to hear. You are more blessed than most other

men, and few have such a name with the Most High as you have. Stay here till tomorrow night, when the Most 58, 59 High will show you in dreams and visions what he intends to do to the inhabitants of earth in the last days.' I did as I was told and slept there that night and the next.

✷   55–6. *see the magnificence of the buildings, so far as your eyes have power to see it all. Then, after that, you shall hear as much as your ears have power to hear:* these words imply that what was seen and heard in the vision could not adequately be comprehended by a mere human being; because of their apparent spontaneity they have been taken as an indication that the narrative is based on an actual visionary experience. Cp. 1 Cor. 2: 9, 'But, in the words of Scripture, "Things beyond our seeing, things beyond our hearing, things beyond our imagining, all prepared by God for those who love him", these it is that God has revealed to us through the Spirit.' The command to enter and see the city implies that the city is thought of as still being present before Ezra; cp. verse 32.

57. See the comment on 6: 32–3.

58–9. As on previous occasions Ezra is commanded to wait for a further revelation, but this time, for no obvious reason, the regular pattern is broken; he is to wait only two nights, not a week, and there is no reference either to fasting or to eating only what grows in the field. *the Most High will show you in dreams and visions what he intends to do to the inhabitants of earth in the last days:* the author indicates precisely the function of the two visions which follow; they describe when and how the end will come and thus supplement the information already given in different places in the dialogues (cp. 4: 33 – 5: 13; 5: 50 – 6: 28; 7: 26–[44], [75–115]; 8: 63 – 9: 13).   ✷

THE VISION OF THE EAGLE AND THE LION
(CHS. 11–12)

✳ In a dream vision Ezra sees a monstrous creature rising
from the sea, an eagle with twelve wings, eight rival wings
and three heads. The wings and heads rule over the earth in
turn and then disappear until, when only one head and two
rival wings are left, the eagle is challenged by a lion which
accuses it of tyrannizing the earth. The lion states that in
accordance with God's predetermined plan the time for the
disappearance of the eagle itself has now come, and the vision
ends with the body of the eagle bursting into flames. As we
subsequently learn, the eagle symbolizes the fourth kingdom
of the vision of Dan. 7, but interpreted to refer to the Roman
Empire not, as in Daniel, to the Greek Empire founded by
Alexander the Great (see the comment on 12: 11–13); the
lion is the Messiah. The wings and heads are Roman emperors, and the rival wings are military commanders or provincial governors who attempted to seize power. However,
although there are good reasons for thinking that the first
two wings represent Julius Caesar and Augustus, and that the
three heads are Vespasian, Titus and Domitian, it is difficult
beyond this to identify the remaining wings and rival wings
with any certainty.

The concern with Roman history and the succession of
emperors reveals something of the purpose of this vision. The
author's intention was to provide comfort and assurance for
his readers by indicating to them where they stood in time.
He wrote during the reign of Domitian, and, as we shall see,
he believed that the end of the Roman Empire and of the
present age would follow shortly after Domitian's death.
This vision offers, therefore, a rather more precise answer
than we have so far been given to the question 'How long?'
(cp. 4: 33).

We saw earlier that the vision of the Woman in Distress
(9: 26 – 10: 59) apparently uses an old folk-tale, but the

vision of the eagle very obviously draws its inspiration from the Old Testament. Several elements in the vision are taken from the Son of Man vision in Dan. 7, and since an explicit link is made with this chapter in 12: 11–12, it seems clear that Dan. 7 was in the mind of the author as he wrote. The vision of the Eagle thus provides us with further evidence of the way in which the Old Testament was used in the apocalyptic writings (see the comment on 3: 4–36). ✻

THE EAGLE

On the second night I had a vision in a dream; I saw, **11** rising from the sea, an eagle with twelve wings and three heads. I saw it spread its wings over the whole 2 earth; and all the winds blew on it, and the clouds[a] gathered. Out of its wings I saw rival wings sprout, 3 which proved to be only small and stunted. Its heads lay 4 still; even the middle head, which was bigger than the others, lay still between them. As I watched, the eagle 5 rose on its wings to set itself up as ruler over the earth and its inhabitants. I saw it bring into subjection everything 6 under heaven; it met with no opposition at all from any creature on earth. I saw the eagle stand erect on its talons, 7 and it spoke aloud to its wings: 'Do not all wake at once,' 8 it said; 'sleep in your places, and each wake up in turn; the heads are to be kept till the last.' I saw that the sound 9, 10 was not coming from its heads, but from the middle of its body. I counted its rival wings, and saw that there were 11 eight of them.

As I watched, one of the wings on its right side rose 12 and became ruler over the whole earth. After a time, its 13 reign came to an end, and it disappeared from sight com-

[a] the clouds: *so some Vss.; Lat. omits.*

pletely. Then the next one arose and established its rule,
14 which it held for a long time. When its reign was coming
to an end and it was about to disappear like the first one,
15, 16 a voice could be heard saying to it: 'You have ruled the
world for so long; now listen to my message before your
17 time comes to disappear. None of your successors will
achieve a reign as long as yours, nor even half as long.'
18 Then the third wing arose, ruled the world for a time
19 like its predecessors, and like them disappeared. In the
same way all the wings came to power in succession, and
in turn disappeared from sight.

20 As time went on, I saw the wings on the left[a] side also
raise themselves up to seize power. Some of them did
21 so, and passed immediately from sight, while others arose
22 but never came to power. At this point I noticed that
two of the little wings were, like the twelve, no longer
23 to be seen. Nothing was now left of the eagle's body
except the three motionless heads and six little wings.
24 As I watched, two of the six little wings separated from
the rest and took up a place under the head on the right.
25 The other four remained where they were; and I saw
26 them planning to rise up and seize power. One rose, but
27 disappeared immediately; so too did the second, vanishing
28 even more quickly than the first. I saw the last two
29 planning to seize the kingship for themselves. But while
they were still plotting, suddenly one of the heads woke
from sleep, the one in the middle, the biggest of the
30, 31 three. I saw how it joined with the other two heads, and
along with them turned and devoured the two little
32 wings which were planning to seize power. This head

[a] *So one Vs.; Lat.* right.

got the whole earth into its grasp, establishing an oppressive rule over all its inhabitants and a worldwide kingdom mightier than any of the wings had ruled. But 33 after that I saw the middle head vanish just as suddenly as the wings had done. There were two heads left, and 34 they also seized power over the earth and its inhabitants, but as I watched, the head on the right devoured the 35 head on the left.

* 1. *I saw, rising from the sea:* cp. Dan. 7: 2–3, 'I saw a great sea churned up by the four winds of heaven, and four huge beasts coming up out of the sea'; see also Rev. 13: 1. *an eagle with twelve wings and three heads:* cp. the descriptions of the beasts in Dan. 7: 4–8, which likewise have monstrous characteristics: 'The first was like a lion but had an eagle's wings . . . another, a beast like a leopard with four bird's wings on its back; this creature had four heads, and it was invested with sovereign power' (Dan. 7: 4, 6). The eagle was appropriate as a symbol of Rome inasmuch as it was the Roman military emblem. The beast which rises out of the sea in Rev. 13: 1 is likewise a symbol of Rome.

2. *I saw it spread its wings over the whole earth:* an indication of its universal power; cp. verses 5–6. *and all the winds blew on it:* a motif taken from Dan. 7: 2. *and the clouds gathered:* the Syriac version reads literally 'and the clouds gathered about it' (similarly the Ethiopic and Arabic), but the Latin omits 'the clouds' and 'about it'. However, the significance of the statement is not clear. In the Old Testament clouds regularly accompany the self-revelation of God (e.g. Exod. 19: 9, 16), but also symbolize the gloom of God's day of judgement (e.g. Joel 2: 1–2); neither idea suits the present passage. It is just possible that the motif has been inappropriately taken from Dan. 7: 13, 'and I saw one like a man coming with the clouds of heaven'.

3. *rival wings* (so the Latin; the other versions support the

reading 'little wings'): military commanders or provincial governors who attempted to seize power; the fact that they *proved to be only small and stunted* indicates their lack of success.

4. *Its heads lay still:* because the time for their rule had not yet come; cp. verses 8–9.

5–6. An allusion to the world-wide power exercised by the Romans in the first century A.D.

8. The emperors obviously could not all rule at the same time, but this fact has to be accommodated to the symbolism of the vision.

9. *the heads are to be kept till the last:* because we know that 2 Esdras 3–14 was written against the background of the Jewish war of A.D. 66–73 and its aftermath (see pp. 102–4), it is possible to identify the three heads as Vespasian and his two sons, Titus and Domitian, with a fair degree of certainty. The author, writing in the time of Domitian, believed that the reigns of these three emperors marked the climax of Roman rule, and expected that the end of this age would follow the death of Domitian; see 12: 28.

10. *the sound was not coming from its heads, but from the middle of its body:* because the Roman Empire itself is speaking, not one of the emperors.

11. *rival wings:* so the Latin, but other versions have 'little wings', and this (or a similar expression) is the term used from now on in the Latin. *eight:* who these were is extremely uncertain.

12–13*a*. The first wing can be identified as Julius Caesar because the next wing is clearly Augustus.

13*b*–17. The long reign indicates that the second wing represents Augustus who came to power after the death of Caesar in 44 B.C. and was in effect sole ruler from 31 B.C. to A.D. 14, although the formal recognition of his status dates only from 27 B.C.

19. *all the wings came to power in succession, and in turn disappeared:* it is not clear whether *all the wings* means all twelve

wings or only, as the N.E.B. implies, the six on the right side
(see the comment on verse 20). In either case there are considerable problems in identifying the twelve wings and eight
little wings. Since the first two wings are Caesar and Augustus,
and since the three heads are Vespasian, Titus and Domitian,
it is possible that the twelve wings are Caesar, Augustus,
Tiberius, Gaius, Claudius, Nero, Vindex, Nymphidius, Galba,
Piso (i.e. M. Piso Licinianus), Otho and Vitellius. The identification of the first six (Caesar and the emperors Augustus,
Tiberius, Gaius, Claudius and Nero) is virtually certain, that
of the second six much less so; these are men who in the
troubled years of 68 and 69 either became emperor for a short
period or were involved in attempts to seize power. However, the main difficulty with this view is the identity of the
eight little wings, and if this view is correct, it would probably
have to be said that we are not in a position to determine
whom they symbolize. Alternatively it might be argued that
Vindex, Nymphidius, Galba, Piso, Otho and Vitellius are

The Roman emperors from Augustus to Domitian	
(Murder of Julius Caesar	44 B.C.)
Augustus	27 B.C.–A.D. 14
Tiberius	A.D. 14–37
Gaius	37–41
Claudius	41–54
Nero	54–68
(Revolt of Vindex and conspiracy of	
Nymphidius	68)
Galba	68–9
Otho	69
Vitellius	69
Vespasian	69–79
Titus	79–81
Domitian	81–96

more naturally identified with six of the eight little wings. But on this view the twelve wings become a problem, for there are now apparently only six rulers left prior to Vespasian (i.e. Caesar, Augustus, Tiberius, Gaius, Claudius, Nero) whom they could represent. This difficulty could be explained by assuming that the numbers were revised after the death of Domitian in an attempt to bring the vision up to date when it had become clear that the end of this age had not yet arrived; against this, apart from the question of the numbers, there are no hints in the text to suggest that it has been revised. There are clearly difficulties involved in both explanations, as well as in others that might be suggested, and no certain conclusion can be reached. On any view it is possible that the figure 'twelve' was used primarily because it was regarded as a significant number (cp. 2 Baruch 53 where the whole of history from Adam to the period after the exile is divided up into twelve periods).

20. *I saw the wings on the left side also raise themselves up to seize power:* the N.E.B. translation implies that the first six (those on the right side) of the twelve wings are referred to in verses 12–19, and the second six (those on the left side) in verse 20. Such a view is certainly possible. However, the reading 'on the left side' is supported only by some Ethiopic manuscripts; the Latin, Syriac and Armenian versions (the Arabic does not mention the side), as well as the remaining Ethiopic manuscripts, all have 'on the right side', and this much stronger attestation suggests that there is no parallelism between the right and left sides in verses 12–19 and 20. Besides this, there are indications that the rival or little wings are meant in verse 20; for *the wings* the Latin actually has 'the wings which followed', the Syriac 'the little wings'; the Latin is ambiguous, but the Syriac quite explicit. Verse 20 could certainly be interpreted without difficulty as referring to the little wings, and if this is so, (1) 'all the wings' in verse 19 means all twelve wings, (2) the detail 'on its right side' (verses 12, 20) has no particular significance.

22. *two of the little wings:* possibly Vindex and Nymphidius who were both involved in plots in the last months of Nero's reign. For a vivid description of the events of this period see the accounts by Suetonius (*The Lives of the Caesars*) and Tacitus (*The Histories*); see the Note on Further Reading, p. 306.

23. This verse refers to the period immediately after the death of Nero in June 68.

24. *two of the six little wings ... took up a place under the head on the right:* the head on the right is Domitian (emperor from 81 to 96), but there has been no entirely convincing identification of the two little wings which joined him, nor is it clear why they should be mentioned here rather than later.

26. *One rose, but disappeared immediately:* possibly Galba who became emperor after the death of Nero, but was murdered in January 69.

27. *the second, vanishing even more quickly than the first:* possibly M. Piso Licinianus who was nominated co-ruler by Galba, but was likewise murdered.

28. *the last two:* possibly Otho and Vitellius who were emperors for brief periods during 69; the former took his own life, the latter was murdered.

29. *one of the heads ... the one in the middle, the biggest of the three:* Vespasian, the general in command of the operations against the Jews, who was declared emperor by his legions and was the one ultimately successful in the struggle for power in the year 69. He reigned until 79.

30. *the other two heads:* his sons, Titus and Domitian.

32. *an oppressive rule:* the author's attitude towards Vespasian was no doubt strongly influenced by the measures taken against the Jews in the aftermath of the Jewish war.

35. *the head on the right devoured the head on the left:* according to rumour the death of Titus (*the head on the left*) was supposed to have been brought about by Domitian (*the head on the right*). The former was emperor from 79 to 81, the latter from

81 to 96. Verse 35 forms the conclusion of the description of the past; the author has now reached the time at which he is writing and what follows is his prophecy of the events that would take place in the last days; cp. the comparable transition that occurs in Dan. 11 between verse 39 and verse 40.   ✲

THE LION

36 Then I heard a voice which said to me: 'Look carefully
37 at what you see before you.' I looked, and saw what seemed to be a lion roused from the forest; it roared as it came, and I heard it address the eagle in a human voice.
38 'Listen to what I tell you', it said. 'The Most High says
39 to you: Are you not the only survivor of the four beasts to which I gave the rule over my world, intending
40-41 through them to bring my ages to their end? You are the fourth beast, and you have conquered all who went before, ruling over the whole world and holding it in the grip of fear and harsh oppression. You have lived[a] long in the world, governing it with deceit and with no
42 regard for truth. You have oppressed the gentle and injured the peaceful, hating the truthful and loving liars; you have destroyed the homes of the prosperous, and razed to the ground the walls of those who had done
43 you no harm. Your insolence is known to the Most
44 High, and your pride to the Mighty One. The Most High has surveyed the periods he has fixed: they are now at an
45 end, and his ages have reached their completion. So you, eagle, must now disappear and be seen no more, you and your terrible great wings, your evil small wings, your

[a] You are the fourth ... lived: *so some Vss.; Lat.* The fourth beast came and conquered ... It has lived ...

cruel heads, your grim talons, and your whole worthless body. Then all the earth will feel relief at its deliverance 46 from your violence, and look forward hopefully to the judgement and mercy of its Creator.'

While the lion was still addressing the eagle, I looked **12** 1 and saw the one remaining head disappear. Then the 2 two*a* wings which had gone over to him arose and set themselves up as rulers. Their reign was short and troubled, and when I looked at them they were already 3 vanishing. Then the eagle's entire body burst into flames, and the earth was struck with terror.

※ 37. *a lion:* identified in 12: 31–2 with the Messiah. The symbolism perhaps goes back to the prophecy concerning Judah in Gen. 49: 9; cp. Rev. 5: 5 where the Messiah is described as 'the Lion from the tribe of Judah, the Scion of David'.

39–40*a. Are you not the only survivor of the four beasts ... ? You are the fourth beast:* the eagle is identified as the fourth beast, i.e. the fourth kingdom, of Dan. 7: 7; cp. 12: 10–12.

40*b*–43. The author, writing under the impact of the events of the Jewish war, accuses the Romans of ruling with cruelty and injustice. In the Latin version of part of verses 40 and 41 the third person was used by mistake instead of the second person; see the footnote.

44–5. The end of the Roman Empire is in accordance with God's plan. The thought underlying these verses is one common to many apocalyptic writings: God has determined in advance the duration of this world and the course of human history (cp. verse 39, 'Are you not the only survivor of the four beasts to which I gave the rule over my world, intending through them to bring my ages to their end?'). However,

[a] *So other Vss.; Lat. corrupt.*

despite holding this deterministic view, the author also believed that men were responsible for their own destiny, as we have seen. So here the downfall of Rome is presented both as part of God's plan and at the same time as a consequence of its despotic and arrogant behaviour.

46. *all the earth will . . . look forward hopefully to the judgement and mercy of its Creator:* not the last judgement, but the judgement of the Roman Empire; this would be followed by the reign of the Messiah; cp. 12: 31–4.

12: 1–3*a. I looked and saw the one remaining head disappear:* the death of Domitian still lay in the future; it would be one of the events of 'the last days'; see verse 28. *the two wings:* see the comment on 11: 24; the death of these two would also be one of the events of the last days; cp. verses 29–30. *Then the eagle's entire body burst into flames:* cp. the fate of the fourth beast in Dan. 7: 11, 'I went on watching until the beast was killed and its carcass destroyed: it was given to the flames.'   ✳

THE INTERPRETATION OF THE VISION

So great was my alarm and fear that I awoke, and said 4 to myself: 'See the result of your attempt to discover the 5 ways of the Most High! My mind is weary; I am utterly exhausted. The terrors of this night have completely 6 drained my strength. So I will now pray to the Most 7 High for strength to hold out to the end.' Then I said: 'My Master and Lord, if I have won your favour and stand higher in your approval than most men, if it is 8 true that my prayers have reached your presence, then give me strength; reveal to me, my Lord, the exact interpretation of this terrifying vision, and so bring full 9 consolation to my soul. For you have already judged me worthy to be shown the end of the present age.'

He said to me: 'Here is the interpretation of your 10
vision. The eagle you saw rising from the sea represents 11
the fourth kingdom in the vision seen by your brother
Daniel. But he was not given the interpretation which I 12
am now giving you or have already given you. The 13
days are coming when the earth will be under an empire
more terrible than any before. It will be ruled by twelve 14
kings, one after another. The second to come to the 15
throne will have the longest reign of all the twelve. That 16
is the meaning of the twelve wings you saw.

'As for the voice which you heard speaking from the 17
middle of the eagle's body, and not from its heads, this
is what it means: After this second king's reign, great 18
conflicts will arise, which will bring the empire into
danger of falling; and yet it will not fall then, but will be
restored to its original strength.

'As for the eight lesser wings which you saw growing 19
from the eagle's wings, this is what they mean: The 20
empire will come under eight kings whose reigns will be
trivial and short-lived; two of them will come and go 21
just before the middle of the period, four will be kept
back until shortly before its end, and two will be left
until the end itself.

'As for the three heads which you saw sleeping, this is 22
what they mean: In the last years of the empire, the Most 23
High will bring to the throne three kings, who will
restore much of its strength, and rule*a* over the earth and 24
its inhabitants more oppressively than anyone before.
They are called the eagle's heads, because they will com- 25

[a] who . . . rule: *so some Vss.; Lat.* and he will restore . . . and they
will rule . . .

plete and bring to a head its long series of wicked deeds.
26 As for the greatest head, which you saw disappear, it
signifies one of the kings, who will die in his bed, but in
27 great agony. The two that survived will be destroyed by
28 the sword; one of them will fall by the sword of the
other, who will himself fall by the sword in the last days.
29 'As for the two little wings that went over to the head
30 on the right side, this is what they mean: They are the
ones whom the Most High has reserved until the last
days, and their reign, as you saw, was short and troubled.
31 'As for the lion which you saw coming from the
forest, roused from sleep and roaring, which you heard
addressing the eagle, taxing it with its wicked deeds and
32 words, this is the Messiah whom the Most High has kept
back until the end. He will address[a] those rulers, taxing
them openly with their sins, their crimes, and their
33 defiance. He will bring them alive to judgement; he will
34 convict them and then destroy them. But he will be
merciful to those of my people that remain, all who have
been kept safe in my land; he will set them free and give
them gladness, until the final day of judgement comes,
about which I told you at the beginning.
35 'That, then, is the vision which you saw, and its mean-
36 ing. It is the secret of the Most High, which no one except
37 yourself has proved worthy to be told. What you have
seen you must therefore write in a book and deposit it
38 in a hiding-place. You must also disclose these secrets to
those of your people whom you know to be wise
39 enough to understand them and to keep them safe. But
stay here yourself for seven more days, to receive what-

[a] He will address: *probable reading; Lat. defective.*

ever revelation the Most High thinks fit to send you.'
Then the angel left me.

* 3*b*–9. Ezra wakes in terror and prays to God to be shown
the meaning of the vision; as we have seen, these are common
motifs in visions of this kind; cp. the comment on 10: 28.

7. *if I have won your favour:* see the comment on 5: 56.
and stand higher in your approval than most men: as he had been
repeatedly assured; cp. 7: [76]; 8: 47–9; 10: 57. *if it is true
that my prayers have reached your presence:* cp. 6: 32.

9. *For you have already judged me worthy to be shown the end
of the present age:* Ezra is apparently alluding to the information given him during the course of the three dialogues.

10–34. The interpretation is given in language that is indirect in character and in some respects no clearer than the
vision itself, although no doubt the author's contemporaries
understood exactly what was meant. The use of language of
this kind is typical of such visions (cp. e.g. the interpretation
in Dan. 7: 23–7) and forms part of the whole apocalyptic
approach, namely that the revelations which are given are
mysteries intended, not for the general public, but only for a
restricted group of wise men who are capable of understanding them (cp. e.g. verses 36–8 and see the comment on
8: 62).

10. *He said to me:* we are not told who the speaker is, and
from this point on it is left quite unclear whether it is the
angel or God who answers Ezra.

11–13. *The eagle . . . represents the fourth kingdom in the
vision seen by your brother Daniel. But he was not given the
interpretation which I am now giving you:* the author indicates
clearly his use and reinterpretation of the vision of Dan. 7.
The eagle is the fourth kingdom (Dan. 7: 7–8, 11, 19–27), but
whereas in Daniel this is the Greek Empire founded by
Alexander the Great, in 2 Esdras 3–14 it is the Roman Empire.
In a somewhat similar way the author of Rev. 13: 1–10 has
drawn on Dan. 7 in his description of the beast which sym-

bolizes the Roman Empire, although in Revelation the term
'fourth kingdom' is not used. For the eagle as a symbol of
Rome see on 11: 1. *The days are coming:* the vision is supposed to have been received during the exile in Babylon, i.e.
at a time long before the Roman Empire came into existence.

14–16. *twelve kings . . . twelve wings:* see the comment on
11: 19. *The second . . . will have the longest reign of all the twelve:*
i.e. Augustus; see on 11: 13*b*–17.

17. *As for the voice which you heard speaking from the middle
of the eagle's body, and not from its heads:* these words suggest a
reference to 11: 10, but cp. also 11: 15. However, the following
verse is not an interpretation of the speech in 11: 7–9 (which
in any case would be out of place at this point), nor of the
speech in 11: 16–17; see below.

18. *After this second king's reign:* so the Latin, but the Syriac
and Armenian versions read 'In the middle of the time of that
kingdom', and these versions probably preserve the original
text. The author has used a detail taken from 11: 10 (the
middle of the eagle's body) as the basis of a piece of interpretation which has no real counterpart in the vision itself.
From an historical point of view verse 18 seems to refer to the
troubled period which followed the death of Nero, and to the
restoration under Vespasian, events which are dealt with in
more detail in verses 19–21 and 22–8.

19–21. *eight lesser wings . . . eight kings:* see the comment on
11: 19. *two of them will come and go just before the middle of the
period:* possibly Vindex and Nymphidius; see the comment
on 11: 22. *four will be kept back until shortly before its end:*
possibly Galba, Piso, Otho and Vitellius; see the comment on
11: 26–8. *and two will be left until the end itself:* cp. 11: 24;
12: 2; as we have seen, there has been no convincing identification of these two little wings.

22–5. *three heads . . . the Most High will bring to the throne
three kings:* the Flavian emperors, Vespasian, Titus and
Domitian (cp. 11: 29–35 and see the comment on 11: 9). The
deterministic view of history held by the author is reflected

clearly here; it was God who controlled what happened to the Romans, and thus he who brought the kings to the throne. *In the last years of the empire:* the author of 2 Esdras 3–14 believed that the end of the Roman Empire (and of the present age) would follow immediately after the rule of these three emperors; cp. verse 25. *who will restore much of its strength:* the Flavian emperors brought a period of peace and stability after the disorders of 68 and 69. In the Latin version the text of verse 23 is slightly out of order; see the footnote. *and rule . . . more oppressively than anyone before:* the accusation again reflects the impact of the events of the war of A.D. 66–73; cp. 11: 32.

26. *the greatest head:* Vespasian; cp. 11: 32–3. *who will die in his bed, but in great agony:* Vespasian died of fever.

27. *The two that survived:* Titus and Domitian; cp. 11: 34.

28. *one of them will fall by the sword of the other:* the death of Titus; see the comment on 11: 35. *who will himself fall by the sword in the last days:* the death of Domitian (cp. 12: 1–2*a*) which for the author still lay in the future; it would be one of the events of *the last days*, i.e. of the end of the present age.

29–30. *the two little wings:* cp. 11: 24; 12: 2*b*–3*a*. As we have seen, there has been no convincing identification of these two; for the author their death also lay in the future. *until the last days:* here literally 'for its end', i.e. for the end of the eagle.

31–4. The Messiah; cp. 7: 26–44 and see the comment on 7: 28 where the name and functions of this figure are discussed. In the present passage his tasks are to judge, convict and destroy the Roman Empire (verses 31–3), and to bring deliverance and happiness to the remnant of God's people who survive (verse 34).

31–3. *As for the lion . . . this is the Messiah:* cp. 11: 36–46 and for the symbolism see the comment on 11: 37. *whom the Most High has kept back until the end:* these words imply that the Messiah is already in existence; he is kept by God in readiness until the time comes for him to act. In 1 Enoch the pre-existence of the Son of Man, who is likewise kept back by God until the end of this age, is stated rather more explicitly; see 48: 6, 'he was chosen and hidden before him (i.e. God) before the world was created', and 62: 7, 'For from the beginning the Son of Man was hidden, and the Most High kept him in the presence of his power.' *until the end:* so the Latin, but the Syriac and other versions add 'of days', thus making clear that the end of this age is meant; the end of this age coincides with the end of the Roman Empire which will be destroyed by the Messiah. The Syriac and other versions continue 'who will spring from the seed of David. He will come and address . . . ' (the Latin is defective here, see the footnote); the belief that the Messiah would be a descendant of David, which was based on such passages as Isa. 11: 1 and Jer. 23: 5, was widespread (cp. e.g. Psalms of Solomon 17: 23, 'Behold, O Lord, and raise up for them their king, the son of David, at the time when you see, O God, that he should reign over Israel, your servant'; in the New Testament cp. Rev. 5: 5; 22: 16, and contrast Matt. 22: 41–6 where this belief is challenged as being inadequate). *He will address those rulers, taxing them openly with their sins . . . He will bring them alive to judgement:* it is interesting to observe that the Messiah brings about the end of the Roman Empire, not in a great battle, but through an act of judgement; cp. 13: 37. In this respect he functions in a similar way to the Son of Man in 1 Enoch whose role is primarily that of the judge of the wicked; cp. e.g. 69: 27, 'and the whole judgement was given to the Son of Man, and he will cause the sinners to pass away and be destroyed from the face of the earth'.

34. This verse describes the reign of the Messiah (see the comment on 7: 28); the destruction of the Romans would be followed by the liberation of those who survived the end of this age and by the establishment of the messianic kingdom. *those of my people that remain:* i.e. those who survive the woes which will occur at the end of this age; cp. 6: 25; 7: 27–8; 9: 7–8. *all who have been kept safe in my land:* as in 9: 8 and

13: 48 the messianic kingdom will be based on the land of Israel. *my land* (literally 'my borders'): at this point the speaker is assumed to be God; for Israel as God's land see the comment on 9: 8. *give them gladness:* cp. 7: 28, the Messiah will 'bring four hundred years of happiness to all who survive'. *until the final day of judgement comes:* the reign of the Messiah is only of limited duration (cp. 7: 28); it will be followed by the day of judgement which will mark the beginning of the new age. *about which I told you at the beginning:* perhaps a specific allusion to 7: 26–[44] where the day of judgement as the sequel to the reign of the Messiah is described in some detail. But the day of judgement forms a constant theme throughout the dialogues (3: 1 – 9: 25).

35. *That, then, is the vision which you saw:* cp. 11: 1.

36. *the secret … which no one except yourself has proved worthy to be told:* these words no doubt reflect the author's convictions about his own status and about the revelation which he had received; see the comment on 6: 32–3.

37. The command to write an account of the vision and to hide it in a secret place is part of the apocalyptic technique; it is intended to explain how Ezra's revelation, which supposedly dated from the period of the exile, only became known at a much later date, i.e. at the end of the first century A.D., the time when it was actually composed. Similar commands, with a similar purpose, are to be found in other apocalyptic writings; cp. e.g. Dan. 12: 4, 'But you, Daniel, keep the words secret and seal the book till the time of the end.'

38. *You must also disclose these secrets to those of your people whom you know to be wise enough to understand them:* see the comment on 8: 62. The apocalyptic revelations are intended only for the wise, who alone are capable of understanding them.

39. *stay here … for seven more days:* cp. 5: 13; 6: 31; 9: 23, and contrast 10: 58. *the angel:* only mentioned in the Armenian version; see the comment on verse 10.   ✳

EZRA COMFORTS THE PEOPLE

40   When all the people heard that seven days had passed without my returning to the town, they assembled and
41 came to me. 'What wrong or injury have we done you,' they asked me, 'that you have deserted us and settled
42 here? Out of all the prophets you are the only one left to us. You are like the last cluster in a vineyard, like a lamp in the darkness, or a safe harbour for a ship in a
43, 44 storm. Have we not suffered enough? If you desert us, we had far better have been destroyed in the fire that
45 burnt up Zion. We are no better than those who perished there.' Then they raised a loud lamentation.

46   I replied: 'Take courage, Israel; house of Jacob, lay
47 aside your grief. The Most High bears you in mind, and
48 the Mighty One has not for ever[a] forgotten you. I have not left you, nor abandoned you; I came here to pray for Zion in her distress, and to beg for mercy for your
49 sanctuary that has fallen so low. Go to your homes now, every one of you; and in a few days' time I will come back to you.'

50   So the people returned to the town as I told them,
51 while I remained in the field. I stayed there for seven days in obedience to the angel, eating nothing but what grew in the field, and living on that for the whole of the time.

✻   40–5. The people come to Ezra and complain that he has abandoned them.

   40. *When all the people heard that seven days had passed:* apparently an allusion to 9: 23. Ezra had waited a week before he had the vision of the Woman in Distress (cp. 9: 26–7),

[a] *So one Vs.; Lat.* in strife.

and a further two nights before the vision of the eagle (cp. 10: 58 – 11: 1). *without my returning to the town:* i.e. to Babylon (cp. 3: 1). Ezra had gone out from Babylon to the 'field called Ardat' (9: 26) and had not returned from there.

42. *Out of all the prophets you are the only one left to us:* Ezra is here regarded as a prophet; cp. 1: 1; 15: 1, and see p. 77.

43–5. The complaint of the people leads naturally into a reference to the fate of Jerusalem, the problem with which 2 Esdras 3–14 begins (cp. ch. 3). Ezra takes up this point in the course of his reply in verse 47.

46–9. Ezra assures the people that they have neither been forgotten by God, nor abandoned by himself; they should return home to await him.

47. *The Most High bears you in mind, and the Mighty One has not for ever forgotten you:* Ezra's words here allude to what had been said in verses 43–5. His positive statement contrasts strikingly with his earlier complaints about God's dealings with Israel and is a further indication of the change of attitude that occurs after 9: 25. *for ever:* so the Syriac version; the Latin 'in strife' (see the N.E.B. footnote) probably goes back to a misunderstanding of the same Greek text as that underlying the Syriac.

51. *I stayed there for seven days in obedience to the angel:* cp. verse 39. Once again it is only the Armenian version that actually refers to the angel; cp. verse 10; the Latin, Syriac and Ethiopic versions have literally 'as he had commanded me'. *eating nothing but what grew in the field:* Ezra maintains the diet prescribed in 9: 24. ✳

THE VISION OF THE MAN FROM THE SEA (CH. 13)

✳ We saw earlier that the vision of the Eagle (chs. 11–12) was intended to provide comfort for the author's contemporaries by indicating when the end of the Roman Empire – and of this age – would occur, but in the course of the vision

the role of the Messiah in the events of the end was also
described (cp. 11: 36 – 12: 3*a*; 12: 31–4). The vision of the
Man from the Sea offers a further description of the role of
the Messiah which, like the vision of the Eagle, is based on the
Son of Man vision in Dan. 7. There are, however, a number
of differences. The vision itself (13: 1–13*a*), although drawing
its primary inspiration from Dan. 7, also makes use of motifs
taken from Dan. 2 and from a wide range of other Old
Testament passages. More importantly, in the interpretation
(13: 25–53) the term 'Messiah' is not used; instead the man
from the sea is identified as 'my son' (cp. e.g. 13: 32). In
addition the functions assigned to this figure differ to some
extent from those assigned to the Messiah in the vision of the
eagle. These differences may suggest that in the composition
of this section (i.e. ch. 13) of 2 Esdras 3–14 the author drew on
other already existing traditions. More important than this is
to ask what was the author's purpose in adding the vision of
the man from the sea. In effect the vision provides a further
comment on the tasks of the Messiah which supplements the
picture already given in the preceding vision: the Messiah
will not merely judge and destroy the Romans, he will
destroy all the nations opposed to him (cp. 13: 25–38) and
will then gather in the land of Israel the twelve tribes to
participate in the messianic kingdom (cp. 13: 39–50).   ✶

THE VISION

13 The seven days passed; and the next night I had a dream.
2 In my dream, a wind came up out of the sea and set the
3 waves in turmoil. And this wind brought a human figure
rising from the depths,*a* and as I watched, this man came
flying*b* with the clouds of heaven. Wherever he turned
his eyes, everything that they fell on was seized with

[a] And ... depths: *so other Vss.; Lat. defective.*
[b] *So other Vss.; Lat.* grew strong.

terror; and wherever the sound of his voice reached, all 4
who heard it melted like wax at the touch of fire.

Next I saw an innumerable host of men gathering from 5
the four winds of heaven to wage war on the man who
had risen from the sea. I saw that the man hewed out a 6
vast mountain for himself, and flew up on to it. I tried to 7
see from what quarter or place the mountain had been
taken, but I could not. Then I saw that all who had 8
gathered to wage war against the man were filled with
fear, and yet they dared to fight against him. When he 9
saw the hordes advancing to attack, he did not so much
as lift a finger against them. He had no spear in his hand,
no weapon at all; only, as I watched, he poured what 10
seemed like a stream of fire out of his mouth, a breath
of flame from his lips, and a storm of sparks from his
tongue. All of them combined into one mass – the stream 11
of fire, the breath of flame, and the great storm. It fell
on the host advancing to join battle, and burnt up every
man of them; suddenly all that enormous multitude had
disappeared, leaving nothing but dust and ashes and a
reek of smoke. I was dumbfounded at the sight.

After that, I saw the man coming down from the 12
mountain and calling to himself a different company, a
peaceful one. He was joined by great numbers of men, 13
some with joy on their faces, others with sorrow. Some
came from captivity; some brought others to him as an
offering.

* The vision falls into three parts: (1) the appearance of the
Man from the Sea (verses 1–4); (2) the defeat of the forces
opposed to him (verses 5–11); (3) the summoning of a peaceful
company (verses 12–13*a*).

2. *In my dream, a wind came up out of the sea and set the waves in turmoil:* cp. 11: 1–2 and Dan. 7: 2, 'In my visions of the night I . . . saw a great sea churned up by the four winds of heaven.'

3*a*. *And this wind brought a human figure rising from the depths:* the author of 2 Esdras 3–14 has rather dramatically altered the sense of Dan. 7, the passage on which he is at this point dependent; in Dan. 7 it is the beasts, symbolizing the forces hostile to God, who rise from the sea, not the 'one like a man' (Dan. 7: 13). *and as I watched, this man came flying with the clouds of heaven:* cp. Dan. 7: 13, 'I was still watching in visions of the night and I saw one like a man coming with the clouds of heaven'; Isa. 19: 1, 'See how the LORD comes riding swiftly upon a cloud.' In the Old Testament clouds regularly accompany a self-revelation of God (cp. e.g. Exod. 19: 9, 16); correspondingly in 2 Esdras 3–14 the fact that the man flies *with the clouds of heaven* is an indication that he, like the 'one like a man' of Dan. 7, has some kind of divine status. In the New Testament cp. Rev. 1: 7 (Jesus 'is coming with the clouds') and Matt. 24: 30. *came flying:* the Latin 'grew strong' (see the N.E.B. footnote) is merely a mistake.

3*b*–4. The things said here about the man from the sea are similar to things said in the Old Testament about God; this is not chance, but is a further indication of the divine status of the Man from the Sea. *Wherever he turned his eyes, everything that they fell on was seized with terror:* cp. Ps. 104: 32, 'When he looks at the earth, it quakes.' *and wherever the sound of his voice reached, all who heard it melted like wax at the touch of fire:* the simile of wax melting before fire is used several times in the Old Testament in passages referring to the self-revelation of God; cp. e.g. Ps. 97: 5:

'The mountains melt like wax as the LORD approaches,
    the Lord of all the earth.'

Cp. also Ps. 68: 2; Micah 1: 3–4.

5. The nations of the world gather to fight in a last great battle against *the man who had risen from the sea*. For the motif cp. Ezek. 38–9, the assault of Gog and his forces on the land of Israel, and see the comment on this passage in the commentary on Ezekiel in this series (p. 254). Cp. also Dan. 7: 21, 25. *from the four winds of heaven:* i.e. from the four quarters of heaven, a way of saying 'from the whole world'.

6. *the man hewed out a vast mountain for himself:* the author is drawing on Dan. 2. In his dream Nebuchadnezzar saw a stone, 'hewn from a mountain, not by human hands', which shattered the statue of gold, silver, bronze, iron and clay, and then became 'a great mountain filling the whole earth' (Dan. 2: 34–5). Subsequently the stone is identified as a kingdom, established by God, which destroys the kingdoms symbolized by the statue (Dan. 2: 44–5). In 2 Esdras 3–14 the mountain is identified in the interpretation as the pre-existent heavenly Jerusalem (verse 36, cp. 7: 26; 10: 27, 38–59). Verse 36 makes clear the link with Dan. 2 by adding a significant detail ('hewn out, not by the hand of man') to its description of the mountain. *and flew up on to it:* in Dan. 2 the stone shatters the statue which symbolizes the kingdoms; in 2 Esdras 3–14 the Messiah stands on the mountain in order to destroy his enemies (cp. verse 35).

7. Ezra cannot *see from what quarter or place the mountain had been taken* because, as a symbol of the new Jerusalem, it belongs to the heavenly world.

10. *he poured what seemed like a stream of fire out of his mouth, a breath of flame from his lips, and a storm of sparks from his tongue:* probably based on Isa. 11: 4, the passage referring to the ideal Davidic king:

'his mouth shall be a rod to strike down the ruthless, and with a word he shall slay the wicked.'

Cp. also Ps. 18: 8, which describes God coming to the aid of the Psalmist:

> 'Smoke rose from his nostrils,
>   devouring fire came out of his mouth,
>   glowing coals and searing heat.'

For a similar motif in the New Testament cp. 2 Thess. 2: 8.

11. *It fell on the host . . . and burnt up every man of them:* in Dan. 7 the fourth beast is destroyed by being burned in fire (Dan. 7: 11). Fire is mentioned elsewhere in the Old Testament as the means by which God destroys those who have incurred his anger; cp. Ezek. 39: 6 (significantly in the context of the Gog prophecy; cp. the comment on verse 5) and frequently in Amos 1–2.

12. *I saw the man . . . calling to himself a different company, a peaceful one:* after defeating his enemies the Messiah will gather those who will be his subjects in his kingdom.

13a. *some with joy on their faces, others with sorrow:* the former are presumably Jews, and the latter gentiles, although the gentiles are not in fact mentioned in the interpretation (but see the comment on verses 49–50). The theme of the conversion of the gentiles occurs in several Old Testament writings; in Isa. 55: 3–5 their conversion is, in an indirect way, the work of the Davidic Messiah. *Some came from captivity:* i.e. Jews in captivity; cp. Isa. 42: 6–7, referring to God's appointment of his servant:

> 'I have formed you, and appointed you . . .
> to bring captives out of prison,
>   out of the dungeons where they lie in darkness.'

some brought others to him as an offering: the words are apparently based on Isa. 66: 20:

> 'From every nation they shall bring your countrymen . . .
> as an offering to the LORD'

Thus the implication of the passage in 2 Esdras is that Gentiles will bring Jews.   *

EZRA REFLECTS ON THE SIGNIFICANCE OF THE VISION

I woke up in terror, and prayed to the Most High. I said, 'You have revealed these marvels to me, your 14 servant, all the way through; you have judged me worthy to have my prayers answered. Now show me the mean- 15 ing of this dream also. How terrible, to my thinking, it 16 will be for all who survive to those days! But how much worse for those who do not survive! Those who do not 17 survive will have the sorrow of knowing what is in store 18 in the last days and yet missing it. Those who do survive 19 are to be pitied for the terrible dangers and trials which, as these visions show, they will have to face. But perhaps 20 after all it is better to endure the dangers and reach the goal than to vanish out of the world like a cloud and never see the events of the last days.'

'Yes,' he replied, 'I will explain the meaning of this 21 vision, and tell you all that you ask. As for your question 22 about those who survive, this is the answer: the very 23 person from whom the danger will then come will pro- tect in danger those who have works and fidelity laid up to their credit with the Most High. You may be assured 24 that those who survive are more highly blessed than those who die.

* 13*b*–20. As on previous occasions Ezra is overcome by fear and asks to be shown the meaning of his dream; for these typical motifs see the comment on 10: 28. But the content of the dream also leads Ezra to reflect on the alternatives that face men: survival until the last days, or death before the end. Distress is inevitable in either case, but he concludes that the former is preferable to the latter.

14. *You have revealed these marvels to me, your servant, all the way through:* cp. 8: 63. The marvels are the revelations about the end which Ezra has received throughout the preceding dialogues and visions. *you have judged me worthy to have my prayers answered:* cp. the rather more tentative words that are used in 12: 7–9.

16. *How terrible . . . for all who survive to those days!:* i.e. to the time when the Messiah will destroy his enemies (verses 5–11), and more generally to the time of distress which will occur at the end of this age (cp. 5: 1–12; 6: 18*b*–28; 9: 1–13). Strictly speaking, Ezra, who has just asked to be told the meaning of his dream, does not at this point know that the vision of the Man from the Sea refers to the Messiah. But it would be wrong to conclude from this inconsistency – as some older scholars did – that verses 16–24 do not belong to the original text. *But how much worse for those who do not survive!:* i.e. for those who die before the time of distress at the end of this age.

17–18. *what is in store in the last days:* the blessings of the messianic kingdom (cp. 7: 28). Those who die before the end will miss not only the distress, but also the reign of the Messiah which will follow.

19. *the terrible dangers and trials:* cp. the comment on verse 16 and the passages mentioned there.

20. It is preferable to survive to the period of distress, and to live through it, in order to enjoy the blessings of the messianic kingdom, than to die before the end.

21–4. Ezra is assured that the righteous who survive to the last days will be protected.

21. *he replied:* it is again left unclear whether it is the angel or God who answers Ezra; cp. the comment on 12: 10.

23. *the very person from whom the danger will then come:* i.e. the Messiah, who will not only destroy his enemies, but will at the same time protect the righteous who are to be the subjects of his kingdom. *those who have works and fidelity laid*

up *to their credit with the Most High:* cp. the comment on
7: [77].
    24. The conclusion which Ezra had reached in verse 20
is confirmed. ✻

THE INTERPRETATION OF THE VISION

'This is what the vision means: The man you saw   25
rising from the depths of the sea is he whom the Most   26
High has held in readiness through many ages; he will
himself deliver the world he has made, and determine
the lot of those who survive. As for the breath, fire, and   27
storm which you saw pouring from the mouth of the
man, so that without a spear or any weapon in his hand   28
he destroyed the hordes advancing to wage war against
him, this is the meaning: The day is near when the Most   29
High will begin to bring deliverance to those on earth.
Then men will all be filled with great alarm; they will   30, 31
plot to make war on one another, city on city, region on
region, nation on nation, kingdom on kingdom. When   32
this happens, and all the signs that I have shown you
come to pass, then my son will be revealed, whom you
saw as a man rising from the sea. On hearing his voice,   33
all the nations will leave their own territories and their
separate wars, and unite in a countless host, as you saw   34
in your vision, with a common intent to go and wage
war against him. He will take his stand on the summit   35
of Mount Zion, and Zion will come into sight before all   36
men, complete and fully built. This corresponds to the
mountain which you saw hewn out, not by the hand of
man. Then my son will convict of their godless deeds   37

the nations that confront him. This will correspond to
38 the storm you saw. He will taunt them with their evil
plottings and the tortures they are soon to endure. This
corresponds to the flame. And he will destroy them
without effort by means of[a] the law – and that is like
the fire.

39 'Then you saw him collecting a different company, a
40 peaceful one. They are the ten tribes which were taken
off into exile in the time of King Hoshea, whom Shalmaneser king of Assyria took prisoner. He deported them
beyond the River, and they were taken away into a
41 strange country. But then they resolved to leave the
country populated by the Gentiles and go to a distant
42 land never yet inhabited by man, and there at last to be
obedient to their laws, which in their own country they
43 had failed to keep. As they passed through the narrow
44 passages of the Euphrates, the Most High performed
miracles for them, stopping up the channels of the river
45 until they had crossed over. Their journey through that
region, which is called Arzareth, was long, and took a
46 year and a half. They have lived there ever since, until
47 this final age. Now they are on their way back, and once
more the Most High will stop the channels of the river
to let them cross.

48 'That is the meaning of the peaceful assembly that you
saw. With them too are the survivors of your own
people, all who are found inside my sacred boundary.
49 So then, when the time comes for him to destroy the
nations assembled against him, he will protect his people
50 who are left, and show them many prodigies.'

[a] by means of: *so one Vs.; Lat.* and.

'My lord, my master,' I asked, 'explain to me why the 51
man that I saw rose up out of the depths of the sea.' He 52
replied: 'It is beyond the power of any man to explore
the deep sea and discover what is in it; in the same way
no one on earth can see my son and his company until
the appointed day. Such then is the meaning of your 53
vision.

✫ In the interpretation the man from the sea is identified as
the Messiah (verses 25-6); he will destroy his enemies (verses
27-38) and gather together the tribes of Israel to participate
in his kingdom (verse 39-50). In a further question and
answer the fact that the man comes from the sea is explained
as indicating that the Messiah will remain hidden until the
time comes for him to act (verses 51-2).

25-6. *The man . . . is he whom the Most High has held in
readiness through many ages:* i.e. the man is the pre-existent
Messiah; see the comment on 12: 31-3 and cp. verse 52.
he will himself deliver the world he has made: so the Latin, the
meaning being that God himself will deliver his world (cp.
verse 29). But other versions support a translation 'through
whom he will deliver the world he has made', and this corresponds better to the general sense of the chapter (the Latin
text is based on a misunderstanding of the original). The
thought here is that the Messiah will be God's agent in the
deliverance of the world. *and determine the lot of those who
survive:* the N.E.B. translation assumes that the subject of this
clause is the same as that of the previous clause, i.e. 'the Most
High'. But the text is perhaps better translated 'and he will
determine . . . ', with the Messiah as the implied subject. The
Messiah will order the conditions of life for those who are
left to participate in his kingdom.

27-8. Cp. verses 9-11.

29-31. These verses have no counterpart in the vision, and
this is perhaps an indication that they are an addition to the

original text. They describe the signs of the end and, as such, are similar in character to 5: 1–12; 6: 18*b*–28; 9: 1–13, passages which are in fact alluded to in verse 32.

29. *The day is near:* cp. 5: 1; 6: 18*b* – the same words are used in the Latin in all three cases. *when the Most High will begin to bring deliverance to those on earth:* cp. verse 26 and the comment on that verse. The fact that God, rather than the Messiah, is seen here as the deliverer (cp. 1 Thess. 4: 14) is perhaps a further indication that verses 29–31 are an addition.

30. *Then men will all be filled with great alarm:* cp. 5: 1.

31. *they will plot to make war on one another, city on city, region on region, nation on nation, kingdom on kingdom:* probably based on Isa. 19: 2:

> 'I will set Egyptian against Egyptian,
>   and they shall fight one against another,
>   neighbour against neighbour,
> city against city and kingdom against kingdom'.

Cp. Mark 13: 8 (and parallels), part of the Marcan account of the signs of the end, 'For nation will make war upon nation, kingdom upon kingdom.'

32. *and all the signs that I have shown you come to pass:* see the comment on verses 29–31. *then my son will be revealed:* cp. 7: 28 and see the comment on that verse. As we have seen (p. 169), the use of 'my son' as a title for the Messiah may reflect Christian influence, but the messianic interpretation of Ps. 2 leaves open the possibility that this is a Jewish title.

33–4. Cp. verses 4–5 and the comment on verse 5. Cp. also Zech. 14: 2 and Rev. 16: 14–16, 'These spirits . . . were sent out to muster all the kings of the world for the great day of battle of God the sovereign Lord . . . So they assembled the kings at the place called in Hebrew Armageddon.'

35. *He will take his stand on the summit of Mount Zion:* cp. verse 6. The passage possibly draws its inspiration from Zech. 14: 4.

36. *and Zion will come into sight before all men, complete and fully built:* the pre-existent heavenly Jerusalem; cp. 7: 26;

10: 27, 38–59; Rev. 21: 2, 9–10. *the mountain which you saw hewn out, not by the hand of man:* cp. Dan. 2: 34, 45, and see the comment on verse 6.

37–8. Cp. verses 10–11. It is noticeable that the interpretation at this point diverges from the sense of the vision. In the vision the *storm*, *flame* and *fire* combine into one and burn up the enemies of the Messiah so that nothing is left 'but dust and ashes and a reek of smoke'. Here each of the three elements is given a separate allegorical interpretation. *my son will convict of their godless deeds the nations that confront him:* as in 12: 32–3 the Messiah is presented as a judge, rather than as a military leader (see the comment on the earlier passage). *And he will destroy them without effort by means of the law:* apparently the thought is of the law as the standard by which the Messiah will exercise judgement. *by means of:* so the Syriac version; the Latin 'and' is corrupt (see the N.E.B. footnote).

39–50. Cp. verses 12–13 *a*. After destroying his enemies the Messiah will bring the ten northern tribes back to the land of Israel; this is a more specific expression of the common belief in the return to Israel in the last days of all dispersed Jews; cp. e.g. Isa. 27: 13; 2 Macc. 2: 18; Matt. 24: 31. At the time at which 2 Esdras 3–14 was written there seems to have been a certain amount of speculation as to the fate of the ten tribes. The deportation of the inhabitants of the northern kingdom to Assyria is described in 2 Kings 17: 1–23, and in verse 23 they are said to be still there. But the exiles from the north are not further mentioned in the Old Testament, and in practice it is likely that they were absorbed into the local population and lost their identity. However, the ideal of the twelve tribes was still maintained (cp. e.g. Matt. 19: 28), and at the end of the first century A.D. the belief is found that the exiled northern tribes were still in existence. Thus Josephus (*Antiquities* 11: 133), having mentioned the Jews (including some from the northern tribes) who returned to Jerusalem with Ezra, states: 'But the Israelite nation as a whole remained in the country. In this way has it come about that there are two tribes in Asia and Europe subject to the Romans, while until now there have been ten tribes beyond the Euphrates – countless myriads whose number cannot be ascertained' (Loeb Classical Library translation of Josephus, vol. 6, pp. 377, 379). So also in 2 Baruch the northern tribes to whom Baruch sends a letter are thought of as dwelling beyond the river Euphrates (77: 22; 78: 1). But the legend found in 2 Esdras 13: 39–50 goes beyond these references; it is an attempt to explain both the assumed existence of the ten tribes and their actual disappearance. The expectation of the return of the ten tribes which occurs here has a parallel in a debate between two rabbis, Aqiba and Eliezer, who were more or less contemporary with the author of 2 Esdras 3–14: the former held that the ten tribes would not return, the latter that they would (Mishnah, Sanhedrin 10: 3; see H. Danby, *The Mishnah*, p. 398). The legend of the ten tribes was subsequently further elaborated, but none of the speculation about their fate has any historical foundation.

40. *the ten tribes which were taken off into exile in the time of King Hoshea, whom Shalmaneser king of Assyria took prisoner:* cp. 2 Kings 17: 1–6. *beyond the River:* i.e. beyond the Euphrates – from a Palestinian standpoint on its eastern side; this was the area in which the places mentioned in 2 Kings 17: 6 lay. Cp. the references in Josephus and 2 Baruch given above.

41. *they resolved to . . . go to a distant land never yet inhabited by man:* this is meant to explain why the ten tribes were not to be found in any known land.

43. *the narrow passages of the Euphrates:* possibly a tributary of the Euphrates is meant, but where exactly is not clear.

44. *stopping up the channels of the river until they had crossed over:* a deliberate parallel seems to be intended with the miraculous crossings of the Red Sea (Exod. 14: 21–31) and of the Jordan (Josh. 3: 14–17), but the fact that a miracle was needed also serves to explain the inaccessibility of the area occupied by the ten tribes.

45. *Their journey through that region, which is called Arzareth, . . . took a year and a half:* a further indication of the remoteness of the land in which the ten tribes were supposed to dwell.

Arzareth: generally interpreted as a corruption of a Hebrew expression *'erets 'ahareth*, 'another land', which occurs in Deut. 29: 28, part of a passage which explains why the Jews were taken into exile, 'The LORD uprooted them from their soil in anger, in wrath and great fury, and banished them to another land, where they are to this day.' Deut. 29: 28 was used in the rabbinic debate mentioned in the note on verses 39–50, and it seems likely that the author of 2 Esdras 3–14 was also alluding to this passage (cp. also verse 40 where the N.E.B. 'a strange country' might also be translated 'another land').

46. *Now they are on their way back:* perhaps better translated 'Now they are about to come back.'

47. *once more the Most High will stop the channels of the river:* the crossing of the Euphrates will again be miraculous (see the comment on verse 44), and implicitly the return of the ten tribes is presented as a new exodus. Cp. Isa. 11: 15–16:

> 'The LORD will divide the tongue of the Egyptian sea
>   and wave his hand over the River
>   to bring a scorching wind;
>   he shall split it into seven channels
>   and let men go across dry-shod.
> So there shall be a causeway for the remnant of his people,
>   for the remnant rescued from Assyria,
> as there was for Israel when they came up out of Egypt.'

48. *the survivors of your own people:* i.e. those who have survived the destruction of the nations and the woes which will occur at the end of this age; cp. 7: 27–8; 9: 7–8. But the text of this verse is uncertain. The N.E.B. gives a possible interpretation of the Latin text which assumes that these survivors are to be distinguished from the ten tribes. However, the Syriac reads 'But those who survive of your people, who are found inside my sacred borders, will be saved', and thus does not make the same distinction. The other versions differ, and it is not clear what the original text was. *all who are found inside my sacred boundary:* the messianic kingdom will be based on the land of Israel; see the comments on 9: 8 and 12: 34.

49–50. A summary of the meaning of the vision. *his people*

who are left: presumably all Israel is meant, both the Jews already in Palestine and the ten tribes. No mention is made in the interpretation of the many other Jews who lived outside Palestine, nor of gentile converts (cp. verse 13), but possibly the ten tribes are intended in a symbolic way to include both these groups. *and show them many prodigies:* the miracles that will be experienced during the reign of the Messiah.

51–2. Further elucidation of a detail of the vision. *explain to me why the man that I saw rose up out of the depths of the sea:* cp. verses 1–3. *no one on earth can see my son and his company until the appointed day:* the Messiah is already in existence (cp. 12: 32; 13: 25–6), but is kept hidden by God until the time comes for his activity. See the comment on 12: 31–3 and the passages from 1 Enoch quoted there which refer to the pre-existence and the concealment of the Son of Man. *his company:* there is no mention in the vision of anyone accompanying the man from the sea, nor has there so far been any mention of companions in the interpretation. But see 7: 28 and the comment on that passage. Presumably again either angels or immortal men such as Enoch or Elijah (cp. 6: 26) are meant.   *

THE CONCLUSION OF THE VISION

The revelation has been given to you, and to you 54 alone, because you have given up your own affairs, and devoted yourself entirely to mine, and to the study of my 55 law. You have taken wisdom as your guide in everything, 56 and called understanding your mother. That is why I have given this revelation to you; there is a reward in store for you with the Most High. In three days' time I will speak with you again, and tell you some momentous and wonderful things.'

57   So I went away to the field, giving worship and praise

to the Most High for the wonders he performed from
time to time and for his providential control of the 58
passing ages and what happens in them. There I remained
for three days.

✻ 53*b*–56*a*. *The revelation has been given to you, and to you
alone:* Ezra's unique position, here attributed to his devotion
to the law and to wisdom, is again stressed, see the comments
on 6: 32–3 and 12: 36. As has already been suggested, statements such as this no doubt give an indication of how the
author regarded his own status. *You have taken wisdom as your
guide in everything, and called understanding your mother:* cp.
Prov. 7: 4:

> 'Call Wisdom your sister,
> greet Understanding as a familiar friend'

there is a reward in store for you with the Most High: i.e. the
reward of life in the age to come; cp. 7: [77]; 8: 33.

56*b*. *In three days' time I will speak with you again:* the
pattern of a week's interval between each revelation is broken
for a second time; see the comment on 10: 58–9. Why this
should be so is not clear, although it is unlikely that it is to be
explained, as was at one time suggested, in terms of the use
within 2 Esdras 3–14 of different sources. Perhaps the shorter
interval is an external indication that the cycle of revelations
is about to reach its climax.

57–8. Transition to the seventh section. *So I went away to
the field:* so the Latin version (literally 'So I set out and went
to the field'), but since Ezra is already in the field (cp. 9: 26;
12: 51), we should perhaps follow the reading of the Syriac
and Ethiopic: 'So I set out and walked through the field.'
*and for his providential control of the passing ages and what
happens in them:* the determinism characteristic of many apocalyptic writings is again stressed; cp. the comment on
4: 37. ✻

271

The writing of the sacred books

✳ The last section of 2 Esdras 3–14 differs completely from the previous six. It consists of a legend which describes how Ezra, warned of the approaching end of his life, asked to be given the inspiration to restore the scriptures (both the books of the Old Testament and the apocalyptic books), and how he subsequently did this. The purpose of this legend is to explain how the scriptures, and more particularly the apocalyptic writings (see pp. 105–8), survived the fall of Jerusalem in 587 B.C. and were thus available at the time at which 2 Esdras 3–14 was written, i.e. the end of the first century A.D. It represents, in other words, an attempt to give authority to the apocalypses by presenting them as genuinely ancient writings. The apocalyptic literature was ultimately rejected by the Jews, and 2 Esdras 14 reflects a situation in which the authority of this literature was already being questioned. The legend builds upon the Old Testament tradition that Ezra established the law as the basis of the life of the community after the exile (Neh. 8), but it differs considerably from this tradition. ✳

EZRA IS TOLD TO PREPARE FOR THE END OF HIS LIFE

14 ON THE THIRD DAY I was sitting under an oak-tree, when a voice came to me from a bush, saying, 2 'Ezra, Ezra!' 'Here I am, Lord', I answered, and rose to 3 my feet. The voice went on: 'I revealed myself in the bush, and spoke to Moses, when my people Israel was in 4 slavery in Egypt, and sent him to lead my people out of Egypt. I brought him up on to Mount Sinai, and kept 5 him with me for many days. I told him of many won-

ders, showing him the secrets of the ages and the end of
time, and instructed him what to make known and what 6
to conceal. So too I now give this order to you: commit 7, 8
to memory the signs I have shown you, the visions you
have seen, and the explanations you have been given.
You yourself are about to be taken away from the world 9
of men, and thereafter you will remain with my son and
with those like you, until the end of time. The world has 10
lost its youth, and time is growing old. For the whole of 11
time is in twelve divisions; nine[a] divisions and half the
tenth have already passed, and only two and a half still 12
remain. Set your house in order, therefore; give warnings 13
to your nation, and comfort to those in need of it; and
take your leave of mortal life. Put away your earthly 14
cares, and lay down your human burdens; strip off your
weak nature, set aside the anxieties that vex you, and be 15
ready to depart quickly from this life. However great 16
the evils you have witnessed, there are worse to come.
As this ageing world grows weaker and weaker, so will 17
evils increase for its inhabitants. Truth will move farther 18
away, and falsehood come nearer. The eagle that you
saw in your vision is already on the wing.'

✳ 1. *On the third day:* cp. 13: 56, 58. *a voice came to me from
a bush, saying,* '*Ezra, Ezra!*': cp. Exod. 3: 4, 'When the LORD
saw that Moses had turned aside to look, he called to him out
of the bush, "Moses, Moses."' In accordance with his role as
the restorer of the scriptures Ezra is presented as a second
Moses. This is indicated in verse 1 by the fact that God speaks
to Ezra from a bush, and by the repetition of Ezra's name, and

[a] *Probable reading; Lat.* ten.

is made explicit in verses 3–8 by the parallel that is drawn between Moses and Ezra.

2. '*Here I am, Lord*', *I answered:* cp. Exod. 3: 4, 'And Moses answered, "Yes, I am here."'

3–4*a*. A summary of Exod. 3: 1–12.

4*b*. *I brought him up on to Mount Sinai, and kept him with me for many days:* cp. Exod. 24: 18 (with its sequel in 31: 18); 34: 28.

5. *I told him of many wonders, showing him the secrets of the ages and the end of time:* this is hardly a summary of the legislation in the Pentateuch given at Mount Sinai; rather it presents Moses as the recipient of apocalyptic visions. There are a number of works associated with the name of Moses which were composed in the Christian era, and of these we know of at least one that is apocalyptic in character, namely the Assumption of Moses (see p. 108 and R. H. Charles, *Apocrypha and Pseudepigrapha*, vol. 2, pp. 407–24; the Assumption dates from the beginning of the first century A.D.). The author of 2 Esdras 3–14 no doubt had in mind such works as the Assumption of Moses in his statement in verse 5, but his words also seem intended to claim the authority of Moses for apocalyptic literature generally.

6. *and instructed him what to make known and what to conceal:* the laws contained in the Pentateuch and the apocalyptic writings. The concealment of the latter is part of the apocalyptic fiction which is intended to explain how these supposedly ancient writings only became known long after they were composed; cp. verses 26, 46 and the comment on 12: 37.

8. *commit to memory:* perhaps better 'keep in your mind'. But in any case the implication is that, like Moses, he is not to make public the secret revelations he has received. *the signs . . . the visions . . . the explanations:* i.e. what is contained in chs. 3–13.

9. *You yourself are about to be taken away from the world of men:* Ezra's life is about to end, not through death, but

through his being 'translated' to heaven. The Old Testament records that two particularly pious men were 'carried away to another life without passing through death' (Heb. 11: 5), namely Enoch (Gen. 5: 24) and Elijah (2 Kings 2: 11), and the same fate is here attributed to Ezra. The actual 'translation' is described in the oriental versions at the end of the chapter, but the passage is not present in the Latin version, and so is not given in the N.E.B. *my son:* the pre-existent Messiah; cp. 7: 28; 13: 32. *those like you:* those already translated to heaven. *until the end of time:* i.e. until the end of the present age.

10–12. The thought of the end of this age leads to a comment that the end will not be all that long delayed. *The world has lost its youth, and time is growing old:* cp. 5: 50–5 and the comment on that passage. *For the whole of time is in twelve divisions:* the division of history into a set number of ages is a common characteristic of apocalyptic writings; cp. the idea, found in Dan. 7 and carried over into 2 Esdras 11–12 (e.g. 11: 39; 12: 11), that there were to be four empires between the exile and the end of this world. *nine divisions and half the tenth have already passed, and only two and a half still remain:* the text is uncertain at this point. The N.E.B. follows the Latin, but with one plausible correction (see the footnote); other versions either omit verses 11–12, or are rather different. The essential point is that the world is nearer its end than its beginning (cp. 4: 48–50).

13. *Set your house in order, therefore:* in view of his impending 'translation' to heaven Ezra is to give his last instructions; cp. verses 27–36. This motif is traditional; it is recorded of several great men in the Old and New Testaments that, shortly before the end of their lives, they gave a last speech or testament; cp. e.g. the speech of Paul to the Ephesian elders in Acts 20: 18–35. *your house:* the house of Israel, *your nation.*

14–15. As further preparation for the end of his life Ezra is to put on one side all the troubles which oppress him.

16–18. Because he is to be taken away from this world,

Ezra will escape the evils which will occur as this age approaches its end. *However great the evils you have witnessed:* the events of the Jewish war of A.D. 66–73 were no doubt primarily in the author's mind. *there are worse to come:* i.e. what are elsewhere described as the 'signs' of the end; cp. 5: 1–12; 6: 18b–28; 9: 1–13. *As this ageing world grows weaker and weaker:* cp. verse 10. *Truth will move farther away, and falsehood come nearer:* cp. 5: 9b–11 and contrast 6: 27–8 which describes the conditions which will apply in the new age. *The eagle that you saw in your vision is already on the wing:* i.e. the Roman Empire already holds power, a sign that the end of this age is near (cp. chs. 11–12). This statement does not, of course, relate to the time of Ezra, but to the time in which the author of 2 Esdras 3–14 lived. ✵

EZRA'S CONCERN TO RESTORE THE SCRIPTURES

19, 20 'May I speak[a] in your presence, Lord?' I replied. 'I am to depart, by your command, after giving warning to those of my people who are now alive. But who will give warning to those born hereafter? The world is shrouded in darkness, and its inhabitants are without 21 light. For your law was destroyed in the fire, and so no one can know about the deeds you have done or intend 22 to do. If I have won your favour, fill me with your holy spirit, so that I may write down the whole story of the world from the very beginning, everything that is contained in your law; then men will have the chance to find the right path, and, if they choose, gain life in the last days.'

23 'Go,' he replied, 'call the people together, and tell 24 them not to look for you for forty days. Have a large

[a] May I speak: *so other Vss.; Lat. omits.*

number of writing-tablets ready, and take with you
Seraiah and Dibri, Shelemiah, Ethan, and Asiel, five men
all trained to write quickly. Then return here, and I will 25
light a lamp of understanding in your mind, which will
not go out until you have finished all that you are to
write. When your work is complete, some of it you must 26
make public; the rest you must give to wise men to keep
secret. Tomorrow at this time you shall begin to write.'

✻   19-22. Ezra acknowledges his responsibility to speak to
those who were then alive, but is concerned as to what will
happen in the future. The scriptures had been destroyed, and
he asks to be given the inspiration to restore them.

20. *after giving warning to those of my people who are now
alive:* cp. the command to do this in verse 13 and the speech
in verses 27-36. *The world is shrouded in darkness, and its
inhabitants are without light:* because the illumination provided
by God's law no longer exists – the reason for this is made
clear in the following verse. For the idea of the law as a light
cp. Ps. 19: 8*b*:

> 'The commandment of the LORD shines clear
> and gives light to the eyes.'

21. *For your law was destroyed in the fire:* the author assumes
that the law was lost in the fire which destroyed the temple
and the rest of Jerusalem in 587 B.C.; cp. 2 Kings 25: 8-9,
'Nebuzaradan, captain of the king's bodyguard, came to
Jerusalem and set fire to the house of the LORD.' *and so no one
can know about the deeds you have done or intend to do:* an
allusion to the narrative and prophetic portions of the Old
Testament. In this chapter 'law' is used in a loose sense to
refer to the Old Testament scriptures generally (for a similar
use cp. John 15: 25; 1 Cor. 14: 21).

22. *If I have won your favour:* see the comment on 5: 56.
the whole story of the world from the very beginning, everything

277

that is contained in your law: here it is quite clear that 'law' is being used in a very general sense.

23–6. Ezra is given instructions to restore the scriptures.

23. *and tell them not to look for you for forty days:* Ezra is again presented as a second Moses (see the comment on verse 1). Just as Moses spent forty days on Mount Sinai when he received the law (cp. Exod. 24: 18; 34: 28; Deut. 9: 9), so Ezra is to spend forty days in the restoration of the scriptures.

24. *Seraiah and Dibri, Shelemiah, Ethan, and Asiel, five men:* the names can all be found in the Old Testament, but not as a group belonging to the time of Ezra. There may be some significance in the fact that *five men* are mentioned inasmuch as it is possible that there is an allusion here to the five famous disciples of Rabban Joḥanan ben Zakkai, the man largely responsible for the survival of Judaism in the period after the fall of Jerusalem in A.D. 70. The five disciples are mentioned in the Mishnah, Aboth 2: 8; see H. Danby, *The Mishnah*, p. 448, or R. H. Charles, Aboth 2: 10 in *Apocrypha and Pseudepigrapha of the Old Testament*, vol. 2, p. 696.

25. *Then return here:* i.e. to the field; cp. 13: 57.

26. *some of it you must make public:* the books of the Old Testament. *the rest you must give to wise men to keep secret:* the apocalyptic writings; see verse 6 and the comment on 12: 37. *wise men:* as we have already observed, the apocalyptic books are only for the learned, not the general public; cp. verses 46–7 and the comment on 8: 62. ✻

EZRA'S LAST WORDS TO THE PEOPLE

27 I went as I was ordered and summoned all the people,
28,29 and said: 'Israel, listen to what I say. Our ancestors lived originally in Egypt as foreigners. They were rescued from
30 that land, and were given the law which offers life. But they disobeyed it, and you have followed their example.
31 Then you were given a land of your own, the land of

Zion; but you, like your ancestors, sinned and abandoned
the way laid down for you by the Most High. Because 32
he is a just judge he took away from you in due time
what he had given. And so you are now here in exile, 33
and your fellow-countrymen are still farther away. If 34
then you will direct your understanding and instruct your
minds, you shall be kept safe in life and meet with mercy
after you die. For after death will come the judgement; 35
we shall be restored to life, and then the names of the just
will be known and the deeds of the godless exposed.
From this moment no one must come to talk to me, nor 36
look for me for the next forty days.'

* As commanded, Ezra summons the people and tells them
not to seek him for forty days (verses 27, 36; cp. verse 23).
But the speech also provides the opportunity for Ezra to give
his last instructions (verses 28–35; cp. verse 13), and in this
respect it has a significant place in the structure of 2 Esdras
3–14. The speech consists of a summary of the main events of
Israel's history from the time in Egypt to the exile, and as
such it seems intended to provide a deliberate contrast to the
summary given in the prayer with which 2 Esdras 3–14 begins.
In ch. 3 Ezra blamed God for the situation in which Israel
found herself, but here the exile is accepted as being the fully
merited punishment for Israel's sin, and God is called a 'just
judge' (verses 29–33). Furthermore, whereas ch. 3 ended on
a note of despair, this speech ends on a note of hope (verses
34–5).

Ezra's words refer ostensibly to the situation which existed
after 587 B.C., but what is really in mind is the situation after
A.D. 70. The contrast between the opening and closing sections
of 2 Esdras 3–14 is a clear indication of the way in which the
attitude of the author has changed (see above pp. 219); he now

acknowledges the reality and the justice of the disaster of A.D. 70, but holds out to his readers hope for the future.

27. Cp. verse 23.

30. *and were given the law which offers life:* cp. 3: 17–22; 5: 27; 9: 30–1. The gift of the law was intended to provide the means of salvation (participation in the life of the age to come), but Israel failed to observe it. For the law as the source of life cp. Ecclus. 17: 11; 45: 5.

31. *Then you were given a land of your own:* the people are addressed as if they were the generation which received the gift of the land of Palestine.

32. *Because he is a just judge:* contrast the complaints uttered in 3: 28–36.

33. *And so you are now here in exile:* i.e. in Babylon, the place in which the book is supposedly set (cp. 3: 1). *and your fellow-countrymen are still farther away:* the ten northern tribes; cp. 13: 40–7.

34–5. *If then you will direct your understanding and instruct your minds:* despite the difficulties of the situation, if the people discipline their lives, there is still hope. *you shall be kept safe in life:* the Latin text could also be translated 'you shall be kept alive'; in this case the reference would be to life in the age to come. *and meet with mercy after you die:* i.e. at the judgement. *For after death will come the judgement; we shall be restored to life:* for the resurrection and the judgement see 7: 31–[44]. *and the deeds of the godless exposed:* cp. 7: 35.

36. Cp. verse 23. ✡

THE RESTORATION OF THE SCRIPTURES

37 I took with me the five men as I had been told, and we
38 went away to the field, and there we stayed. On the next
day I heard a voice calling me, which said: 'Ezra, open
39 your mouth and drink what I give you.' So I opened my
mouth, and was handed a cup full of what seemed like

water, except that its colour was the colour of fire. I took 40
it and drank, and as soon as I had done so my mind began
to pour forth a flood of understanding, and wisdom grew
greater and greater within me, for I retained my memory
unimpaired. I opened my mouth to speak, and I con- 41
tinued to speak unceasingly. The Most High gave under- 42
standing to the five men, who took turns at writing down
what was said, using characters[a] which they had not
known before. They remained at work through the forty
days, writing all day, and taking food only at night. But 43
as for me, I spoke all through the day; even at night I was
not silent. In the forty days, ninety-four[b] books were 44
written. At the end of the forty days the Most High 45
spoke to me. 'Make public the books you wrote first,'
he said, 'to be read by good and bad alike. But the last 46
seventy books are to be kept back, and given to none
but the wise among your people. They contain a stream 47
of understanding, a fountain of wisdom, a flood of knowledge.' And I did so.   48

✻ Ezra carries out the instructions which had been given to
him and, under divine inspiration, miraculously restores the
scriptures.

37. *I took with me the five men as I had been told:* cp. verse 24.
and we went away to the field: i.e. Ardat (9: 26); cp. verse 25.

38–41. Ezra had prayed for inspiration, and this is now
granted to him (cp. verses 22, 25). He is told to drink a cup of
liquid which fills him with understanding and wisdom and
enables him to dictate the scriptures.

39. *a cup full of what seemed like water:* the description of the
means of inspiration is unique, but may perhaps be compared

[a] *Probable reading, based on other Vss.; Lat. corrupt.*
[b] *So other Vss.; Lat. corrupt.*

with Ezek. 2: 8 – 3: 3 (Ezekiel is inspired to prophesy by eating a scroll) and Rev. 10: 8–11. *except that its colour was the colour of fire:* the fire is possibly intended to symbolize the spirit; cp. verse 22 and Acts 2: 3–4, 'And there appeared to them tongues like flames of fire ... And they were all filled with the Holy Spirit.'

42. The five men are also given inspiration which enables them to copy out the scriptures at Ezra's dictation. *using characters which they had not known before:* an allusion to the Jewish tradition that Ezra was the inventor of the square Hebrew letters which are still in use today. *the forty days:* cp. verse 23.

43. *even at night I was not silent:* in order to complete the work within the forty-day period.

44–7. Ninety-four books are copied at Ezra's dictation, but of these only the first twenty-four are to be made public; cp. verse 26.

45. *Make public the books you wrote first:* the books of the Old Testament. Their number (twenty-four – the Syriac version actually gives this figure, but the number is in any case clear from the context; see verse 46) reflects the arrangement of the Hebrew Bible, namely the five books of the Pentateuch, the eight books of the Prophets (Joshua, Judges, Samuel, Kings, Isaiah, Jeremiah, Ezekiel, the Twelve Minor Prophets [counted as one]) and the eleven books of the Writings (Psalms, Job, Proverbs, Ruth, the Song of Songs, Ecclesiastes, Lamentations, Esther, Daniel, Ezra–Nehemiah [counted as one], Chronicles); see in this series, *The Making of the Old Testament*, pp. 105–32.

46. *But the last seventy books are to be kept back, and given to none but the wise among your people:* the apocalyptic writings; see verses 6 and 26 and the comments on both passages.

47. *They contain a stream of understanding, a fountain of wisdom, a flood of knowledge:* these words are important inasmuch as they give some indication of the way in which the author

regarded the apocalyptic writings; for him they were in some sense a form of wisdom.

48. *And I did so:* after these words the Syriac version adds

'in the seventh year, in the sixth week, after five thousand years of creation and three months and twelve days. And at that time Ezra was carried away and taken to the place of those who are like him, after he had written all these things. He was called the scribe of the knowledge of the Most High for ever and ever.'

A similar ending is found in all but one of the other oriental versions of 2 Esdras 3–14, and it is likely that the ending was omitted from the Latin version when chs. 15 and 16 were added to 2 Esdras 3–14. For the 'translation' of Ezra to heaven see the comment on verse 9.   *

2 ESDRAS 15–16

Prophecies of doom

* We have already seen that chs. 15 and 16, often referred to in modern writings as 6 Ezra, do not belong with chs. 3–14, but are a quite separate work (see pp. 76–7). The origin of these chapters is, however, not entirely clear. They seem to have been deliberately composed as an appendix to 2 Esdras 3–14, although there is some evidence to suggest that they also circulated independently. But it would appear not unlikely that the author of this appendix took over and adapted for his purposes traditions that were already in existence. In form these chapters consist of a series of prophecies which are only loosely strung together and in which there is no attempt to develop a sustained argument. The prophecies imitate the style of, and draw their inspiration from, Old

Testament prophecy. As in the case of chs. 1 and 2, chs. 15 and 16 have survived in their entirety only in Latin. The indications are, however, that these chapters were composed in Greek, and were written as an appendix to chs. 3–14 when the latter had already been translated into Greek. A papyrus fragment containing a Greek text of 15: 57–9 has been found.

The background to 2 Esdras 15–16 is a period of persecution; the author threatens judgement to the oppressors and attempts to comfort and encourage those who are being persecuted. These latter are apparently Christians, and the work is apparently a Christian composition, but although there are a number of parallels with the New Testament, the Christian colouring is not very marked. However, in its present form it does seem likely that 2 Esdras 15–16 is a Christian work, and its character is perhaps to be explained – as was hinted above – by the assumption that the Christian author made use of already existing Jewish traditions; but if this is correct, neither the date nor the place of composition of 2 Esdras 15–16 is very clear. Christians were subjected to persecution at various times throughout the second and third centuries, and a date at any time within this period is theoretically possible. But allusions have been detected, particularly in 15: 28–33, which make it seem likely that they were composed in the latter part of the third century. The place of composition is more difficult to determine. References to events in the east suggest the eastern part of the Roman Empire; it is not possible to be more precise. ✳

GOD'S VENGEANCE ON THE WICKED

15 PROCLAIM TO MY PEOPLE the words of prophecy
2 which I give you to speak, says the Lord; and have them written down, because they are trustworthy and
3 true. Have no fear of plots against you, and do not be
4 troubled by the unbelief of those who oppose you. For

everyone who does not believe will die because of his
unbelief.[a]

Beware, says the Lord, I am letting loose terrible evils 5
on the world, sword and famine, death and destruction,
because wickedness has spread over the whole earth and 6
there is no room for further deeds of violence. Therefore 7
the Lord says, I will not keep silence about their godless 8
sins; I will not tolerate their wicked deeds. See how the
blood of innocent victims cries to me for vengeance, and
the souls of the just never cease to plead with me! I will 9
most surely avenge them, says the Lord, and will hear
the plea of all the innocent blood that has been shed.
My people are being led to the slaughter like sheep. I will 10
no longer allow them to remain in Egypt, but will use 11
all my power to rescue them; I will strike the Egyptians
with plagues, as I did before, and destroy their whole
land. How Egypt will mourn, shaken to its very founda- 12
tions, when it is scourged and chastised by the Lord! How 13
the tillers of the soil will mourn, when the seed fails to
grow, and when their trees are devastated by blight and
hail and terrible storm![b] Alas for the world and its inhabi- 14
tants! The sword that will destroy them is not far away. 15
Nation will draw sword against nation and go to war.
Stable government will be at an end; one faction will 16
prevail over another, caring nothing in their day of
power for king or leading man of rank. A man may want 17
to visit a city, but will not be able to do so; for ambition 18
and rivalry will have reduced cities to chaos, destroyed
houses, and filled men with panic. A man will violently 19
assault his neighbour's house and plunder his goods; no

[a] Or *in his unbelief*.   [b] *Probable meaning; Lat. obscure.*

pity will restrain him, when he is in the grip of famine and grinding misery.

20 See how I summon before me all the kings of the earth, says God, from sunrise and south wind, from east and south,[a] to turn back and repay what they have been
21 given. I will do to them as they are doing to my chosen people even to this day; I will pay them back in their own coin.

22 These are the words of the Lord God: I will show sinners no pity; the sword will not spare those murderers
23 who stain the ground with innocent blood. The Lord's anger has overflowed in fire to scorch the earth to its foundations and consume sinners like burning straw.
24 Alas for sinners who flout my commands! says the Lord;
25 I will show them no mercy. Away from me, you rebels!
26 Do not bring your pollution near my holiness. The Lord well knows all who sin against him, and has consigned
27 them to death and destruction. Already disaster has fallen upon the world, and you will never escape it; God will refuse to rescue you, because you have sinned against him

✻ 1–4. The person addressed is instructed to announce the prophetic message which God gives to him.

1. *Proclaim to my people the words of prophecy:* the person addressed is commissioned as a prophet; cp. 1: 1; 12: 42, and see p. 77. *which I give to you to speak:* literally 'which I will place in your mouth'; cp. Jer. 1: 9.

2. *and have them written down:* the command to have the prophecies written down appears to build on the theme of ch. 14 and was perhaps intended to provide a link between chs. 15–16 and chs. 3–14. *because they are trustworthy and true:* cp. Rev. 21: 5.

3. *Have no fear of plots against you:* cp. Jer. 1: 7–8.

[a] south: *probable reading; Lat.* Lebanon.

5–19. God is about to take vengeance on the wicked because of their persecution of the innocent; in consequence the world will be overwhelmed by chaos and destruction.

8. *See how the blood of innocent victims cries to me for vengeance:* cp. Gen. 4: 10, 'The LORD said, "What have you done? Hark! your brother's blood that has been shed is crying out to me from the ground"'; cp. also Rev. 6: 10.

10a. *My people are being led to the slaughter like sheep:* cp. Ps. 44: 22; Isa. 53: 7.

10b–13. God will deliver his people from Egypt and once more afflict the land *with plagues*. It is often thought that the immediate occasion for the prophecy contained in these verses was the occurrence in Alexandria of a devastating plague which followed shortly after a period of war and famine. These events took place during the reign of the Emperor Gallienus (260–8) and are mentioned in Eusebius, *Ecclesiastical History*, VII.21.22 (see H. J. Lawlor and J. E. L. Oulton, *Eusebius. The Ecclesiastical History* (London, 1927–8), vol. 1, pp. 232–4). However, the deliverance from Egypt and the plagues are presented as a repetition of God's action on behalf of his people at the time of the exodus. *but will use all my power to rescue them:* literally 'but will bring them out with a strong hand and an outstretched arm'; in the Old Testament the expression 'with a strong hand and an outstretched arm' is used several times in reference to God's deliverance of his people from Egypt; cp. e.g. Deut. 4: 34.

14–19. The reference to judgement on Egypt leads into a description of the chaos that will overtake the earth as the end approaches. This passage, in common with other passages in chs. 15 and 16, is similar to the descriptions of the signs of the end in the gospels (cp. Mark 13 and parallels) and in 2 Esdras 3–14 itself (cp. e.g. 5: 1–12).

15. *Nation will draw sword against nation and go to war:* cp. 13: 31; Matt. 24: 7.

18. *for ambition and rivalry will have . . . filled men with panic:* cp. 13: 30; Luke 21: 26.

19. Cp. 6: 24.

287

20–7. The theme of judgement is continued. Verses 20–1 are directed specifically at 'the kings of the earth' who persecute God's chosen people; they are to be repaid in kind for their deeds. Verses 22–7 refer to two groups: the sinners who shed innocent blood (verses 22–3, cp. verses 7–10) and apostates (verses 24–7).

25. *rebels:* literally 'apostate sons' – it is presumably Christian apostates who are meant. ✶

A HORRIBLE VISION

28 How terrible the sight of what is coming from the
29 east! Hordes of dragons from Arabia will sally forth with countless chariots, and from the first day of their advance their hissing will spread across the land, to fill all who hear
30 them with fear and consternation. The Carmanians, mad with rage, will rush like wild boars out of the forest, advancing in full force to join battle with them, and will
31 devastate whole tracts of Assyria with their tusks. But then the dragons will summon up their native fury, and will prove the stronger. They will rally and join forces,
32 and fall on them with overwhelming might until they are routed, until their power is silenced, and every one
33 of them turns to flight. Then their way will be blocked by a lurking enemy from Assyria, who will destroy one of them. Fear and panic will spread in their army, and wavering among their kings.

✶ This section of 2 Esdras 15–16 has often been thought to allude, in a cryptic style similar to that of Dan. 11, to specific events of the third century (and thereby to provide an approximate date for the composition of these two chapters). Under the Sassanid king Shapur I (240–73) the Persians made a series of attacks on the Roman province of Syria, and in 260 they again overran the area; Shapur conquered Antioch for a third time and was able to pursue his campaign into Asia Minor. However, Shapur was not completely successful and on his return he was defeated in battle by the forces of the city of Palmyra under the leadership of Odenathus. For this and for other services Odenathus was given various honours by the Emperor Gallienus and was placed in overall control of Roman forces in the east. But he was murdered by a relative in 267, and his wife Zenobia effectively assumed power.

29. *Hordes of dragons from Arabia:* the Palmyrene forces under Odenathus. It is a little surprising that these are mentioned first, since the attack of Odenathus came after Shapur's campaign (verse 30). The dragon symbolism was possibly suggested by the idea that the wilderness was the home of snakes and serpents; cp. Deut. 8: 15; Isa. 30: 6.

30. *The Carmanians:* the Persian forces under Shapur I. Carmania (Kirman) was the name of the southern province of the Parthian Empire, the region from which the Sassanid dynasty came. *Assyria:* here a symbolic name for Syria.

31–2. The defeat of Shapur by the forces of Odenathus.

33. *Then their way will be blocked by a lurking enemy from Assyria, who will destroy one of them:* apparently an allusion to the murder of Odenathus. ✲

JUDGEMENT ON BABYLON

See the clouds stretching from east and north to south! 34
Their appearance is hideous, full of fury and tempest.
They will clash together, they will pour over the land a 35
vast storm;[a] blood, shed by the sword, will reach as high
as a horse's belly, a man's thigh, or a camel's hock. Terror 36, 37
and trembling will cover the earth; all who see the raging
fury will shudder and be stricken with panic. Then vast 38

[a] storm: *probable meaning; Lat. obscure.*

289

storm-clouds will approach from north and south, and
39 others from the west. But the winds from the east will
be stronger still, and will hold in check the raging cloud
and its leader; and the storm*a* which was bent on destruction will be fiercely driven back to the south and west
40 by the winds from the east. Huge mighty clouds, full of
fury, will mount up and ravage the whole land and its
inhabitants; a terrible storm*a* will sweep over the great
41 and the powerful, with fire and hail and flying swords;
and a deluge of water will flood all the fields and rivers.
42 They will flatten to the ground cities and walls, mountains and hills, trees in the woods and crops in the fields.
43 They will advance all the way to Babylon, and blot it
44 out. When they reach it, they will surround it, and let
loose a storm*a* in all its fury. The dust and smoke will
reach the sky, and all her neighbours will mourn for
45 Babylon. Any of her survivors will be enslaved by her
destroyers.

✻ Shapur's attacks on the Roman provinces in the east
coincided with attacks on the borders of the Roman Empire
in Europe by various groups of peoples, of which the Goths
represented the most serious danger, and for a time the
empire, which had been seriously weakened internally, must
have seemed to be on the point of collapse. It was against this
background that the prophecy in 2 Esdras 15: 34-45 appears
to have been composed. Using the image of storm-clouds the
author depicts the nations overwhelming the Roman Empire
and carrying their attack as far as Rome itself (verses 44-5).
In 2 Esdras 15-16, as in Revelation, Babylon is a symbol for
Rome (cp. Rev. 14: 8). It may be that specific historical

[a] storm: *probable meaning; Lat. obscure.*

events underlie some of the statements in this prophecy (e.g. in verses 38–9), but if so, it is not possible to identify these events precisely. It is, however, equally likely that the whole thing is to be read as a prophecy of the future; inspired by the events of his day, the author believed the end of the Roman Empire to be near at hand, and in symbolic language he described the way in which this would come about.

35. *as high as a horse's belly:* cp. Rev. 14: 20.
43. *Babylon:* i.e. Rome.   ✶

JUDGEMENT ON ASIA

And you, Asia, who have shared the beauty and the 46 splendour of Babylon, alas for you, poor wretch! Like 47 her you have dressed up your daughters as whores, to attract and catch your lovers who have always lusted for you. You have copied all the schemes and practices of 48 that vile harlot. Therefore God says, I will bring upon 49 you terrible evils: widowhood and poverty, famine, sword, and plague, bringing ruin to your homes, bringing violence and death. Your strength and splendour will 50 wither like a flower, when that scorching heat bears down upon you. Then you will be a poor weak woman, 51 bruised, beaten, and wounded, unable to receive your wealthy lovers any more. Should I be so fierce with you, 52 says the Lord, if you had not killed my chosen ones 53 continually, gloating over the blows you struck them, and hurling your drunken taunts at their corpses?

Paint your face; make yourself beautiful! The harlot's 54, 55 pay shall be yours; you will get what you have earned. What you do to my chosen people, God will do to you, 56 says the Lord; he will consign you to a terrible fate. Your 57

children will die of hunger; you will fall by the sword, your cities will be blotted out, and all your people will
58 fall on the field of battle. Those who are up on the mountains will be dying of hunger, and their hunger and thirst will force them to gnaw their own flesh and drink
59 their own blood. You will be foremost in misery, and
60 still there will be more to come. As the victors go past on their way home from the sack of Babylon, they will smash your peaceful city, destroy a great part of your territory, and bring much of your splendour to an end.
61 They will destroy you – you will be stubble, and they
62 the fire. They will completely devour you and your cities, your land and your mountains, and will burn all
63 your forests and your fruit-trees. They will make your children prisoners and plunder your property; and not a trace will be left of your splendid beauty.

* The announcement of judgement on Babylon (Rome) is followed by the announcement of judgement on Asia; God will hand her over 'to a terrible fate' (verse 56) because of her persecution of his chosen people. In this passage 'Asia' has sometimes been thought to represent Palmyra under Odena- thus and Zenobia, and it has been held that there are allusions here to the fate of this city which for a short time enjoyed considerable importance. We have already seen that after his defeat of Shapur I in 260 Odenathus, as an ally of Rome, achieved a position of power and influence in the east. He was murdered in 267, and his widow, Zenobia, took effective control of Palmyra. Her ambition eventually led her to attack Asia Minor and Egypt, but she was defeated by the forces of the Emperor Aurelian (270–5), and Palmyra was besieged and captured. It is possible that these events are alluded to here, and in particular that the fall of Palmyra is referred to in verses 60–3. However, these verses make better sense if they are read as a prophecy of a future judgement, and not as a cryptic account of past events. It is, furthermore, also possible that in this passage (15: 46–63) 'Asia' is used to refer to the Roman Empire in the east, just as in 16: 1 Babylon, Asia, Egypt and Syria are used together to refer to the totality of the Roman Empire. This passage can then be understood as a prophecy of judgement on the provinces in the east which follows not unnaturally on the prophecy of judgement on Rome itself (15: 34–45).

47–8. Apparently inspired by Rev. 17: 4–5:

'The woman was clothed in purple and scarlet and bedizened with gold and jewels and pearls. In her hand she held a gold cup, full of obscenities, and the foulness of her fornication; and written on her forehead was a name with a secret meaning: "Babylon the great, the mother of whores and of every obscenity on earth."'

Cp. also Rev. 14: 8; 18: 2–3.

49. Cp. Rev. 18: 7–8.

55. *The harlot's pay shall be yours*: possibly intended ironically – in the Old Testament death is the punishment for a woman who became a prostitute; see Gen. 38: 24; Lev. 21: 9; Deut. 22: 21.

56. Cp. verse 21.

60. *As the victors go past on their way home from the sack of Babylon*: cp. verses 43–4. ✻

THE IRREVERSIBLE JUDGEMENT

Alas for you, Babylon and Asia! Alas for you, Egypt **16** and Syria! Put on sackcloth and hair-shirt, and raise a 2 howl of lamentation for your sons; your doom is close at hand. The sword is let loose against you, and who will 3 turn it aside? Fire is let loose upon you, and who will put 4

5 it out? Calamities have been let loose against you, and
6 who is there to stop them? Can any man stop a hungry
lion in a forest, or put out a fire among the stubble once
7 it has begun to blaze? Can any man stop an arrow shot
8 by a strong archer? When the Lord God sends calamities,
9 who can stop them? When his anger overflows in fire,
10 who can put it out? When the lightning flashes, who will
not tremble? When it thunders, who will not shake with
11 dread? When it is the Lord who utters his threats, is there
any man who will not be crushed to the ground at his
12 approach? The earth is shaken to its very foundations,
and the sea is churned up from its depths; the waves and
all the fish with them are in turmoil before the presence
13 of the Lord and the majesty of his strength. For strong is
his arm which bends the bow, and sharp the arrows which
he shoots; once they are on their way, they will not stop
14 before they reach the ends of the earth. Calamities are let
loose, and will not turn back before they strike the earth.
15 The fire is alight and will not be put out until it has burnt
16 up earth's foundations. An arrow shot by a powerful
archer does not turn back; no more will the calamities be
recalled which are let loose against the earth.

* The dominant theme of this passage is that the judgement
of God, which is seen already to have begun in various
disasters which are taking place, cannot be stopped, but must
run its course. The passage is addressed to Babylon, Asia,
Egypt and Syria, and these four serve here to represent the
entire Roman Empire. The disasters are described in such
vague terms that they cannot be related to a specific historical
situation. But it seems likely that this passage was written
against the general background of the period of internal

instability and external danger which overwhelmed the Roman Empire from the death of Alexander Severus (235) to the accession of Diocletian (284), and that it belongs to more or less the same time as the prophecies of judgement in ch. 15.

2. *Put on sackcloth and hair-shirt:* conventional signs of mourning; cp. e.g. 2 Sam. 3: 31.

6. *Can any man stop a hungry lion in a forest?:* cp. Amos 3: 8, 'The lion has roared; who is not terrified?' The chain of rhetorical questions in verses 3–11 is to some extent reminiscent of the chain of questions in Amos 3: 3–8.

12. Cp. 2 Sam. 22: 8, 16, and the parallel Ps. 18: 7, 15.

14. Cp. Jer. 30: 24.

15. Reflected here is the belief that at the judgement the earth will be consumed in fire; cp. e.g. 2 Pet. 3: 7, 10; the Hymns from Qumran, III.29–31:

> 'The torrents of Satan shall reach
>   to all sides of the world.
> In all their channels
>   a consuming fire shall destroy
>   every tree, green and barren, on their banks;
> unto the end of their courses
>   it shall scourge with flames of fire,
> and shall consume the foundations of the earth
>   and the expanse of dry land.
> The bases of the mountains shall blaze
>   and the roots of the rocks shall turn
>   to torrents of pitch;
> it shall devour as far as the great Abyss.'

(Translation from G. Vermes, *The Dead Sea Scrolls in English*, 2nd ed. (Harmondsworth, 1975), pp. 159–60) *

THE HORRORS OF THE LAST DAYS

17 Alas, alas for me! Who will rescue me on that day?
18 When troubles come, many will groan; when famine strikes, many will die; when wars break out, empires will tremble; when the calamities come, all will be filled with terror. What will men do then, in the face of calamity?
19 Famine and plague, suffering and hardship, are scourges
20 sent to teach men better ways. But even so they will not abandon their crimes, nor keep in mind their scourging.
21 A time will come when food grows cheap, so cheap that they will imagine they have been sent peace and prosperity. But at that very moment the earth will become
22 a hotbed of disasters – sword, famine, and anarchy. Most of its inhabitants will die in the famine; and those who
23 survive the famine will be destroyed by the sword. The dead will be tossed out like dung, and there will be no one to offer any comfort. For the earth will be left
24 empty, and its cities a ruin. None will be left to till the
25 ground and sow it. The trees will bear their fruits, but
26 who will pick them? The grapes will ripen, but who will tread them? There will be vast desolation everywhere.
27 A man will long to see a human face or hear a human
28 voice. For out of a whole city, only ten will survive; in the country-side, only two will be left, hiding in the
29 forest or in holes in the rocks. Just as in an olive-grove
30 three or four olives might be left on each tree, or as a few grapes in a vineyard might be overlooked by the
31 sharp-eyed pickers, so also in those days three or four will be overlooked by those who search the houses to
32 kill. The earth will be left a desert, and the fields will be

overrun with briers; thorns will grow over all the roads and paths, because there will be no sheep to tread them. Girls will live in mourning with none to marry them, 33 women will mourn because they have no husbands, their daughters will mourn because they have no one to support them. The young men who should have married 34 them will be killed in the war, and the husbands wiped out by the famine.

✻ The thought of judgement leads once again into a description of the horrors that will occur as the end approaches; see the comment on 15: 14–19. The passage employs a number of traditional motifs which are familiar from the Old and New Testaments.

18b–20. *What will men do then, in the face of calamity?:* at the moment of crisis men will not know how to respond.

19. *Famine and plague, suffering and hardship, are scourges sent to teach men better ways:* the thought underlying such passages as Amos 4: 6–12.

20. Cp. Hag. 2: 17.

21. A brief time of plenty just before the end will give men a false sense of security; cp. Luke 12: 16–21.

22. For the thought cp. Isa. 24: 17–18a.

23. *The dead will be tossed out like dung:* cp. Jer. 9: 22.

28. *For out of a whole city, only ten will survive:* cp. Amos 5: 3. *in the country-side, only two will be left:* cp. Matt. 24: 40–1; Luke 17: 34–5.

29–31. Apparently inspired by Isa. 17: 4–6:

> 'On that day Jacob's weight shall dwindle
>   and the fat of his limbs waste away,...
>   as when one beats an olive-tree
>   and only gleanings are left on it,
>   two or three berries on the top of a branch,
>   four or five on the boughs of the fruiting tree.'

32. Cp. Isa. 7: 23.
33–4. Cp. Jer. 7: 34; Rev. 18: 23.   *

ADVICE TO THE LORD'S SERVANTS
AS THE END APPROACHES

35 But listen to me, you who are the Lord's servants, and
36 take my words to heart. This is the word of the Lord.
37 Receive it, and do not disbelieve what he says. Calamities
38 are here, close at hand, and will not delay. When a pregnant woman is in the ninth month, and the moment of
her child's birth is drawing near, there will be two or
three hours in which her womb will suffer pangs of
agony, and then the child will come from the womb
39 without a moment's delay; in the same way calamities
will come on the earth without delay, and the world will
groan under the pangs that grip it.

40 Listen to my words, my people; get ready for battle,
and when the calamities surround you, be as though you
41 were strangers on earth. The seller must expect to have
42 to run for his life, the buyer to lose what he buys; the
merchant must expect to make no profit, the builder
43 never to live in the house he builds. The sower must not
44 expect to reap, nor the pruner to gather his grapes. Those
who marry must expect no children; the unmarried must
45 think of themselves as widowed. For all labour is labour
46 in vain. Their fruits will be gathered by foreigners, who
will plunder their goods, pull down their houses, and
take their children captive. If they have children, they
47 will have been bred only for captivity and famine; any
who make money do so only to have it plundered. The
more care they lavish on their cities, houses, and property,

and on their own persons, the fiercer will be my indig- 48
nation against their sins, says the Lord. Like the indig- 49
nation of a virtuous woman towards a prostitute, so will 50
be the indignation of justice towards wickedness with all
her finery; she will accuse her to her face, when the
champion arrives to expose all sin upon earth. Do not 51
imitate wickedness, therefore, and her actions. For in a 52
very short time she will be swept from the earth, and
the reign of justice over us will begin.

✶ 35–9. The Lord's servants are warned that the evils which
will precede the end of this age and the judgement of God are
about to take place, and that nothing will delay their occurrence.

37. *Calamities:* of the kind described in 15: 14–19; 16:
17–34.

38. The illustration from child-birth is a reminder that in
the New Testament the signs that precede the end are called
'the birth-pangs of the new age' (Matt. 24: 8; Mark 13: 8).
Cp. 4: 40; I Thess. 5: 3.

40–52. When the moment of crisis comes, God's people
must be prepared to act as though they 'were strangers on
earth' (verse 40), to dissociate themselves completely, that is,
from all the concerns of human life (verses 41–4). The reason
for this is that at that moment all labour will prove to be
worthless. The things for which men work will be taken from
them, and God's anger will be particularly roused against the
sins of those who lavish care on themselves and their property
(verses 45–8). The judgement will mark the end of wickedness
and the beginning of the reign of justice, and God's people
are warned not to 'imitate wickedness' (verses 49–52).

41–4. The thought resembles that of I Cor. 7: 29–31.
must expect to have to run for his life: 'must be ready to run for
his life' would better convey the sense (and similarly in the
following examples).

46. *Their fruits will be gathered by foreigners:* cp. Lev. 26: 16; Deut. 28: 33, 51.

50. *when the champion arrives to expose all sin upon earth:* literally 'when he comes who will vindicate him who exposes all sin upon earth' – a reference to the coming of God at the judgement. Both God and his agent (in the context we are no doubt meant to see an allusion to Jesus) will be involved in this. ✳

FURTHER ADVICE: SIN CANNOT BE HIDDEN FROM GOD

53 The sinner must not deny that he has sinned; he will only bring burning coals on to his own head if he says, 'I 54 have committed no sin against the majesty of God.' For the Lord knows all that men do; he knows their plans, 55 their schemes, and their inmost thoughts. He said, 'Let the earth be made', and it was made; and 'Let the heavens 56 be made', and they were made. It was by the Lord's word that the stars were fixed in their places; the number 57 of the stars is known to him. He looks into the depths with their treasures; he has measured the sea and every-58 thing it contains. By his word he confined the sea within the bounds of the waters, and above the water he sus-59 pended the land. He spread out the sky like a vault, and 60 made it secure upon the waters. He provided springs in the desert, and pools on the mountain-tops as the source 61 of rivers flowing down to water the earth. He created man, and placed a heart in the middle of his body; he 62 gave him spirit, life, and understanding, the very breath of Almighty God who created the whole world and 63 searches out secret things in secret places. He knows well 64 your plans and all your inward thoughts. Alas for sinners

who try to hide their sins! The Lord will scrutinize all
their deeds; he will call you all to account. You will be 65
covered with confusion, when your sins are brought
into the open, and your wicked deeds stand up to accuse
you on that day. What can you do? How can you hide 66
your sins from God and his angels? God is your judge:
fear him! Abandon your sins, and have done with your 67
wicked deeds for ever! Then God will set you free from
all distress.

* Sinners are advised not to attempt to deny that they have
sinned because nothing can be kept hidden from God, the
creator of the world. On the day of judgement all sins will be
exposed, and those who have tried to hide their sins will be
overcome with shame. The best policy is to abandon sin; the
man who does this will be kept safe by God.

53. *The sinner must not deny that he has sinned:* cp. 1 John 1: 8.
he will only bring burning coals on to his own head: a reinterpretation of Prov. 25: 22; cp. Rom. 12: 20.

54–63. God's omniscience is shown by the fact that he is
the creator of the world. The passage is very loosely based on
Gen. 1, but there are reminiscences of other Old Testament
passages as well.

54. *For the Lord knows all that men do:* cp. Ecclus. 15: 18–19;
39: 19.

55. *He said, 'Let the earth be made', . . . 'Let the heavens be
made':* not exact quotations, but cp. Gen. 1: 6–10.

56. *It was by the Lord's word that the stars were fixed in their
places:* cp. Gen. 1: 14–19. *the number of the stars is known to
him:* cp. Ps. 147: 4.

57. Cp. Job 38: 16.

58. *By his word he confined the sea within the bounds of the
waters:* cp. Gen. 1: 9; Job 38: 10–11; Prov. 8: 29. *and above
the water he suspended the land:* cp. Pss. 24: 1–2; 136: 6.

59. *He spread out the sky like a vault, and made it secure upon the waters:* cp. Gen. 1: 6–8. The idea that God 'stretched out the skies' occurs in a number of places in the Old Testament; cp. e.g. Isa. 44: 24.

60. *He provided springs in the desert:* cp. Ps. 107: 35.

61–2. *He created man:* cp. Gen. 1: 26–7. *he gave him spirit, life, and understanding, the very breath of Almighty God:* cp. Gen. 2: 7.

63. *He knows well your plans and all your inward thoughts:* an idea that finds frequent expression, in various different ways, in both the Old and the New Testaments; cp. e.g. Ps. 44: 21; Heb. 4: 12–13.

64–5. God will judge the sinners, and *on that day* of judgement there will be no possibility of hiding sin. ✳

ENCOURAGEMENT FOR THOSE WHO FACE PERSECUTION

68 Fierce flames are being kindled to burn you. A great horde will descend on you; they will seize some of you
69 and make you eat pagan sacrifices. Those who give in to
70 them will be derided, taunted, and trampled on. In place after place[a] and in all the neighbourhood there will be
71 a violent attack on those who fear the Lord. Their enemies will be like madmen, plundering and destroying
72 without mercy all who still fear the Lord. They will destroy and plunder their property, and throw them out
73 of their homes. Then it will be seen that my chosen people have stood the test like gold in the assayer's fire.
74 Listen, you whom I have chosen, says the Lord; the days of harsh suffering are close at hand, but I will rescue
75 you from them. Away with your fears and doubts! For

[a] In place after place: *possible meaning; Lat. obscure.*

God is your leader. You who follow my commandments 76
and instructions, says the Lord God, must not let your
sins weigh you down, nor your wicked deeds get the
better of you. Alas for those who are entangled in their 77
sins, and overrun with their wicked deeds! They are like
a field overrun by bushes, with brambles across the path
and no way through, completely shut off and doomed to 78
destruction by fire.

✻ As 2 Esdras 15–16 began with threats of judgement on
those who were persecuting God's people, so it ends with
encouragement for those who faced persecution.

68–73. The author warns that 'there will be a violent
attack on those who fear the Lord' (verse 70). Some will be
compelled to eat food that had been used in sacrifices, others
will be driven from their homes. The only consolation is that
the persecution will show the true quality of those who remain
faithful. It has sometimes been thought that these verses were
written in the light of events that had already occurred, and
they certainly give that impression. More specifically, it has
been suggested that it was the persecution of Decius in the
year 250 that was in the mind of the author, but the evidence
is insufficient to determine whether this is so or not.

68. *pagan sacrifices:* literally 'that which has been sacrificed
to idols'. The eating of food that had been used in pagan
sacrifices posed a problem at various times to both Jews and
Christians; cp. e.g. 2 Macc. 6: 7–9, 21; Acts 15: 20; 1 Cor. 8.
In the persecution of Decius Christians were commanded to
take part in pagan sacrifices.

73. *my chosen people have stood the test like gold in the
assayer's fire:* cp. Isa. 48: 10; Zech. 13: 9; 1 Pet. 1: 7.

74–8. A final exhortation. Persecution is imminent, but
God will rescue those whom he has chosen. They should

303

have courage, and not allow themselves to be overcome by
the deadly effects of sin.   ✳

✳   ✳   ✳   ✳   ✳   ✳   ✳   ✳   ✳   ✳   ✳   ✳   ✳

POSTSCRIPT

2 Esdras is a composite work which reflects the circumstances
of three quite different periods. The largest and most important component within it, i.e. chs. 3–14, was written in
response to the crisis of faith which overwhelmed Judaism
in the years following the unsuccessful outcome of the revolt
of A.D. 66–73. By the very nature of things its response to that
crisis was expressed in the thought-forms and ideas of its own
day, and thus it speaks of such topics as God, sin, or life after
death in terms that may seem alien in the twentieth century.
It also contains some specific prophecies about the end of this
world order; the author believed that the end of this age
would follow shortly after the death of the Emperor Domitian,
and the fact that his prophecies, in common with many comparable biblical prophecies, were unfulfilled may likewise
make his work seem strange or irrelevant. Despite this, there
are two reasons why 2 Esdras 3–14 is still a work of considerable interest and importance; it represents a very serious
attempt, at a specific point in time, to grapple with the difficulties of belief in God, and it provides a valuable picture of
the kind of theological ideas which were current in some
Jewish circles at more or less the same time as that at which
many New Testament writings were composed.

Although 2 Esdras 3–14 is a Jewish work, it seems, like
other apocalyptic writings, to have fallen out of favour
amongst the Jews, and it owes its survival to the fact that it
was taken over by the Christian Church. Within the Christian
Church 2 Esdras 3–14 was held in high regard, and it was
because of this that, in a time of persecution in the latter part
of the third century A.D., a Christian author added chs. 15 and

16. Despite some uncertainties, it seems reasonably clear that these two additional chapters were composed from the outset as an appendix to chs. 3–14, the purpose of which was to make the earlier work refer more directly to a new situation. The author of this appendix urges his readers to stand firm in the face of persecution. The fact that he should have made this addition is an indication that, nearly two centuries after it was originally composed and in rather different circumstances, 2 Esdras 3–14 was still thought to have a relevant message to convey.

2 Esdras 1–2, a Christian work dating in all probability from the mid-second century A.D., is quite distinct from the remainder of 2 Esdras. The author takes up the question of the relationship of the Church to Judaism. His answer, that Israel has been completely rejected, and that the Church has taken her place, is no longer satisfying, but the question he raises is one of fundamental importance to practising Christians and Jews.

A NOTE ON FURTHER READING

A number of other commentaries on 2 Esdras are available. Those by W. O. E. Oesterley, Westminster Commentaries (London, 1933) and by J. M. Myers, Anchor Bible (Garden City, New York, 1974) cover the whole of 2 Esdras and are somewhat more detailed than the present volume. The commentary by G. H. Box, *The Ezra Apocalpyse* (London, 1912), is even more detailed, but deals only with chs. 3–14; it provides a mass of helpful information, but needs to be used with very great caution. Box reproduced the substance of this commentary in his contribution to the second volume of R. H. Charles, *The Apocrypha and Pseudepigrapha of the Old Testament* (see below).

The events which form the immediate background to 2 Esdras 3–14 are vividly described by Josephus in the *Jewish War*; the wider background, the history of the Roman Empire in the first century A.D. (and particularly in the troubled period which followed the death of Nero). is described in equally vivid terms by Suetonius (*The Lives of the Caesars*) and Tacitus (*The Histories*). English translations of all three works are available as Penguin Classics, or, together with the text, in the series The Loeb Classical Library. For a concise modern treatment of Jewish history in this period see M. Noth, *A History of Israel*, 2nd ed. (London, 1960); for Roman history see M. Cary and H. H. Scullard, *A History of Rome down to the Reign of Constantine*, 3rd ed. (London, 1975).

English translations of most of the apocalyptic and

related writings mentioned in this commentary (including 2 Esdras 3–14 itself) are available in vol. 2 of R. H. Charles, *The Apocrypha and Pseudepigrapha of the Old Testament in English* (Oxford, 1913; reprinted 1963), but for the Apocalypse of Abraham see the translation edited by G. H. Box (London, 1918). For 1 Enoch see also M. A. Knibb, in consultation with E. Ullendorff, *The Ethiopic Book of Enoch* (Oxford, 1978) (from which the translations in this commentary have been taken). K. Koch, *The Rediscovery of Apocalyptic* (London, 1972) provides a very lively and helpful account of the character of the apocalyptic writings.

A number of other Jewish and Christian writings have been mentioned or quoted in this volume, and for convenience a list of readily available English translations is given below:

The Dead Sea Scrolls: G. Vermes, *The Dead Sea Scrolls in English*, 2nd ed. (Harmondsworth, 1975).

The Mishnah: II. Danby, *The Mishnah* (Oxford, 1933).

Philo: F. H. Colson, G. H. Whitaker and R. Marcus, The Loeb Classical Library edition of the works of Philo.

The Shepherd of Hermas: Kirsopp Lake, The Loeb Classical Library edition of the Apostolic Fathers, vol. 2.

Eusebius, *Ecclesiastical History*: H. J. Lawlor and J. E. L. Oulton, *Eusebius. The Ecclesiastical History* (2 vols., London, 1927–8).

INDEX TO 1 ESDRAS

INDEX TO 2 ESDRAS

INDEX

Odenathus (prince of Palmyra) 289, 292

Old Testament, use of, in 2 Esdras 77, 80, 82, 101, 116, 236–7; examples 79, 80, 83, 84, 85, 95, 116–17, 121, 123, 136–7, 140, 146, 156, 194–6, 203, 239, 249, 256, 258–9, 297, 301

Old Testament books 282

Otho (Roman emperor) 241, 243, 250

Palestine 87, 89, 110, 116, 136, 169, 280

palms (given to the righteous in heaven) 99, 100

Palmyra 289, 292

paradise 93–4, 121, 167, 172, 178, 191, 210

patriarchs 87, 88, 145

Paul 275

Pelatiah (Jewish leader of the period after the exile) 134

Perizzites 83

persecution of Christians 287, 303

Persians 288–9

Phaltiel (Jewish leader) 134

Pharaoh 80

Philistines 83

Philo (Jewish philosopher) 201

Piso (M. Piso Licinianus, co-ruler with Galba) 241, 243, 250

prayer 133, 136, 155–6, 218

pre-existence: of the blessings of the new age 209; of the heavenly Jerusalem 266; of the Messiah 251–2, 265, 270; of the soul 200

prophets 87, 88, 89; rejection of 85, 192

Psalms of Solomon (collection attached to the name of Solomon) 160, 252

pseudonymity *see* apocalyptic writings

Rachel (wife of Jacob) 227

Red Sea 268

Remiel (name of an angel) 128

resurrection 93, 128, 142, 170, 280

robes (worn by the righteous in heaven) 97, 100

Roman Empire: as the 'fourth kingdom' 236, 249; existence of a sign that the end is near 276; in 2 Esdras 1–2 78, 90; in 2 Esdras 15–16 290, 292–3, 294; Jewish communities in 137–8; to be judged by the Messiah 168, 245–6, 252, 256

Roman history (alluded to in 2 Esdras 11–12) 104, 239–44, 249–51

Romans: Jewish revolt against 102–3; Jerusalem destroyed by 167

Rome 90, 116, 132, 147, 290–1, 292

sacrifice 103, 233, 234

Salathiel (name given to Ezra) 115

salvation of the just 175, 193, 206, 213, 215, 217

Samuel 188

Sarah (wife of Abraham) 227

Saul 188

scriptures, restoration of 101, 272, 277–8, 281–2

Septuagint 88, 159, 203

Seraiah (companion of Ezra) 278

Seraiah (last chief priest of the pre-exile temple) 102

Shalmaneser (Assyrian king) 268

Shapur I (Sassanid king) 288–9, 290, 292

Shealtiel (uncle or father of Zerubbabel) 115

Shelemiah (companion of Ezra) 278

Sheol 128, 201, 210

Shepherd of Hermas 78, 99

Shiloah 136

Sidon 80

signs of the end: in 2 Esdras 1–2 95; in 2 Esdras 3–14 131–3, 149–51, 167, 212–14, 262, 266, 276; in 2 Esdras 15–16 287, 297, 299

sin: all men sinners 174–5, 178, 205; causes of 117, 118, 125, 184, 191, 210; fate of sinners 174–5, 178, 191, 210, 216–17